The state flower is the blossom of the saguaro cactus, the largest cactus found in the United States. The saguaro (sah-*war*-oh), or Giant Cactus (*Carnagiea gigantea*), is found in Arizona and northern Mexico with a very few scattered along the Colorado River in California. This cactus grows to a height of from forty to fifty feet, lives to an age of from 150 to 200 years. Its pure white waxy flowers appear in garlands on the tips of the long arms of the plant in May and June.

STATE FLOWER

he 21st Arizona state legislature, second regular session, designated e palo verde (genus *Cercidium*) as Arizona's state tree. The palo erde (from the Spanish meaning "green stick" or "green pole") is one the beautiful trees of the desert and desert foothill regions. When blooms, generally in April or May, depending on elevation, it is a aze of shimmering yellow gold. There are two native species of palo erde Cercidium in Arizona, the blue palo verde (*Cercidium floridum*), aracterized by a blue-green color of the branches and leaves; and e foothill palo verde (*Cercidium microphyllum*) characterized by e yellow-green color of branches and leaves. Both bear a profusion yellow blossoms when in bloom.

TATE TREE

State symbols art by George Avey courtesy of Arizona Highways Magazine

ARIZONA
its people and resources

ARIZONA

Revised, Second edition
by
Members of the Faculty of
The University of Arizona

ts people and resources

THE UNIVERSITY OF ARIZONA PRESS
Tucson, Arizona

THE UNIVERSITY OF ARIZONA PRESS

I. S. B. N.-0-8165-0262-5
L. C. No. 72-81017

CONTENTS

ILLUSTRATIONS

RESEARCH AND THE FUTURE

MAPS, CHARTS, AND DIAGRAMS

THE POINT OF VIEW

Roosevelt Dam on the Salt River, an early action
step to deliver more water to a fast-growing state.

ARIZONA HERE AND NOW

AFTER MORE THAN 100 YEARS as a political entity, Arizona as the 1970s began was a living example of man's repeated mastery over his environment.

The area — a territory in 1863, a state since 1912 — continued into its second century of life as a governmental unit containing some of the more sophisticated studies of the space age. .

Geologically old, its crater-dotted lava plateaus were furnishing a dramatic training ground, simulating the dead surface of the moon, for astronauts preparing for a second walk by man on that planet.

But it retained in its mountains and deserts the homes, little changed by time, of the largest number of Indians of any state.

Students of its universities were studying and documenting the traces of an ancient past. Archaeologists and anthropologists were seeking to reweave the fabric of the lives of those who departed centuries ago, leaving the imprint of their skills in pit house and cliff house and long-dry canals.

Others were striving to interpret in diverse ways the full picture of the last century — the hundred years or so in which modern Arizona evolved from its pioneer past. They were recording its burgeoning population, the harnessing of its wild rivers to place water on its semiarid lands and to furnish power for the multitude of uses called for by the new technologies, increasing vastly the production of wealth from the state's natural resources.

President Lincoln established the Territory in 1863 and appointed the first strong civil government for Arizona. But it was nearly a year before the first session of the territorial legislature was convened in Prescott.

The infant agricultural industry of that period, born in the Mormon settlement of Beaver Dams (later known as Littlefield) in 1864, has become a mammoth operation in fields of cotton, feed grains, citrus fruits, grapes, and vegetables.

The livestock industry, which moved into the broad, free grasslands of the territory, following the Civil War, and increased despite the Indian troubles which plagued it, continued to grow and branch out. Starting essentially as a cow and calf state, Arizona has broadened its livestock base to include feeding, finishing and packaging operations. Product quality, not mere numbers, has become the aim.

Mabel Weadock
Ancient style of Papago building used in 20th century.

[3]

Purebred foundation beef herds, based on Scottish and English breeds, have long since displaced the long-horn, and new hybrids have joined them in fenced pastures to harvest the annual crop of nutritious range grasses which can be marketed in no other fashion.

Conservation practices, conducted under federal and state laws and enlightened individual use, have reclaimed and preserved thousands of acres of grazing land for the use of coming generations.

These changes have not concerned Anglo-Americans alone. For example, sheep of the modern Navajo and cattle herds of the once warlike Apache show the effects of top bloodlines and compete successfully with the stock of their Anglo neighbors in the marketplace.

The much-discussed "population explosion" in the sixties has had a unique and two-edged effect on agriculture. Small farms, citrus groves, vineyards, cotton fields, and even cattle range, in the vicinity of metropolitan areas have ceased to be food or fibre-producing acres and have become housing projects. In the 1960s complete communities grew up on what had been range lands or farms.

The problem of increasing food production on shrinking acreage was disturbing economists and ecologists alike.

Animal scientists at the University of Arizona were researching again the possibilities of eliminating the open range as a part of the production cycle for beef, planning to conduct the entire program — breeding, calving, feeding and to market — on a dry feedlot basis.

Don Keller
Feedlots have expanded the state's cattle-raising.

Ray Manley
Prize cattle are not uncommon on Arizona ranches.

Automated controlled feeding, its efficiency already proven, will replace range and pasture which, in turn, will be taken over by the home builder and community developer.

This demand for additional living space resulted in the expansion of cities, pushing their borders out into what had been suburban countryside. In 1960 Phoenix had within its city limits 187.4 square miles. By 1970, annexation had brought within the city limits of the state capital 247.7 square miles.

In Tucson the city area was 70.88 square miles in 1960 and in 1970 the city claimed jurisdiction over 76.91 square miles.

In 1960 Del Webb founded Sun City on the former Marinette Cotton Ranch. Population in 1970, 14,000.

Beyond these limits the suburban areas spread thickly into the surrounding rural acreage, creating as they expanded new metropolitan problems of government to be solved by the boards of supervisors, established under the constitution of the state, essentially for rural government.

But the population demands had to be met and the county officials found themselves involved in health and welfare problems for both urban and rural communities and responsible for numerous services, sanitary and otherwise, which had before been obligations of the city. Urban-type zoning, streets, roads, parks and highways, and school affairs as well, were seen as ever-broadening problems for county government of the seventies.

As Arizona reached the seventies, more than a half-million people in the state were engaged in wholesale and retail trade, a long stride from February, 1856, when Solomon Warner led a merchandise-laden pack train of thirteen mules from Yuma to open Tucson's first general store.

Manufacturing, practically unknown in the 1860s in Arizona, a century later employed 93,700 people annually and exported products valued at $98 million per year. Non-electrical machinery, instruments and related products, electrical machinery, lumber and wood products made up the bulk of the manufactured items.

At the beginning of the 1970s, records maintained since 1874 credited the state with having produced 45 billion pounds of copper since that date, with the total growing at the rate of 1.5 billion pounds per year. To this was added a huge tonnage of other metals, bringing an annual return for all mineral production from Arizona mines of $1,159,863,000 in 1970. This included 53.4 percent of all of the copper mined in the United States in that year.

In a century mining had changed from the hand labor of a single man or group of men to a highly complex series of engineering skills involving the use of specially designed equipment with which to move ore. The discovery and application of flotation and other modern methods of extraction of metal from mineral-bearing rock made profitable use of low-grade ores. The mineral treasure of the state — its presence known since the conquistadores marched over it seeking the Cities of Gold — was being uncovered in the huge open pit mines, and turned into tangible wealth for the use of man.

Fred Wehrman

Tucson's dense downtown area was cleared in the late 1960s to make room for public buildings and civic center.

Transportation in the 1870s might be by burro pack.

Precision manufacturing at Motorola's Arizona plant.

At the Ray, Arizona, silicate ore leach plant, low-grade copper ores are recovered by new techniques.

Ray Manley

Ray Manley

Kennecott sulfuric acid plant helps fight pollution.

At the beginning of the 1970s the mining industry of Arizona, which dates back to the work of the early Hopi Indians digging for salt, was planning to use the awesome force of atomic power to wrest more wealth from beneath the mountains of the state.

Under the pressure of a national, state, and local campaign for clean air, the industry also was seeking a method other than smelting to refine metals.

Arizona's growth during its first century of life as a political entity was accompanied by dramatic changes in transportation facilities. They ranged from the initial crossing of the state by the frontier road of the Morman battalion, to the coming of the Butterfield stages in October, 1858, and the arrival of the railroad in 1880.

First the covered wagons and the military roads quickened the coming of the frontier merchants, while the railroad created swift expansion of the livestock and mining industries, providing an outlet to markets. The railroad also expedited immigration into the area.

But transportation in Arizona on the eve of the seventies had once again acquired a new look, as railroad passenger service, for nearly ninety years a major factor in the state economy, was almost entirely phased out, even with the advent of Amtrak.

Travelers took to the air, to private automobiles or to the major bus lines.

Air travel's impact on the state was attested by the nine airlines which serviced the Sky Harbor Airport in Phoenix and the seven lines which served the International Airport in Tucson. The Tucson airport claim

Arizona's World War II legacy of U.S. Air Force planes in mothballs at Davis-Monthan Air Force Base, Tucson.

Loading a 747 at Phoenix's Sky Harbor airport.

Al Ruland Photo, City of Phoenix

to being international rested on its being the clearing point for both customs and immigration between the United States and Mexico. Sky Harbor Airport had also achieved international status.

Phoenix logged 3,005,873 passenger flights in 1971 while Tucson registered 943,362.

Although passenger service was reduced to a minor factor in the operation of the two major railroads crossing Arizona, both the Santa Fe in the north and the Southern Pacific in the south greatly increased their freight tonnage, particularly in the field of perishables, moving heavy freight trains on passenger train schedules.

This increased tonnage resulted from a number of factors in freight-train operation. The century in the Southwest had seen the change from burro-back and the twenty-mule-team freighter to piggy-back, pre-packaged freight, picked up at the shipper's loading dock and delivered to the customer's door, nearly a continent away.

Roller-bearing cars, powered by speedy diesel-electric units, with liquid-cooled refrigerator cars which required no icing stops, maintained passenger train schedules, delivering produce from border to border in field-fresh condition. A major vegetable producer was one of the pilot users of this system in Arizona and southern California.

Railroad pipelines deliver fuel across modern Arizona.

People yes, plants no, at Arizona-California border.   *Ray Manley*

The elimination of the old "seventy-car law" permitted radio-controlled trains of 110 cars or more to be handled with speed and efficiency.

These were large factors in the business of the Southern Pacific as it moved ever-increasing shipments of produce from the west coast of Mexico to the eastern markets. This produce shipping was also instrumental in making Nogales, Arizona, one of the busiest ports of entry on the border.

With the state spending $90,872,189 on new and improved highways in the 1970-71 fiscal year (federal aid included) the travel by private passenger cars increased greatly. More than 5 million cars were logged into the state at the various ports of entry, while registration figures on Arizona passenger cars rose to 827,579. Commercial truckers registered 187,462 vehicles while non-commercial trucks totalled 128,303.

The cross of the Christian religion accompanied the sword of the conquistadores, and the black robe of the Jesuit and the brown habit of the Franciscan order were found in the vanguard as the Spaniards extended their explorations and conquests into Apachería.

These clergy were men of many facets. They were teachers who brought a concept of deity that asked no human sacrifice, but could be grasped by a primitive people long attuned to the Father image of the Sun and to the beneficence and warmth of the Earth Mother. They were also explorers, cartographers, tillers of the soil and builders who taught, along with religion, the skills needed to exploit the resources of a great land, the potential of which had not been touched.

Education, which entered Arizona with the sword

and the cross, received its initial governmental support in 1864 when the First Territorial Legislature convened in Prescott. The legislators set aside $1,500 for education, and passed an act to raise money for public schools. They appropriated $250 for the first public school, then being conducted at San Xavier Mission by Fr. Carlos E. Messea, an Italian Jesuit who was to become well known in the education field in California.

The legislature, in this first session, also established a University and authorized a board of regents to operate it. The population of the Arizona Territory at the time numbered 4,573 according to a census made for Gov. John N. Goodwin by U. S. Marshal Milton B. Duffield.

Following the arrival of a stable government, people began to flow into the great open valleys and mountains of the Territory. Young and vigorous men and women were drawn to the lure of new country — to its mines, its farms, its broad ranges, and its business opportunities. They brought families or created new ones and along these streams of population children and schools thrived.

In the early 1970s, when the Thirtieth Arizona State Legislature convened, its members were confronted by the task of providing for a school population of 588,968 in the tax-supported schools of the state. This included 344,753 elementary school pupils, 136,900 high school students and 107,315 students in various insti-

Ray Manley
Ties are still strong between mission padres and
Arizona Indians at San Xavier on the Papago reservation.

Arizona State University at Tempe grew to be a major center of higher education during the 1960s.

Pima College at Tucson opened its doors in 1970.

Natural Bridge, a neighbor of the Grand Canyon.

tutions of higher learning. These last included the University of Arizona, authorized more than a century before, Arizona State University at Tempe, Northern Arizona University at Flagstaff, and eleven junior colleges scattered about the state.

The growth of education during the slightly more than 100 years of Arizona's political life may be seen in the amount of money devoted to it by the state. In comparison to the $250 appropriation by the First Territorial Legislature to a public school fund, the Thirty-first Arizona State Legislature, in preparing its budget for 1971-72, was asked by the Board of Regents for $93,361,891 for the three state universities alone, a figure which was scaled down to $85,342,290 for the fiscal year ending in 1972. This did not include the per diem per pupil for elementary and high schools.

As Arizona entered the decade of the seventies, more than half of the taxpayer's dollar went to education.

Out of the total cost of $624,279,456 for running the state in the opening fiscal year of the seventies, $326,465,830 was expended for education.

The lure of Arizona's recreational areas was seen in the fact that 10,403,500 visitors were being checked in to the twenty national parks and monuments in the state in a single season.

A novel facet of Arizona's pleasure travel is that in a state not known for an overabundance of water, there were 45,390 pleasure boats registered in 1970.

A pertinent feature in the attractiveness of the state for the outdoorsmen among visitors and residents is the unique pattern of ownership of land within Arizona and the uses of that land. In 1970, out of the total of 72,688,000 acres in the state 44.68 percent was federally owned land; 27.03 percent was Indian reservation land; 12.66 percent was state land and only 15.63 percent was privately owned.

In each instance, federal, state, or Indian lands are contributing to the requirement of the camper, hunter, and fisherman. The modern national forest camps are not only located in areas of spectacular scenery, but also are equipped with good sanitary facilities, built-in fireplaces, cooking grills, tables, and in many cases with electric power hook-ups available.

Department of the Interior concessions for the camper, boatman, and fisherman abound at Lake Mead and Lake Powell on the Colorado River, while similar services are to be found around the Salt River lakes.

In the White Mountain country the Apache tribe's recreation service has been maintaining camping facilities at more than one thousand sites in some of the most spectacular scenery in Arizona. Both federal and state fish hatcheries contribute to keeping the fresh water lakes and streams stocked, maintaining a good fish population despite heavy use. Hunting and fishing license fees have financed a large portion of the work of the state fish and game commission. Hunting and fishing permit revenues and other tribal funds provide for policing and stocking of Apache recreation areas.

Highway 73, east of McNary — beauty and no billboards.

Dale Sutton

Fishing and camping, Hawley Lake, Apache Reservation.

U.S. Army

Arizona military personnel learn computer technology.

active, but its old cavalry garrison was gone. In its place was the headquarters of STRATCOM, the world wide Strategic Communications Command, a portion of the U. S. Army Electronic Proving Grounds, the Safeguard Communications Agency, and the U. S. Army Intelligence School.

Modern communities and complex technologies had also developed around such military installations as Davis-Monthan Air Force Base in Tucson where, by 1971, more than 9000 military and 2700 civilian personnel were employed. In the Phoenix metropolitan area, Luke and Williams Air Force bases also added to population.

But there had been a much earlier conquest by man over his environment in this area. Less than fifty miles from the fort, archaeologists uncovered from deep in the earth bones of an elephant which had died with bone arrowheads in head and body and traces of old fire pits and stone fleshing tools. Here, more than 11,000 years ago, Cochise man hunted and killed huge animals, now extinct, leaving only the traces of the bones of pachyderms and tapir, horses and bison, and the charcoal from his cooking fires.

These evidences of the early residents of the state are treasured exhibits in the Arizona State Museum. Along with many other artifacts, unearthed from border to border, they help to tell the story of how Arizona's people, from the days of the mammoths to those of atomic fission, have struggled with manifold difficulties to wrest liveability from their environment.

Even before territorial days, Arizona was an active home for military units, located there either for protection of the frontier or in training for wars elsewhere. More than fifty sites at one time or another bore the designation fort or camp — the majority of them during the Indian wars.

At the beginning of the seventies all were gone or converted to other than military uses except one.

Fort Huachuca, in Cochise county, built in 1877 as an operating base against the Apache Indians, was still

STRATCOM at Fort Huachuca in southeastern Arizona provides ultra-modern communications for U.S. defense.   *U.S. Army*

ARIZONA'S
PEOPLE
AND THEIR. PAST

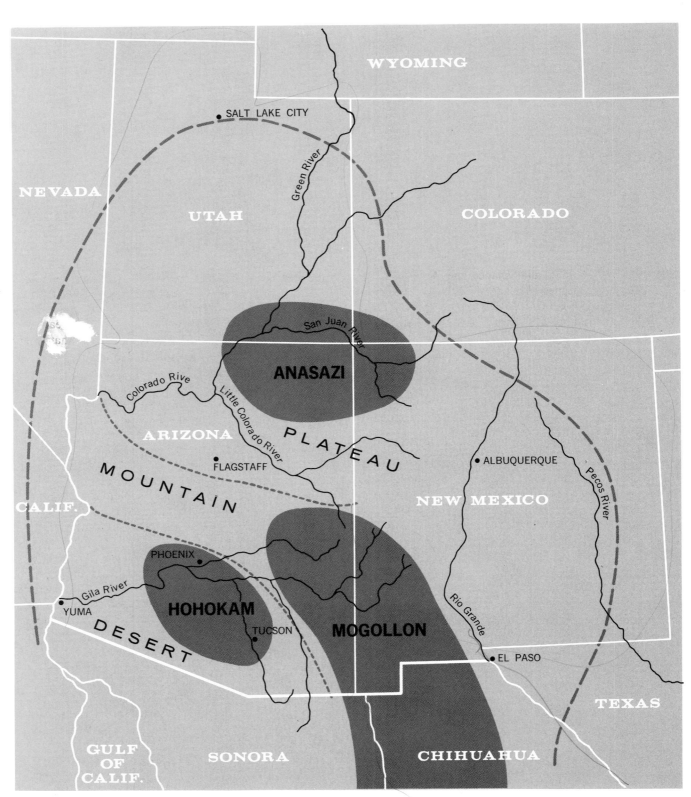

Fig. 1.1 Approximate location of the three principal culture centers in about A.D. 700.

Emil W. Haury
Anthropologist

1

BEFORE HISTORY

THE NATURAL FORCES that shaped the Arizona landscape in geologic times also left a subtle imprint upon the lives of its present-day inhabitants. This is evident in the occupations of the people — in mining, cattle growing, arid land agriculture, tourism, and even in the out-of-doors homelife and forms of recreation. The influences of environment were just as emphatically stamped upon the lives of the native people who preceded our modern society by fifteen millennia. It is with this range of time that the archaeologist deals.

Archaeologists generally speak of large segments of the American continents as archaeological areas within which ancient societies developed and shared common ways of life. The Southwest is one of these areas, and the state of Arizona and most of New Mexico constitute its core. Parts of adjacent states to the north, west, and south are also included in this particular area (Fig. 1.1).

The story of man's adjustment to his environment begins with geography. Three startlingly different zones are evident in Arizona. From south to north, these are first, the flatlands of the desert, extending from sea level to almost three thousand feet, excluding the crests of the mountain ranges. Blessed with abundant arable land, but deprived by altitude and limiting precipitation factors, this land supports little more than thorny trees, brush, and cactus. Except for a few streams and springs, surface water is scarce.

Second, diagonally from the northwest to the southeast through the state stretches a mountainous belt with an altitude varying from the upper desert limits to twelve thousand feet. Surface water is abundant, stemming from generous rainfall. Forests and grass cover the area, but good farming acreage is sparse.

The third zone is the northern plateau with an elevation of about one mile. Much of this region is barren upland, but it includes vast stretches of juniper and piñon. It is studded with colorful mesas and cut by intricate networks of canyons. Although very beautiful,

the area lacks water and productive soil, two ingredients essential to prosperous living.

Each of these three land types supported and nurtured native populations before the European conquest. Nature imposed restrictions upon what could be done by a people solely dependent upon the resources of the land. Thus, to a marked extent, uniform human cultures arose in each of these zones. The sharp boundaries separating their territories disappeared only after each group had mastered its local environment. Once that was done, migrations from zone to zone began.

Within the time limits of the Christian Era, therefore, the archaeologist recognizes the rise of three principal old tribal entities who left in the wake of their decline and fall hundreds of ruins broadcast over the Arizona landscape. Each distinct tribe centered in one of the three geographical areas.

Because these societies left no records from which the archaeologist can name them, the archaeologist has classified them arbitrarily. Beyond the Mogollon Rim, the northern uplands, or the Colorado Plateau, contained the Anasazi (Basketmaker-Pueblo) culture. Anasazi is a Navajo word meaning "The Ancient Ones." The Navajo Indians, recent immigrants into the Southwest, use this word when they speak of those who built and left the ruins on the lands which they now occupy.

The Mogollon people centered in the mountain belt, particularly in the eastern half. Not knowing what these people called themselves, archaeologists found it fitting to apply to them the name of an early Spanish general, also given to the Mogollon Rim in Arizona and Mogollon Mountains in New Mexico.

In the south, the earliest inhabitants of the desert area are called Hohokam, a word borrowed from the Pima language meaning "All Used Up."

Several other groups in the northwestern quarter of Arizona have been identified by archaeologists, for

[17]

example the Patayan and Sinagua. But they were of minor importance when compared with the three major ancient peoples.

No one knows when man first set foot in Arizona. By conservative reckoning, this was from twelve thousand to fifteen thousand years ago. As archaeologists better understand the evidence they accumulate and study, this estimate for man's arrival may be pushed back in time. It is certain that the earliest Arizonans must claim kinship with the enormous reservoir of humanity in Asia. It is reasonably certain that they were attracted to this part of the world by the abundance of big game upon which their lives at that time depended — the elephants, camels, horses, sloths, and bison that lived in another geologic era. These first people were hunters, on the move, a simple folk, leaving behind only occasional traces of their presence in campsites and in the remains of animals killed with their primitive weapons.

The bones of an elephant (Columbian Mammoth), with eight spear points in the head and rib cage, mutely evidence the hunting skill of this early man. These remains were discovered imbedded deeply in the earth along Greenbush Creek near Naco, Arizona. At the Lehner ranch near Hereford, in the San Pedro River valley, big game hunting was common. Here were found the bones of nine pachyderms, several horses, bison, and tapir, slaughtered around a water hole in a fossil stream. Spear points and stone butchering tools were uncovered at the same site. Even the remains of two fires upon which some of these animals may have been roasted were discovered. With the aid of skills developed by the geologist and the atomic physicist, particularly by the use of carbon dating, the age of the events described above has been dated back at least eleven thousand years.

Evidence of these early inhabitants has also been found in Ventana Cave on the Papago Indian Reservation, one hundred miles west of Tucson. Sundry stone tools, scattered bones of a variety of extinct animals, and charcoal from their fires have been unearthed beneath fifteen feet of refuse — the accumulation of centuries of debris left by later occupants.

These archaeological discoveries illuminate the first chapter of Arizona's history. They are preserved in the excellent exhibits of the Arizona State Museum on the campus of the University of Arizona.

What we know of man in Arizona from this point on is related to the disappearance of the animals upon which he subsisted. The climate, fauna, and flora of those days were much different. With the glacial retreat of the last Ice Age came the end of big game. But man's hunting skill also hastened the doom of the animal herds. When man was deprived of his primary food source, he was forced to adjust to other foods or to perish.

The Cochise people form the next connecting link in man's early history. Their record stretches over at least eight thousand years. Temporally, they are sandwiched between the elephant hunters and the more highly developed people of the Christian Era. Archaeologists have named these people after Cochise County, where many traces of them were first found in the alluvial valley deposits brought to view by the heavy arroyo cutting which began in the last decades of the nineteenth century.

While the earliest of these Cochise people knew and hunted the extinct animals, the loss of the big game forced them to turn to smaller quarry, the species of animals we know today. They also turned to a greater dependence upon plant foods. Thus, they became gatherers primarily, demonstrating their capacity to adjust to a changing environment. They developed appropriate stone tools for collecting and preparing vegetal foods. Campsites of this period have produced large quantities of such tools. Among these, and undoubtedly the most important, was the functionally related pair of grinding stones consisting of the nether stationary unit against whose surface the movable hand-held stone was operated. This was the prototype of the mano and metate associated with the farming societies of later times.

Until approximately 2000 B.C., the Cochise people collected foods provided by nature. At that time, or thereabouts, a cereal grain in the early stages of domestication came to them by way of the people in Mexico. This grain was a primitive form of corn, or maize, in which each kernel was separately sheathed in a husk and attached to a small cob. The introduction of this new food changed man into a planter and food producer, for corn does not reseed itself, but must be planted and tended. This was a revolution of major proportion in Southwestern culture history. To some extent, man could now begin to control his environment. He could produce more than he could consume. But the capacity to store the surplus food was essential to the success of the system. It took some time for the widespread adoption of corn, but by the beginning of the Christian Era, most of the people in the Southwest were well on their way to a sedentary agricultural life.

About this time, two other vegetal plants, squash and beans, were introduced to enrich and stabilize the economy. It is at this point that archaeologists begin to use the regional tribal distinctions associated with the three physiographic provinces of Arizona. The respective histories of these three tribal groups can be traced through their artifacts with increasing reliability and completeness to the present.

The Hohokam, the Mogollon, and the Anasazi experienced special problems in dealing with their environments — the desert, the mountain zone, and the plateau, respectively. But of these problems, water was primary. It was difficult to know where to find it, and how to use and control it for the benefit of all. A second major problem was obtaining food, both in collection and in production. These early peoples had to coax crops from an unyielding soil and were handicapped by contrary elements of nature. A third difficulty

Fig. 1.2   Fourteenth-century irrigation canal was part of early Hohokam engineering project.

was found in living from day to day. They were forced to develop smoothly operating social, political, and religious systems. While the three groups shared numerous traits, their differences distinguish them from one another. Although the specific origins of the Anasazi and Mogollon are unknown, their roots dip back into the culture of the old Cochise people. The Hohokam were believed to have been immigrants from Mexico several centuries before the time of Christ. All were stimulated to adopt higher living standards by the introduction of new crops, new agricultural practices, and new arts, such as pottery making, from the more highly developed cultures of Mexico.

It was the Hohokam who built the irrigation canals that drew water from living streams, diverting it to thirsty fields far distant from the source. Several hundred miles of such engineering projects have been traced in the Salt and Gila river valleys. Some of those canals match modern ones in size. In fact, in pioneering days, a few of the Hohokam ditches were restored to use by cleaning them out, patching breaks in the banks,

and turning water into them. No Indian achievement north of Mexico, in pre-Conquest times, surpasses the Hohokam canal system for planning, expenditure of effort, and for the evident inter-community organization that produced it. They were master-farmers, producing corn, beans, squash, and cotton in an arid land by irrigation and water control. Some form of canal irrigation may have existed by 300 B.C., but the system reached its height between 1000 and 1400.

By developing such an intricate system of canals, the Hohokam accomplished another important objective: they had freedom of choice for the location of their villages. Ordinarily the village or town site was picked because of the existence of natural water. But canals, going far from streams, opened new possibilities of mobility and location — the kind of emancipation from the environment achieved in modern society often only by digging wells. The classic example of this mobility of location, dating from the canal period, was the large settlement of Los Muertos, six miles south of Tempe, excavated by Frank Hamilton Cushing in 1887–88.

There, hundreds of people lived in the desert, six miles from the Salt River, sustained by the thin lifeline of a canal. No other prehistoric people in the Southwest matched this feat. From this fact the archaeologist deduces the existence of a political and social organization that had community welfare at heart.

Some of the desert dwellers, such as those living on what was later the Papago Reservation, were not fortunate enough to have access to live streams. Here control of the surface runoff was the key to successful living. Gathering ditches were one answer. One of these ran in a westerly direction for nearly ten miles from the base of Baboquivari Peak. It cut across numerous small natural drainages on the gentle piedmont slope, collecting the rain water and directing it to fertile ground in the lowland. This was a precarious form of irrigation, but it must have worked at least much of the time.

The discovery that irrigated agriculture was practiced in Mexico during the first millennium B.C. has helped modern archaeologists to understand what happened in the valleys of the Gila and Salt rivers. The Hohokam learned the art of irrigation from their kinsmen in Mexico. It was Hohokam genius, however, that modified the principles they knew to meet the demands of the local environment. To many people, the Hohokam, more than any other group of prehistoric Southwesterners, exemplify man's capacity to rise to the challenge of a harsh environment by understanding it and turning its hidden advantages to his favor, thereby setting the stage for the development of what we choose to call civilization.

As it did on all other farming people, the miracle of agriculture left a deep imprint on Hohokam society. The growing season of plants, and labor investments in canals and fields, anchored the people to the soil. This meant permanent villages in which the labors of a few could produce food for many. Food surpluses permitted the release of time and energy for other pursuits which contributed to the advance of Hohokam culture.

Impressive and solidly constructed domestic and religious architecture was not among the great Hohokam achievements. For more than a thousand years the family home was a roofed-over pit in the ground, looking like an earthen mound from the outside. With a side entrance, the inside was comfortable in both summer and winter, an efficient shade in spite of its simplicity. Until the 1950s, archaeologists had not found any architectural remains that might have been used primarily for religious observances. The kiva, either large or small, a common feature in Mogollon and Anasazi ruins, was apparently entirely lacking. But in 1958, scientists from the Arizona State Museum cleared the debris away from an earthen mound situated near Gila Bend, disclosing a flat-topped, pyramidal temple base. The age of this structure was close to A.D. 1100, and it is one of the many links that relate the Hohokam to the high civilizations of central Mexico.

Another prominent feature in some Hohokam sites is the ball court, in which the Indians played a game doubtless similar to that for which the stone-walled courts found in Toltec and Maya ruins were used. An old ball made of native rubber, found in a pottery jar near Casa Grande, hints that balls of this kind were used in the game. As in Mexico, there were probably religious aspects to the game, but of these nothing is known. The evidence suggests that the ball game was played in special arenas as early as A.D. 700 and that the custom persisted at least until 1400. During this period there was a reduction in the length of the court and a shift in orientation from east-west to north-south. It is probable that the kickball races of the Pima and Papago Indians represent a faint echo and survival of the early formalized game.

The effect of a sedentary farming life on the Hohokam is best seen in their arts and crafts. As the original Arizona cotton growers, a plant that came to them from Mexico perhaps before A.D. 300, the Hohokam also became producers of fine textiles. The unfortunate custom of cremating the dead with their finery has destroyed many of the products of the loom, but scraps have survived in a few rock shelters, such as Ventana Cave, where the Hohokam once lived. From these scraps it is evident that, in addition to the simple weaving of cloth, a number of complicated techniques were used. Tapestry, twill, gauze, and an ingenious lace-like cloth known as weft-warp openwork provided means for decorating cloth. Evidence of these is found among the neighbors of the Hohokam to the north and east, who obviously were inspired by Hohokam achievement, and many of whom were almost certainly supplied with raw cotton from Hohokam fields through trade.

In terms of quality, Hohokam pottery was not of the best. But what it lacked in quality of body it made up for in form and design. Shapes run a wide gamut from the conventional to the eccentric (Fig. 1.4) and some of these, such as the legged vessels, also suggest affinities with the people of Mexico. The buff-colored pottery was painted with a red-brown iron oxide pigment, producing what the archaeologist calls red-on-buff of various kinds. This pottery is readily distinguishable from that of other Southwestern people. Most characteristic of the designs were repeated life forms which, with a few cursive brush strokes and without detail, achieved an amazing degree of animation. Careful stratigraphic studies at Snaketown on the Gila River Indian Reservation and in other ruins have traced at least fifteen hundred years of Hohokam pottery history.

The Hohokam talent for modeling clay is best revealed in figurines which usually copied the human form. The occurrence of many of these with cremated dead suggests ritual use. In some instances it appears that efforts were made to capture the personality of a real person.

Stone sculpture was also an outstanding Hohokam

Fig. 1.3 Snaketown archaeologists found housefloors revealing a thousand years of architectural history.

Fig. 1.4   Pottery of the Hohokam is distinguished by its shapes, designs, and red-on-buff color.

trait, best exemplified by slate palettes for mixing pigments and small receptacles with bas-relief decoration. Sculpture was limited to small objects, differing in this respect from the monumental works of the Mexican Indians.

Because the Hohokam were nearer to the sea than any other Southwestern Indians, they found sea shell to be a material which could readily be fashioned into a large variety of ornaments. They excelled all Indians north of Mexico in this art, and capitalized upon their ability to acquire shell easily by trading it, both raw and shaped, to tribes far and near. Their crowning achievement was the development of an etching technique, whereby a pattern was obtained by immersing a shell painted with a wax in an acid which was probably the fermented juice of the saguaro fruit (Fig. 1.5). This technique was apparently unique to the Hohokam and was invented by them by A.D. 1100, some 400 years before the same principle was employed in Europe by craftsmen to decorate metal armor.

The custom of cremating the dead began in the Southwest long before the time of Christ. The incinerated bones of the deceased were generally enshrined in earthenware pots, sometimes with lavish accompaniments. Only those which resisted fire, such as objects of stone, bone, and shell survived, but fragments of cloth and other perishable objects are occasionally found among the ashes. The loss of these objects, as well as the destruction of the physical remains of the people by fire, has seriously limited the archaeologist's ability to write as fully as he would like about all the aspects of the Hohokam people and their culture.

Particularly important is the role the Hohokam played as the recipients and modifiers of the elements of high Mexican civilizations. Of all Southwestern people, they mirrored the achievements of Mexico most clearly, accepting what they wanted and changing it to fit their situation. The direct import of a few things, such as copper bells and pyrite-encrusted mosaic plaques, is evidence of trade contacts. Some archaeologists see the Hohokam as migrants from Mexico. They were unique among ancient Southwestern tribes in their effective adjustment to desert living and in their imaginative combining of native and imported ideas.

By A.D. 1400, the Hohokam went into an eclipse as a virile group. Throughout the Southwest, this was a period of drastic changes, which caused the decline of other groups as well as the Hohokam. Paradoxically, archaeologists at the beginning of the 1970s knew less about the period between A.D. 1400 and 1700 than about the culture history of the millennium before 1400, but there are reasons for believing that the Pima and Papago Indians are the modern descendants of the Hohokam.

Standing in sharp contrast to the Hohokam were the mountain-dwelling Mogollon people. By comparison they were a drab people, their culture more difficult to define, their contributions to the total culture history of the Southwest undistinguished. They inhabited the Arizona-New Mexico border country south of the White Mountains, stretching down into Mexico for an undetermined distance (Fig. 1.1). While there is some dispute over the origin of the Mogollon, the evidence seems clear that their roots are in the Cochise culture. The mountains gave them ready access to water and plentiful game, but little land for farming save in a few favored localities. Like that of many forest inhabitants, their life was simple, a response to environmental limitations.

Yet they were among the earliest Southwestern

people to grow corn and to make pottery. At first this was unpainted. Later, it was decorated with red-earth pigments on a brown base. Superficially this resembled the pottery of the Hohokam, a likeness born of the common inspiration for both traditions from Mexico, but tribal distinctiveness is disclosed by the difference in the method of manufacture and the surface treatment. The introduction of potterymaking may be dated to the second or third century B.C., long before the art was learned by the Anasazi, their neighbors to the north. Corn reached them somewhat earlier than this.

Mogollon villages consisted of loosely arranged clusters of houses, partly underground and partly above, entered by means of covered ramps leading to floor level from the east. The idea of building walls of stone was foreign to them until late in their history. In most villages a large pit structure, much larger than those designed for family living, has been found. This is believed to have been a building for community ceremonial use. It is a reminder that, despite a simple and rigorous existence, the social, political, and religious aspects of Mogollon life may have been complex.

The material goods of the culture not destroyed by time and soil were mostly rough tools of stone, tips for arrows, metates for grinding corn, thin rock slabs for tilling the soil, grooved mauls for work requiring

Fig. 1.5 The Hohokam ornamented seashells with acid etching.

Arizona State Museum, University of Arizona

heavy blows, small stone bowls for pulverizing pigments, and similar items. The Mogollon excelled at producing the tubular stone pipe, technically the most difficult to make. A few simple bone tools were also used, and gambling pieces of the same material reveal at least one of their diversions. They knew the art of basketry and in late times, after A.D. 700, they wore cloth of cotton, a fiber almost surely imported from the Hohokam.

The Mogollon Indian was of medium build and stature, with a round head, not greatly different from many modern Indians. He wore few, if any ornaments, though he may have painted his body to offset this lack. At death he was tightly folded and placed in a shallow pit and was rarely accorded the luxury of accompanying food containers or tools.

Since the northern frontier of the Mogollon touched on the Anasazi, and beyond the western boundary was the Hohokam domain, cultural blending was inevitable, especially because the Mogollon were a culturally impoverished lot and their neighbors were not. The net result of this was a submergence of the old simple Mogollon way of life, and the rise of a more complex society basically Anasazi, also tinged with Hohokam, in which a few old Mogollon elements were retained. Archaeologists are greatly interested in a cultural transformation of this kind because it reveals some of the processes of change. Although the Mogollon left an undistinguished record, having given little to their neighbors but having received much more, they added special and challenging problems to the archaeological past. Their modern descendants, if any, have not been identified.

On the plateau to the north of the Mogollon was the homeland of the Anasazi. These people are the best known of all of the prehistoric Southwesterners because archaeologists have studied their ruins for nearly a century and because, until recent years, most expeditions focused their attention on this tribe. Furthermore, the Anasazi have received prominence through the designation of many of their abandoned homes as national monuments.

Much of the plateau is arid, and vast stretches have neither arable land nor readily accessible surface water. These two factors determined the deployment of the population, and because of these the population density was spotty over the plateau, varying from great centers such as Black Mesa and the Hopi country, the White Mountains, Mesa Verde, the Chaco Canyon, to the sparsely inhabited Painted Desert. The diversified environment of the plateau required the development of specialized techniques before the land could be made to produce foodstuffs in sufficient quantities to support towns. The Anasazi rose to this challenge with an amazing degree of skill. The compelling requisites of water and soil determined the extent to which a community could expand, and expansion was the tribal pattern,

demanded by defense, group activities in farming, and proper conduct of religious ceremonies.

The Four Corners country, where Arizona, New Mexico, Colorado, and Utah come together, is generally regarded as the heartland of the Anasazi, and it is here that their oldest remains are found. These date from about the beginning of the Christian Era. Prior to this time the Anasazi were probably a nomadic people, but the earliest archaeological evidence is from the time when they were just adopting agriculture. Within a few centuries their living pattern was established. Their permanent dwellings, in or out of caves, resembled those of the Hohokam and Mogollon; these were often clustered in loose village arrangements. The bow and arrow replaced the spear-thrower or *atl-atl,* and pottery-making and the bean were added to the culture. Skills of the artisan were developed in basketry, and in the creation of woven sandals and sashes. Even music made its appearance with the development of flutes. The dog was domesticated. All this represents great progress by the Anasazi people in adaptation to and control over the environment.

Then started a long upward climb, the molding of a new way of life a thousand years in the making. These steps are traceable in the thousands of ruins that dot the plateau. The climax of Anasazi achievements was from about A.D. 1000 to 1400. This was the time when the homes were often built in caves widely scattered through the canyons creasing the plateau (Fig. 1.6). But infinitely more pueblos, as Anasazi towns are known, were built in the open because there simply were not enough caves to supply natural shelter for all. It is incorrect, therefore, to think of Anasazi people as cliff dwellers only. They established their residence wherever land and water permitted, and if a cave was available, so much the better.

Due to a method of dating which was developed on the University of Arizona campus, archaeologists have been able to speak of the age of Anasazi remains with a definiteness not possible for any other New World ruins. Dendrochronology, or the study of tree-rings, as applied to the ruins of the Southwest, was the brainchild of Dr. A. E. Douglass. The timbers that went into the Anasazi residences are the main sources for the raw data upon which this system depends. When the archaeologist is able to refer to past events in terms of dated decades, quarter or half centuries, rather than in the vagueness of a relative chronology lacking calendar years as we know them, half of the battle to interpret prehistory is won. The Anasazi story has been enormously enriched because of this method of studying the past.

Fig. 1.6   A typical Anasazi "apartment house" — White House Ruins, Canyon de Chelly.
Tad Nichols

With the mastery of agricultural techniques, food surpluses followed. The ability to store excess food in jars, baskets, and bins (even to the point of tiding the people over lean years) provided the stability that resulted in an expanding population, large communities, specialization in the arts, and, inferentially, increasing complexity in the social, religious, and political systems.

The evolution of pueblo architecture from simple beginnings was one of the finest accomplishments of the Anasazi. The joining of room to room whether of stone or adobe, and the stacking of rooms to a height of four or five stories was the Anasazi method for packing people into the least possible space. The reason for this crowding is not clear since there was no shortage of land. While most towns grew by accretion in response to the expanding population, a few of them show planning as though following an architect's design. The monotony of solid room blocks was broken by plazas, providing easier access to the rooms and good space for outdoor activities. The plazas of our oldest Western towns are surely traceable to this old Indian custom.

Another noteworthy architectural feature was the underground kiva with specialized furnishings. As in the modern pueblo Indian villages where kivas are in use today, the prehistoric kivas were probably owned by the male members of the clans, and were used both as club houses and for secret religious rites. The great kivas, as much as seventy feet in diameter and strongly roofed, were the most impressive buildings ever erected in the Southwest until the Conquest. They served the larger communities as a place where rites vital to the group as a whole, such as rain-producing ceremonies, were performed.

A familiar sight on all Anasazi ruins of this climax period are the numerous fragments of pottery. Much of this has black patterns on white backgrounds, the most distinctive of all Anasazi hallmarks (Fig. 1.7). Many other kinds are also present, such as multi-colored pottery and the rough-surfaced cooking and storing pottery known as corrugated. All of these have special significance to the archaeologist because the shapes, colors, and designs show differences from place to place and time to time.

Other arts also reached a high level of perfection. Textiles of cotton (Fig. 1.8), robes of feather cloth, sandals in a great variety of weaves, baskets, personal ornaments, ritual finery — all of these have been found by archaeologists.

The Anasazi dead were normally buried in the

Helga Teiwes Photo, Arizona State Museum, University of Arizona

Fig. 1.7   The white background is characteristic of Anasazi pottery. These pieces date from about A.D. 600 to 1300.

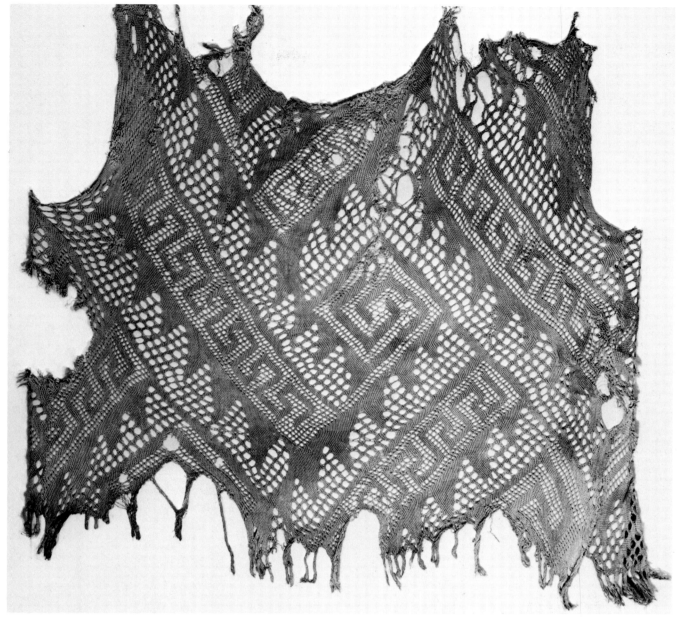

Fig. 1.8 A fourteenth-century cotton lace shirt from the Upper Tonto Cliff Ruin.   *Arizona State Museum, University of Arizona*

refuse heaps. From the graves come many of the objects that help archaeologists characterize the society. The skeletons reveal that these Indians have living descendants among such tribes as the Hopi, Zuñi, and the Rio Grande pueblos of New Mexico.

By A.D. 1400 some of the larger centers, thriving only one to two centuries before, had already been abandoned. The frontiers were shifting, mainly to the south out of the Four Corners country. The reasons for this still puzzle archaeologists. No satisfactory answer has yet been discovered, but it is certain that the causes were complex, interlocking, and that they influenced most of the Southwest.

This movement of people resulted in centers even larger than before, but far fewer in number. These enjoyed a brief spurt of cultural energy. By 1500,

however, only the Hopi, Zuñi, and Rio Grande centers remained. Chroniclers of the Spanish Conquest, which began in 1540, record only seventy pueblo towns, and by then most of the old glory was lost. The number today stands at about twenty-six. Perhaps a factor in the concentration of the Anasazi during the fifteenth and sixteenth centuries was the arrival of wandering hunters, the Navajo and Apache Indians. Upsetting as their presence must have been, these nomads did no more than speed up the Anasazi decline; they did not initiate it.

Anasazi history, like that of the Hohokam, matches the worldwide pattern of the rise and fall of ancient societies. Though obscured by time, their achievements have lent drama to Arizona's past.

Russell C. Ewing
Historian

2

THE SPANISH PAST

"AWAY UP HERE IN THE FAR NORTH, thousands of miles from Spanish centers at Mexico City, Guatemala, Bogotá, Santiago, and Buenos Aires, lay the outer fringes of the Spanish Empire — the northern borderlands. Remote they were, indeed, but what a history they have had!" Thus writes the Southwest's most distinguished historian, Herbert E. Bolton, in a panoramic presentation of Southwestern exploration called *Outpost of Empire*.

His exclamatory remark, "What a history they have had!" stemmed partly from his profound knowledge of the history of Arizona, which, for the greater part of 300 years, was one of Spain's most outlandish frontiers; and for twenty-five years, from 1821 to 1846, it was Mexico's most isolated political entity. But outlandish and isolated as it was, it was the home of scores of Indian tribes, and by the middle of the nineteenth century it was to be a meeting place of two Old World cultures, Spanish and Anglo, not to mention a few German and Italian culture bearers who served as missionaries during the seventeenth and eighteenth centuries. Some came to seek precious metals or to husband the land, while others came to garner souls, to explore, or to seek military and political glory.

The recorded history of Arizona began on a June day in 1527, when 600 men in five ships left Sanlucar, Spain, "to conquer, occupy, and colonize 'the provinces of Florida,'" which then constituted the Gulf of Mexico coastal areas from the tip of the Florida peninsula to the Rio Grande. This was to be the ill-fated Narváez expedition. On board were Alvar Nuñez Cabeza de Vaca, the treasurer of the enterprise, together with Alonso del Castillo, Andrés Dorantes, and the Negro slave Estevanico. These, according to experts, are said to have been the first Europeans to reach Arizona.

About a year later, after re-outfitting in Española (Haiti) and Cuba, the expedition made a landfall near Tampa Bay; and thus was begun one of the Southwest's most tragic ventures. Hostile Indians, lack of sufficient supplies, and a storm which sent the greater part of the expedition's fleet to the bottom of the Gulf took the lives of the greater part of Narváez's army. Four of the survivors, Cabeza de Vaca, Castillo, Dorantes, and Estevanico were to be held captive by Texas Indians for six years, while a fifth, Juan Ortiz, was to live with the Florida Indians for ten years before being rescued by Hernando de Soto.

These six years of captivity of Cabeza de Vaca and his companions were hard years; but they were profitable years, for Cabeza de Vaca gained an insight into the habits of the natives which enabled him, as a medicine man, to travel westward from tribe to tribe as a welcome healer. His route through Texas and New Mexico need not concern us here. Of more immediate importance is whether he and his three companions were the first Europeans to reach Arizona. If so, what route did they fellow?

Investigators of this rather troublesome problem are not in agreement. About half of them maintain that Cabeza de Vaca did not enter Arizona, while one extremist is sure that Narváez's treasurer crossed into Arizona by way of Zuñi. Another has the courage to say that all four of the survivors made their way across the lower San Pedro River and thence west into the Santa Cruz Valley. Two students of the matter, Carl O. Sauer and Cleve Hallenbeck, without doubt the most careful investigators of the entire Cabeza de Vaca route, are authorities for the statement that the three Spaniards and the Negro slave stepped into the southwestern corner of the state near Indian Wells. From this point, according to Sauer and Hallenbeck, Cabeza de Vaca followed a course by way of Tule Springs and over the low Peloncillo Mountains into the San Simón Valley, thence southwest across the valley through the pass between Dos Cabezas and the Chiricahua Mountains. This route is further marked out as proceeding along the western slopes of the Chiricahua Mountains, and then following a somewhat vaguely defined course to San Bernardino Valley. And quite as vague at this point is the matter of chronology. When did Cabeza de Vaca reach Arizona? Late in 1535? Early in 1536? A conservative and safe guess is that it was early in 1536. At any rate it is known that he completed his overland journey at Culiacán, Sinaloa, on April 11 of the latter year.

Cabeza de Vaca may have been a marathon hero to his countrymen, but of far more importance to them than admiration of his endurance was what he had to say about the marvels of the north. For example, when he told them he had reason to believe there were large and rich cities in the region, word soon got around that this must be another Mexico, another kingdom of the Aztecs. Or perhaps these were the long-lost Seven Cities, a fable as old as medieval Spain. In any event, it was a matter worth looking into. Even cautious and stolid Viceroy Mendoza was willing to spend the king's money on an army which he would send north in search of these reportedly rich cities.

But there must first be a reconnaissance expedition. Who would be in charge of it? Not Cabeza de Vaca, for he was to return to Spain and then later go off to Paraguay for more high adventure. Nor could the viceroy persuade either Castillo or Dorantes to retrace their steps up the Pacific coast; but perhaps the viceroy might wish to buy Estevanico, the Negro slave. Mendoza saw the wisdom of this, purchased the slave, and scoured the Valley of Mexico for an experienced and literate man who would lead the expedition and use Estevanico as a guide.

Someone now suggested the name of Friar Marcos de Niza as the most suitable person to take charge of the reconnaissance expedition, for it was known that he had had an enviable reputation as an explorer in both South and Central America. Moreover, he was at the present moment in Mexico City. Mendoza responded favorably to the suggestion and offered the job to the friar, who promptly accepted the assignment.

Route Is Legendary

The details of Friar Marcos' route are shrouded in mystery. He and a few Indian guides left Culiacán in March, 1539, following a trail blazed by Estevanico, who had been sent ahead with instructions to keep the missionary advised on the character of the country. The slave sent back tales of the marvelous splendor of the great cities which he had discovered, but aside from the fact that is pretty well established that he approached the present international boundary line from the upper Sonora River, it is not at all clear whether he continued on north to the Zuñi pueblos by way of the San Pedro or through the San Simón Valley. And there are some who even doubt that Marcos entered Arizona. This, however, is an extreme point of view, as is the remark that

the good friar wrote his name on some rocks near present-day Phoenix. The conservative point of view, and one held by most historians today, grants that Marcos barely crossed into Arizona near Lochiel. And somewhere in this region he learned that the Indians had killed Estevanico, which seems to have occasioned Marcos' rapid retreat to Culiacán.

Of immediate importance, as was the case with Cabeza de Vaca's observations, was what Marcos had to say about the people in the far north, and not about whether he had entered this or that river valley. So when Marcos said that he had seen one of the Seven Cities, Cíbola, "larger than the city of Mexico," with portals of turquoise, Viceroy Mendoza promptly organized an army to take possession of what appeared to be another Tenochtitlán, or Mexico City.

Command of the army was given to Mendoza's young friend, Vásquez de Coronado, who had only recently been appointed governor of Nueva Galicia, a vast west-coast province extending indefinitely northward from about present-day Guadalajara. Young men eager for adventure and possible wealth hastened to join Coronado's army, which was to consist of 336 men; and Friar Marcos, now Franciscan provincial, went along as guide and carried instructions to lay the foundation for future missionary work on this distant frontier. Also, a few of the soldiers' wives were permitted to join the expedition, and several hundred Indians were sent as servants and herdsmen. The herdsmen must have been busy indeed, for there were at least 1,500 animals in the caravan, including horses, cattle, rams, and sheep. Castañeda, one of Coronado's lieutenants, places the figure as high as 6,500!

Final preparations for the expedition were made at Compostela, capital of Nueva Galicia, and on February 23, 1540, the army began its march northward. Culiacán, the farthest northern outpost of Nueva Galicia, was reached early in April. Here Coronado pondered a statement he had recently received from Melchior Díaz, the *alcalde mayor* of Culiacán, who in the previous November had been sent by Mendoza "to go with some mounted men and to see if what he might discover conformed to the report of Father Fray Marcos."

Díaz, with fifteen horsemen and a band of Indians, had made a round trip to the north which lasted for about four months. They are known to have reached the Sonora, San Pedro, and Arivaipa valleys and to have gone as far north as Chichilticale near the Pinaleño Mountains. What is not known, however, is the precise location of Chichilticale, or Red House, supposedly to have stood at the foot of these mountains. Bolton places it on 76 Ranch near Eagle Pass, where "there are extensive pueblo ruins, one of which may well be the remains of the structure . . . called Chichilti-cale."

In Díaz' statement to Coronado the elusive site is mentioned, but Coronado was more interested in what the *alcalde* had to say about Indians and cities than about archaeological sites. In the main, though somewhat less

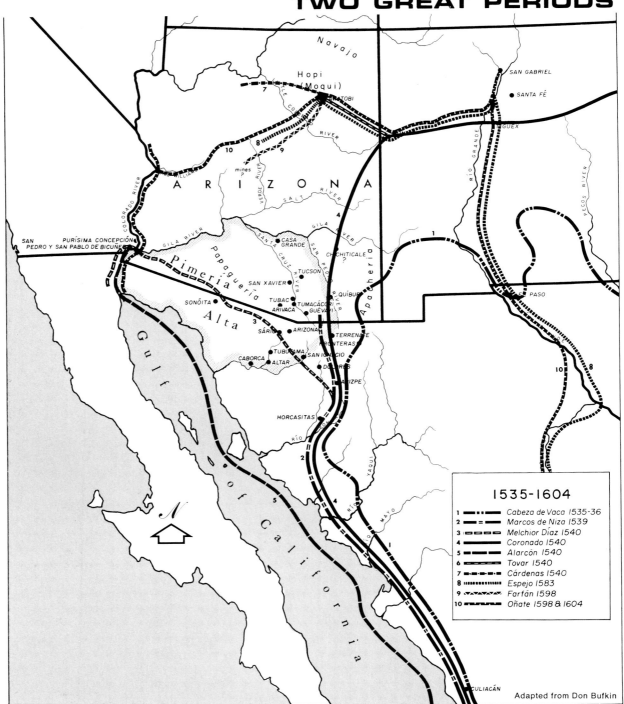

Fig. 2.1 Two and a half centuries before the American Revolution, Spain began a first great period of exploration, pressing thousands of miles northward from Mexico City and other more southern centers of colonial power.

dramatic in the telling, Díaz corroborated the essentials of Friar Marcos' report. Díaz makes no claim to having seen the cities, but his native informants assured him that "there are seven villages," that "the whole group is called Cíbola," that "they have plenty of maize, beans, and melons," and that "they do have turquoises in quantity."

There was no turning back now, even though Díaz' account of the fabulous north was a pale image of the Franciscan's report. But, owing to the barrenness of the route which Díaz said the army would have to follow, Coronado reorganized his expedition into two contin-

gents. One of these, a select group of about 100 soldiers and all the friars, was to serve as a vanguard under the command of Coronado. The other and larger part of the army was to remain at Culiacán under the direction of Tristán de Arellano with orders to follow the general in a fortnight.

The Coronado Trail Begins

On April 22 Coronado set out with his vanguard, following a route which had been marked out by Díaz and Marcos through the Sonora Valley and down the

[30]

PANISH EXPLORATION

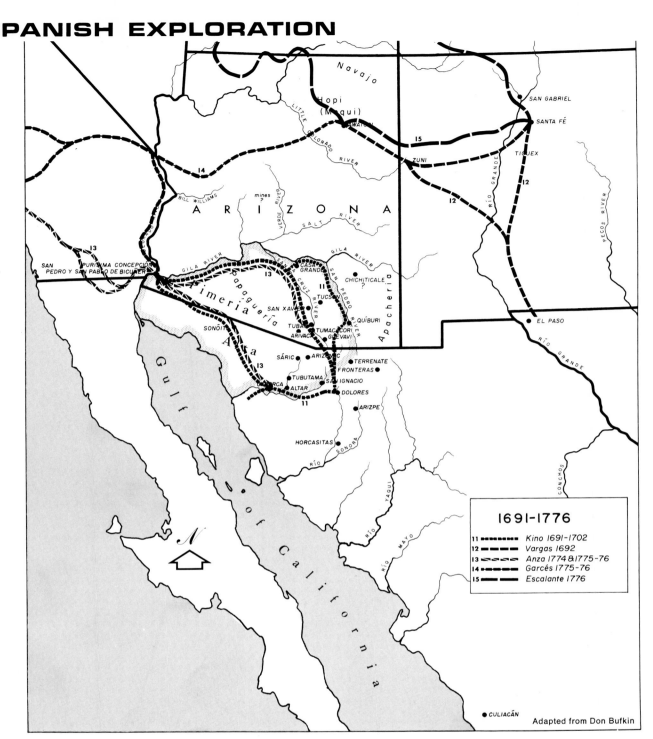

Fig. 2.2   In 1691 Padre Kino gave impetus to a second thrust, following a dormant interval of eighty-six years during which various missionary enterprises were short-lived on the northern borderlands.

San Pedro to a point just below Benson. It was now July, and the natives appeared to be friendly, especially the Sobaipuris, who lived on the San Pedro, or Nexpa as the Indians called it. Coronado's army now marched a little east of north through Galiuro Range and across Arivaipa Valley to Eagle Pass. Here again the records speak of the Red House, which, writes Castañeda, "must have been despoiled by the natives of this region, who are the most barbarous people thus far encountered." But this did not discourage Coronado from asking the natives how far it was to the Western Sea. "I found that it was fifteen days' journey distant from the sea,

although the father provincial had said that it was only five leagues distant and that he had seen it. We all felt great anxiety and dismay to see that everything was the opposite of what he had told your Lordship."

Coronado's interest in the Western Sea did not arise from idle curiosity: the viceroy was sending three ships up the Gulf of California coast with needed supplies for the army. The captain of the flotilla, Hernando de Alarcón, would certainly find it a bit difficult to deliver his cargo to a point some 200 miles inland. "Great anxiety and dismay," indeed!

Alarcón's vessels had left the port of Culiacán

shortly after the departure of Coronado's army, including the contingent under Arellano. The voyage was slow, but finally, on August 26, the fleet sailed into the shallow waters at the head of the Gulf. A few days later the ships reached "a mighty river with so furious a current that we could scarcely sail against it." They had discovered the Colorado River, which Alarcón chose to call the Buena Guía, or Good Guide, a phrase that appears on the motto of the coat of arms of Mendoza.

In order to make better headway against the turbulent stream and not to be wrecked on sand bars, Alarcón anchored his ships near the mouth of the river and proceeded upstream with two launches and twenty men. But the going was still most difficult, and at times it was necessary for the crews to fasten ropes to their boats and pull their crafts up the river. Nor did the Indians contribute to the peace of mind. About "two hundred and fifty Indians in warlike mood . . . came toward us with a loud outcry, their bows and arrows ready." But Alarcón was an able diplomat; before many days had passed the Indians were assisting the Spaniards in their struggle against the current and bringing "so much food that we had to lighten our boats twice." Moreover, the Indians were duly impressed with Alarcón's insistence that he was the Son of the Sun!

Where was Coronado's army? All the way up the Gulf, Alarcón had sought in vain for news of the general. But now the natives of the Colorado had encouraging words for Alarcón. One Indian told him that "he had been in Cíbola, that it was one month's travel from his country," and that he had obtained a "dog and other articles from a bearded negro . . . He had heard that the chieftain ordered him killed." Others, too, had heard of Cíbola, and some said they had learned of Coronado's arrival there. This set things in motion. Alarcón promptly called for volunteers to take a message to Coronado. But no one, either Spanish or Indian, accepted the exciting challenge to carry the message to Cíbola.

Somewhat displeased with his failure to contact Coronado, Alarcón prepared to retrace his course, but only after he had reached a point on the Colorado just above the Colorado-Gila junction. Yet there remained one final, desperate effort to get in touch with Coronado: the captain sat down and wrote letters summarizing his experiences, then buried the letters at the foot of a tree on which he inscribed, "Alarcón came this far; there are letters at the foot of this tree." Alarcón now set his sails to a friendly wind which sent his ships to the sheltered ports of Nueva Galicia.

While Alarcón was exploring the Colorado and Coronado was drawing near to Cíbola, the main army under Arellano had bivouacked in the Sonora Valley to await further orders from the general. This gave Arellano the opportunity to send a party of his men to the Gulf in search of the sea expedition. The ships were nowhere in sight, but there were plenty of tall Indians. One "was so large that the biggest man in the army did not come up to his chest." This special detail returned to the Sonora Valley in time to learn that orders had come from the north with instructions to proceed at once, but to leave a small contingent in the valley as a sort of half-way base. The couriers who delivered the orders were none other than Friar Marcos and Melchior Díaz. The Franciscan, in poor health and no longer in the confidence of Coronado, was encouraged to return to his duties in Mexico. Díaz was commissioned to take charge of those who would remain behind in the valley, and also to search for the elusive ships of Alarcón.

A Perilous Trek

Shortly after Arellano moved to join Coronado, Díaz began his memorable march west through the land of the Papagos and the Yumas. With him went twenty-five Spaniards and several Indians as servants, guides and interpreters, and a herd of sheep was driven along for food. It was late September, and the route was northwest, perhaps on one of the Southwest's most perilous trails, the Devil's Highway. Details of the journey are not known, for it appears that none of the participants in this hazardous venture wrote of their experiences. Fortunately, however, the garrulous Castañeda was close enough to the event to provide us with a reasonably accurate synopsis of what occurred.

After a march of 150 leagues, Díaz reached the Colorado near the mouth of the Gila, where the inhabitants were "like giants, exceedingly tall and muscular." The Spaniards also noted that the Indians carried firebrands with which they warmed their hands and bodies; and for want of a better name, the soldiers called the Colorado the Río del Tizón, or Firebrand River, a name which was more commonly applied to the river than Alarcón's Buena Guía.

Of course Alarcón was not to be found, but the Yumas told him that the Son of the Sun had only a few weeks earlier turned down the river. In posthaste Díaz and his men went in search of the captain. Three days later they reached a place about half way from the Gulf to Yuma, and, behold! here was the tree at whose foot lay the buried letters. They were promptly dug up and read. Castañeda does not provide us with any quotations from the letters, but he does say that the letters made it clear to Díaz that Alarcón had returned to New Spain, or Mexico. What a treasure it would be if these letters were extant! Perhaps Díaz destroyed them in a rage of disappointment.

Díaz retraced his steps to the vicinity of Yuma, where, after a brush with the Indians, he and his party crossed to the east bank of the river. Then, swinging south and west, the group went in search of the "other coast," which apparently meant the western shore of the Gulf. After about a week's march, tragedy struck when Díaz was accidentally impaled on his own spear while in pursuit of a greyhound that was molesting the sheep. The expedition promptly turned back, recrossed the river and headed for the Sonora Valley. All but Díaz made it. He lies buried somewhere along the Devil's Highway.

At this point it would be well to ask, who discovered the state of California? The usual story is that Rodríguez Cabrillo, in 1542, was the first European to see the Golden State. But how about Alarcón? Melchior Díaz?

The Search for Cities Continues

By now, Coronado and his army had reached Cíbola and were preparing to establish headquarters in the upper Rio Grande Valley. Cíbola had been a great disappointment. Where were the Seven Cities? Possibly there were seven, but they could hardly be compared with the Aztec capital. This was Zuñi country, and the only pueblo of any consequence, at least from the point of view of the Spaniards, was Háwikuh, which Coronado chose to name Granada, "both because it has some similarity to it and in honor of your Lordship" (Mendoza). One wonders what the people back home might have thought of this comparison.

But the natives were most obliging. Once they became aware that the Spaniards were in search of the fabulous, it was easy to send the white conquerors on their way. To the northwest, said the Zuñi, was Tusayán, a province with seven cities. "Seven" runs deep in Spanish folklore, but here was an occasion when the number was founded on hard mathematical reality. Following the directions given them by the Indians, some twenty-three soldiers led by Zuñi guides discovered seven towns in Tusayán. This was Hopi country, or the land of the Moquis, as the Spaniards were to call it.

It was now mid-July, 1540. Ensign Pedro de Tovar was in command of the Tusayán expedition. A Franciscan friar, Juan de Padilla, "who had been a warrior in his youth," and who at one time had been with Cortés, was brought along to teach the natives the Gospel. The Hopis were in no mood to extend Tovar a welcome. "They had heard that Cíbola had been conquered by very fierce men who rode animals that ate people," writes Castañeda. Hence, in a hostile spirit, the Hopis made it quite clear that the white intruders must remain well beyond the limits of the town. To this the Spaniards objected, and most especially Father Padilla, who apparently still viewed such situations with the eye of a soldier. "Indeed, I do not know what we have come here for," he said. Tovar and his companions accepted this remark as a call to arms, and within a short while the natives were scurrying towards their mesa-top homes. Primitive weapons were no match for what were then modern instruments of warfare — long, well-tempered lances, and gunpowder and lead, not to mention "animals that ate people."

It may be assumed that some of the natives were killed in the scuffle, though the records are none too clear on the matter. It is well known, however, that the Hopi chiefs did now consent to talk things over on a friendly basis, and as peace offerings the natives gave the Spaniards food and a few turquoises. Tovar was pleased to accept the gifts but demonstrated more interest in what the natives had to say about a deep gorge in the west than in a donation of maize, flour, and piñon nuts. But since Tovar was not authorized to go beyond Tusayán, he and his squad returned to Háwikuh.

General Coronado's imagination was aroused by the story of the deep gorge. Perhaps a great river flowed through it on which sailed the ships of Alarcón. This was something that had to be investigated. So, on August 25, Captain García López de Cárdenas was sent with a command of twenty-five horsemen to find this geographical curiosity. A three-weeks' march carried them through the Painted Desert and the Hopi settlements to the rim of Grand Canyon. Here, near Grand View, they looked out upon one of nature's greatest scenic wonders; but Cárdenas and his men must have been a hard lot, because, so far as we know, not one of them has left us a description of the natural beauty of the canyon. To them "it looked like an arroyo." And where was the great river Coronado hoped they would find? There was certainly a stream off in the distance, "a fathom across." Six feet! The natives quickly corrected this optical illusion by saying that it was "half a league wide." A mile and a half! This the Spaniards would not believe until three of the more agile of the party spent the greater part of one day within the depths of the canyon. We have the names of two of these pioneer Arizona mountain climbers, Captain Melgosa and Juan Galeras, who said they had gone one-third of the distance to the bottom of the canyon where they could see that "the width given by the Indians was correct." The Indians knew their geography; and an unnamed member of Coronado's army said the river was "as large or much larger than the one at Seville." Further details of this, as well as of many other tantalizing but clouded events of the Coronado expedition, may some day come to light, if the lost report of the official chronicler of the army, Pedro de Sotomayor, is found. It is known that he accompanied Cárdenas to the Grand Canyon of the Colorado River.

Water Not In Evidence

It was a great disappointment to Cárdenas and his men that they had not reached the river on which they might find Alarcón's ships bulging with supplies; moreover, the party was in desperate need of water. Perhaps there were rivers to the south and west, or at least a spring or a lake. But neither spring nor lake was to be found, not even a water hole. So, after a trek of four days, and after being told by their native guides that there was no water to be found for three or four more days, Cárdenas gave orders to turn back. This was fortunate decision, for within a few days they had reached a waterfall, near which were some fine crystals of salt. "They . . . gathered quantities of it which they brought and distributed when they returned to Cíbola." Dr. Katharine

Bartlett, an authority on early explorations in northern Arizona, places the discovery of the salt deposits near the mouth of the Little Colorado. And salt, like water, is essential to pioneering on any frontier. Thus, although the records are silent in this respect, there is good reason to believe that Coronado's men placed the crystals in their knapsacks; perhaps the crystals would be used to season a steak or lamb chop some evening in front of the campfire along the trail.

Meanwhile, two other contingents of Coronado's army were on the march. Captain Hernando de Alvarado, at the head of a party of about twenty men, was exploring the country to the east of Cíbola, to turn back only after reaching the Canadian River. And from its rendezvous in the Sonora Valley, Captain Arellano's command was pushing north along Coronado's trail.

Leaving a handful of men at San Gerónimo, a name which the Spaniards had attached to their Sonora encampment, Arellano and his troops had begun their march a few days before Díaz went in search of Alarcón. Assuming that they followed Coronado's route, they entered the San Pedro Valley and proceeded thence to Chichilticale. "They found the natives cheerful and submissive everywhere, and without fear," writes the chronicler, Castañeda, who was a member of Arellano's army. And the Indians were generous with their food supply, for, in the vicinity of a placed called Vacapán, which Bolton identifies as Arivaipa, they presented the soldiers with quantities of *tuna* preserves. The gift satisfied the hunger pangs of the Spaniards, but it had some serious side effects. For the greater part of twenty-four hours the soldiers were "drowsy with headaches and fever, so that the Indians could have done great harm to them if they had wished," says Castañeda. This was further proof of the "submissive" nature of the Indians.

The "army Señora," as the soldiers chose to call it, recovered from its bad case of indigestion and moved on to other adventures along the trail. A day's march beyond Chichilticale the army was interrupted by a flock of mountain sheep which aroused the hunting instincts in some of the advanced guard. The soldiers gave chase, but, writes Castañeda, who accompanied the hunters, the sheep "are fleet in rough country, so we could not overtake them and had to let them go." The chase was perhaps in the neighborhood of Eagle Pass, and Castañeda left the first written record of these Arizona animals.

Three days later, Arellano's army "learned another bit of natural history" when it reached what apparently was the Gila River. Here they stopped to examine a horn, "a fathom long and as thick at the base as a man's thigh. By its shape it looked more like the horn of a buck than of any other animal. It was worth seeing." Indeed it was, not only because of its astounding size, but also because Coronado had placed it on the trail to mark the route to Cíbola.

The travelers now pushed on into the high country where, within a day's journey from Cíbola, "there arose in the afternoon a bitter cold whirlwind, followed by a heavy snowfall, which brought considerable hardship to the Indian servants." They came from the warm climes of the south, and there was now "plenty to do taking care of them and carrying them on horseback while the soldiers walked." Thus, pioneering did strange things to ethnic relationships; but the frontier was no place for race snobbishness, especially in situations where an Indian guide and interpreter spelled the difference between success and failure of an enterprise.

Arellano's contingent pushed on to Cíbola without other incidents of note. Here they were joined by the discoverers of Grand Canyon and by some of the men who had gone east with Alvarado to the Canadian River. In his march across the Rio Grande Alvarado had reached the heart of the Pueblo country, a region which he strongly recommended as an excellent site for winter quarters for Coronado's army. The recommendation was promptly seized upon. Coronado thus established his headquarters in the province of Tiguex, and in the following spring went in quest of fabulous Quivira, only to return to the Rio Grande for another winter and disappointment; and in April, 1542, Coronado was forced to abandon his enterprise and lead his men back down the trail to Nueva Galicia and to the misfortunes of a courageous but, in the eyes of jealous contemporaries, an unsuccessful and incompetent discoverer. All of this, of course, is significant history but falls outside the scope of the present narrative.

Dormant for Four Decades

Forty years were to pass before interest was renewed in this far frontier of New Spain, as all of present-day Mexico was called during the colonial period. The coastal plains of the Gulf of California had served and would continue to serve, after the opening of the seventeenth century, as a corridor to Arizona. A second corridor, the great Central Plateau of Mexico, became an avenue to New Mexico and northern Arizona, and by 1570 soldiers, miners, and missionaries had reached a point on the Conchos River, a little more than eight hundred miles down the plateau from Mexico City. Here, in the Conchos Valley, two settlements were founded, Santa Bárbara and San Bartolomé, both of which were to become bases for the Spanish advance into New Mexico during the closing years of the sixteenth century. And the authorities had anticipated the importance of this distant frontier when, in 1562, they had created the province of Nueva Vizcaya, comprising a region in the northwest beyond a line of some indefiniteness stretching from about Saltillo, Coahuila, to the southern limits of the present state of Sinaloa.

An advance of well over six hundred miles north of this line was occasioned in the opening years of the 1580s by reports at Santa Bárbara and San Bartolomé of northern Indians who had a culture worth exploiting; moreover, so the story went, there were large settlements of people in the area with little or no knowledge of Christianity. If the reports were true, why not send missionary, soldier, and miner to take possession of the country for the King of Spain? And how about the rumors of English activities in the north? For after all, Francis Drake had only recently sailed the coast of California and had taken possession for his monarch. Perhaps he had discovered the elusive Strait of Anián. If he had, then the English were in a favorable position to sail from the Atlantic to the Pacific, or the South Sea as it was often called, and thence to the riches of the Orient. International rivalry for this part of the continent was in the making.

Thus, on June 5, 1581, a party of about twenty-eight persons, comprised of three Franciscans, nine soldiers, and some sixteen Indian servants, left Santa Bárbara for the land of the Pueblos. Traveling by way of the Conchos and the Rio Grande, they reached a point not far from present Bernalillo and visited Acoma and Zuñi. Chamuscado, in command of the soldiers, became disappointed in his search for gold and silver and ordered his men to return to Santa Bárbara. Two of the missionaries, Agustín Rodríguez and Francisco López, chose to remain with the Pueblos, even though the third friar, Juan de Santa María, had been killed by the Indians. None of this expedition, either missionary or soldier, had stepped within the present limits of Arizona; but there is evidence that somewhere in the vicinity of Zuñi they had heard of the Hopi villages, "where there were five large pueblos with many people. According to the signs which the Indians made," writes a member of the party, "they understood that two of the pueblos were very large, and that in all of them large quantities of cotton were raised, more than any other place which they had seen."

The Franciscans at Santa Bárbara feared for the lives of Rodríguez and López. A rescue party was therefore promptly organized, and a wealthy Mexican, Antonio de Espejo, offered to finance the expedition and to accompany it in its search for the friars. The offer was accepted, and on November 10, 1582, the party set out from San Bartolomé, following the route which had been opened up by Chamuscado and the Franciscans in 1581.

This enterprise is known to history as the Espejo expedition, which was comprised of some fifteen soldiers, together with Fray Bernaldino Beltrán and some Indian servants and interpreters, and over a hundred horses and mules. Reaching the New Mexico country, they learned that both Rodríguez and López had been killed by the Indians. Thus, Beltrán believed that he had accomplished his mission and was therefore anxious to return to the Conchos settlements. But Espejo and his soldiers had come to see the sites and to look for mines. One expedition for this purpose reached the northern part of Arizona.

By the middle of March, 1583, the party had reached the Zuñi pueblos, where the Indians told Espejo about Coronado's visit to the region and said that there were mines west of Háwikuh and that not very far away was the province of Mohose, another name for the

Moqui, or Hopi, country. These were tales which drew Espejo and nine adventurous soldiers on west, together with some friendly Zuñi Indians. The rest of the party, including Beltrán, remained behind. The route they followed was no doubt over a well-trod Indian trail to the Hopi villages: generally west to the Puerco River, which they crossed at a point about twenty miles east of the present town of Holbrook, thence northwest and north across Leroux, Cottonwood, and Jeddito washes. Perhaps they were following the same trail that Tovar and Cárdenas had used some forty years earlier.

On April 17, after a march of ten days, Espejo's party was greeted near Jeddito Wash by "a few of the bravest" Hopis from Awátobi, or Aguato as the natives called it. The Indians protested their interest in peace; and by "sunset so many people came from Aguato in a short time with tortillas, tamales, roasted ears of green corn, maize, and other things, that although our friends (the Zuñi) were many, they had half of it left over," writes Diego Pérez de Luxán, who was one of the nine Spaniards who accompanied Espejo on this *entrada* into Arizona. And a great feast it must have been, for Espejo tells us that he had 150 Zuñi Indians in his entourage, not to mention "three Christian Indians" who had been in Coronado's army and had chosen to remain in Cíbola.

After the banquet, and after Espejo had given the Hopis "some presents of little value" as tokens of friendship, the Spanish captain asked the Hopis to build a corral for the horses. "We . . . told them that the horses we had with us might kill them because they were very bad, and that they should make a stockade where we could keep the animals, which they did." So states Espejo. Luxán says, "We asked them to build a fortress of dry masonry in which we could keep the horses, because the friendly Indians told us that we could not trust them." But a close examination of the documents leads one to the conclusion that neither man was telling the whole truth. The region was teeming with Indians — so it seemed to Espejo and Luxán. How could ten soldiers hope to cope with the 50,000 Indians Espejo said he saw, especially if they took to the warpath? Luxán was a bit more conservative in his estimate of the number of Indians in Hopi land: "The Lord willed . . . that the whole land should tremble for ten lone Spaniards, for there were 12,000 Indians in the province with bows and arrows, and many Chichimecos whom they call Corechos." Thus it would be worth a guess to say that the "fortress" was designed quite as much for defense as for corralling the horses.

Espejo and his little army now marched on to Aguato (Awátobi), Gaspe (Walpi), Comupaui (Shongopovi), Majanani (Mishongnovi), and Olalla (Oraibi). Six days were spent visiting the villages, and possession of each "was taken for his majesty in the main plaza with a salvo of harquebus shots." The natives everywhere were generally friendly and exceedingly generous. On one occasion the chiefs gave the soldiers "4,000 cotton *mantas,* some colored and some white." The

Spaniards were pleased with the gift, but some of them were more interested in what the Hopis had to say about mines than in praising the natives for their mastery of the art of weaving. Perhaps these were the mines from which the Zuñi people said ore had been taken and given to Coronado.

The Party Divides

The mines, so the Hopis said, were to be found far to the west, where the country was arid and difficult to traverse. Moreover, it was a region of "many barbarous people who could kill us by throwing mere handfuls of dirt," says Luxán. Espejo therefore believed it would be wise to divide his party into two equal parts, one to go in search of the mines, the other to return with the baggage to Cíbola. The five who chose to prospect for mines might lose their lives, but there was good reason to believe that the remaining five would succeed in reaching Cíbola.

On April 30, both contingents began their march from Aguato, and both were destined to complete their missions without loss of life. Espejo, leading what no doubt was the first band of white prospectors in Arizona, headed southwest. A march of five leagues carried them to a waterhole. "We named this place El Ojo Triste," writes Luxán. This was an appropriate name — Sad Waterhole — for the reason that it was virtually dry and "was insufficient for the horses, so they were two days without water." On the following day, May 1, they continued their march and spent the night on the banks of the Little Colorado, "a fine, beautiful river . . . containing many groves and willows." According to Dr. George P. Hammond, the recognized authority on the Espejo expedition, the party had reached a point not far from the mouth of Cañon Diablo.

Continuing southwest, through a country "of many large pools of rainwater . . . rich in . . . pastures and cedar forests . . . and ash trees," and after a two-day march, they set up camp at a spot some ten or fifteen miles south of the present city of Flagstaff. Here, for the first time since leaving the Hopis, they were molested by Indians, who were attracted to the camp by their curiosity to see the strange animals which the Spaniards were riding. But, says Luxán, the Indians "fled when they heard them as they found the sound unfamiliar." (The horses must have neighed.) So these "warlike mountainous people," as the soldiers described them, chose to remain at a respectable distance along the entire route. This was a fortunate development, at least for the Spaniards, for within a day or two Espejo was to move into the country of the Yavapai, a people whom the white man at a later time had great difficulty in conquering.

The last stage of the journey, of some forty or fifty miles, was over rough, forbidding country to Sycamore Creek, which the soldiers named Río de las Parras, or River of the Vines, since "this river is surrounded by an abundance of grapevines." Espejo approached the creek by descending a steep rise, "so steep and dangerous that a mule belonging to Captain Antonio de Espejo fell down and was dashed to pieces." That night and the next day, May 6, they spent near the Sycamore. On the following morning they broke camp and pressed on some six leagues, marching "at times close to the Parras river." Here they found an abandoned native village, though not far away they saw some Indians "seated around with their heads low, singing of the peace they wished with us." This was good news, as was the discovery of mines on the following day. At least the discovery of the mines was good news to Espejo, who says, "I found them, and with my own hands I extracted ore from them, said by those who know to be very rich and to contain much silver." But Luxán disagreed with his chief: "We did not find in any of them a trace of silver, as they were copper mines, and poor." But both are in general agreement on matters relating to the natives and the geography of the country. The discovery was close to the Verde River, which the Spaniards named the Río de los Reyes (Kings River), on whose banks were "Castilian grapes, walnuts, flax, blackberries, maguey plants, and prickley pears." The Indians raised maize, lived in good houses, and were very friendly; and by signs they told Espejo that beyond the mountains was a very large river, "eight leagues in width and (which) flowed towards the North Sea." They were no doubt referring to the Colorado, but they had it flowing in the wrong direction, if we are to believe Espejo's narrative. Or the Spaniards may have misunderstood what the natives said, for the correct reference should have been to the South Sea, as the Pacific was called during a great part of the colonial period.

Having reached their objective, Espejo and his men did not tarry on the banks of the Verde. On the eighth they gathered together their effects and began their return journey to Zuñi over a course somewhat different from the one they had taken to the mines. Unfortunately, the records are silent on the route which they were now to follow, aside from the laconic remark of Espejo that, "We endeavored to return by a different route so as to better observe and understand the nature of the country, and I found a more level road than the one I had followed in going to the mines." They made their way to the vicinity of Awátobi, and thence to Zuñi, where they arrived on May 17. Thus, within a week after leaving the Verde they were back in Zuñi, a distance of well over 300 miles, which is something of a record for horseback riding through a region of steep mountains, deep ravines, and thick forests, a challenge to the best of equestrians.

The Espejo expedition, after a few months of exploration in New Mexico, made its way back to San Bartolomé, arriving there on September 20, 1583. The report that Beltrán and Espejo made about the deaths of Rodríguez and López was sad news; and the tales the missionary and the captain had to relate about a land of numerous Indians and rich mines, not far from which the natives said there was a lake of gold, created an atmosphere of expectant activity along the northern frontier and at points as far south as Puebla. Espejo himself had visions of returning to New Mexico, though for reasons none too clear he was not again to be sent north. In Puebla one enthusiast for exploration asked for authority to lead an expedition to search for a northern strait that, so he said, connected the South Sea with the North Sea and lay well beyond the upper limits of New Mexico. Others, not waiting for official approval, made *entradas* across the Rio Grande, one of which turned northeast and went as far as the Platte River. But it was not until the closing years of the sixteenth century that another official expedition was sent to New Mexico.

The Oñate Expedition

The leader of this party was none other than Juan de Oñate, the wealthy son of a still wealthier father, who was one of the discoverers of the bonanza silver mines at Zacatecas. By marriage, Oñate the younger was also one of Mexico's "400" of the day. His wife was the granddaughter of Cortés and great-granddaughter of Montezuma. Thus, wealth and family position, plus a strong desire to make a name for himself, enabled Oñate to obtain a contract for the conquest and settlement of New Mexico. In return for bearing the expenses of the expedition, he was granted extensive privileges as governor and captain-general of the enterprise; but jealous rivals and a change in viceroys delayed his departure for nearly two years.

Finally, on February 7, 1598, under orders to conquer and to colonize New Mexico with a party of missionaries, 400 men, and several families, Oñate started his northward march from the Conchos River Valley. With some minor variations, Oñate followed the route opened by his Spanish predecessors to New Mexico, and not far from the present site of El Paso he took formal possession of the region in the name of the Spanish crown. Pushing on up the valley, he reached the pueblo of Caypa, which he made his headquarters and from which he was to send soldiers to explore the country and to conquer the Indians. Oñate's subsequent subjugation of the Pueblos in New Mexico is one of the Southwest's great epics.

Espejo's mines, together with Indian accounts of pearls, which convinced Oñate that the South Sea must be nearby, attracted the governor and some of his men to the west. And not the least of these attractive forces was the possibility of finding the South Sea, for New Mexico could then "trade with Peru, New Spain, and China," says Oñate. So, on October 6, 1598, Oñate and some of his men, including Captain Marcos Farfán, who was second in command, began their westward march. Their route no doubt was over a well-beaten path from the Rio Grande to Zuñi. Here they spent several days, during which time Farfán made a short *entrada* into Arizona in search of a salt spring which the natives said was nine leagues away. The Indians knew what they were talking about, for Farfán says he found the "best saline in the world . . . a league around . . . and . . . a depth of over a spear's length." This saline was certainly not the one that Coronado's men had discovered somewhere near the mouth of the Little Colorado, since it only took Farfán three days to make the round trip to the spring. Yet, no one has been able to identify the site of the discovery.

On November 8, Oñate's entire party set out for the Hopi villages, probably over the same trail that Espejo had followed. It was mid winter, the snow was falling, and the soldiers and animals suffered from the lack of sufficient water. They seem, however, not to have been molested by the Indians, and reached the Hopi villages after a three days' march. Here — perhaps at Awátobi — Oñate decided to send eight men under the command of Farfán to find the mines, while the governor himself and the rest of the party would return to the Zuñi province and there await the return of Farfán. Neither Farfán nor Oñate tell us why this decision was made. Perhaps the governor did not wish to submit his entire group to dangers of a severe winter and hostile Indians.

On November 17, Farfán and his companions started down the trail for the "rich mines." Perhaps they followed the one used by Espejo. Authorities are not in agreement, either as to the route, or as to the sites of the mines which Farfán discovered. Bolton traces the route somewhat parallel to that of Hammond's description of Espejo's trail, though Bolton is not in agreement with Hammond on the site of the mines. According to Bolton, the mines were on Bill Williams Fork, not near the Verde. Bartlett contends that there were two possible routes which Farfán could have followed, though she has a preference for Espejo's line of march. Both Hammond and Bartlett believe the mines were in the Verde Valley, and the latter scholar is willing to commit herself to the precise spot: "undoubtedly . . . the present location of the United Verde Copper Company at Clarkdale."

Whatever the route may have been, Farfán has given us the first classic description of the region as to its geography, ethnology, flora, and fauna. The details, of course, cannot be included within the limits of this paper. Suffice it to say that he found the Indians peaceful and numerous and the land abounding in game and in tall pines and fertile valleys. There were times when the going was difficult, but Farfán does not dwell on this. The important thing was the objective, which he reached on November 23.

On the following morning, six Indians led Farfán to a mine, "which was at a good height . . . There they found an old shaft, three *estados* in depth [16 ft. +], from which the Indians extracted the ores for their personal adornment and for the coloring of their blankets, because in this mine there are brown, black, water-colored, blue, and green ores." Nearby was a large dump, and Farfán noted that there was a wide vein of rich ore which "crossed over to another hill." And at still another point they found a vein "two arms' length in width" which they named San Francisco. "The veins are so long and wide," says Farfán, "that half of the people of New Spain can have mines there." Bonanza! The soldiers promptly staked out some thirty claims, for themselves and for their companions at Zuñi.

The discovery of the ores did not engage the entire attention of Farfán. After all, so the story went, the South Sea was not far away; and the captain's native informants at the mines corroborated the story by saying that there was a great river in the west, on whose banks lived "immense settlements of people" and which emptied into a sea. Good news, indeed; but Farfán was not commissioned to go in search of the sea. It was his duty to make a prompt report of his discovery of the mines. Thus, by what appear to be forced marches, the expedition retraced its route to Zuñi, carrying with it samples of ore. Fatigue, however, compelled seven members of the party to spend a few days in the Hopi country while Farfán and one soldier hurried down the trail to Zuñi, which they reached by December 11.

The governor was pleased with the results of Farfán's discovery, but conditions in the Rio Grande Valley were of more immediate importance than organizing an expedition for further ventures in the west. That could wait; and it did. It was not until 1604 that Oñate was able to return to Arizona, though there is some evidence that one of his men, Vincente de Zaldívar, in 1599, led a party of twenty-five men westward, to "a point which he was told was three days from the sea." If this is true, he must have been in, or passed through a part of, Arizona.

Oñate's journey to the Gulf of California is one of the most notable chapters in the history of Arizona explorations. On October 7, 1604, Oñate set out from his capital in New Mexico, with an army of thirty men, "most of them raw recruits," says one of Oñate's fellow countrymen, who, about twenty years later, was to write one of the best accounts of the journey. Attached to the army were two Franciscans, Juan de Buenaventura and Francisco de Escobar. The latter left a dairy of the enterprise.

The Route to the River

Despite our sources, which are none too plentiful for the expedition, it is most difficult to trace with accuracy the route followed to the Colorado. Bolton and Bartlett quite naturally agree on the route to the Hopi villages but are in disagreement on the course taken from there to Bill Williams River. Bolton seems to place this segment of the route somewhat west and north of Bartlett's, though both of them agree that the party reached the forks of the Bill Williams, thence down the river to the Colorado, which Oñate called Buena Esperanza, or Good Hope. From this point it is not difficult to trace Oñate's route. He turned up the Colorado to, perhaps, a point near Needles, then faced about and traveled down the east bank of the river to the mouth

of the Gila, to which they gave the name of Nombre de Jesús, or Name of Jesus. Leaving some twenty horses here to graze, "so that they might be in condition to make the return trip to the provinces of New Mexico," Oñate and his men proceeded down the river to the Gulf, where, on January 25, 1605, "We took . . . possession . . . for the glory and honor of God our Lord." The Spaniards knew their geography well enough to know that they had not reached the South Sea but the Gulf of California. And how about the pearls that were supposed to be found? The natives were familiar with these lustrous gems, "but," writes Escobar, "we could not find a single one among the Indians, even though the governor did his best."

Oñate may have been disappointed in not having found the South Sea and a land of pearls, but he and his companions heard many exciting stories from the natives living on the banks of the Colorado. Mohave Indians from the vicinity of Needles spoke of the great Lake of Copalla where the natives wore bracelets of gold and from whose shores migrated the people who settled in Mexico. The Spaniards took this to mean the Aztecs. The story was repeated and elaborated on as the Spaniards traveled down the river. There was also an island of gold and silver, said the Indians; and as proof that there was silver to be found, the Indians pointed to the silver plates which the Spaniards carried and said that they were of the same metal which the Indians west of the Colorado used for cooking utensils. Some of the soldiers may have believed this tale, but Father Escobar had his doubts: "Only an examination of the metal, in case it exists, as so many Indians affirm, will dispel my doubts." Then there was the account of an island ruled by a chieftainess, "very corpulent, very broad, and with big feet." Here, too, was silver, and most of the men of the island were bald. And, so the stories went, there was a nation of people whose ears were so long that five or six persons could stand under each ear, and not far away were natives who slept under water, not to mention a tribe whose people had only one foot, and still another which slept in trees. Moreover, the Indians wanted the Spaniards to know that there were people in the region who lived solely on the odor of their food, and others who slept standing up. Escobar entered all of this in his diary, not because he was willing to believe "such monstrous things," but merely as a matter of record. "Each one may believe what he wishes," he writes. Perhaps the soldiers were a bit more credulous than the friar.

Oñate now felt that it was time to return to the Rio Grande; and after five or six days of exploring near the mouth of the river, the expedition started its return journey. At the junction of the Gila and the Colorado the soldiers stopped to round up the horses they had left behind on their way down the river, only to learn that the Indians had eaten about half of the animals. This was a serious loss, but the Spaniards were wise enough to know that they should not punish the natives. So far, the Indians everywhere had been quite friendly. A battle with the Indians here would only cause trouble further up the trail. After all, according to the records, there were twenty thousand Indians living just along the east bank of the Colorado between its mouth and the Gila! This no doubt then was a prudent decision, for the tribes remained peaceful all along the route, which, apparently, was the one the expedition had taken on its outward journey. They reached their New Mexico capital, San Gabriel, on April 25, 1605, "all sound and well, and not a man missing," writes one of the early Spanish chroniclers of New Mexico.

Exploring Epoch Ends

Thus ended the first great period of exploration in Arizona (1540–1605). During the next seventy-five years, despite the fabulous stories and the evidence of rich mines, Spanish activity in the region was mainly confined to missionary enterprises in the northwestern parts of the present state, enterprises, however, which were short-lived and seldom successful. And the center of Spanish interest in the area continued to be in the Hopi country. The Navajo, to the north and east of the Hopi, were relatively insignificant at the time of discovery, and it was not until the opening years of the eighteenth century that the Spaniards made any concerted attempt to conquer and then to Christianize these natives.

The religious conquest of the Hopis began in 1629 when three Franciscans, Francisco de Porras, Andrés Gutiérrez, and Cristóbal de la Concepción — all from New Mexico — were commissioned to found missions among the Moqui. In the spring and summer of that year, "with their crucifixes at the neck and staffs in their hands" and accompanied by twelve soldiers, the three missionaries made their way from the Rio Grande and Zuñi to the Hopi villages. They reached Awátobi on August 20, St. Bernard's day, and in honor of the occasion they gave the saint's name to the village. "Here," writes a contemporary, "the friars were received with some coolness, because the devil was trying in all possible ways to impede and obstruct the promulgation of the divine law." According to the record, the devil was obtaining considerable help from an apostate Indian who had entered the village shortly before the arrival of the missionaries and the soldiers. The Spaniards, so he said, were coming to burn the villages, "steal their property, and behead their children." Moreover, he warned the Indians not to be deceived by the men in the party who wore trousers and vestments, for they were imposters and would sprinkle water on their heads, a ceremony which would certainly kill the recipients. Thus, the missionaries and soldiers walked into an atmosphere of hostility, and for two nights the Spanish guards were on the alert for an Indian attack.

The Indians chose not to attack the Spaniards, but the spirit of hostility lingered on, even though the missionaries tried to win the friendship of the natives by distributing trinkets such as knives, beads, rattles, and hatchets, "in order to make them feel that the friars came to give rather than to ask of them." But then there was to be a sudden change in the attitude of the Hopis, a change for the better which the Franciscans said was brought about through a great miracle, or the healing of a blind Hopi boy by Father Porras. Shortly thereafter, so say the priests, this resulted "in the conversion of a thousand Indians." This was a turn of events which angered the Hopi shamen, who now awaited the opportunity to rid the country of the white man's priests. Nearly four years passed, however, before the opportunity presented itself, when, on June 28, 1633, Porras died from eating food which had been poisoned by the Indians. The Franciscans thereupon withdrew from the Hopi villages, though there is some evidence that, during the years 1647–72, the friars did return for short periods of time. Then, shortly before the Pueblo Revolt of 1680, the Franciscans again undertook to Christianize the Hopis, only to meet their deaths during the revolt. Though we know very little about the careers of these martyrs, we do have their names; Fray José de Figueras, who was killed at Awátobi; Fray José Trujillo at Shongopovi; and friars José de Espeleta and Augustín de Santa María at Oraibi. It is at this time, too, and no doubt owing to fear of Spanish vengeance, that the Hopis removed their towns from the foot of the mesas to more defensible positions on the summits, where their villages may still be seen. But the Spanish soldiers were not sent out immediately to punish the natives, for the reason that the Spaniards themselves had been defeated by the Pueblos and were compelled to retreat to El Paso. Here they remained for more than a decade before they were able to reconquer the New Mexican Indians.

The successful reconquest of New Mexico was accomplished under the leadership of Diego de Vargas, one of Spain's ablest frontier governors. In the fall and winter of 1692, Vargas and his army made their first effective march into the upper Rio Grande Valley and to the Hopi settlements. Here, at the Hopi villages, which the governor reached on November 18 with an army of sixty-three picked soldiers and two missionaries, the natives at first showed signs of hostilities. But the well-armed soldiers, together with Vargas' apparent intentions to treat the Indians in a friendly manner, caused the natives, with the exception of those at Oraibi, to agree to live in peace with the Spaniards. Vargas then planned to use force, if necessary, to bring the Oraibi people to terms, a plan, however, that did not meet the approval of the governor's lieutenants. The weather was severe, the horses and mules were all but exhausted, and there was not a single water hole on the route they would have to follow to the village. The lieutenants therefore argued that the loss of their horses would be a disaster for the army. Vargas heeded the advice of his lieutenants, and on November 24 the army began its return march to the Rio Grande by way of Zuñi.

But Vargas had learned something else about the country. To the west of the villages, so he had been told, were rich silver and quicksilver mines in the Sierra Azul and Cerro Colorado, two more of the many fabulous sites in early Arizona history. In the Sierra Azul, said one of the Indians, was an "ochre deposit . . . in a large round pool, in the form of a reddish liquid which sometimes moved and changed in color." The story was not new to Vargas, for he had heard of the Sierra Azul even before he had left El Paso, and he now hoped that his journey to the Hopis would enable him to verify the story. And, as was so common in the history of the conquest of the northern borderlands of New Spain, Indians were very anxious to spin yarns about silver and gold mines, especially when they discovered that this was one sure way to encourage the Spaniards to move on. Vargas, however, was not prepared to go in search of the Sierra Azul, though he did obtain some samples of ore which the natives said came from the mines. A few months later, the ore was assayed and found to be very low grade. Nevertheless, the Sierra Azul myth continued to stir the imaginations of the Spaniards for many years.

The Hopis, with the exception of those at Oraibi, may have promised Vargas that they would remain friendly, but Vargas and his army were soon to discover that none of the Indians in the region intended to keep their promises. Throughout the rest of the colonial period the Hopis remained recalcitrant and often allied themselves with the Navajos, the Utes, and the Pueblos in their attacks upon the Spaniards. During the Pueblo revolt of 1680 and the lesser uprisings of 1696, many of the natives of the Rio Grande fled to the Hopi country and were not to return to their homes in the east. A few, however, in 1748, were forced to abandon their town of Payúpki, on the Middle Mesa, and to settle at Sandía. And in the eighteenth century several notable punitive expeditions were sent against the Hopi, one of the most significant under the command of Governor Felix Martínez in 1716. He spent twenty days in the Moqui province with an army of sixty-eight soldiers, a dozen or more members of the Santa Fé cabildo, and a group of 255 "loyal Indian auxiliaries." But this show of force did not frighten the natives to the point of making peace with the governor. They chose to fight, a decision which cost them the loss of several lives and many head of livestock, as well as the destruction of a great part of their maize fields. Nevertheless, they were not to be conquered, and Martínez was compelled to retreat to the Rio Grande. And it was during this period, too, (1680–1750) that the Apache menace grew to serious proportions, all the way from the upper Rio Grande and northern Arizona to the Spanish settlements in Sonora and Sinaloa.

Thus, the sixteenth and seventeenth centuries had been a period of spying out the land, searching for the fabulous, and attempting to subjugate the Indians in northeastern Arizona. This was a story which was to continue throughout the eighteenth century, though the scene was to change and a few new elements were to be introduced into the historical development of Arizona. The main lines of Spanish approach were no longer to be from the Rio Grande but from Sinaloa and Sonora. Of course the Indian frontier was to pose its problems, yet missionary, soldier, miner, and farmer came to stay.

The northwest frontier of New Spain had come to rest for half a century, from 1540 to 1591, in the vicinity of Culiacán. But in the latter year, with the coming of the Jesuits to the Sinaloa Valley, foundations were laid for a hundred-year march, valley by valley, to the present boundaries of Arizona. The Jesuits carried the Cross and founded the missions until 1767, when they were expelled from all the Spanish dominions; but theirs was not labor lost, for the Franciscans were promptly sent to replace Loyola's sons. Both, Jesuit and Franciscan, like their brethren in northern Arizona, were to win the martyr's crown. And both marched side by side with the soldier, who at times found it most difficult to view frontier conditions in the same manner as his missionary companions. Then there was the miner, Indian and Spaniard, who often found himself at cross-purposes with missionary and soldier. Thus, from all of this, arose difficult administrative problems for the authorities in Guadalajara, Mexico City, and far-away Spain.

In an effort to meet these problems, new jurisdictional areas proceeded along with the advance of the frontier, such as Sinaloa, Ostimuri, Sonora, Pimería Baja, Pimería Alta; and in the closing years of the eighteenth century, as one desperate effort to integrate the administration of the entire northern borderlands of New Spain, the famous Interior Provinces was created and placed under the direction of a commandant general, whose headquarters were to be at Chihuahua City. This vast region, as was the case in nearly every administrative reform for the borderlands, was established only after careful planning for improving the military defense of the region against both Indians and hostile European powers. The Spanish authorities were therefore careful to select their most competent subjects to make the necessary investigations and recommendations for frontier reforms. Hence it was that Pedro de Rivera, in the years 1724 to 1728, made a tour of inspection of the military outposts across the entire frontier and recommended some important reforms. In 1766, the Marqués de Rubí was sent all the way from Spain to inspect the military posts, especially with a view towards checking the depredations of the Apaches. In 1769, one of the king's most important ministers, José de Gálvez, visited Sonora and, on the basis of his and Rubí's reports, brought about the creation of the Interior Provinces. Six years later, Inspector Commandant Hugo O'Conor set about, with some success, in putting into effect the several recommendations for reorganizing the northern military frontier.

Fig. 2.3 Padre Kino, seeking a land passage to California, defined the peninsula and the mainland with fair accuracy.

Donald B. Sayner Collection

The Fort and the Mission

The two most significant institutions, then, were the presidio, or military garrison, and the mission. The presidio — usually a walled fort — was located at a strategic point near potable water and sufficient pasturage for horses. The command of the post was commonly in the hands of a captain, commissioned either by the local governor or by officialdom in Mexico City. The second in command was either a standard bearer or a lieutenant, and the normal complement of the garrison varied from twenty to fifty men, some of whom were assigned to the nearby missions. Here it was their duty to protect the resident missionaries and to accompany them on

their visitation to outlying Indian villages. There seems to have been no specific term of enlistment, if "enlistment" is the proper word, and the soldier's paymaster and supply officer was the captain of the presidio. The records are therefore replete with instances of graft at the expense of many a soldier. Yet, despite the hardships faced by these frontier soldiers, there are few if any accounts of mutiny but many instances of the presidial's excellent fighting qualities. Occasionally, one might desert, a practice which is hardly unique in the history of armies. Occasionally, too, in times of emergencies, the presidials were assisted by town militia.

The mission system came to the New World shortly after the Columbian discovery and followed the course of the Spanish empire everywhere in the Americas. As noted above, the missions on the northern frontiers of New Spain were assigned to the Jesuits and the Franciscans. Of course, the first duty of the missionary was to propagate his faith, but he was never to overlook the fact that he was also one of the king's principal economic and political agents. It was the missionary who brought European crops to the frontier, taught the Indians the most advanced methods of agriculture and animal husbandry, and supplied nearby presidios with the products of the fields and mission shops. It was the missionary also who often served as the frontier diplomat and ambassador. By the processes of acculturation, mission Indians were brought within the sphere of the Spanish political system, and the archives are full of missionary reports on ways and means for dealing with rival European powers.

Kino in the Borderlands

The first of these missionary diplomats in southern Arizona was the famous Jesuit, Eusebio Francisco Kino. Born in Italy and educated for the priesthood in Germany, he was to be sent to Baja California and northern Sonora. His assignment to Baja California was short-lived, owing to the fact that the authorities on the mainland were unable to provide adequate supplies for the peninsular enterprise. Kino and his companions were therefore recalled, and the Jesuit, upon the advice of a friend, accepted an appointment, in 1687, as missionary to the Pimas, who lived on the northern borders of Sonora. In March, he chose an Indian village on the upper San Miguel as the site of his mission, which he named Nuestra Señora de los Dolores. From this point and until his death in 1711 Kino was to make no less than thirty major expeditions, which took him at various times to the native settlements on the Altar, the San Pedro, the Santa Cruz, the Gila, and the Colorado. Nor did he neglect to make a trip or two to the Gulf coast in search of geographical knowledge. This was Pima Land, or Pimería Alta, extending north and south from the San Ignacio River to the Gila, and east and west from the San Pedro to the Gulf. It was a region which was administered as a part of the province of Sonora, and the province itself was included within the kingdom of Nueva Vizcaya.

It has been said that during Kino's day Pimería Alta had a population of some 30,000 Indians. The most numerous group, the Pima tribe, lived in villages near the head waters of the Sonora, the San Ignacio, the Altar, the San Pedro and the Santa Cruz. There were also a few who resided in the region between Gila Bend and the Casa Grande. The Sobaipuris lived on the San Pedro and had their principal village at Quíburi, whose ruins may still be seen a short distance north of present day Fairbank. These, too, were of Piman stock, differing mainly from the Pimas to the west in their warlike

characteristics. (The Sobaipuris had to be warriors, for they faced the Apaches to the east.) Another Pima-speaking group, the Sobas, were found along the lower San Ignacio and Altar rivers, and their principal town was at Caborca. Astride the present international boundary and generally west of the Santa Cruz Valley was still another Piman people, the Papagos, whose struggle for existence in their arid environment brought about culture traits which differed from their linguistic brothers on the rivers. Scattered in villages along the Gila, from about the bend to near the river's mouth, were the Cocomaricopas. At the junction of the Colorado and the Gila lived the Yuman peoples, south of whom, and extending to the delta, were the Quíquimas. (The Colorado River people, especially south of the Gila, present an interesting problem in ethnography, both as to names and numbers. Even a cursory comparison of the Oñate documents with those of Kino and his contemporaries proves the point.)

These, then, were the Indians whom Kino and his companions taught the European way of life; and native leaders often became the Jesuit's acculturation instruments. At Dolores was powerful Coxi, chief of many of the western Pima villages. It was Coxi, christened Don Carlos by Kino, who persuaded his people that the Spaniards were the Indians' friends and would bring them happiness. The natives responded by building Kino's church, which was dedicated on April 26, 1693. At Quíburi was Chief Coro, who remained a pagan but was always faithful to Kino, and who served both Spaniard and Indian alike by sending his Sobaipuri warriors against the Apaches. Down the Altar Valley, a short distance south of Caborca, was El Soba, warlike leader of the natives in the valley but willing to assist Kino on the missionary's treks to the Gulf.

But native chiefs alone, despite their friendship for Kino, could not maintain "peaceful coexistence," especially in the Altar, where, in 1695, the Indians rose in rebellion and killed Father Francisco Xavier Saeta, a young Sicilian priest who had only recently been sent to establish a mission at Caborca. Though for nearly a year there had been unrest in the outlying villages, or *rancherías,* before the Pimas went on the warpath, neither Kino nor his missionary companions were apprehensive about Indian loyalties in southwestern Pimería. For reasons none too clear, the rebellion began at Tubutama, north of Caborca, and on April 2 a band of natives, in the guise of peace, entered Saeta's quarters and "filled his poor body with arrows till he resembled Saint Sebastian," writes Bolton. The rebels then turned on some of the father's servants, whom they also slew, and then marched up and down the valley, in the wake of plunder, fire, and death.

To Kino and his associates this was a most unhappy turn of events. The leaders of the uprising must certainly not go unpunished, but would it be wise to use sword and gun to reestablish peace? Violence might only lead

Fig. 2.4 Caborca, Sonora, in the late 1960s restored its Kino mission.

J. W. Baugh

The Chain of Missions

to further violence. It would be enough to bring only the leaders to trial and justice, not the rebels in general. But this was a plan which went awry when fifty Indians appeared at El Tupo, near present day Magdalena, for peace talks. Some of the soldiers, like their later Anglo-Saxon counterparts, believed that "the best Indian is a dead Indian." There then ensued what was long known in the history of Pima Land as La Matanza — The Slaughter. The Pimas thereafter did settle down to peaceful ways, but for reasons other than the massacre at El Tupo. Fifty-six years later, in 1751, the Pimas were again to strike at the Spaniards, on both sides of the modern international border, bringing about far more serious consequences than the rebellion in Kino's day.

Kino was to found twenty-five missions, three of which, San Gabriel de Guevavi, San Cayetano de Tumacácori, and San Francisco Xavier del Bac, were to be in the Santa Cruz Valley, between Tucson and Nogales. There is some difference of opinion on the dates of the founding of Guevavi and Tumacácori, though it has been clearly established that San Xavier was founded in April, 1700, Kino himself taking part in the construction of a mission church. "On the twenty-eighth," he writes, "we began the foundations of a very large and spacious church and house of San Xavier del Bac, all the people working with much pleasure and zeal." But the beautiful "White Dove of the Desert," though bearing the name

Tucson

San Xavier Del Bac

Sonoita △

Tubac 1752
Tumacacori △
Quevavi △

Quiburi

Ootcam △
TUCUBAVIA △

Busanic △
San
Bernardo
Aquimuri △

Santa
Barbara △

Baconacos △
Bugato
San 1741
Lazaro

Terrenate

Sarica △

Siboda △

Cocospera △

CANANEA ○

Cuquiarachi

Fronteras
1690

Cuchuta

Santa Teresa △
Atil △

Tubutama ▲

Imuris △

Remedios △

Bacoachi ▲
Vescuachi △

Teuricachi △

Caborca ▲

Pitiquito △

Oquitoa △

Tupo △

San Ignacio ▲

Magdalena △

Bavispe ▲

Bacerac ▲

Bisaning △

Alfar
1752

SANTA ANA

Dolores △

Saracachi △
Cucurpe ○

Arizpe ▲

Chinapa ▲

Huachinera ▲

NACOZARI ○

Oputo △

Tuape △

Sinoquipe ▲

Cumpas △

Santa Magdalena
de los Tepocas
(probable location) △

Opodepe ▲

Banamichi ▲
SAN JUAN BAUTISTA
Huepac ▲
Aconchi ▲

Opusura ▲
(MOCTEZUMA)

Guasavas △

Bacadehuachi ▲
Satachi △
Serva △

Nacori △

Mochopa

Nacameri △

Baviacori △

Terapa △

Tepachi △

Populo △
1742
Horcasitas ○
Los Angeles △

Ures ▲

Batuc ▲
Tepupa △

San Mateo
Teopari △

Carrizal
(probable location) △

Hermosillo

Pitic
1741

San Pedro
de la Conquista
de los Seris

Santa
Rosalia △

Alamos △

RIO SONORA

Matape ▲
Nacori △

Bacanora △

Sahuaripa ▲
Santo Tomas ▲
Pondia △
Arivechi ▲

ISLA
TIBURON

San Jose de
Pimas △

Rebeico △

Soyopa △

Tacupeto ▲
Tarachi △

Tecoripa ▲

Tonichi △

Onapa △

Natori △

Suaqui △

Onavas △

Movas △

Yecora △

Maicoba △

N

San Jose Laguna
and
San Jose de Guaymas

Cumuripa △

Nuri △

Tezopaco △

Tepahui △

Guaymas

Buena Vista △

BAROYECA ○

Belem △
Huriuwas △
Rahum △
Potam △

1765

Vicam △

Torin △

Bacum △

Cocorit ○

Ciudad
Obregon

Conicari △

Tesia △

Camoa △

Navojoa ○

CIUDAD
ALAMOS ○

Cohurimbo △

Eichoja △

Santa Cruz
de Mayo △

OFUERTE

MISSIONS of SONORA
1614 – 1826
— L E G E N D —

▲ MISSION CHURCH IN USE ▲
△ MISSION CHURCH RUINS △
◻ PRESIDIO
○ TOWN

SCALE   IN   MILES

0   25   50 miles

Compiled by GEORGE ECKHART
Drawn by DON BUFKIN

Fig. 2.5   Jesuits established dozens of missions north from the Río Mayo to the Santa Cruz.

Kino had given to his mission, was built by the Franciscans in the closing years of the same century. Guevavi may have been founded in 1701, and Tumacácori a year or two later.

It was not until 1691 that Kino made his first *entrada* into Arizona, accompanied by one of his closest friends, Father Juan María de Salvatierra. They descended the Santa Cruz Valley as far as Tumacácori, and visited Guevavi. They were favorably impressed with the fertile countryside and the friendly natives; and in the following year Kino returned to the valley, visited Bac, where they encountered an Indian population of 800, and then turned east to the San Pedro, which was then referred to as the Río de San Joseph de Terrenate, or de Ouíburi. Thus Kino had begun his contacts with the northern groups of Pimería Indians, contacts which were to continue until his death in 1711 at the Sonoran mission of Santa María Magadalena. And it is most fortunate that he was to write a detailed account of his experiences and observations, under the title of *Favores Celestiales,* which was later translated by Bolton as *Kino's Historical Memoir of Pimería.* It is from these, together with the writings of the superb diarist, Juan Matheo Manje, who was often Kino's companion on the trail, that students have drawn most of their facts on the early history of southern Arizona.

For example, it was Kino and Manje who have given us our first written records of the famous Casa Grande, together with priceless accounts of the Indians and the land on which the natives lived. Along the lower Colorado, in 1699, they heard echoes of folk-tales which Oñate had listened to eighty-four years earlier. But they had a new one for Kino and Manje, though it was one which was rather common in many quarters of the Southwest. The tale related to The Woman in Blue, who at one time had visited the Colorado people, dressed in white, grey, and blue, and who wore a veil. She spoke to them in a language they did not understand, and they shot her with arrows, leaving her for dead. But she came to life and "left by the air."

Kino had not gone to the Colorado to listen to yarns. He was much more interested in facts of geography, especially those relating to Baja California. As a young man, he had been taught to believe that Baja California was a peninsula. This, of course, was correct; but in New Spain he was told there was no peninsula in the area, that California was an island. This Kino doubted, and by questioning the Indians and observing the Gulf coast he reasoned that his initial concept was true. To inform the world of his conclusions he drew the first fairly accurate map of the peninsula and the mainland in 1701.

Kino was by no means the only famous Jesuit in Pimería Alta. Padre Agustín de Campos, one of the ablest of linguists, reached Pimería Alta shortly after Kino began his work at Dolores, and for twenty-three years Campos followed the example set by Kino. Beginning in the 1720s bands of Jesuits with un-Spanish

Esther Henderson

Fig. 2.6   A national monument since its restoration is San Cayetano de Tumacácori, Kino mission in the Santa Cruz Valley.

sounding names — Keller, Sedelmayr, Steiger, Nentvig, Rhuen — entered the Pima missions, and before the expulsion of 1767 many more were to arrive from Mexico and Spain. But, with few exceptions, very little is known about any of them. They still await their Herbert E. Bolton or Francis Parkman.

Two Highlights of History

Between the time of the death of Kino and the expulsion of the Jesuits, there were two notable events which made their marks on the history of Pimería Alta. One relates to the discovery of silver; the other, to the Pima revolt of 1751.

A dozen or so miles southwest of the twin cities of Nogales is a site which is sometimes called Arizona. Perhaps the big state of Arizona owes its name to this small spot on the map. Everyone is not in agreement

J. W. Baugh Photo, Eckhart Mission Collection

Fig. 2.7   After Padre Kino's remains were found in Magdalena, a tomb was erected over the burial site.

on the origin of the application of the state's name, but students of Southwest history all admit that the spot on the map, in 1736, was far more important than the vast area to the north. For it was in the Sonora hills at Arizona, which in the eighteenth century commonly went by the names of Arizonac, Aranzazu, or San Antonio de Padua, that one of the most remarkable discoveries in the mining history of the Southwest was made.

Late in October or early November, 1736, Antonio Siraumea, a Yaqui miner, while searching for mines in the hills near the settlement, discovered large nuggets and slabs of silver lying close to the surface. This set off a mining rush, the first of its kind on this frontier. The hills were soon swarming with hopeful prospectors, many of whom struck it rich — at least for a time. Word got around that the metal was virgin silver, a rumor which, in the main, proved to be true. This was a matter that needed official investigation, for the king's interests were at stake; therefore, the captain at the nearby presidio of Terrenate, Juan Baustista de Anza, father of the founder of San Francisco, hastened to the scene. Upon his arrival, he learned that much of the silver had already found its way into the pockets of many a Spanish store-keeper. Moreover, he was soon to learn that no less than 4,000 pounds of silver in the form of large balls and slabs, had been taken from a comparatively small area; and one such ball or slab was so large and heavy that it had to be broken into manageable pieces. Anza promptly placed an embargo on all the silver which

had been discovered, for there was a highly important legal problem to be solved. If the silver was the product of normal mining procedures, the king would be entitled to one-fifth of it. If it were a treasure trove, as some believed, then the state might lay claim to all of it. And supposing the Aztecs had hidden it here on their march to the Valley of Mexico, a point of view held by many a frontiersman of the day. Yet, there was the possibility that God in His wisdom had cached the metal for the use of the missionaries, so said some of the Jesuits. It was the Jesuits also who provided Anza with legal briefs on mining law. Fathers Joseph Toral, Cristóbal de Cañas, and Juan de Echagoyan, from their missions on the southern limits of Pimería Alta, in detailed and well-documented opinions, informed the captain that the discovery presented some knotty problems, but it was their belief that most of the silver belonged to the state. In effect, this was also to be the decision of authorities in Mexico City. Thus the discoverers were to be denied their claims to the silver. But this did not stop the silver rush, and doubtless many hopeful prospectors sank picks into the Arizona hills north of Arizonac. Yet there is no evidence that any comparable deposits of silver were found, and within a few months the prospectors set aside their picks and settled down to a more normal life.

Life remained normal until the early winter of 1751, when the Pimas once again rose in rebellion against their Spanish masters. The uprising, which began in November at Sáric, a mission in the upper Altar, was to be the most serious Indian revolt in the history of Pimería Alta. The causes of the uprising are not clear, though it is known that Luis Oacpicagigua, native governor and captain general of the Pimas, had long been hostile to the Spaniards and was waiting for the opportunity to lead his people in violence against the white men. By November 20, he thought the opportunity had arrived, and instructions went out to all of his people to destroy the white man and all his property. Within two days, Father Tomás Tello was murdered at Caborca, and Father Enrique Rhuen and some of his servants were killed at the Papaguería mission at San Miguel de Sonoita. The revolt had also taken its toll in the Santa Cruz Valley and on the several scattered ranches. Father Francisco Paver, in charge at San Xavier and anticipating trouble, hurriedly made his way to Guevavi with three soldiers and his *mayordomo*. At Guevavi, Paver was joined by Father José Garrucho and others fleeing from the ravages of the Indians, and all retreated to the presidio of Terrenate. A few hours later San Xavier, Guevavi, and the Spanish farms at Arivaca lay in ruins. Meantime, down the Altar Valley at the mission of Tubutama, padres Jacobo Sedelmayr and Juan Nentvig, the latter of whom had escaped the hostiles at his mission of Sáric, were fighting off the attackers. Behind the barricaded walls of Sedelmayr's house, the fathers and a handful of Spaniards and loyal natives succeeded in keeping the Indians at bay, though two of the defenders were killed. After more than a day's fighting, Sedelmayr and his group made their way to a ranch at Santa Ana and later moved to Mission San Ignacio. Thus, within three or four days no less than 100 persons had lost their lives.

Reports of the uprising had reached the presidio and capital of Sonora, San Miguel de Horcasitas, where Governor Diego Ortiz Parrilla organized an army to subjugate the rebels. After nearly four months of campaigning, Oacpicagigua and his people, upon assurance that they would not be seriously punished for their deeds, agreed to return to their villages and to live in peace with the Spaniards. There was also to develop a serious quarrel between the governor and the missionaries, a situation quite common to the history of the Spanish borderlands. In this instance, missionary and soldier, searching for the causes of the uprising, accused each other of being responsible for native unrest and rebellion. The facts of the quarrel reached the ears of the authorities in Spain, and, after some eight years of studying vast quantities of documentary records relating to charges and countercharges, the king's attorney ordered "that this matter be placed in perpetual silence." In other words, the royal authorities did not want to hear any more about it.

In order to maintain peace in Pimería, word had also come from Mexico City that a presidio was to be established in the heart of Pimería Alta. The word arrived in the form of a decree issued by the viceroy, dated January 31, 1752, with instructions that a force of fifty men was to be assigned to a permanent garrison, the site of which was to be chosen by Parrilla. On March 18, Parrilla ordered the founding of the presidio, though it was several months before the governor and his advisers made their final decision for the site of the military post, which was to be Tubac. The first commander of the establishment was the experienced frontier officer, Captain Thomás de Beldarrain; and Parrilla has left us the muster roll containing the names of these early Arizona pioneers.

Ousting of the Jesuits

Sixteen years after the Pima Revolt, but not consequent upon that event, came the expulsion of the Jesuits from all of the Spanish dominions. The causes for the expulsion are not well known, but the entire affair had tremendous repercussions, both in the Old and in the New World. On this frontier — Pimería — the Jesuit missions were assigned to the Franciscans, whose record of achievement matches that of the Jesuits. Among the more notable ones who played a significant role in the history of Arizona during the Spanish period were Fray Francisco Garcés, an expert in Indian psychology and the beloved missionary at San Xavier; Fray Pedro Font, superb diarist and keen analyst; padres Juan Díaz, Matias Moreno, and Thomás Eixarch, all three of whom, together with Garcés, were to meet a martyr's death across the river from Yuma in 1781; and padres Francisco Escalante and Francisco Domínguez, both of whom were to cross northern Arizona in a famous expedition from Santa Fe in 1776.

Fig. 2.8 An altar detail from Cocóspera exemplifies colonial transmission of European arts to New Spain.

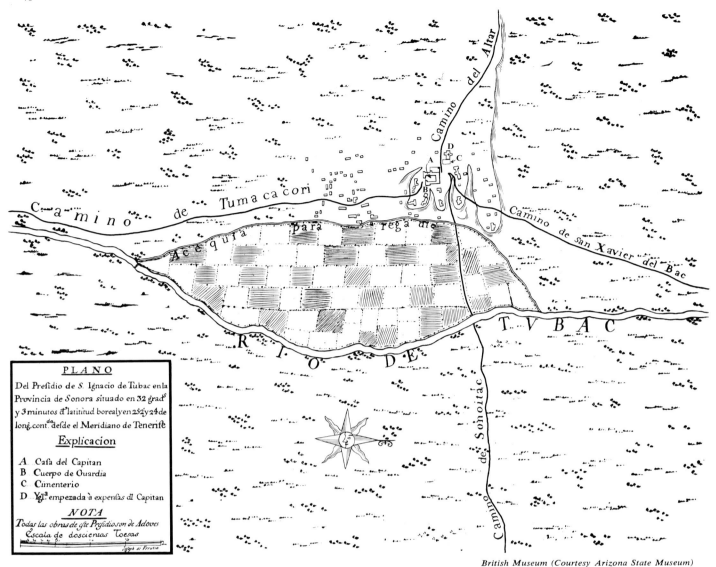

Fig. 2.9   Twenty-four years before the founding of Tucson as a Spanish pueblo, the viceroy established a presidio at Tubac.

Quite as important as this array of famous names were those of soldiers and colonists. Lieutenant-Colonel Juan Bautista de Anza, commanding officer at Tubac and son of a distinguished father who had also served his king in Pimería, explored a route to San Francisco in 1774, and in the following year, 1775–76, led a colony of 240 persons from Tubac and as far south as Culiacán to found the great city by the Golden Gate. It was a caravan of soldiers with their wives and three missionaries, two of whom, Garcés and Eixarch, stopped off at Yuma, while Father Font continued on to California and kept a detailed diary of the expedition. And of course Anza had not overlooked the essentials of logistical support, including such important items as 695 horses and mules and 355 cattle.

It must have been an impressive sight when, on October 23, the caravan moved out from Tubac and began its march up the Santa Cruz Valley. Eight days later Anza and his colonists were at the Casa Grande, where Font made a thorough study of the place and drew a ground plan of the ruins. He was deeply impressed with what he saw and amused with what he heard. The Indians felt compelled to relate the "true" history of the site. The builder of the Great House, said the local historian, was The Bitter Man, whose servants were the wind and the clouds, and whose pretty daughter was married to a good-for-nothing. This made for trouble, but eventually The Bitter Man managed to set things aright. Then came the The Drinker to the country, whose principal assistants were the Humming Birds and the Coyote. He, too, had his troubles. He became so angry with his people that he flooded their lands, burned their skins with the sun, and turned some of the natives into saguaros. For the record, Font wrote all of this in his diary, and more; but he says, "we laughed a little at these yarns."

The expedition made its way down the Gila to the Colorado, reaching the junction of the two rivers on November 28. Here they were greeted by Chief Palma, a long-standing friend of both Anza and Garcés. This

Yuman chieftain, together with Father Garcés who on former occasions had visited the natives in the region, had convinced Anza of the feasibility of an overland route to California. Palma had been rewarded for his faithfulness by a medal which Anza had given him in the previous year, 1774, when Anza and a party of soldiers passed through the Yuman villages on their initial reconaissance from Caborca to Monterey. Palma now returned the honors by providing a fiesta in the best fashion, after which the colonists, with the exception of Garcés and Eixarch, were assisted across the river and continued their march to Monterey and San Francisco.

Eixarch and Garcés remained behind with instructions to await the return of Anza. Eixarch settled down to the serious endeavor of converting the natives; Garcés, who was happiest on the trail with Indian companions, explored up and down the Colorado, "Padre Garcés," writes Font, "is so fit to get along with Indians, and go among them, that he seems just like an Indian himself." He ate their food, no matter how disgusting it was to the more delicate palates of the Spaniards; and, as a psychologist, he carried with him "a linen print of Maria Santísima with Niño Dios in her arms, having on the other side the picture of a lost soul." Here was an effective visual aid. The Indians, said Garcés, had their choice, either of following the teachings of the Most Holy Mary, or of becoming the lost soul on the other side of the picture. Usually, it was an easy choice.

Eixarch was not so ingenious and went off in despair to Caborca, only to return a few weeks later to be present upon the arrival of Anza from California. But Garcés was not at the Yuma villages when the lieutenant-colonel reappeared on the banks of the Colorado. The friar had been exploring and showing his linen print to the natives. At the time of Anza's return to the Colorado, Garcés was in the California mountains and was preparing to extend his peregrinations to the Hopi country and possibly to the Rio Grande Valley. Therefore, he set his course eastward, through the Mohave country, and reached the Colorado at a point well north of Yuma, just two weeks after Anza and his party had left for Sonora. Here Garcés employed guides and headed east through the mountains, intent on reaching New Mexico. No one has yet taken the trouble to mark out his route with care, but it is reasonable to infer that it must have been close to the Santa Fe Railway route as far as Peach Springs. In any event he reached the Hopi villages, and would have continued on to Zuñi had the natives been more friendly. His only choice now was to face about, but only after he had sent a letter to the missionary at Zuñi in which he urged the opening of a northern route to Monterey. This proved to be something of a coincidence, for at that very moment Father Escalante at Zuñi had the same plan in mind. Garcés did not wait for a reply, but turned west and reached Yuma on August 27, 1776 and September 17 he was once again back at his mission of San Xavier.

The Founding of Tucson

The year 1776, as every schoolboy knows, is an important date in the history of our country; but perhaps he does not know that this was also a year of some significance in the history of Arizona. Not only was this the year in which Anza led his colony from Tubac to found San Francisco while Garcés made his famous explorations, but it was also the year of the founding of Tucson as a Spanish pueblo and the date of the Escalante expedition along the northern borders of Arizona. In July of that year, fathers Escalante and Domínguez, accompanied by a small band of soldiers and guides, left Santa Fe on a northwesterly course with plans to reach Monterey. They were forced to abandon their quest in the vicinity of present-day Provo, Utah, and then turned south, entering Arizona near the northern end of Lydel Wash on October 16. From then until November 24 they followed a winding trail along the north side of Grand Canyon, crossed the river just north of the present interstate line, made their way to the Hopis, and thence to Zuñi, which they reached on November 24. The old Pueblo — Tucson — was founded in the same year, when orders were given to remove the troops at Tubac and station them at the old Indian settlement of Tuquisón. The transfer was in accord with plans for ultimately moving the frontier of settlement to the Gila and the Colorado. Moreover, Tucson was at a strategic location for checking the marauding Apaches.

The designs for establishing missions and a presidio at the mouth of the Gila had been suggested by the Jesuits, who at one time in the 1740's had visions of pushing the mission frontier as far north as the Hopi villages. But the Apache barrier north of the Gila, together with the historical claims of the New Mexican Franciscans to the Moqui country, checked these ambitions of the Pimería Jesuits. Finally, however, the Gila-Colorado suggestion was given official approval and support in 1780, when a small army of soldiers and their families, accompanied by fathers Garcés, Díaz, Moreno, and Eixarch, was sent to establish two missions and a presidio on the west bank of the Colorado. The sites for the three establishments were opposite the modern town of Yuma; but the Indians were no longer the friendly natives they had been a year or two earlier. Even Palma, who had been one of the Spaniards' staunchest friends, turned against the white settlers. The natives protested the manner in which the Spaniards seized the Indians' land; the Spaniards were angry at the exorbitant prices the natives asked for provisions. On July 17, 1781, the Yumas took matters into their own hands by massacring nearly all of the white settlers, including the four missionaries and Rivera y Moncada, a former governor of California. Punitive campaigns were made during 1781 and 1782, but with few tangible results. The Indians remained hostile, and Yuma, Anza's bridge to California, was closed for the remaining years of the Spanish period.

The Mountain Men Arrive

During the closing years of the eighteenth and the opening decades of the nineteenth centuries, Spain's hold on Arizona was tenuous. The Hopi and Navajo maintained their independence. A handful of troops and civilians remained close to the walls of the presidio of Tucson in the face of Apache raids, while the missionaries at Tucson, San Xavier, Tumacácori, and Guevavi worked diligently but not always successfully with their native charges. Then came the 1820s when a new tide was setting in from the east: white men, with un-Spanish names — Pattie, Young, Williams, Robidoux — pushed down the Gila, thence up the Salt, the Verde, and the Colorado with traps for the beaver.

Primarily these were men from the St. Louis fur trade — Sylvester Pattie and his son, James Ohio, who recorded the times in his memoirs, *Personal Narrative of James O. Pattie,* Ewing Young, Bill Williams who worked along the Gila, and Antoine Robidoux, "king of the Colorado fur trade," who worked west to the Colorado from Taos, summer rendezvous of the trappers.

They came into Apachería — a term which might at that time have been applied almost to the entire present state of Arizona. In the thirties and forties the area south of the Gila was almost wholly in Apache hands. The mission communities of Tumacácori and San Xavier had been deserted. White settlers remained only at Tubac and Tucson. North of the Gila was the wilderness home of the marauding Apaches.

The trappers and traders did not try to tame the wilderness, but adapted themselves to it and to Indian ways, much as the French fur traders northeast on the continent had done in earlier years.

Apache wrath was not directed toward these *couriers du bois,* and the early relationships were not unfavorable. The Apaches were concentrated in the 1820's on keeping Mexicans and Spaniards out of the mining business, and from this concentration radiated much of the hostile energy that kept the generations at war.

In 1832, Juan José, elderly chief of the Mimbreño Apaches, permitted Mexican miners at Santa Rita in southwestern New Mexico to remove large quantities of copper ore. This angered younger members of the tribe who moved to Warm Springs under the leadership of Black Knife. Joining with Mangas Coloradas in 1835, the younger group attacked the Santa Rita mine.

Subsequently the governor of Durango, Mexico, made the error of offering bounty for Apache scalps, and fur trapper James Johnson fatally compounded this error by accepting the offer. He invited Warm Springs and Mimbreño Apaches to a feast and a massacre, in which old Juan José was killed, and Mangas Coloradas escaped to wage war for thirty years with the support of most of the Apaches of the Southwest. Under his leadership such powerful subchiefs as Delgado and Victorio alternately stirred and banked the embers that ignited the Apache wars of Arizona history.

Such was the land of the Apaches in the days of the Mountain Men. These English-speaking frontiersmen carried with them the harbinger of another day, the day of Manifest Destiny. They were trailblazers. Others that followed would soon have their chance to tame a wilderness which had vexed the Spaniards for nearly 300 years.

Harwood P. Hinton
Historian

3

FROM FRONTIER TO STATEHOOD

ON DECEMBER 16, 1846, a dusty column of American volunteer infantry, followed by a small train of creaking wagons, marched into the Mexican village of Tucson. The United States and Mexico had been at war for eight months, and this group, a battalion of Mormons led by Philip St. George Cooke, Lieutenant Colonel of volunteers, was part of Gen. Stephen W. Kearny's Army of the West, raised to conquer and to hold New Mexico and California. Finding that the Mexican garrison had already withdrawn, Cooke halted in the military plaza, and as the inhabitants watched he sent a soldier to implant the Stars and Stripes in one of the towers on the presidial walls. Cooke's stay in Tucson was brief — but the act was a forecast of things to come. Within eight years the vast northern borderland of Mexico stretching from Texas to the Pacific would become a part of the United States.

For more than a decade, American politicians had clamored for government action to acquire Mexican California and the British-held Oregon country. It was the "Manifest Destiny" of the American people, they cried, to possess this Western country. When attempts were made through negotiation and purchase to obtain the land, the British withdrew gracefully from Oregon; but the Mexican government, still smarting from the loss of Texas, closed its northern borders and grew belligerent. With the firing on American troops occupying the disputed zone between the Nueces River and the Rio Grande, war came on May 13, 1846.

The history of American Arizona began on August 18 with General Kearny's arrival in Santa Fe, the capital of the Mexican province of New Mexico. Instructed by his superiors to establish a temporary civil government, the general on September 22 promulgated the so-called Kearny Code, which had been drawn from existing Spanish and Mexican law, but mainly from legal experience in Missouri and Texas. This document provided the basic framework for a provisional civil government in the newly acquired territory and included provisions guaranteeing the basic rights enjoyed by all Americans. Kearny selected Charles Bent, who was part owner of Bent's Fort and had married into a Taos family, to be Territorial governor; Donaciano Vigil, a New Mexican experienced in civil and military affairs, was appointed secretary, and three other citizens of New Mexico — Antonio J. Otero, Joab Houghton, and Charles Beaubien — became judges. Colonel Sterling Price was placed in charge of the American troops occupying the territory. These appointments marked the introduction of American institutions into the Spanish-Mexican Southwest. The temporary government set up by Kearny would function fitfully for four years.

On September 25, General Kearny led a dragoon column out of Santa Fe for California. Near Socorro he met Kit Carson, who was carrying dispatches from Lieutenant Colonel John C. Frémont to Washington, and pressed him into service as a guide. Here also, he selected one hundred soldiers to continue with him and sent the rest back to Santa Fe. Transferring his baggage and arms from wagons to pack animals, Kearny left the Rio Grande near the present New Mexico town of Truth or Consequences and moved west into the mountains. While the soldiers were encamped at the headwaters of the Gila, the Mimbres Apache Chief Mangas Coloradas visited them. Professing friendship for the Americans, he traded fresh mules and offered to help fight the Mexicans. Kearny now began a strenuous march west along the banks of the Gila, eventually reaching the Pima villages, where he rested his men and recruited his animals. The column then continued downriver, crossing the Colorado River on November 25, and proceeded on into California. The first military east-west crossing of present-day Arizona had consumed exactly one month.

Before Kearny crossed the Colorado, another American force was marching through the Southwest. Colonel Cooke's Mormon Battalion, numbering some

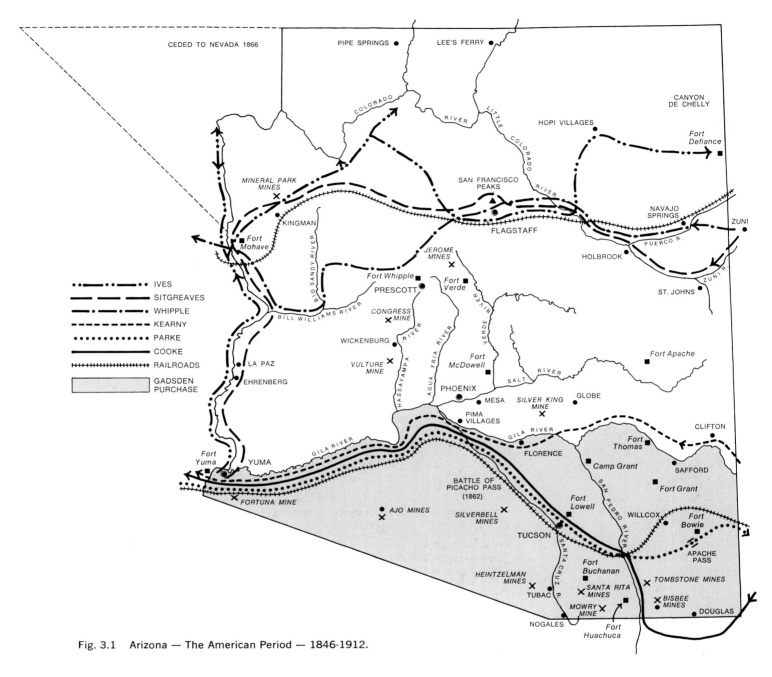

Fig. 3.1 Arizona — The American Period — 1846-1912.

four hundred men, had left Santa Fe in late October with orders to swing southwest through less mountainous country with a train of wagons and blaze a road overland via Tucson to California. Although three veteran guides, Antoine Leroux, Pauline Weaver, and Baptiste Charbonneau, accompanied him, Cooke found his march determined by the availability of water. Heading west from the Rio Grande, then south down the Janos road, he maneuvered his vehicles through a treacherous defile near Guadalupe Canyon at the junction of the modern boundaries of Arizona, New Mexico, and Sonora; on December 2, the battalion arrived at the rancho of San Bernardino. Once the site of extensive cattle operations, the buildings and walls were now in ruins. Here, Apaches again appeared and traded with the Americans.

Cooke now turned his caravan north. Traveling down the east bank of the San Pedro River, the battalion passed the abandoned rancho San Pedro and on December 11 fought the only battle of its campaign. A foraging party riding through the tall grass near the river suddenly aroused some wild cattle, descendants of the San Bernardino's vast herd, and a number of bellowing animals charged the Mormon column. Several of the bulls tried to gore the mules, while others rammed into the wagons and scattered the soldiers in the excitement. The attack was only momentary and no one was killed.

At a point near Benson, Cooke crossed the river, climbed to the tableland above, and pushed west for the presidio of Tucson. Entreaties from the Mexican commander, Antonio Comaduran, to bypass the presidio were ignored. Cooke needed supplies and pressed on. He entered Tucson on December 16 and found that the Mexican garrison had departed. Camping on the banks of the nearby Santa Cruz River, the Americans obtained flour and grain and marched north, reaching the Pima villages on December 21. Turning down the Gila, Cooke crossed his wagons over the Colorado on January 9-11, 1847, and arrived in San Diego twenty days later. In June, most of the Mormons, their one-year enlistment ended, hastened east to rejoin families and relatives who had come overland to found a settlement at the Great Salt Lake.

Still a third military expedition crossed Arizona during the Mexican War. In the early summer of 1848, a dragoon battalion led by Major Lawrence P. Graham left Monterrey, Mexico, with orders to take station in California. This force crossed Chihuahua, swung north through Sonora, and entered Arizona near the present site of Nogales. After descending the Santa Cruz to Tucson, Graham followed Cooke's route to California.

The three expeditions that crossed Arizona during the war obtained valuable information on the Southwest. They learned about travel across the desert plains, the attitudes of the Apaches, and the weakness of the Mexican settlements. The Cooke route never developed into a wagon road. When the gold rush in California occurred, parties following southwestern trails generally left El Paso, crossed Chihuahua to the San Bernardino rancho, continued to the headwaters of the Santa Cruz, and turned north to the Gila. An alternate route by 1849 was charted through what became Stein's Pass and Apache Pass by way of Tucson to California.

The war with Mexico officially ended on July 4, 1848, when President James K. Polk proclaimed peace. By the Treaty of Guadalupe Hidalgo, signed in February, the United States received New Mexico (including Arizona north of the Gila), California, and parts of Nevada, Utah, Colorado, and Wyoming. Americans now faced the problems of exploring and governing this vast territory.

The Territory of New Mexico was created in 1850. A slate of officials appointed in Washington, D.C., and headed by Governor James Calhoun took over in Santa Fe. Elections were held, and a legislature and Territorial delegate chosen. The legislature adopted a code, and designated five counties. Four of these extended west across the uninhabited region north of the Gila to the Colorado. Later, the fifth, Doña Ana County, would be extended across the Gadsden Purchase when it was added to the Territory of New Mexico. From the beginning, this vast western district was ignored in Santa Fe. The only evidence of local rule was a justice of the peace in Tucson and the occasional sending of a criminal east nearly 300 miles to Mesilla, the seat of Doña Ana County, for trial. Eventually, the western part of New Mexico, which extended from Utah south to the Sonoran border, would be separated to form the Territory of Arizona.

The Gold Rush of 1848 and the rapid development of California aroused interest in establishing closer ties between the Pacific Coast and the States. California politicians joined Eastern railroad promoters in pressuring Congress to employ the army in exploring, marking, and guarding overland routes. New Mexico and Arizona were greatly benefitted by the government activity that followed. During the period from 1851 to 1858, millions in federal funds were spent in opening wagon roads, charting railroad routes, building forts, fighting hostile Indians, and subsidizing mail and stage service through this sparsely settled domain.

The question over the southern boundary of New Mexico Territory continued to rankle. The 1848 treaty, instead of specifically stipulating longitude and latitude, had merely declared that the boundary running west of El Paso should follow Disturnell's map, which had been used during the negotiations. The inaccuracy of this map became apparent when the Joint Boundary Commission began its work. The surveyors ran the line from the Pacific Coast east to a point below present Yuma, then reassembled at El Paso in the fall of 1850 to proceed west. Here, through the use of instruments, they found that the Disturnell map showed El Paso thirty-four miles too far north and the Rio Grande over one hundred miles too far east. The Mexican Commissioner urged that the longitude and latitude on the map, although inaccurate, be followed, but John R. Bartlett, in charge of the American party, balked — then agreed to compromise away some three million acres in the Mesilla Valley. The Anglo citizens upriver rose in dismay, and the governor of New Mexico threatened to call for troops to defend the southern border. With these developments, Congress refused to honor the compromise.

The New Mexico boundary problem was resolved in 1853. In May the newly elected president, Franklin Pierce, sent James A. Gadsden to Mexico to settle the dispute and to purchase additional territory. By December Gadsden had reached an agreement with the Mexican government and for ten million dollars had acquired a strip of land (29,640 square miles) south of the Gila. Known as the Gadsden Purchase, this area was officially added to New Mexico on June 29, 1854. Although the United States hoped to obtain a port on the Gulf of California the final draft did not provide one. The marking of the southern boundary of the Gadsden Purchase was completed in August, 1855.

During the 1850s the army played a major role in opening and protecting the routes of travel across western New Mexico. In September, 1849, Lieutenant Cave J. Couts, with a detachment belonging to the Joint Boundary Commission, arrived at the Colorado River, and established Camp Calhoun on the California side, opposite the mouth of the Gila. During his brief stay, he afforded protection and aid to goldseekers and emigrants bound for California. On November 1, the Howard party arrived from the Pima villages. During the journey a son had been born to Mrs. Howard and named Gila. The child may well be the first to be born of American parents in Arizona. A year later Captain Samuel P. Heintzelman moved the military camp to the site of the old Garcés mission and renamed it Camp Yuma.

Overland traffic at Yuma Crossing was heavy. Several ferries were put into use to transport travelers, wagons and teams, and livestock across the Colorado. Particularly important was the ferry operated by Louis J. F. Yaeger, who later became a prominent merchant-freighter in the Yuma area. Most of the people came in large parties, because of the need for protection from hostile Indians along the Gila. The crosses near the big bend of the Gila marking the site of the Oatman massacre were a grim reminder of the dangers present. Here, in February, 1851, Royce Oatman, foolishly pushing ahead of an emigrant party, perished with his wife and several children. Two daughters, Olive and Mary, were carried into captivity; the younger sister died, but Olive was later ransomed from the Mohaves.

In the autumn of 1851, the army established its first fort in present-day Arizona. Located about fifty miles northwest of the Zuñi villages, Fort Defiance was placed in the heart of the Navajo country to reduce the raiding on the settlements along the upper Rio Grande. A large, four-company post, it also was the agency headquarters for the first Navajo agent, H. L. Dodge. About the same time that work was begun on Fort Defiance, Lieutenant Lorenzo Sitgreaves, of the Corps of Topographical Engineers, set out to explore from Zuñi west along the thirty-fifth parallel to the Colorado. The party, guided by Antoine Leroux and accompanied by a small military escort, included an assistant engineer, a physician, several draftsmen, and a group of packers. The expedition crossed the Little Colorado, circled north of the San Francisco Peaks, and moving westerly, reached the Mohave Valley on November 5. Turning south along the east bank of the Colorado, the explorers straggled into Camp Yuma a few weeks later. Sitgreaves' report provided the first major description of the terrain, plants, animals, Indians, and mineral possibilities north of the Gila.

Between 1853 and 1858 three more government parties marked routes near the Sitgreaves trace. The first was led by Lieutenant Amiel W. Whipple, who had previously served with the Boundary Commission. His mission was to chart a railroad route along the thirty-fifth parallel from Fort Smith, Arkansas, across New Mexico to the Colorado River. Whipple left Albuquerque in November, 1853, with a corps of assistants and a detachment of soldiers and generally followed Sitgreaves' path. After suffering many hardships, he crossed the Colorado on February 29, 1854, and continued into California.

The next expedition passing over the Sitgreaves-Whipple route was conducted by Edward F. Beale, former Superintendent of Indian Affairs in California. Instructed to open a wagon road along the thirty-fifth

parallel, Beale left Zuñi in August, 1857, with wagons and teams, a flock of sheep, and a herd of twenty-five camels. Although the camels were loaded with five hundred pounds of supplies each, they proved to be amazingly versatile as beasts of burden on the deserts of the Southwest. They could bear greater loads than could mules and traveled farther on less water and forage. Beale crossed the Colorado in October, and continued west to Fort Tejon. He had noted the obstacles to wheeled traffic, the need for bridges and grading, and the availability of water. To test the practicability of winter travel over the road, Beale and twenty men returned east in February to New Mexico. Because of Mohave attacks on immigrant trains on Beale's Road, the army early in 1859 established Camp Mohave, a two-company post, near Beale's Crossing on the Colorado.

Perhaps the most interesting army expedition north of the Gila was led by Lieutenant Joseph C. Ives. On January 11, 1858, Ives departed from Fort Yuma on a small steamboat named the *Explorer* to ascend the Colorado to the head of navigation. Three months later, the slow-moving steamer encountered obstacles in Black Canyon, below the present Hoover Dam, and Ives was forced to send it back to Yuma. Landing his party at the Mohave villages, he organized a pack train and headed northeast with Hualapai guides. He skirted the great bend of the Colorado, and descending Diamond Creek, walked out onto the floor of the Grand Canyon. After briefly entering Cataract Canyon to the east, where his party contacted the Havasupais, Ives followed an overland trail to visit the Moquis, reaching Fort Defiance in May. His report was probably the most fascinating and profusely illustrated ever compiled on the northern region.

Equally important army surveys were also made south of the Gila. In January, 1854, before the actual transfer of the Gadsden strip, Lieutenant John G. Parke, informed that the Mexican government had granted permission for a railroad survey along the thirty-second parallel, set out from San Diego with a scientific corps and a dragoon detachment. Traveling up the Gila to the Pima villages, Parke passed through Tucson, then proceeded east to the San Pedro River, and on to the Rio Grande. The following spring he retraced his steps, making a more detailed record of the country. The Southern Pacific Railroad later drew on Parke's reports in building its line through the Southwest.

Another government undertaking in the Gadsden strip was the Leach Road. In October, 1857, James B. Leach began marking a highway to run from El Paso via the Gila to the Colorado. From Mesilla its path swung north through Cooke's Canyon and west by Stein's Pass to the San Pedro. Here, the road turned down the river, bypassing Tucson, and at the junction with the Gila headed west to Yuma. Because it missed the settlements, was unprotected from Indians, and was constructed when clouds of war were affecting Western travel, the Leach Road never realized its full potential.

While attempts were being made to open roads, private enterprise sought aid in building a transcontinental railroad across the Southwest. Railroad promoters not only enjoyed influence in the halls of Congress, but formed syndicates, founded newspapers, and sought federal subsidies to further their plans. They felt that a railroad to the Pacific would help bind the sections together, open frontier areas, and provide outlets to world markets. Of the many schemes advanced in the 1850s, only one affected the future of Arizona. This was the plan of the Texas Western Railroad Company to gain right-of-way and support in order to tie the lower Mississippi Valley to the Pacific coast. In 1854 the company retained Andrew B. Gray, a veteran surveyor, to project a route and to make estimates from West Texas along the thirty-second parallel to San Diego. It was hoped that agricultural lands and mines could be developed along its path as a basis for settlements, which in turn would make the case for federal aid more attractive.

The opening of the mines in the mountains south of Tucson was part of the larger railroad scheme. During the early summer of 1854, two men — Charles D. Poston of San Francisco and Herman Ehrenberg, a mining engineer — entered the newly acquired Gadsden strip from Sonora. They came to investigate the mines in the Santa Cruz Valley, mines which had been opened in Spanish times and subsequently abandoned because of Apache raids. Poston was probably representing a syndicate tied to the Texas Western Railroad. The two men collected specimens from the old silver mines in the mountains bordering the valley and at the copper workings over a hundred miles to the west at Ajo. Traveling on to Camp Yuma, they showed their discoveries to Captain Heintzelman, then hurried on to California. Soon afterward, in October, 1854, Peter R. Brady, who had been with the A. B. Gray railroad survey was sent with a party by a San Francisco firm, the Arizona Mining and Trading Company, to begin development of the Ajo mines. This was Arizona's first copper mining company.

In search of Eastern investors, Poston took the silver ore to New York, and after months of disappointment, found interested parties in Cincinnati, Ohio. Here, he again met Heintzelman, who was now stationed across the Ohio River at Newport Barracks. The officer introduced him to the Wrightson brothers, William and Thomas, publishers of the *Railroad Record,* who were promoting the development of Western railroads and mines. In March, 1856, the Sonora Exploring and Mining Company was formed in Cincinnati and was capitalized at two million dollars. Heintzelman was president, William Wrightson secretary, and Edgar Conkling the general agent. Named "commandant and managing agent," Poston was authorized to spend up to one hundred thousand dollars to gather and outfit a work force, obtain claims, and bring the Tubac mines into production.

Arizona Historical Society

Fig. 3.2 Charles D. Poston promoted separate territorial status for Arizona.

Landing in Texas, Poston recruited men in the San Antonio vicinity, purchased wagons and equipment, and set out overland for New Mexico. He arrived in Mesilla, seat of Doña Ana County, and received permission from the probate clerk to act as his deputy in the Santa Cruz Valley. The party reached its destination in September, reconditioned the old Mexican barracks at Tubac, and erected a company store. Prospecting parties began scouring the mountains on both sides of the Santa Cruz for outcroppings and old mining shafts. Mexican families arrived from Sonora to work for the company. Arrastras (crushing vats) were laid out, crude adobe ovens built, and mesquite cut for charcoal. Arrangements were made to transport the ore south to the Gulf and also east to Missouri. Fortunately, the surface ore was rich; otherwise, the operation would have failed at the beginning. Tubac, the first company town in Arizona, grew rapidly. Glowing letters by Poston appeared in the *Railroad Record.* Subsidiary mining companies were organized to open additional mines, and prospecting was extended to the south and east. A newspaper, the *Weekly Arizonian,* was started in 1859, and the population soared to over five hundred inhabitants, temporarily eclipsing Tucson some sixty miles to the north.

The increased activity in the Santa Cruz Valley attracted the attention of the Apaches, who came down from their mountain strongholds to prowl the countryside for booty. The Santa Cruz was on the western edge of the Apachería, which extended east through the Chiricahua Mountains and north beyond the Gila into the

Tonto and White mountains. Even before Poston arrived, travel had become so hazardous that the citizens of Tucson had urged the Military Department of New Mexico to erect a fort in their midst. In response to these pleas, the government in 1856 ordered four dragoon companies from New Mexico to the Santa Cruz Valley. Strangely, the Mexican garrison had remained at Tucson nearly two years after the Gadsden Purchase had passed to the United States! It finally left in the spring preceding the arrival of the Americans. The dragoons reached Tucson in mid-November and went south to locate a post near the confluence of Sonoita Creek and the Santa Cruz. In June, 1857, Major Enoch Steen, the commander, moved his men up the Sonoita to some thermal springs and established Fort Buchanan. This post served the dual purpose of protecting local settlers from Indians and exerting United States authority on the Mexican border. Ranches sprang up in the vicinity to supply both the post and the mining town of Tubac.

The citizens in the Santa Cruz Valley also clamored for improved communications with California and the East. To a great extent the steamboat and the stage supplied their needs. Steamboat traffic on the Colorado dated from 1852, when George A. Johnson, a contractor supplying Camp Yuma, put the *Uncle Sam* into service. At the mouth of the Colorado, he picked up freight and passengers brought by schooner from California and took them upriver to the post. Two years later, this vessel ran aground and sank, and the *General Jesup* was placed in use. During the next two decades, steamer traffic grew to large proportions with vessels going upriver regularly, as far as Hardyville. The most popular means of travel was by stage. The San Antonio & San Diego Mail Line, supported by a government mail subsidy, began operations in 1857, passing semi-monthly through Yuma, Tucson, and on to Mesilla on the Rio Grande. A year later the Overland Mail Company, under John Butterfield, secured the mail contract and started running stages semi-weekly from Missouri via El Paso and Tucson to California.

As travel and settlement increased, the responsibility of dealing with the Indians loomed larger. Forts established in their midst kept the Yumas and Mojaves under control, while the Pimas, Maricopas, and Papagos continued to be friendly. In 1859 Congress appropriated funds to survey a reservation on the Gila for the Pimas and the Maricopas and authorized regular gifts and clothing for them. John Walker of Tucson was appointed their agent, reporting to the Indian superintendent in Santa Fe. Responsibility for the Apaches was placed in the hands of Dr. Michael Steck, whose headquarters generally were at Fort Stanton, northeast of present day Alamogordo. To pacify the Chiricahua, Gila, and Coyotero (White Mountain) bands, Steck appeared annually at a prearranged rendezvous with wagons loaded with supplies and gifts. During the late 1850s, the Apaches became especially troublesome. Military

campaigns such as the Gila Expedition in 1857 served only to increase their hostility. The army established Fort Breckinridge in 1860 near the confluence of Aravaipa Creek and the San Pedro to provide additional protection. In April, 1861, when Lieutenant George N. Bascom tried to seize the Chiricahua chieftain Cochise during a conference at Apache Pass, the stage was set for increasing warfare between the Indian and the white man in the Southwest.

Even before the Sonora Exploring and Mining Company opened the silver mines around Tubac, there was a surge of interest in creating a new territory in southern New Mexico. The movement began in the Mesilla Valley, where local citizens felt both ignored and unrepresented in Santa Fe. In January, 1855, James A. Lucas, a representative from Mesilla, urged the Territorial legislature to ask Congress to organize a new territory to be called Pimería — but he found no support. Two memorials were drafted in 1856. The first petition, drafted in Spanish in midsummer in Mesilla, called for the separation of the area south of 34° 20' and its establishment as the Territory of Arizona. It failed to gain an audience in Washington. The second petition was approved at a meeting in Tucson on August 29, 1856. Bearing two hundred and sixty signatures, it recited the usual grievances regarding courts, voting apparatus, representation, and Indian protection. Among those signing were Arizona pioneers Herman Ehrenberg, Mark Aldrich, Edward E. Dunbar, Solomon Warner, Peter R. Brady, Frederick A. Ronstadt, Granville H. Oury, William H. Kirkland, Julius Contzen, Juan Elías, and Ignacio Ortiz. The Tucson memorial was sent to Washington but died in committee. Although Charles Poston may have had a hand in drafting the Mesilla and Tucson petitions, his name did not appear on either.

The movement gained momentum. In December, 1857, Senator William M. Gwin of California introduced the first bill in Congress to organize a new territory in southern New Mexico. He had collaborated with Lieutenant Sylvester Mowry, an officer stationed at Camp Yuma, who had become deeply involved in the quest for territorial status for the Gadsden Purchase area. With Heintzelman's help Mowry had obtained an extended leave, which he used for lobbying in Washington. In March, 1858, a memorial from Mesilla bearing one thousand signatures reached Mowry in the capital and was introduced in the Senate. Both bills, however, failed to gain headway. In July Mowry resigned his commission, and by autumn he had returned to Arizona to spark the territorial movement. Major Heintzelman, on military leave, visited the Tubac mines, and met and encouraged Mowry in his efforts. Additional support came in January, 1859, when one of the Cincinnati promoters, William Wrightson, arrived to superintend the Santa Rita Silver Mining Company, a subsidiary of the Sonora Company.

By February, 1860, ten bills to organize Arizona Territory had failed. A call now went out to hold a convention in Tucson in April to form a provisional government. When it assembled on April 2, James A. Lucas of Mesilla presided. Delegates were there from a number of the lower Rio Grande towns and from the villages and ranches in the Santa Cruz Valley. The convention drafted a constitution, declared Arizona to include all of New Mexico south of 33° 40', and designated four counties: Doña Ana, Mesilla, Ewell, and Castle Dome. Dr. Lewis S. Owings of Mesilla was elected governor, Ignacio Orrantia, lieutenant governor, and Lucas, secretary. Mowry was selected to be territorial delegate. The proceedings, constitution, and Owings' inaugural address were printed by the Tucson *Arizonian* and were bound as the first book ever published in Arizona. Unlike many extralegal governments on the frontier, this government actually tried to function.

While the Tucson convention was in session, another major effort was being made in Congress to create Arizona Territory. On April 3, Senator Joseph S. Green of Missouri introduced a bill calling for the creation of the territory, but the spectre of slavery caused the ensuing debate to drift, and the measure had no chance of passage. When the November elections brought Republican victory, there was a rush to organize new territories in Colorado, Nevada, and Dakota. But at this point there was no one in Washington to argue for Arizona. In the Southwest, sympathies were with the South as it struggled to find accommodation in the Union.

In the spring of 1861, the provisional government of Arizona cast its lot with the Southern Confederacy. This deed was precipitated by actions on the part of Texas, where careful plans were made to incorporate New Mexico and California in the Confederate fold. If this could be accomplished, a railroad from Texas to the Pacific would be more easily secured, rich mines might be acquired, and additional territory added. Philemon T. Herbert, an El Paso attorney, and Simeon Hart, a wealthy miller in the same city, were agents appointed by the secession convention in Austin to enter New Mexico to stir up enthusiasm for the Confederate cause. The spokesman for their activities was the *Mesilla Times*. In late March secession conventions in Mesilla and Tucson passed resolutions supporting the Confederacy. When news of the outbreak of hostilities reached Mesilla, there was a celebration, and the Confederate flag was hoisted and saluted. By midsummer many of the Southern-born regular officers in the Southwest resigned to serve the Confederacy. Lieutenant Colonel Edward R. S. Canby succeeded to command of the garrisons scattered throughout New Mexico Territory.

Anticipating an invasion from Texas, Colonel Canby ordered the western posts in his jurisdiction abandoned and the soldiers concentrated on the Rio Grande. In mid-July, Forts Breckinridge and Buchanan were burned, and the garrisons marched for Fort Craig, north of Mesilla. By this time, also, the mining companies at Tubac had closed down, and bands of savage Indians and lawless whites were roaming the countryside. Only in the Patagonia Mountains near the border, where Sylvester Mowry had built a fortified camp to protect his newly acquired mine, was there security. To the north, Tucson became virtually isolated from the outside world when the Overland Mail ceased running.

The military struggle for New Mexico began in July. Marching from El Paso, Lieutenant Colonel John R. Baylor and three hundred mounted Confederates from Texas pushed up the Rio Grande and occupied Mesilla on July 27. From Fort Fillmore, across the river, Major Isaac Lynde, commanding eleven Union companies, made a feint at the town and skirmished briefly. Then, believing himself in danger, Lynde hastily evacuated Fillmore and headed for the Organ Mountains, hoping to reach Fort Stanton. Overtaken in San Augustine Pass by Baylor, he surrendered his entire command—which was promptly paroled. Baylor returned to Mesilla and on August 1 proclaimed himself military governor of the Territory of Arizona. A week later a mass meeting in Tucson elected Granville Oury the territorial delegate to the Confederate Congress in Richmond. The Confederacy recognized Arizona as a separate territory on February 14, 1862, with boundaries generally coinciding with those designated by the Tucson convention in 1860.

The Confederate invasion of New Mexico proved unsuccessful. In February, 1862, Brigadier General Henry H. Sibley, at the head of some three thousand Confederates, arrived in Mesilla and took command of operations in New Mexico. Moving his force up the east bank of the Rio Grande, Sibley at Valverde threw back Union and volunteer soldiers sent against him by Colonel Canby from Fort Craig. Continuing up the river Sibley occupied Albuquerque and Santa Fe — then turned northeast to seize Fort Union, the major military depot in the Southwest. But on March 25 at Glorieta Pass, a column of Colorado troops under Colonel John P. Slough savagely attacked the Confederates and destroyed their supply train. His forces shattered, Sibley began retreating down the Rio Grande and by May had evacuated New Mexico.

Confederate occupation of Arizona was equally brief. On February 28, Captain Sherod Hunter arrived in Tucson with a mounted company from the Rio Grande. His mission was to occupy Tucson and send pickets west along the Gila to report on Union troop movements at Yuma, which had been redesignated Fort Yuma. Arriving with Hunter was Colonel James Reily, who was charged with obtaining assistance and supplies in Chihuahua and Sonora for the Confederates. In Tucson, Hunter confiscated food and animals, destroyed Union stores, and arrested or chased from town those who defied him. There were, however, many Tucsonans who welcomed the soldiers, for they provided protection from the Apaches. Early in March Reily and an escort left on what proved to be an unsuccessful trip into Sonora, and Hunter rode north with a detachment to the Pima villages. There, he seized Ammi White, who operated a gristmill, and a few days later by a ruse captured a detachment of Union soldiers probing along the Gila.

As early as September, 1861, plans had been made to send an army from California to drive the Confederates from New Mexico. In November advance companies arrived at Yuma and the following month Colonel James H. Carleton, a veteran of the Southwest, was placed in command. Torrential rains hampered the gathering of supplies, but by mid-February, 1862, Carleton's column of about fifteen hundred men was ready to move. When word came that Confederates were at the Pima villages, soldiers were dispatched east to investigate. After being fired on near Gila Bend, the Californians reached the villages, only to find the Confederates in retreat. With twelve men Lieutenant James Barrett set out in pursuit, and on April 15 he overtook a Confederate picket at Picacho Pass, forty-five miles northwest of Tucson. In the running skirmish, Barrett and two of his men were killed, and two Confederates were wounded. This engagement has been called the "Westernmost battle of the Civil War." As Captain Hunter now saw that further efforts were futile, he evacuated Tucson and returned east to join Sibley on the Rio Grande. Advance units of Carleton's column rode into Tucson on May 20 and raised the Stars and Stripes.

Carleton, now a brigadier general, arrived early in June with the main body of his army. On June 8 he placed the "Territory of Arizona" under martial law and required all citizens of Tucson to take the oath of allegiance to the United States. A military depot called Camp Lowell was established in town, and detachments were sent to establish temporary outposts at Tubac and old Forts Buchanan and Breckinridge.

Learning that Sylvester Mowry, while operating the Patagonia mine, had given aid and supplies to Hunter's Confederates, Carleton ordered the ex-officer arrested and his mine shut down. Mowry was tried and confined at Fort Yuma for several months, then released. To support the local military establishment, heavy taxes were levied on businesses and saloons in Tucson. Then in late June, leaving a skeleton force behind, Carleton marched east for the Rio Grande. A horde of hostile Apaches under Mangas Coloradas and Cochise attacked his advance in Apache Pass, but were beaten off by artillery fire. Camp Bowie was established at this site soon afterward. In September, General Carleton succeeded Colonel Canby in command of the Military Department of New Mexico.

The Civil War left few scars on the land. The Confederate Territory of Arizona, born in the heat of enthusiasm and hope, lasted less than nine months — about the same length of time as the Confederate attempt to conquer New Mexico. Tucson itself had been occupied less than two months. Animosities kindled during this interlude quickly vanished in the common struggle for more tangible goals.

In the spring of 1862 the drive for separate territorial status for Arizona was resumed in Congress. Although many of the individuals who had worked tire-

Fig. 3.3   Fort Bowie was founded in 1862 because of the Indian menace to travel through Apache Pass.

Arizona Historical Society

lessly in the 1850s toward that end were no longer on the scene, Poston, Heintzelman, the Wrightsons, and others who had investments in the Santa Cruz Valley formed a strong lobby in Washington, and continued to push for the new territory. On March 12, James M. Ashley, an Ohio Republican who chaired the House Committee on Territories, introduced a bill calling for the organization of Arizona Territory. Unlike most of the memorials and petitions brought to Congress earlier, Ashley's measure provided for a north-south boundary at approximately the 109th meridian. Debate over the bill dragged through the spring, with extended discussion centering on the need to protect and develop the mines around Tubac. The opposition repeatedly pointed out that the 1860 census showed that Arizona had a population of less than twenty-five hundred whites, including soldiers. After New Mexico delegate John S. Watts and several others strongly urged separation of Arizona from New Mexico, emphasizing its great underdeveloped mineral wealth, Ashley's bill finally passed the House on May 8.

In the Senate the Arizona bill met tough opposition. Here, during the summer, Ben Wade, powerful Ohio Republican and chairman of the Senate Committee on Territories, championed the measure — but was unable to override the stiff opposition to creating a territory with so few people. The matter was postponed until February, 1863. During the interim, Poston, Heintzelman, and the Wrightsons pressed the issue with influential senators. On February 19 debate over the Arizona bill was resumed, and with the aid of Senator James A. McDougall of California and Wade of Ohio, the measure passed. On February 24, 1863, President Abraham Lincoln signed into law the bill creating the Territory of Arizona.

The officials selected to launch and govern the new territory were typical of their times. Governor John A. Gurley of Ohio and Chief Justice John N. Goodwin of Maine were lame duck congressmen; Secretary Richard C. McCormick of New York and several others had been defeated at the polls earlier. Still others, like Indian Superintendent Charles Poston, had never held public office before.

In August Gurley died at his home in Cincinnati, and Chief Justice Goodwin was named governor. By the early fall of 1863, the Arizona Territorial officials, with a military escort, were on their way down the Santa Fe Trail to New Mexico.

The officials arrived in Santa Fe on November 14 and stayed nearly two weeks. Here, Goodwin made a study of the New Mexico Territorial Code, which he would follow until the Arizona legislature met and enacted one. General Carleton also discussed at length the recent gold strike on the headwaters of the Hassayampa River in central Arizona and said he was constructing a military post there named Fort Whipple. Located by Joseph R. Walker, a famous mountain man and guide, with the aid and encouragement of Carleton,

the discovery lay near the railroad survey along the thirty-fifth parallel. As the Arizona organic act specified no capital, Carleton urged that the new Territorial seat be located near the Walker diggings. When Goodwin's party left Santa Fe, they headed for the mines, accompanied by an escort of New Mexico militia and a heavily loaded wagon train.

On the morning of December 27, the caravan halted at Navajo Springs, forty miles west of Zuñi and just inside the Arizona line. Two days later ceremonies proclaiming the new territory were held. Speeches were made and official oaths taken. On January 22, 1864, the officials reached Fort Whipple and were greeted by thirteen ringing blows on an anvil. In the weeks that followed, they toured the mines, filed numerous claims, and made trips to acquaint themselves with the area. In April Governor Goodwin briefly visited Tucson, Tubac, and the Sonoita Valley, swinging north to the site of Fort Breckinridge before returning to Prescott.

By May, 1864, the governmental machinery in Arizona was in motion. By proclamation Goodwin in April established three judicial districts and ordered U.S. Marshal Milton B. Duffield to take a Territorial census. When the report came in, the population was announced to be 4,573 whites. A month later, Fort Whipple was moved south some twenty miles, and the officials took up residence in the little mining community located nearby on Granite Creek. After the townsite was surveyed, Secretary McCormick was among the first to purchase property. Erecting a building, he launched on March 9 the *Arizona Miner,* the first newspaper published north of the Gila. Named Prescott, this settlement was designated as the Territorial capital in May. On July 18 an election was held, and nine councilmen and eighteen assemblymen were chosen to form a legislature. Indian Superintendent Poston won the position of Territorial delegate to Washington.

The First Territorial Legislature convened in Prescott on September 26. The legislators passed laws encouraging railroad and toll road companies, establishing schools, providing for a militia, and creating the four counties of Yavapai, Pima, Mohave and Yuma. Perhaps the most important action was the adoption of a Territorial code. This body of law was drafted by Judge William T. Howell from the legal experience of New York and California, and when approved it officially set Arizona Territory apart from New Mexico. Memorials also were sent to Congress requesting aid for improving navigation on the Colorado and asking for the establishment of Indian reservations. With the adjournment of the legislature on November 10, all attention shifted back to the mining activity in Arizona.

During the late 1850s and early 1860s, the interest in mines had by no means been restricted to the Tubac area. In 1856 the Arizona Mining and Trading Company had brought machinery from California to the silver-copper deposit at Ajo, about one hundred twenty

Fig. 3.4   First officials of the Arizona Territory were (standing, left to right) Henry F. Fleury, the governor's private secretary; U.S. Marshal Milton B. Duffield; U.S. District Attorney Almon P. Gage; and (seated) Associate Judge Joseph P. Allyn; Governor John Goodwin; and Secretary Richard C. McCormick.

miles west of Tubac, and had placed Edward E. Dunbar in charge. But financial difficulties, transportation problems, and lack of a market doomed this venture to an early failure. Then in 1858 prospectors discovered gold placers on the Gila about twenty miles east of Camp Yuma, and a place called Gila City sprang up. As the California mines were depressed, hundreds of men crossed into Arizona, swelling the population to over five hundred. Within two years, however, the scarcity of water and exhaustion of the placers ended the boom.

Along the Colorado north of Yuma more rich placers were found. In the midst of this discovery the town of La Paz was born. A booming mining and supply center, La Paz was briefly considered as a site for the Territorial capitol. However, when the Walker strike occurred in the spring of 1863, the river population left for the interior. In a very short time, Lynx Creek, Big Bug, Vulture, and Rich Hill became widely known names. Hungry miners attracted a ranch and cattle population. The freighting business boomed. By the late 1860s, ore worth millions of dollars had been taken from the Arizona mines.

To protect the routes of travel and the mining camps from increasing Indian depredations, Carleton began the reoccupation in 1862 of the forts at Mohave, Buchanan and Breckinridge, and established Camps Lowell (Tucson), Bowie (Apache Pass), Whipple (Prescott), and Verde (Verde Valley). Most of these became bases for operations against hostile Apaches.

A Territorial militia, which included friendly Pimas and Maricopas, was also formed to strike the Apaches, and occasionally volunteer groups, impatient with the army, would organize and conduct their own forays into Apacheland.

Carleton's solution for the Indian problem was harsh and grandiose. The first part of his plan involved vigorous campaigns to crush and collect the scattered bands. The Indians would then be placed on military reservations in Arizona and New Mexico, where they could be settled, fed, and taught the rudiments of white civilization. Those who refused to go on a reserve would be exterminated. By such a policy he hoped to bring peace and security to the Southwest. The plan was launched early in 1863 when Carleton laid out the Bosque Redondo Reservation near Fort Sumner on the Pecos River in eastern New Mexico. Orders then went to his commanders to hunt down the Apaches. After brief but successful operations, Colonel Christopher Carson rounded up the Mescaleros in the mountains near Alamogordo and moved them to Bosque Redondo. In Arizona, however, the troops from Camp Bowie and other posts could not bring the Apaches to bay.

In dealing with the Navajos, Carleton realized his greatest success. In the years following Kearny's occupation of Santa Fe in 1846, a series of commanders had tried unsuccessfully to extract treaties from the Navajos, and in 1851 Fort Defiance was established to block their raids on the upper Rio Grande settlements. In the spring of 1861, however, the post was abandoned. In the fall of 1863, Colonel Carson reoccupied Defiance and with a large number of soldiers began systematically driving the Navajos back into their ancestral stronghold, Canyon de Chelly, in northeastern Arizona. Navajo fields of grain were burned wherever found, sheep slaughtered by the thousands. By April, 1864, the Navajos were starved into submission. Under military escort, over eight thousand Indians were moved overland four hundred miles to Bosque Redondo. Here, they remained for four years, suffering terrible privations. Finally, in 1868 the Navajos signed a treaty of peace with the United States and were taken back to Arizona. An agency was established at old Fort Defiance for them. The troubles with the Navajos were over.

The Apache problem remained insoluble. On January 20, 1865, Arizona was separated from the Department of New Mexico and was attached to the Department of California. When General John S. Mason, the new commander, arrived at Fort Whipple, he found that there were less than three thousand soldiers scattered through Arizona at nine posts. Unlike his predecessor, Mason encouraged the Apaches to come to the posts for rations. Fort Goodwin on the Gila became the most successful "feeding station," being visited by both White Mountain and Pinal bands. There was a citizen outcry in Tucson and Prescott, however, against his "soft" policy toward the Apaches, and Mason was replaced.

From 1866 to 1870, a series of commanders struggled to protect the settlements from the Apaches. Finally, on April 15, 1870, the Department of Arizona was created and was placed under General George Stoneman. Following in Mason's footsteps, Stoneman incurred the wrath of the citizenry when he ordered at least one-half of the eighteen posts in Arizona to be abandoned. Politicians, contractors, and merchants, particularly a clique called the Tucson Ring, immediately cried out. The reduction of the federal payroll would be a serious blow to the infant economy.

Beginning in 1871, the federal government took definite steps to end the Apache menace in Arizona. This action was precipitated by a massacre on April 30 of over one hundred defenseless Indians settled near Camp Grant, a fort built at the site of old Fort Breckinridge. Aided by Papagos and Mexicans, a group of Tucsonans, enraged by stock depredations and the lack of military protection, organized under William S. Oury and Jesús Elías and at dawn attacked the Apache camp near Grant. They brutally murdered women and old men and captured twenty-nine children, who were turned over to the Papagos as slaves.

Almost simultaneously, the authorities in Washington had decided to replace Stoneman with Brevet Major General George Crook. Also, Vincent Colyer, a member of the Indian Commissioners, soon was given special powers and ordered to go west and to place the Apaches on reservations. Crook arrived in Arizona first but found his hands tied until after Colyer's visit. The commissioner faced a hostile press when he reached Camp Grant, but he contacted several Indian tribes and designated reservations for some four thousand Apaches. Six months later General O. O. Howard also attempted pacification

Fig. 3.5 In the heyday of silver in Arizona, wagons such as these hauled ore from mine to mill. *Arizona Historical Society*

of the Indian. He then sanctioned the creation of San Carlos Reservation, which became the largest Apache reserve in the West, and arranged to meet the old Chiricahua chieftain Cochise. Howard designated Cochise's mountain homeland as the Chiricahua Reservation.

Finally, in the fall of 1872, after sending out warnings for all hostile bands to surrender, Crook unleashed his forces north of the Gila. His commanders moved swiftly with pack trains, scoured the countryside, and drove the Apaches toward the Tonto Basin, northeast of present-day Phoenix. In late December, soldiers surrounded an Apache party seeking refuge in a cave in a bluff above the Salt River Canyon. Firing at the roof of the opening, which caused the bullets to ricochet, they killed over seventy Indians, including women and children. This affair was later called the battle at Skull Cave, because for years the skeletons of the slain were plainly visible. A few months later Crook's forces surprised an Apache band at Turret Butte, to the north in the Verde Valley, killing and capturing a number of warriors. By the spring of 1873 the Apaches were coming in to surrender and were being assigned to reservations. The Indian wars north of the Gila were over. For his success, Crook received the star of a regular brigadier general.

In the late 1860s, many new settlements had sprung up in Arizona. On the Colorado, Hardyville, a river port near Fort Mohave, and Ehrenberg, farther south, became major centers for freighting and stage travel to Prescott. Across from Fort Yuma, Arizona City was struggling into existence as a jumping-off place for travel up the Gila. From this point also, the California firm of Hooper and Company was freighting east over the Butterfield route. The firm reoccupied the old stage stations and rebuilt the adobe structures, shops, and corrals at Maricopa Wells. At this point two important roads branched. One ran northeast across the Salt River to Forts McDowell and Verde on the Verde; the other went south to the Tucson vicinity. A road also tied Prescott with Albuquerque, and another ran east from Tucson to the lower Rio Grande Valley. Because of the Indian menace, it was not until early in 1869 that regular stage operations were resumed across Arizona. In time, a county road system was also developed to supplement the other routes.

The political scene during the early years was dominated by Richard C. McCormick, who served first as Territorial secretary, then as governor. A fiery young Irishman reared in wealth in New York, "Little Mac" had been a newspaperman before entering politics. Making an unsuccessful bid for Congress in 1862, he had served briefly in the newly created Bureau of Agriculture before his appointment as secretary for Arizona. When Governor Goodwin was elected delegate in the fall of 1865 and went east, McCormick became acting governor, and the following year, governor. From the first he began building a personal political machine through the use of his newspaper, the *Miner,* and through deals with special interest groups. The charge of being a "car-

Arizona Historical Society

Fig. 3.6   General Crook commanded in Arizona during the Apache wars.

petbagger" soon was leveled against him. Through his influence, for example, the 1867 legislature voted to move the capital from Prescott to Tucson, and the following year he was elected delegate largely on votes in the Tucson area. To support his machine, he bought a controlling interest in the Tucson *Arizonian* — and later founded the *Citizen.* He probably helped create the Tucson Ring, a coterie involved in controlling government contracts in Arizona.

McCormick also was a Territorial booster. He wrote numerous articles, stressing the needs and advantages of Arizona. Some of these were published in Eastern newspapers and were reprinted for distribution. As governor he eagerly sought federal funds for roads and stage and mail lines, pushed for a larger army in Arizona and additional military posts, and championed liberal mining laws. As Territorial delegate from 1869 to 1875, Richard McCormick was intimately involved in most of the major decisions regarding appointments and government policy in Arizona.

In April, 1869, Anson P. K. Safford was sworn in as governor and arrived in Tucson in early July. Reflecting the prevailing view of the settlers, Safford fell into line with the Tucson Ring and others who were clamoring for a large-scale war against the Apaches. Paralleling his strong stand on the Indian question was his equally active interest in mining and in railroads. Like McCormick, Safford was an incorporator of the Atlantic and Pacific Railroad, projected along the thirty-fifth parallel. He was also to be a prime mover in the development of the Tombstone mines.

Safford is best remembered for his untiring efforts to establish a public school system in Arizona. He viewed with dismay the opposition in Utah and New Mexico to public schools, and at the same time he saw the need for further Americanization of the Spanish-American population in Arizona. At Safford's request, the Sixth Legislature drew on the experience in California and in 1871 passed the first important school law. This measure made the governor ex-officio superintendent of public instruction, set up a board of education, designated each county probate judge as county school superintendent, and established a system of local taxation. To push implementation of the law, Safford began a horse and buggy campaign, urging the Board of Supervisors in each county to establish school districts. Within two years there were eleven public schools in operation. When Safford resigned the governorship in 1877 because of ill health, the number of schools in Arizona had increased manyfold.

The last of the so-called carpetbagger governors was John C. Frémont. A national hero and the first Republican candidate for president in 1856, General Frémont by the mid-1870s was in dire need of financial support. Approaching party leaders for aid, he was appointed governor of Arizona, replacing John P. Hoyt. In the fall of 1878 the Frémonts reached Prescott, which had been redesignated the capital the year before. Within a few months the new Territorial executive became involved with Judge Charles Silent and others in grandiose mining, irrigation, and real estate schemes. He also approved the creation of the Arizona Development Corporation, a lottery whereby funds could be raised to build a statehouse and to help finance public schools. The Postmaster General halted this operation. As Frémont was out of Arizona for extended periods on private business ventures, both Territorial officials and legislators began clamoring for his removal. In the spring of 1881 the ill-fated politician resigned. Frémont's departure closed an era in Arizona politics. Thereafter, the officials appointed in Washington to govern the Territory were more responsive to local interests, more party oriented, and more successful in promoting Arizona's future.

Beginning in the late 1860s, a slump in mining activity occurred in Arizona. In many districts, the gold placers played out; in the shaft mines complex ores were encountered. The lack of transportation, the problem of the Indian, and insufficient capital precluded further mining development. Fortunately the picture brightened in the mid-1870s. Prospectors reported silver veins in the Pinal Mountains, in the Tombstone Mountains, in the Bradshaws south of Prescott, and in Mohave County north of the Bill Williams River. In 1878 Congress remonetized silver, encouraging Western production. The age of the great silver bonanzas in Arizona was at hand.

The story of Tombstone epitomized what happened in numerous other districts. In 1877, while prospecting a few miles east of the San Pedro River, Ed Schieffelin found a mineral outcrop and filed a claim in Tucson. Obtaining a grub stake, Ed and his brother Al and a friend, Richard Gird, opened a mining district in the spring of 1878 that quickly became famous throughout the West. By the early 1880s, Tombstone boasted a population of some ten thousand and was the largest town in Arizona. In 1881 Cochise County was created with Tombstone as county seat.

The effect of the Tombstone strike on the surrounding area was instantaneous. Tucson boomed as a supply center for the mines. Cattlemen arrived from Texas and New Mexico with herds to feed the hungry miners and to establish ranches. Prospectors scoured the neighboring mountains and found additional ore bodies, especially to the south in the Mule Mountains, where the copper town of Bisbee soon flourished. The peak year for the Tombstone mines was 1882, when silver worth over five million dollars was produced. Then came flooding of the shafts below the five hundred-foot level, halting much of the work. The town slowly began to decline, and in less than a decade its hour of glory had passed.

Although best remembered for its rich silver mines and the rough frontier personalities who walked its streets, Tombstone left an even greater legacy: it played a major role in bringing the first transcontinental railroad into Arizona. This, in turn, signalled the beginning of a new age. Thereafter, the influence of industrialism gradually permeated society and government and brought Arizona closer to the mainstream of American life.

Within six months after the magnitude of the Tombstone discovery became known, the Southern Pacific Railroad made plans to lay track across Arizona. Coupled with the attraction of hauling ore and freight for the mines was the fear that the Texas and Pacific Railroad, already building west from Shreveport toward El Paso, might gain right of way and other concessions in New Mexico and Arizona. As the Southern Pacific in 1877 had completed a line from Los Angeles to Fort Yuma and had constructed a bridge over the Colorado, the officials obtained a charter from the Arizona legislature to extend the trackage east along the thirty-second parallel. On March 20, 1880, the first train arrived in Tucson. It was symbolic that the silver spike handed to railroad officials to celebrate the tie with the outside world had been fashioned from the ore of a Tombstone mine. By late 1881 the Southern Pacific had been pushed across southern New Mexico to meet the Texas and Pacific east of El Paso. Railroad towns sprang up, and farms and ranches were established along the route. The dream in the 1850s of a transcontinental railroad across the Southwest was at last realized.

A second east-west line across Arizona was also under construction to the north along the thirty-fifth parallel. In May, 1880, the Santa Fe Railroad, building under a federal charter granted in 1866 to the Atlantic and Pacific, started grading crews west from Albuquer-

Arizona Historical Society
Fig. 3.7   Henry C. Hooker, beef contractor
and prominent rancher.

Arizona Historical Society
Fig. 3.8   Jacob Hamblin, Mormon trail-
blazer in Northern Arizona.

que. After encountering numerous obstacles, particularly in bridging deep canyons in central Arizona, the Santa Fe reached the Colorado across from Needles in August, 1883, where it joined with the Southern Pacific. The towns of Winslow, Holbrook, Flagstaff, Williams, and Kingman owed their early prosperity to the railroad. Branch lines later were built to connect with Prescott, Phoenix, and the Grand Canyon. To the south, the Gila Valley, Globe, and Northern Railroad (later a part of the Arizona Eastern) branched north from Bowie to the upper Gila Valley settlements. By 1900 a railroad network tied together the major centers of the Territory, affording rapid and adequate transportation for both travel and freight.

Paralleling the mining boom of the late 1870s was the rise of extensive cattle ranches in Arizona. The first large-scale markets for beef developed in the post-Civil War years with the building of permanent military posts, the creation of Indian reservations, and the rise of mining communities. Until the mid-1870s California contractors controlled the markets, sending buyers as far east as Texas and south into Sonora for trail herds. Although the first tribe to receive regular beef rations was the Mohaves on the Colorado River Reservation, the growing Apache reserve at San Carlos eventually provided the most lucrative market. One of the subcontractors, Henry C. Hooker, was aware of this when he decided to establish a ranch in the Sulphur Springs Valley south of the reservation. By the early 1880s his Sierra Bonita Ranch was widely known throughout the Southwest.

The Tombstone strike spurred the development of the sprawling Empire Ranch southeast of Tucson and John Slaughter's San Bernardino spread on the border

near present-day Douglas. North of the Gila, the Aztec Land and Cattle Company in the late 1880s secured a vast tract of land from the Santa Fe Railroad and for years was one of the largest outfits in the Territory. South of its range occurred the celebrated Graham-Tewksbury feud, a vendetta between two ranching families in the Tonto Basin.

By the mid-1880s the open-range cattle business was passing. To protect their herds from diseases carried by imported stock, to prevent rustling, and to control markets, the large producers organized local associations and became politically active, influencing the legislature in 1885 to establish a Livestock Sanitary Board. Attempts were also made to develop winter pastures in the Salt River Valley. Improved stock was brought into Arizona, the first large herd of Herefords being placed on Colin Cameron's San Rafael ranch in 1883. By the nineties, with the cattle market depressed and pastures overgrazed, cattlemen abandoned the idea of trying to fatten their animals to maturity, and began shipping them out to feeder farms in other states. By 1900 most Arizona ranches were restricted to breeding operations. This, however, changed later (see chapter 24).

The sheep industry in Arizona had less spectacular growth. During the 1850s, some fifty-five thousand sheep were driven from the Rio Grande Valley in New Mexico to California, but it was not until twenty years later that sheep ranching in Arizona began on a large scale. The earliest sheep raiser probably was Juan Candelaria, who in the late 1860s drove a large flock of merinos from New Mexico into what later became Apache County. Although there were large flocks in Pima and other southern counties by the 1880s, Flagstaff developed as a center for the industry, with the Daggs brothers the major sheepmen. The coming of the railroad helped considerably in marketing the wool. Mutton at that time was not in demand. Because of friction with cattlemen, and for other reasons, a group of sheepmen met at Flagstaff in 1886 and formed the Arizona Sheep Breeders and Wool Growers Association. Like cattlemen, sheep raisers began wintering their flocks in the Salt River Valley, following well-defined "driveways" from summer pastures in the mountains down to the warmer climes below. In 1891 Arizona producers marketed five million pounds of wool from seven hundred thousand sheep, realizing twenty-five cents per pound.

In the mid-1880s the army ended the Indian menace in Arizona. During the previous decade the reservations in the Territory were constantly plagued with conniving agents, unpredictable contractors, intractable warriors, and military interference. On the giant San Carlos reserve, disgusted Apache chieftains repeatedly gathered their followers and headed for Mexico. When this occurred, the call went out for cavalry to chase the bands and protect the countryside. In 1882 General Crook returned to Arizona and turned his attention to the problem of policing the reservations. In May, 1885, when over one hundred Chiricahuas fled San Carlos, Crook organized an expedition and followed the renegades into Mexico. His Apache scouts located them, and Crook met the chieftains near the old San Bernardino ranch in March, 1886. The Apaches agreed to return, but on the trail north Geronimo changed his mind and fled again. Crook was criticized for his laxity in handling the operation and was replaced by General Nelson A. Miles, who forced the hostiles to surrender in September. The renegades and their families were deported by train to Florida. The Indian "wars" in Arizona were over.

In the meantime, additional settlements had arisen in the central valleys of Arizona. With forts and mining camps furnishing ready markets for hay and vegetables, local contractors in the mid-1860s began cutting the tall grass growing in old Indian ditches along the Salt River Valley and selling it at Fort McDowell. Then, in 1867, ex-Confederate Jack Swilling and several friends from Wickenburg cut a ditch on the north bank of the Salt, built a brush dam to divert the water, and planted crops. During the following year, a number of families settled on both banks of the Salt and built additional ditches. Swilling and William A. Hancock promoted the development of the adobe settlement called Phoenix, while about ten miles to the east and on the south bank, Charles T. Hayden built a gristmill and helped lay the foundations for the present town of Tempe. In 1871 Phoenix became the county seat of newly created Maricopa County. In 1889 it became the capital of the Territory. Before the decade ended Mormon groups had settled at Tempe and still farther east on the Salt at Mesa. These towns were farming communities with surrounding fields producing food crops for domestic consumption and grain for military and reservation needs.

Farmers also were settling on the Gila about this time. Florence was established in 1868, many of the first inhabitants coming from nearby Adamsville, where an irrigation attempt had failed. It became a supply center for the neighboring Pima Reservation and for the silver mines discovered north of the river in the Pinal Mountains. In 1873 a land office was located there, and two years later Florence was made the seat for newly formed Pinal County. To the east, in the upper Gila Valley, Anglos found scattered Mexican settlements when they arrived in the early 1870s. Solomonville, for example, arose near the little village of San José in 1874. When prospectors from Silver City, New Mexico, entered the Clifton-Morenci area to work the copper deposits, they found evidences of earlier Mexican placer activities.

Other Mormon colonists also entered Arizona. From Kanab, in southwestern Utah, Mormons traveled southeast, crossed the Colorado River at Lee's Ferry, and started missionary work among the Hopis at Moenkopi and Tuba City. Others settled in Mohave County at Pipe Springs, which was connected to Utah by a telegraph line in December, 1871, and at Fredonia, the northernmost community in Arizona. Over a road blazed by the famous Mormon explorer, Jacob Hamblin, came wagon trains to establish towns in the Little Colorado Valley. St. Johns, Joseph City, Show Low, and a dozen other places in east-central Arizona sprang to life. Through a

Arizona Historical Society
Fig. 3.9   Rev. John B. Salpointe promoted Catholic work in Arizona after the Civil War.

cooperative association called the United Order, these hardy pioneers built successful irrigation works and tamed the desert. Despite the attempt in the early 1880s to disenfranchise them, the Mormon settlers persevered, and many became prominent citizens of Arizona.

Other civilizing influences were at work at this time. In February, 1866, Father John B. Salpointe arrived in Tucson from Santa Fe with several assistants to bolster the Roman Catholic Church in Arizona. Designating Tucson as the home parish, he sent priests to Yuma and later into central Arizona to work. In 1868 Arizona was designated a Vicariate Apostolic with Salpointe as vicar. Recalled to Santa Fe to succeed Archbishop John B. Lamy, Father Salpointe left behind a heroic record of service. During his nineteen years in Arizona, five parishes had been created, the Sisters of St. Joseph had started a school and had staffed St. Mary's Hospital (opened in 1880) in Tucson, and San Augustine Cathedral had been constructed. The tireless priest indeed had been a beacon in the wilderness. On May 8, 1897, the Diocese of Tucson was created. The Protestants also were active. By the early 1880s the Presbyterians, Congregationalists, Methodists, Baptists, and Episcopalians had organized congregations in Tucson and were building churches in the other major towns in the Territory.

Although the arrival of the railroad signalled the beginning of modern Arizona, it was the rise of the copper industry that brought maturity. For the local economy, copper development came at an opportune time. In the 1880s many of the spectacular silver discoveries were playing out, and the government payroll for the large military establishment fell off abruptly with the end of the Indian problems. Copper buoyed up the local economy by bringing in large Eastern and foreign investments to build towns, smelters, and shortline railroads. This, in turn, spurred the development of agriculture, banking, and other service industries. Together, railroads and copper also heavily influenced county and Territorial politics.

Although prospectors uncovered many copper ledges at an early day, it was not until the advent of rail transportation that concerted efforts were made to bring copper mines into full production. By the mid-1880s at least six major deposits had been located at Ray, Jerome, Globe, Clifton-Morenci, Bisbee, and Ajo, but only the districts at Globe, Clifton-Morenci, and Bisbee were active. The key year was 1888, when copper production in Arizona was valued at $5.3 million, while silver and gold production combined totalled only $3 million. The booming electrical industry requiring millions of miles of copper wire, the increase in geological knowledge, and the resiliency of copper to economic depressions stimulated large-scale development. Such figures as James Douglas, James Colquhoun, L. D. Ricketts, and John C. Greenway became well known throughout the Territory. Among the major companies were the W. A. Clark interests, Phelps Dodge, Arizona Copper Company, Ltd., and Calumet and Arizona.

Arizona Historical Society

Fig. 3.10   John C. Greenway was an outstanding leader in the copper industry.

A number of company towns sprang up. Many Mexican-Americans settled in these towns to labor deep in the earth. From Cornwall came "Cousin Jacks" to build and operate plants; from southeast Europe came Italians and others to open stores. Absentee ownership prevailed, with all the problems the system entailed. After 1900 labor unrest occurred in several of the copper towns, some of it indigenous and shortlived, while in other instances it resulted from national unions' attempts to organize. This problem reached its apogee during the summer of 1917, when company officials at Jerome and Bisbee tried to break up unionism by deporting large groups of workers.

Banking in Arizona was also stimulated by the copper industry. H. S. Van Gorder and Charles Mills, local Phelps Dodge officials, played a major role in establishing the Gila Valley Bank at Solomonville; this financial institution later merged with the Valley Bank to become the Valley National Bank. Douglas money helped found the Bank of Douglas, which proved to be one of the soundest in the country. As was true in other parts of the Arizona economy, many of the early banks had intimate ties with financial circles in California.

Among the prominent merchants in the late nineteenth century were the Goldwaters, the Zeckendorfs, and the Babbitts. In the early 1860s, Michael and Joseph Goldwater opened a store in the booming river town of La Paz, but shortly moved their business downriver and laid out Ehrenberg. Their store became a supply center for the Colorado River mines and a popular meeting place for businessmen, contractors, and politicians. The Goldwaters also invested money in mining ventures, the Vulture Mine in particular. As the population followed the mining strikes inland, so did the Goldwaters, establishing stores at Phoenix, Prescott, and Bisbee. Eventually, both Mike and Joseph returned to California, turning the Goldwater interests over to Mike's sons, Morris and Baron. Morris became mayor of Prescott, a bank president, and chairman of the Democratic Territorial Central Committee. Baron settled in Phoenix, figured in local civic affairs, and devoted his time to the family store. His son, Barry, later served as United States Senator from Arizona and was the Republican candidate for president in 1964.

The most prominent merchants in southern Arizona were the Zeckendorfs, who centered their operations in Tucson. In 1854 Aaron Zeckendorf opened a store in Santa Fe, and in 1867 he sent his brother Louis with a wagon train to Tucson. Louis sold its contents to a local storeman, Charles T. Hayden, who later moved to the Salt River Valley. The following year William Zeckendorf arrived to establish a branch for A. & L. Zeckendorf. Offering both a retail and a wholesale outlet, the firm enjoyed trade with northern Sonora and lucrative

army and Indian contracts. A nephew, Albert Steinfeld, joined the business in 1872 and in time purchased William's interest. Steinfield was a farseeing merchant who soon turned his attention to promoting copper mines, irrigation projects, banking, and real estate. Louis Zeckendorf and Steinfeld became entangled in a lawsuit in 1903, and the former closed out his interests in Arizona. Steinfield emerged as the most prominent and ultimately one of the wealthiest merchants in Tucson.

In the mid-1880s, from Cincinnati, Ohio, came the Babbitt brothers — David, William, George, Charles, and Edward — to settle in Flagstaff. They went into cattle ranching, established a mercantile business with branches in the towns along the Santa Fe line, and set up trading posts on Indian reservations in northern Arizona. Public-spirited citizens, they promoted both the civic and the educational development of the Territory. Many other prominent Arizona businessmen of this period could be mentioned — Solomon Barth, Carlos Jácome, Eugene F. Sanguinetti, to name but a few.

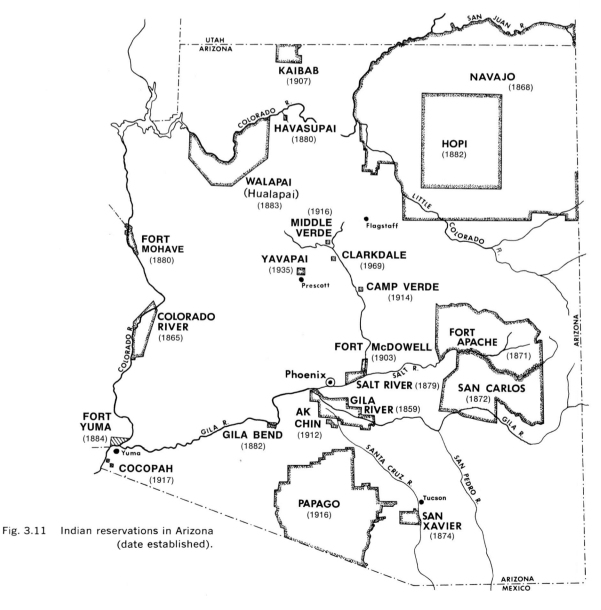

Fig. 3.11   Indian reservations in Arizona
(date established).

Fig. 3.12 Michael Goldwater, merchant
grandfather of the 1964 presidential candidate.

By the 1890s vigorous attempts were being made
to develop large-scale irrigation works in the Salt River
Valley. The canals constructed thirty years earlier had
been primarily for domestic and community purposes.
Later, water was diverted to grow alfalfa and cotton,
but the vagaries of weather, unpredictable streamflow,
and temporary dams made commercial production
impossible. Despite these conditions, Alexander J.
Chandler, veterinarian for the Livestock Sanitary Board,
enlisted financial help from the D. M. Ferry Seed Company in Detroit and founded the Consolidated Canal
Company. Entering into an agreement with the Mesa
City Canal, Chandler built a modern irrigation system
that eventually placed him in control of eighteen thousand acres on the south bank of the Salt.

When an extended drought struck the valley in the
early 1890s, the farmers sought both local and national
support for a large storage reservoir. The Reclamation
Act of 1902 brought the aid they desired. The Salt River
Valley Water Users Association was formed, and through
a federal loan and supervision a dam, a reservoir, and
a complex of channels were built. With the completion of Roosevelt Dam in 1911, over 250,000 acres were
placed under irrigation. Cotton, alfalfa, and grain sorghum spurted forward to become Arizona's major farm
crops. In the years that followed, other government-
sponsored projects were completed on the Gila, Colorado, and Lower Colorado rivers.

Interest in statehood began to stir in the late 1880s.
The coming of the railroad and the rise of the copper
industry brought a measure of stability and provided
foundations for permanent growth. Regarding themselves as second-class citizens because of their Territorial

status, many Arizonans viewed statehood as a means to
gain political self-determination, economic freedom, and
control over their own destiny.

The Democratic party took the lead in the movement. In 1889 outgoing Governor Conrad Zulick
branded the Territorial system of government as "repug-
nant to the enlightened sense of the American people"
and as a brake on progress and prosperity. On January
6, 1890, Delegate Marcus A. Smith, a Democrat, introduced a statehood bill in the House of Representatives,
but it failed to arouse interest. The Sixteenth Territorial
Legislature then issued a call for a Constitutional Convention to meet in Phoenix in September, 1891. Although
dominated by the Democrats, the delegates split over
the issue of Mormon voting, woman suffrage, and free
silver. The constitution sent to Washington was rejected
by a Republican Congress sensitive to the issue of silver
and opposed to additional Democratic states. In 1900
the Republican national platform carried a plank favor-
ing new states in the Southwest. The Republicans won,
but nothing was done.

Finally, in 1902, an Omnibus Bill was introduced to
secure statehood for Arizona, New Mexico, Oklahoma,
and Indian Territory. During the ensuing debate, the
idea of joining Arizona and New Mexico into one state
was advanced. Although the amendment was defeated,
joint statehood was seized upon by Senator Albert J.
Beveridge and other Republicans as a device to delay
and scuttle the Omnibus Bill. In Arizona a great outcry
arose against joint statehood with New Mexico. Corporate interests predicted that the new capital would
be Santa Fe, not Phoenix, and that the larger, Spanish-
speaking population in New Mexico would dominate
the new legislature. Both Democrats and Republicans

Fig. 3.13 Alexander Chandler, pioneer in irrigation.

Arizona Historical Society

Fig. 3.14   G. W. Hunt served as state governor
for seven terms.

closed ranks in protesting jointure. In February, 1906, joint statehood was approved for Oklahoma and Indian Territory, and the following month the Senate agreed to permit a referendum, whereby Arizona and New Mexico could vote separately on joint statehood. In November New Mexico voted in favor of the idea, but Arizona voted five to one against it, and jointure was dead.

Statehood for Arizona seemed imminent. Because of Republican party problems in New Mexico, President Theodore Roosevelt postponed action on statehood, passing on to his successor in 1909, William H. Taft, the final decision on the matter. A statehood bill was started through Congress early in 1909, but again Senator Beveridge blocked its passage. His Committee on Territories then drew up a new bill, which was reported out in March, 1910. It included a number of safeguards for admitting the two territories. These included an anti-polygamy clause for voting, the setting aside of one million acres of government land in each territory to satisfy county railroad bondholders, protection for school land, and a requirement that all members of the new state legislature be able to speak and understand English. Perhaps the most unique provision was the requirement that the new state constitution be approved by Congress *and* the President. This was intended to dampen attempts by local Democratic and labor groups to write such reform guarantees as initiative, referendum, and recall into the new constitutions. On June 18 Congress passed the Arizona-New Mexico statehood bill and two days later President Taft signed it into law.

Arizona now prepared to draft a constitution. Territorial Governor Richard E. Sloan issued a call for election of delegates to a Constitutional Convention. The corporate interests, which controlled at least a half dozen newspapers in Arizona, advised that delegates be selected by popular vote, rather than by the county system, in the hope that reform-minded representatives could be trimmed away. But the fifty-two delegates who arrived in Phoenix in early October, 1910, were chosen by the regular system. George W. P. Hunt, of Gila County, a Democrat who would be state governor seven times, presided over the convention; Morris Goldwater, of Yavapai County, was vice president.

Although President Taft visited Phoenix during the convention and warned against "crank constitutions," the Arizonans drafted a document replete with reform features. Woman suffrage, direct election of senators, direct primaries, as well as referendum, initiative, and recall were included. An uproar followed, and a movement began to oppose ratification. In February, 1911, however, Arizonans voted for the new constitution, and it was sent to Congress. On August 14 Taft vetoed the joint resolution calling for Arizona statehood because of the recall provision, but seven days later agreeably signed a second resolution which provided for statehood if Arizonans voted to remove the recall clause from their constitution. In December Arizona dutifully eliminated the recall provision, and elected its first slate of state officers. On February 14, 1912, Taft signed a proclamation admitting Arizona to the Union. Arizona was a state at last!

In fifty years Arizona had progressed from an undeveloped frontier territory to a progressive, industrial state. Roughly one-half of that period had been characterized by large-scale military operations against hostile Indians, by spectacular but ephemeral mining strikes, by the rise of cattle and sheep ranching, and by a gradual influx of settlers to possess the soil and to build homes. The arrival of the railroad in the 1880s marked the transition to the modern age. The rise of the copper industry, the development of commercial agriculture through irrigation, and the beginnings of merchandising and banking all provided foundations for continuing growth. With her basic economic, social, and political institutions firmly established by 1912, Arizona entered the Union on a high note of optimism.

Fig. 4.1 Arizonans at school, work, or play, are a mixture of races and cultures that is typically American.

Helga Teiwes Photo, Arizona State Museum, University of Arizona

Jean Barstow
Anthropologist

4

THE PEOPLE

ARIZONA IN THE LATE TWENTIETH CENTURY still recalls in many ways its history as a frontier area. Only in the few decades past has its growth shown patterns and trends long apparent in other parts of the United States — rapid urbanization and decline of the rural population, and the shift from an economy based entirely on primary resources to one dependent also on industry, manufacturing, and services. At the outset of the seventies, the state was still relatively underpopulated compared to most of the rest of the nation, with the total number of Arizonans reaching only about two million — considerably smaller than most large cities of the United States. But the state is growing rapidly, both in terms of its economy and its population. Predictions are that sometime during the first half of the seventies, population increase will reach about 100,000 yearly. Roughly one-half of these will be newcomers to the state.

Making up Arizona's population in the early seventies was an unusual diversity of ethnic groups. At least one quarter of the state's inhabitants were of non-Anglo stock, and within each main human segment or ethnic group — Indians, Mexican-Americans, Blacks, Chinese, and Japanese — there were substantial differences in cultural heritage. Although a detailed analysis of the history of their origin and participation in the state's growth would be necessary for understanding the role of each of these groups, a broad overview suggests some of the numerous reasons for the diversity of the population in the 1900s.

One of the decisive influences in creating this diversity was the shift in political control which took place in the Southwest in the mid-nineteenth century. Before the U.S. victory in the war against Mexico in 1847, Spanish-speaking persons had played a dominant role in settling the region. Successful in relegating a portion of the local Indian population to a subordinate position, they had managed also to defend themselves against other groups of raiding Indians. With the Treaty of Guadalupe Hidalgo at the end of the war, however, control passed definitively into the hands of Anglo settlers from the United States. By 1887, these settlers, backed in some cases by the U.S. cavalry, had eliminated almost completely the threat of Indian attack and competition for land and resources.

The nearly exclusive Anglo control over development of the state's natural wealth brought about obvious and profound changes in Arizona's ethnic makeup. Early patterns of migration to the Arizona Territory already reflected consistently the labor needs of the growing enterprises directed by Anglos — agriculture, mining, and ranching. Many of the early migrants — Chinese, Mexicans, and Blacks — along with segments of the

Fig. 4.2   Head Start groups provide common language and learning.

Indian population, provided the labor required for exploitation of the state's resources. Certain patterns of population growth — the immigration of Mexican farm laborers, for example — persisted well into the twentieth century. Only after World War II did another decisive shift with such far-reaching effect take place in Arizona's overall development.

Since that time, dominance of the state's economy by the older enterprises — mining, agriculture, and ranching — has been yielding gradually to the increasing importance of the manufacturing, retail, and service industries. In turn, migration patterns have responded to this reorientation, with its differing labor needs. After the war, high demand for skilled workers and professionals was partly responsible for a preponderance of Anglos among newcomers to the state. At the same time, increasing mechanization of both mining and agriculture began to create an excess labor force, discouraging further large-scale migration of low-skilled labor. Long-range effects of this growth of industry and the displacement of low-skilled workers are expected to become more intensified as the century advances.

Change Characterizes Sixties

Throughout the 1960s the changing roles of the ethnic groups in Arizona were highlighted for a number of reasons. With funds provided by federal poverty programs, studies and projects in previously neglected areas were undertaken. In many cases, programs called for participation of community members, leading indirectly to the emergence of local leaders and community action movements. At the same time, in Arizona as throughout the nation, ethnic groups, especially Indians, Mexican Americans, and Blacks have called for changes in economic and social opportunities. Among the state's ethnic groups, widespread unemployment, low educational achievement, poor housing conditions, and high incidence of disease have been documented thoroughly since the 1960s. In order to eliminate these conditions, spokesmen for the groups, or for their poorer factions, have been insisting that the community itself control its future participation in the state's growth. Such demands for community autonomy are particularly striking among some of the Indian groups in Arizona.

Of all the ethnic groups in the state, the Indians have been held most restrictively to a marginal role since the nineteenth century. As early as the 1860s Indians were being isolated on reservations by the Anglo population. Because of differences among the Indian tribes, and variations in Anglo policies for dealing with them, the impact of the reservation system was by no means uniform on the Indian population. In many cases, relocation deprived the groups of the very basis for their traditional subsistence activities — and consequently of self-sufficiency and autonomy. Some tribes were reduced to living on rations distributed by reservation authorities. Others were able to maintain sub-

Arizona State Museum, University of Arizona

Fig. 4.3   An Arizonan — one of many thousands with Indian ancestry.

sistence patterns or adopt innovations offered by Anglo society. In spite of varying effects of the system, one pervasive influence is noted frequently both by Indians and non-Indians: the reduction of tribes to a position of political powerlessness. Associated feelings of individual powerlessness were experienced by many Indians as well, because of the influence of educational programs designed to replace Indian culture with Anglo institutions. Until the 1960s the implicit assumption behind nearly all federal policies, especially in education, was that Indians would inevitably, although perhaps gradually, become integrated into Anglo society. Conservative policy-makers virtually equated integration with the total disappearance of Indian culture. Even the most liberal policies, designed as alternatives to conservative programs, offered the Indians plans modeled after white institutions, such as the legislation outlined during the New Deal, providing for formation of Indian tribal governments. Overlooked by both types of policy-makers was the obvious fact that Indians were already integrated into Anglo society, but in a marginal and powerless role. By the middle of the 1900s the inadequacy of most programs based on the concept of integration had long been clear. Total assimilation, implying the elimination of Indian-Anglo differences, had not taken place. Certainly there has never been a question of such change for most Indians. In addition, a legacy of problems remained to be solved: lower levels of educational achievement and employment, and higher incidences of poverty and disease among Indians than in the U.S. population as a whole. As an alternative approach to dealing with these conditions, both federal policy-makers and Indian leaders began advocating Indian direction and control of reservation programs previously handled by the Bureau of Indian Affairs and other federal agencies. The Indian leaders who are assuming these responsibilities are confronted with the task of designing more effective programs. In their experimentation, they are faced with serious obstacles to Indian social and economic development.

The reservation system itself represents in many cases a severe limitation on creating change. In the early seventies the total population of reservation Indians in Arizona had reached about 110,000. But it was clear that reservation economies alone were not sufficient to maintain the population. On the Navajo reservation, less than one-half of the people who wanted work in the late sixties could find on-reservation jobs. In order to provide more employment opportunities, some experimental programs have aimed at encouraging industries to locate on reservations. Under this type of arrangement, worked out with federal funding by the Bureau of Indian Affairs Economic Development Agency and tribal councils, industrial parks were developed in the

late sixties on the Gila River Indian Reservation, shared by Pima and Maricopa Indians, and on the Papago Reservation. Yet this alternative is not feasible for all reservations. The poorer tribes, living in relative isolation and without resources, have little hope of attracting industry.

Disparities Among Tribes

A quick survey of Indian landholdings and economies reveals great differences in tribal resources and development. All in all, Indians control about one quarter of the state's land. By far the largest holdings are those of the Navajos, located in the northeast corner of the state, and totaling about nine million acres. By the turn of the century the Navajos had built up a prosperous economy based on sheep and livestock raising. When oil was discovered on their lands in the twenties, a business committee was formed to handle the tribe's resources. In addition to oil, other resources — gas, uranium, and lumber — have made the Navajos the most prosperous Indians in the state. In comparison, many other tribes had only begun to diversify their sources of income in the early 1970s. Stock raising has

Fig. 4.4   Many Indian Arizonans continue to live in environments combining traditional aspects with the limitations of poverty.
Arizona State Museum, University of Arizona

Fig. 4.5   Apaches in northern Arizona have increased tribal income by development of forested areas for recreational use.

long been important for the Apaches on both the San Carlos and Fort Apache reservations, but both were developing recreation areas during the sixties to provide additional tribal income. The Papago Indians, who occupy three different reservations in the south-central part of the state, and the Hualapai, in the area near the Grand Canyon, still depend more than do the Apaches on livestock raising alone. Other tribes continue to rely on farming. The Havasupai, living in the Grand Canyon, can supplement their farm income only by guiding visitors around their area of the canyon. The Hopi, living on a separate reservation within the vast Navajo lands, still raise crops of melons, beans, squash, and corn. Discovery of oil on the Kaibab reservation on the Utah border has created the possibility of diversification for the predominantly agricultural economy of the Southern Paiutes. Among the poorest Indians of the state are the Yavapais living near Prescott, and the four groups living in the southern part of Arizona — Cocopas, Quechans, Mohaves, and the Chemehuevis.

Irrigation farming was a traditional economic activity of the Cocopas and the Quechans on the Colorado River Reservation. With the diverting of the waters of the Colorado into the Salton Sea, a source of water for this farming was affected adversely. By the seventies, however, the Colorado River Reservation was developing irrigation farming through the assistance of the

federal government, and was increasing tribal income by leasing land to outsiders. Quechan subsistence patterns were upset by the wage economy introduced at the time of the Gold Rush, and much of the cultural tradition of the group has disappeared. During the sixties both the Quechan and Cocopa tribes had begun making some beadwork items for the market.

For several reservations, the sale of Indian arts and crafts has provided substantial income — Navajo rugs and silver work, Kachina dolls and jewelry of the Hopi, pottery from various Pueblo Indians, and basketry made by the Papagos. This type of income, however, is restricted to groups who can produce on a fairly large scale for the market.

Expansion of reservation lands represents another possibility for the development of tribal economies, but one which has been difficult thus far. Because of the federal trusteeship over Indian lands, the change in reservation boundaries would require either an executive order or an act of Congress.

In view of these limits on the growth and diversification of reservation economies, it is not surprising that Indians continue to become more dependent on wage labor away from the reservation or on welfare payments. Arizona's rising urban Indian population — estimated very roughly at 20,000 in the early seventies — reflects in part this dependence on wage labor, which has been increasing steadily since World War I. By the sixties, about 12,000 Indians were living in Phoenix and about 6,000 in Tucson. Within these urban areas there were well-defined communities of Yaqui Indians. Of Mexican origin, many Yaquis immigrated from Sonora during the Díaz regime and found farm labor jobs in the Tucson and Phoenix areas. Lacking recognition as a U.S. Indian tribe, the Yaqui have been in a particularly difficult situation because they have not had access to services which are available to other Arizona Indians.

Indian Poverty Persists

On the whole, off-reservation employment has not provided a solution to the poverty suffered by Indians on the reservations. Job opportunities have been mostly for unskilled labor — for miners, seasonal farm workers, and laborers on construction and irrigation projects. Vocational education for the most part has not focused on preparation of Indians for professional roles, with the result that patterns of low-skilled employment and underemployment persist. The Indian worker's low wages and frequent unemployment are reflected partially by the average-income figures for the entire U.S. Indian population, which fell 75 percent below the national average in the late sixties. Unemployment rates for Indians were running ten times higher than those for the rest of the population.

Helga Teiwes Photo, Arizona State Museum, University of Arizona

Fig. 4.6 A Navajo woman demonstrates the art of weaving rugs.

Special Collections, University of Arizona

Fig. 4.7 Visitors to the reservation in the 1970s can still find Papagos dwelling in stick houses like this one from 1894.

Fig. 4.8   A Navajo leader at the turn of the century, wearing silver and turquoise necklaces in the old style.

Education has always been presented as an answer to the problems of bi-cultural participation for ethnic groups. Until recently, however, Anglo education served to reinforce many cultural differences by imposing white values on Indian children. A good proportion of the Indian population has never successfully completed fundamental instruction. By the late sixties the average level of formal education for Indians was only one-half that of the average non-Indian throughout the United States. Drop-out rates ran twice as high as the national averages. In Arizona, a survey illustrated the failure of most schooling to convey even rudimentary knowledge: 80 percent of working-age Papagos in the late sixties reported having difficulties with the use of English. Such ineffectiveness of earlier programs is expected to be compensated for in part by increasing Indian control in the sixties over planning and administration of reservation schools. Several community schools dating from this period typify the trend towards Indian administration. On the Navajo reservation, both the Rough Rock Demonstration School, built in 1965, and Navajo Community College, opened in 1969, are administered by Indians and offer curricula designed to meet the needs of the entire community: adult education courses, English as a second language, and programs in Navajo culture and history, in addition to other subjects. On the Gila River Reservation, the Blackwater School, formerly run by the BIA, has been taken over by the Indian community. Associated with Arizona's universities, a number of Indian studies programs have been developed: for example, a minor in Indian studies at the University of Arizona, courses in Papago language through the University of Arizona Continuing Education program, and offerings at Tucson's Pima College. Both Northern Arizona University and Arizona State University's College of Education have programs for training Indian teachers. In Tempe, the Cook Christian Training School has been training Indian community workers to lead in the development of community action programs.

Indian Participation Increases

In the field of health, Indian participation is emerging also, within the Division of Indian Health of the U.S. Public Health Service. Community health representatives — native-speakers — are learning to establish better communications between the Health Service and the reservation population.

Indian political organization was also developing in the sixties. Indians have been active with such state agencies as the Arizona Commission on Indian Affairs. They have also worked closely with an advisory organization of non-Indians — the Indian Development District of Arizona. Because the proportion of Indian voters is relatively small in terms of the total electorate, direct political influence of Indians through voting will probably remain limited. Additional representation for Indian interests at the state and national level might be achieved through strengthening of organizations such as the National Congress of American Indians and the National Indian Youth Council. At the local level stronger inter-tribal organizations might better express the interest of the state's poorest tribes, who are most in need of assistance for furthering their economic and social development.

Mexican-American Power Significant

In contrast to the Indians, Arizona's Mexican-American population has greater potential for political influence in the state. By far the largest ethnic group, the Mexican Americans made up about fifteen percent of the state's population in the 1960s and were concentrated most heavily in Pima and Maricopa counties. The term Mexican American, however, obscures the diversity of the ethnic community, which includes recent immigrants as well as U.S. citizens of the second or third generation. The entry of Mexicans to the U.S. has fluctuated greatly since the late 1900s, and immigration restrictions have been extremely inconsistent, with the only discernible continuity in policy being the adjustment of regulations to facilitate the influx of laborers needed for the country's economic expansion. In the 1860s laborers immigrated on a large scale to work on agricultural projects in the Salt River Valley, and in the seventies and eighties, dam construction and irrigation projects depended on imported Mexican labor. Mine owners and cattle ranchers also relied heavily on Mexican as well as Indian workers. By the 1920s a high point in immigration was reached, with a liberal immigration policy reflecting the nation's general economic prosperity. A complete reversal of this trend came suddenly with the Depression. Mexican Americans, in some cases regardless of whether or not they were citizens, were sent back to Mexico if they were drawing on diminishing welfare funds of local governments. From the early fifties to 1964, the government intervened, through the *bracero* program, to provide contracted farm labor and to control illegal entry of laborers to the Southwest. Operation Wetback, initiated in the fifties, was an associated program, whose purpose was to locate and deport illegal workers. Since the job certification requirement was put into effect, prospective immigrants must give proof of having a permanent job in the U.S., specifically, one which will not displace any domestic laborers.

The lack of consistency evident in the succession of U.S. policies, and the seeming arbitrariness with which they are at times enforced, have been a constant source of distrust and tension between the Mexican-American community and local authorities. By placing in question the citizenship of many Mexican Americans in the Southwest, immigration policy has aggravated the difficulties experienced by many of those attempting to adjust to living in this country.

José Galvez

Fig. 4.9   A small family shrine adds a gracious note to this home in the shadow of urban renewal near downtown Tucson.

Not Enough Skilled Labor

The present employment patterns of the Mexican-American population reflect a continuing dependence on agricultural labor. At least one quarter of the male working-age population was engaged in farm labor during the sixties. In terms of their proportion to the total population, Mexican Americans also have been over-represented in unskilled labor jobs such as truck driving, warehouse labor, construction, work with heavy equipment, and hospital jobs. By 1970, relatively few had managed to move into technical, professional, and administrative positions, with larger numbers in whole-sale and retail trade occupations. Perhaps the most notable change in employment is the increasing participation of women in the work force, frequently in domestic or clerical positions, or in low-skilled assembly line jobs for industry. Comparatively low income rates for the Mexican-American population suggest the combined effects of lower-paying jobs and higher rates of unemployment among Mexican Americans than in the general population. In 1960, from 55 to 60 percent of the Mexican-American families living in the Inner City area of Phoenix had to get by on $3,000 or less per year. Throughout the Southwest the picture is much the same: in the 1960s, Mexican Americans had only forty-seven cents for every dollar of the median annual income of Anglos. One explanation for the narrow range of Mexican-American employment is the failure of vocational training and employment to reach those who need it most. Another consideration, however, is discrimination, both overt and covert, against hiring and promotion of Mexican Americans in many fields. To some extent public schools are also responsible for perpetuating existing employment patterns, since they have often actively or inadvertently discouraged Mexican Americans from entering institutions of higher education.

In 1960, the median number of years of schooling completed by Mexican Americans twenty-five years of age and older fell 42 percent below the median for Arizona's Anglo population. Drop-out rates were among the highest for the ethnic groups, indicating both the pressures on children from low-income families to go to work, and the lack of effective counseling in the schools. Some proposed reforms have centered around demands for bilingual education programs, while in colleges and universities, Mexican-American student organizations have pressed for courses in Mexican-American studies. The most active groups in Arizona have been MASA, the Mexican-American Student Association, and the more radical MECHA, or Movimiento Estudiantil de Chicanos de Aztlan. At Pima College, in Tucson, courses in community development available in the early seventies were preparing students to work in the Mexican-American communities or *barrios*.

José Galvez

Fig. 4.10   Mexican-American women join the labor force in greater numbers all the time, but usually in low-paying jobs.

Fig. 4.11   College bound! Higher education offers both a challenge and a goal to young Mexican-Americans in Chicano groups.

A similar emphasis on community involvement characterizes several other groups. The United Farm Workers Organizing Committee, based in Tolleson, has been working with Arizona's farm laborers. In Tucson, a group of west-side *barrio* residents organized as the El Rio Coalition in the early seventies to demand conversion of a local golf course into a public park. In the region south of Phoenix, both Yaqui Indian and Mexican-American residents have formed a community group known as the Guadalupe Organization. Since 1968, the Southwest Council of La Raza in Phoenix has been concerned with obtaining technical support for programs in housing, economic advancement, and education for the Mexican-American population of the entire Southwest.

Historic Organizational Base

Throughout the history of the state, Mexican-American organizations have played an influential role in community affairs. On the whole, participation in such groups has been greater in Tucson than in Phoenix, and dates from the last decade of the 1800s. At that time a number of Tucson's upper-class Mexican Americans formed the Alianza Hispano-Americana, primarily as a defense league. The body had decreased in importance by about 1910, but numerous other middle- and upper-class social and professional organizations have been formed since that time. After World War II in particular, organizations of returned veterans and informal social clubs began to flourish.

Although interstate political organizations such as the League of Latin American Citizens never gained much support in Arizona, a number of independent, politically oriented clubs grew up in Tucson in the 1930s. Most have been affiliated with the Democratic Party, but have stressed the need for greater represen-

tation of Mexican-American interests. During the early sixties, the American Coordinating Council of Political Education, a Mexican-American organization, was active in ten out of fourteen Arizona counties, backing its candidates for local office. Throughout the following years, representation in local government has been increasing gradually. With the growing emphasis on community autonomy and on reviving the Mexican-American cultural heritage in the Southwest, a third political party has been formed. In February of 1971, the *La Raza Unida* party organized in Tucson, patterned after the party of the same name which had been successful in local elections in South Texas. In view of the heavy Mexican-American population concentrated in some Arizona counties, success of the party here, at least in local government, seemed possible.

Fig. 4.12   Another "third" political party — La Raza Unida.

U.S. Army Photo, Fort Huachuca

Fig. 4.13   Dr. Carl H. Boatright, U.S. Army captain and chief of the Department of Hospital Clinics at Fort Huachuca.

The Black Segment

Blacks in Arizona make up a much smaller proportion of the state's inhabitants than do Mexican Americans — about four percent of the total population. Like Indians, Blacks have had far less potential for political influence through voting, since during the sixties they still comprised only two percent of the electorate. Yet

they face problems which are comparable to those of both Indians and Mexican Americans, in employment and education, complicated by the persistence of discrimination and de facto segregation. Employment of a significant part of the Black population still means farm labor, which drew many to Arizona from the Southeastern states. Though some Blacks had arrived in Arizona in the mid-1800s, substantial numbers began to arrive only in the latter part of the century, attracted largely by the demand for laborers in the cotton industry. During the two world wars, this demand was stepped up. In addition, military training at Fort Huachuca during World War II and the growth of the defense industries in the post-war period led to an increase in Black migration, which has come to include many more skilled workers and professional people. Since the end of World War II, mechanization of farm industries has resulted in an increasing urbanization of former farm workers. By 1960, two out of three Blacks in Arizona were living either in Phoenix or Tucson. Despite the formation of a middle-class black community in both of these cities, employment of most of the population in low-skilled positions is still evident. Particularly among young people, unemployment rates are much higher for the Black than for the Anglo population. Studies in the sixties revealing underemployment of Blacks in terms of their percentage to the total population included municipal and state governments. Evidence of underpayment of Black professionals has also been brought out. As a reaction to such covert discriminatory practices, some firms have recruited Blacks for job training and subse-

José Galvez

Fig. 4.14   Vergie Bell, editor's secretary on a Tucson daily — example of establishing oneself in the community structure.

quent hiring, but so far these programs have reached only a small segment of the population.

Since 1965, the Arizona Civil Rights Commission has worked to review complaints of discrimination on the part of employers, trade unions, and state agencies. Both the NAACP and the Urban League have been active in Arizona, but civil rights leaders have had a difficult time organizing effective programs partly because of the small size of the Black community. In the early seventies, a voter registration drive was planned as a part of a nationwide effort to reach Blacks between the ages of eighteen and twenty-one. Among students, pressure for greater representation of Blacks was perhaps strongest throughout the sixties and early seventies. In coordination with the Black Student Union at the University of Arizona, a Tucson Black People's Community Organization formed in the spring of 1970. Its goal was to obtain more funds for schools in poor areas and to expose the overcharging practices of some businesses. On various campuses, the Black Student Union and Black Student Alliance groups have stressed the need for Black Studies programs.

The Chinese and Japanese Communities

Among the state's smallest ethnic groups are the Chinese Arizonans. By the 1970s the Chinese population had reached about 5,000, with the largest numbers in Phoenix and Tucson, far fewer in Yuma, and in the northern part of Arizona an extremely sparse population. It was during the 1880s, when employment was available in railroad construction and mining, that the greatest numbers of Chinese first came to the state. Many arrived via Mexico, where they had worked in mining camps as cooks, waiters, and laundrymen. At that time, Chinese businesses, especially groceries and restaurants, rapidly became well established in Prescott, Tucson, and Tombstone. During the eighties, resentful Anglo merchants, who were being undersold by the Chinese, led a boycott against their businesses. By the nineties such feelings had reached a peak in Tucson, and the Chinese were forced to move to the southwest side of town. Around 1912, the Chinese Chamber of Commerce formed in Tucson to represent and protect Chinese interests. In the 1960s three chambers of commerce were still active in Phoenix, Tucson, and Yuma. Members were mainly local businessmen. After World War II, the Tucson Chinese Community Center was founded, offering a youth recreation center and courses in Chinese to young children. The Chinese Welfare Council, a national organization, plays a limited role in Arizona's Chinese community, partly because most activity, mutual aid included, is still centered around the traditional Chinese family organization. Occupational patterns within the community are changing progressively, with the emergence of a larger number of Chinese in professional positions. Local political parties stress maintenance of interest and ties with the Republic of China:

José Galvez

Fig. 4.15 Elmer Carrier, principal of an Arizona junior high school.

there is a local Kuomintang party and a Chinese Anti-Communist League.

Even smaller than the Chinese community is Arizona's Japanese population, concentrated mainly in Maricopa County, and more sparsely in Pima County. In the early 1900s, Japanese Americans were living mainly in Coconino, Mohave, and Yavapai counties. In the Coconino area, jobs were available in the lumber industry, and mining jobs were open in all three counties. During World War II, about 30,000 Japanese were moved to two relocation centers in Arizona. Following the war, many moved into the Salt River Valley and the Glendale area, where they took up truck gardening and citrus fruit raising. Numerous flower farms are cultivated by Japanese residents of the Baseline Road area south of Phoenix. By 1960, the population in that city had reached 967, and Tucson's Japanese population had reached 110. Neither the Japanese nor the Chinese population was being significantly increased by migration to the state during the late sixties.

Migration of Anglos

The majority of newcomers to Arizona throughout the decade of the sixties were Whites. Up until 1950, most had come from Texas and California, but since then, points of origin have often been the states of Illinois, Ohio, Michigan, and Pennsylvania. On the whole, the white population of the entire Southwest has been predominantly of Anglo stock. In the last half of the nineteenth century some other European and Slavic immigrants came to the state for employment in mines, but never in numbers comparable to the concentrations of these groups in the eastern U.S. In the early 1870s, Mormon settlers, also of Anglo stock, began populating the northern part of the state, establishing communities first in the Valley of the Little Colorado and in the White Mountains. In the late seventies, settlement took place in the Gila River Valley near Safford and in the Salt River Valley near Mesa. By the late 1960s, the major concentration of the Mormon population of about 84,000 persons was in the Phoenix area, including Tempe and Mesa. Mormons have played a significant role in local and state politics. In addition they have established numerous centers on university and college campuses, and have worked extensively with Arizona's Indian population.

During the second half of the 1900s, economic forecasts were pointing to a probable continuous increase of migration by professionals and white-collar workers to Arizona. Overall rapid growth of the population was attested to by the expansion of cities and suburbs, and the design and construction of entire communities, as housing shortages were nonetheless becoming serious in some urban areas. As the state was entering this new era of development, earlier generations of Arizona's residents were surveying the outlook for the coming decades. Problems of education, housing, and health for major sectors of the population were evident. For Arizona's ethnic groups, the persistence of discrimination and lack of adequate education were making solutions to these problems more complicated. Spokesmen for the state's earliest inhabitants — Indians and Spanish-speaking persons — along with later generations of migrants to the state, were calling for a larger role in the state's development. They have emphasized that the myth of the gradual assimilation of ethnic groups has lost any credibility it might once have had. In view of this, the issue of importance throughout the rest of the century is not likely to be the integration of these groups into the rest of the population by some kind of transformation process. Clearly they have long been integrated, through their participation in the state's development. Instead, emphasis on community initiative and involvement will probably continue to increase the role played by each sector of the state's population.

ARIZONA'S
LAND AND
RESOURCES

Fig. 5.1 This shaded relief map shows the major landform features of the state of Arizona.

Melvin Hecht
Geographer

5

THE PHYSICAL ENVIRONMENT

ARIZONA HAS A MAXIMUM north-south length of 392 miles and a maximum east-west width of 338. Bounded on the north, east, and south by Utah, New Mexico, and Old Mexico, respectively, and on the west and northwest by California and Nevada the state includes an area of 113,956 square miles. Within those boundaries is a spectacular range of contrasts in elevation, scenery, climate, and vegetation. Near Yuma a riverine greenbelt, desert shrubs, and bare rocks line the Colorado River, whose perennial flow of water comes from drainage basins in seven states. The San Francisco Peaks near Flagstaff have boreal forests of spruce and fir, but only after heavy rains do the waters in the streams which flow off the peaks reach the intermittent Little Colorado a few miles away. Pine-topped mountains in central Arizona rise above streams and canyon lakes that are famous as boating and fishing resorts, but the valleys and ranges along the southwestern border mark the Jornada del Diablo — the Devil's Highway — once lined with the bones of early travelers west who failed to reach the widely spaced watering places along this early trail to the Coast.

The key to much of this contrast is the variation in altitude within the state. The Colorado River floodplain is barely one hundred feet above sea level at the Mexican border near Yuma, while the San Francisco Peaks reach the highest elevation in the state at 12,655 feet. Elevations vary widely over short distances, but three major physiographic regions can be recognized. These are the Sonoran plains and mountains in the southwest, a belt of high mountains and narrow valleys trending northwest through the center of the state, and the land of high plateaus and mesas north of the mountains. These have been designated as the Sonoran, mountain, and plateau regions, respectively. Other classifications of the state are based on special features such as geology, climate, rock and soil types, and vegetation. All classifications,

however, are related in some way to the basic physiographic divisions.

The Sonoran region is characterized by isolated mountain ranges, rising abruptly from low, broad valleys or plains. Most of the ranges are elongated toward the northwest or north and occupy less area than do the intervening valleys. The valley floors step up in elevation from near sea level in the southwest corner of Arizona to two thousand feet or more near the mountain region. The desert ranges themselves are less than two thousand feet high over most of the area, but peaks above seven thousand feet are found in the eastern part.

The desert region grades into the mountain region, which has a greater density of mountains, with individual ranges at elevations as high as eight thousand to ten thousand feet. The average elevation of this province is above five thousand feet, with the highest and most mountainous part in the central section of the state. The central mountain region is in the zone that receives the greatest amount of rainfall in the state, while the high ranges on the northwest and southeast ends of the mountain belt rise directly from arid or semi-arid valleys.

The plateau region is an area of flat-topped mesas and plateaus, lying at elevations above five thousand feet, incised by deep canyons and surmounted locally by volcanic peaks such as the San Francisco Mountains at Flagstaff. The plateau is separated from the mountain region along the Grand Wash Cliffs on the west and the Mogollon Rim through the center of the state.

The topographic configuration of Arizona is related directly to its geological structure and history. The plateau region belongs to the Colorado Plateaus province, which extends north and east into Utah, Colorado, and New Mexico. The desert and mountain regions are part of the Basin and Range physiographic province which extends from southern Oregon and Idaho southward into Mexico and eastward into New Mexico and

West Texas. These are frequently designated as the Sonoran Desert and Mexican Highland sections of the province.

Geologically it has been established that the structural boundary between the Plateau and Basin and Range provinces is not along the Mogollon Rim, but farther south, within the mountain region, and that the change from one structural province to the other takes place across a transitional zone. Other classifications, such as those based on climate and vegetation, may also cut across the basic topographic divisions of desert, mountain, and plateau.

Because the state as a whole slopes downward from east to west, Arizona lies within the drainage system of the Colorado River. In the northern part of the state the principal tributaries of the Colorado are the Virgin and Little Colorado rivers, while in the central and southern parts the main tributaries are the Williams and Gila rivers. The Mogollon Rim and the White Mountains, located in east-central Arizona, are primary watersheds for the northern and central parts of the state. Streams rising on the north side of the Rim and on the northeastern slopes of the White Mountains drain into the system of the Little Colorado River, while streams whose headwaters are on the south side of the Rim and on the southern and western slopes of the White Mountains empty into the system of the Gila and Salt rivers.

In southern Arizona, the principal rivers — the Santa Cruz and the San Pedro — run north, rising in the highlands of the Arizona-Mexico boundary area and draining into the Gila. The Santa Cruz, originating in the San Rafael Valley, flows south first, into Sonora, and then fishhooks back north to reenter at Nogales. These streams, like the majority of others in the state, are intermittent, dependent for their streamflow upon local precipitation or runoff from the mountain reaches.

In territorial days many of these now-intermittent streams were narrower, shallower, and running throughout the year. Several varieties of fish were found in abundance, and game birds lived in the tall marsh grasses along the banks. On the rolling uplands, grass taller than a man provided lush grazing. But an erosion cycle which started in the late 1890s began cutting, deepening, and widening river channels, especially in the southern part of the state.

As in so many human communities, early Anglo settlements in Arizona were usually near rivers with perennial surface water flow. Superior alluvial soils added to the attractiveness of the riverine sites. Many early settlements were made along small streams in the hills and mountains, close to mines and military posts. Settlement thus has increased in all three physiographic regions. Summer recreation colonies in the wooded mountain and plateau regions now obtain water from both surface and ground sources, as do the greatly expanded urban settlements of the plains and basins adjoining the Salt and Middle Gila rivers. In the valleys and basins of the south and southeast, cities and farms depend almost wholly upon ground water.

William D. Sellers
Meteorologist

6

THE CLIMATE

THE RANGE OF TEMPERATURES in Arizona is extreme. Average annual values vary from the middle seventies on the desert plains bordering the Gila and Colorado rivers to the middle forties in the pine country of the central part of the state. Summer temperatures above 120°F. have been reported at all towns along the lower Colorado River south of Hoover Dam and along the Gila River west of its confluence with the Salt River. The record high of 127°F., as of 1969, is held jointly by Parker and Fort Mohave, both on the Colorado. At the other extreme, several towns in the higher elevations have observed temperatures lower than 30° below zero.

Fort Valley, an experiment station northwest of Flagstaff, and Maverick, a former lumber camp high in the White Mountains southeast of McNary, have recorded lows of 33° below zero. The state's warmest and coldest towns are, respectively, Mohawk, located about fifty miles east of Yuma, and Maverick. In July the average temperatures for these two locations differ by almost twenty-five degrees, the average at Mohawk being 94.3°F. and at Maverick 59.9°F. Thus, Arizona offers a wide range of thermal climates, varying from the long hot summers and short mild winters of the warm deserts, to the short cool summers and long icy winters of the cold highlands.

[Arizona has three basic climates: desert, steppe, and highlands,] which cover, respectively, about thirty, fifty-three, and seventeen percent of the state. Climatologists use average annual precipitation and mean temperature of an area to determine into which of these classifications each area should be placed. A simplified map of these three areas (Fig. 6.1) shows each subdivided into warm and cold, depending on whether the average temperature of the coldest month is above or below 32°F. Temperature and precipitation records from 176 weather stations were used in constructing the map. However, most of these are located in the central and southeast parts of the state, leaving large areas where the climatic classification is determined primarily on hypothetical correlations between climate and vegetation.

Arid Conditions

The deserts and steppes are characterized by a lack of precipitation, the former more so than the latter. Practically all of the rain that falls in these regions evaporates; appreciable runoff and subsurface storage occur only during the wettest period. As a result, the vegetation cover is restricted and consists mainly of creosote bush, cacti, and sagebrush on the deserts, and mesquite, piñon-juniper and various types of grass on the steppes. In these dry regions irrigation is a must for successful farming. The highlands, on the other hand, normally receive sufficient precipitation during the year to support a moderately dense vegetation growth, with enough left over for substantial runoff onto the surrounding arid plains. This is particularly true of the cold highlands, which possess some of the finest and most extensive pine forests in the world, and where precipitation is reasonably dependable from year to year. In the warm highlands precipitation is less dependable, varying greatly in amount and intensity from one year to the next.

Annual precipitation in Arizona varies from about three inches on the warm deserts to more than thirty inches in the highlands. Most of this falls in the summer or winter, with only rare storms occurring in the other seasons. The late spring is especially dry. For example, Wellton, a small desert town located about thirty miles east of Yuma, has received measurable amounts of rain in May and June on only eleven days, in the past 37 years, an average of one rainy day every three or four years in these months.

Precipitation is heaviest and most dependable in summer, particularly in the highland regions of the state,

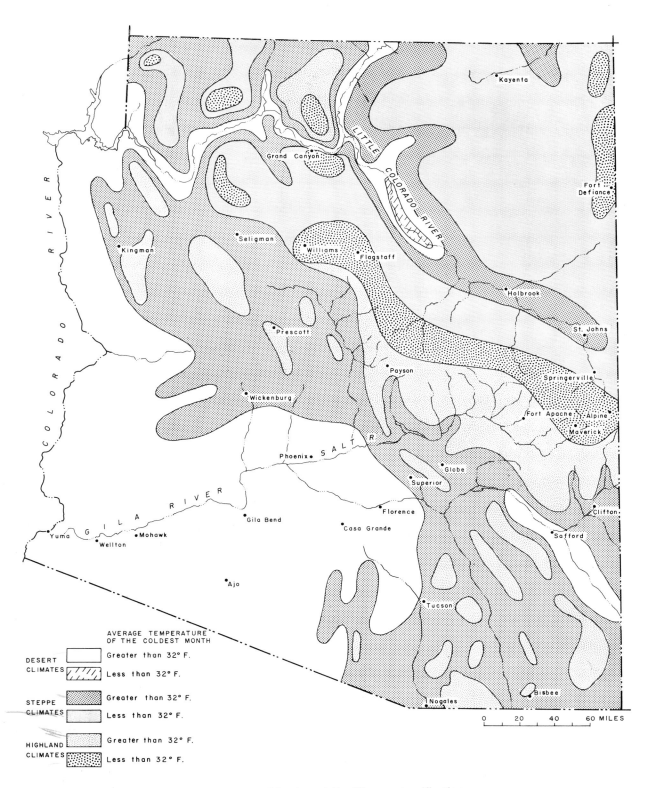

AVERAGE TEMPERATURE
OF THE COLDEST MONTH

DESERT CLIMATES
Greater than 32° F.
Less than 32° F.

STEPPE CLIMATES
Greater than 32° F.
Less than 32° F.

HIGHLAND CLIMATES
Greater than 32° F.
Less than 32° F.

0   20   40   60 MILES

Fig. 6.1   Climates of Arizona, based on modification of the Köppen classification.

which rarely experience a dry afternoon between the second week of July and the first week in September. Occasional cloudbursts may send torrents of water streaming down onto the surrounding valley floors, filling the washes and gullies to overflowing and doing considerable damage to roads and poorly located homes. Once in a while these storms may hit the desert towns, where they can be especially destructive. The inadequate sewer systems in many of these communities have not been built to handle more than moderate amounts of runoff.

Summer thunderstorms in the southern half of the state are frequently accompanied by hail, which, since 1950, has been responsible for property and crop damages estimated at more than $2,000,000. In one particularly violent storm that struck Phoenix on a September afternoon, losses due to hail alone amounted to about $680,000.

Summer rains are associated primarily with very warm, moist, and unstable air which sweeps around the southern and western margins of a semi-stationary high pressure area over the Atlantic Ocean and advances into Arizona from the Gulf of Mexico. Widespread and frequently severe showers and thunderstorms develop in this air when it is forced to ascend over the numerous mountain ranges of the southern and eastern sections of the state. These storms are most intense over the mountains during the midafternoon when surface heating and the general convergence of air, associated with upslope mountain winds, are at a maximum. In the lowlands the

Mabel Weadock

Fig. 6.3   Wet weather may prevail at high elevations.

Fig. 6.2   Summer lightning illuminates the Arizona desert landscape.

Institute of Atmospheric Physics, University of Arizona

Institute of Atmospheric Physics, University of Arizona

Fig. 6.4   In mountainous regions of Arizona, storm clouds are a frequent feature of late summer afternoons.

heaviest summer rains usually occur in the late afternoon or early evening when the valley floors are considerably warmer than the surrounding cloud-covered mountains.

Not all of the warm-season rainfall is of the type described above. A small part is associated with tropical disturbances which develop off the west coast of Mexico at about 15° N. latitude. These storms usually dissipate as they move north, but they are occasionally intense and extensive enough when they reach the thirtieth parallel to produce heavy rainfall over most of Arizona. This type of storm differs from the more common summer type in that it is more widespread, has no tendency to occur at certain hours of the day, has a lesser intensity but longer duration, and is only rarely accompanied by thunder and lightning. Almost three-fourths of the towns in the state have received their heaviest twenty-four hour rainfall from storms believed to have been of tropical origin.

Rainfall in Winter

Winter precipitation is generally less intense but more widespread than that of summer. Part of this precipitation is associated with the storm belt of the middle latitudes, which occasionally advances far enough south for its margins to affect Arizona. It is only when these cyclonic storms move in directly from the Pacific Ocean across the northern and central parts of the country that

measurable amounts of rain can occur. When the storms move in a north-to-south direction east of the 105th meridian, about all Arizona can expect is plenty of wind and subnormal temperatures, particularly in the northeast part of the state.

Probably the heaviest rains of winter are associated with the so-called "Kona" storms or "cold lows" of the subtropical Pacific Ocean. These very intense disturbances form in the vicinity of the Hawaiian Islands and move slowly eastward to the coast of southern California. In this region, or slightly inland, they often remain stationary for several days. But once they get caught in the strong upper-level westerly flow they move rapidly northeastward across the United States. These storms normally pass directly over Arizona, frequently advancing very slowly, and since they retain most of their moisture supply while moving in from the Pacific, they can produce several days of moderate to heavy rain and snow, often accompanied by lightning and thunder.

Rainfall is sporadic in all seasons of the year and practically always falls in very small amounts. For example, along the lower Gila River during summers over a decade, 55.3 percent of the hourly precipitation totals were less than 0.05 inch, 76 percent were less than 0.11 inch, and 1.2 percent greater than 0.50 inch. These values are representative of much of Arizona.

Winter precipitation, dependent as it is on the location of the middle latitude storm track, is extremely variable from one year to the next. In some years, when the storm track is north of its normal position, drought conditions may prevail throughout Arizona from September through June, while in others, when the storm track moves south, the state may receive enough precipitation to veil temporarily its inherently arid condition.

The driest sections of Arizona in winter are generally the cold steppes, particularly those located north of the Little Colorado River. These areas are effectively sealed off from all the major sources of winter moisture by an enveloping curtain of high mountain ranges and plateaus, notably the White and San Francisco mountains and the Mogollon Plateau to the south and southwest, the Wasatch Mountains of Utah, and the Rocky Mountains to the northeast. These barriers, however, do not prevent the occurrence of unusually strong winds, particularly during the winter and spring. When a storm system passes over the area, winds with speeds in excess of thirty miles per hour may blow for several days, first warm from the south and then bitterly cold from the north.

All parts of Arizona have, at one time or another, received at least a trace of snow, but amounts are usually measurable only in the mountain sections of the state, where seasonal totals vary from one to five feet. The slopes of the higher mountains offer excellent opportunities for winter sports, even in the desert regions. Early season snowstorms are very unpredictable; therefore, it is a good policy for hunters and hikers to be prepared

for the worst if they go into the mountains in the late fall months.

Climate — Favors Growth

The mild dry winters of the southern Arizona desert have been a very important factor in the rapid population growth of the area. Temperatures in the coldest month usually range from the middle thirties in the early morning to the high sixties in midafternoon. Below-freezing temperatures are rare, being restricted for the most part to the period near sunrise, and to low altitude areas which are strongly affected by the drainage of cold dense air off the surrounding terrain during the night.

Despite the high temperatures, many people find the summer climate of the Arizona desert less uncomfortable than that of the eastern parts of the country, primarily for two reasons: first, the extreme dryness of the air, with relative humidities often falling below ten percent in May and June, helps to relieve the severity of the heat by increasing evaporation; and second, virtually all homes and buildings are air-conditioned, either by refrigeration or by the less expensive evaporative coolers. During periods of low humidity even the cheapest evaporative coolers are quite effective. However, in some of the heavily irrigated sections high humidities, particularly during the summer rainy season in July and August, render evaporative coolers rather ineffective, and the

Fig. 6.5   The cold steppes north of the Colorado River are among the driest sections of Arizona in winter.

Henk Moonen, University of Arizona

trend has been increasing toward the installation of refrigerative cooling.

The warm steppes of Arizona are slightly cooler, wetter, and more humid than the warm deserts throughout the year; however, the accent is still on heat and aridity. These regions have the prime advantage of being located close to the highlands, which offer refreshingly mild days and cool nights during the hot summer months. In winter, the warm steppes, particularly those in southern Arizona, are a popular center of recreational activity for visitors to the state. The temperature range between day and night in the cooler months is large, often exceeding forty degrees, with the early morning minimum lying in the upper twenties and the afternoon maximum in the low seventies.

Perhaps the most rugged climate in Arizona is found on the cold steppes, which are confined almost entirely to the northeastern corner of the state. Winters are cold, dry, and windy; the temperature normally falls below zero on four to six days between November and March. The summers are quite warm, especially in the northern part of the region, where afternoon temperatures above 90°F. may be expected on fifty to sixty-five days during the warmer months. However, summer nights are cool; temperatures usually drop to the fifties by sunrise.

Arizona Climatic Data

| Location | Daily Mean Temperatures (°F) | | | | Annual Precipitation Total (inches) | |
| | January | | July | | | |
	Max.	Min.	Max.	Min.	Rain	Snow
Ajo	63.9	40.8	103.0	77.0	9.10	T
Alpine	45.5	9.5	77.7	43.5	20.73	64.9
Bisbee	57.3	34.3	88.7	64.2	18.44	10.2
Casa Grande	66.2	33.5	106.9	75.3	8.20	0.1
Clifton	58.7	33.2	100.2	72.2	12.54	1.3
Flagstaff	41.0	14.2	80.6	50.5	20.27	69.4
Florence	66.2	36.3	105.6	74.2	9.84	0.2
Gila Bend	68.5	37.4	108.7	76.9	5.69	T
Globe	56.7	31.0	97.5	67.5	15.75	4.4
Grand Canyon	40.7	18.1	84.3	54.1	15.81	61.6
Holbrook	48.0	18.5	93.7	59.5	8.64	9.9
Kingman	55.8	30.9	97.6	66.8	10.63	3.9
Nogales	62.8	29.5	94.2	65.0	15.60	2.7
Payson	52.5	19.4	89.5	55.7	21.48	25.0
Phoenix	65.1	39.2	103.6	77.5	7.67	T
Prescott	50.4	19.9	89.1	56.2	19.32	29.7
Safford	60.2	28.4	99.2	68.3	8.95	1.3
St. Johns	48.2	16.1	90.1	56.0	11.59	21.6
Seligman	50.5	20.6	90.8	54.7	10.85	16.8
Springerville	47.7	14.5	82.2	51.4	12.11	26.3
Superior	61.4	45.2	96.6	75.0	17.49	1.6
Tucson	64.7	35.2	99.6	72.5	10.91	0.9
Wickenburg	63.6	29.9	102.4	69.1	10.99	0.1
Williams	44.5	16.8	84.2	51.5	21.88	67.2
Yuma	67.1	42.4	105.8	76.5	3.38	T

T — Trace, an amount too small to measure.

Geology Faculty,
University of Arizona

7

GEOLOGY

THE GEOLOGIC HISTORY OF ARIZONA is preserved in the records of rocks formed during five great eras of geologic time. These are, from oldest to youngest, the Older Precambrian, Younger Precambrian, Paleozoic, Mesozoic, and Cenozoic. Not all of the events that characterized these time divisions can be recognized at any one place, but the historical sequence can be pieced together by correlating rocks and structures from one area to another. The time scale by which geologic events are correlated is shown in Figure 7.1, as are the major rock units and geologic activity recognized in Arizona.

Divisions of the geologic time scale are not of uniform duration; rather, they are intervals characterized by major episodes in the history of the earth and the life on it. Radioactive age determinations of rocks from many parts of the world allow an approximate dating in years of events in the scale. The details of geologic history are not known with equal certainty for all parts of geologic time. Paleozoic and younger rocks contain fossils of plants and animal life which allow correlation of rock units over wide areas. Because rocks of the Precambrian eras contain almost no fossil remains, and because these older rocks in many places have been eroded, deeply buried, or crushed in mountain building, the historical geology of Precambrian time is difficult to interpret.

General Chronology of Rock Units and Structural Events

OLDER PRECAMBRIAN ERA. The oldest known rocks of Arizona are exposed in the bottom of the Grand Canyon and in the cores of mountain ranges in central, southern, and western Arizona. They consist of metamorphic and crystalline rocks such as schist, gneiss, granite, and quartzite and, locally, of volcanic and sedimentary strata that have been little changed or altered.

Detailed studies of the Older Precambrian Vishnu, Yavapai, and Pinal schists of the Grand Canyon and of central and southern Arizona show that these rocks originally consisted of thick sequences of sedimentary strata, largely mudstone and sandstone, with locally thick piles of basaltic lavas. The accumulation of as much as twenty thousand or more feet of such rocks suggests deposition in a great sinking, elongated trough, or geosyncline. The orientation of this trough is not known, but the long axis possibly extended northeast through the state.

Minor disturbances affected the rocks locally during their accumulation, but there is no evidence of major mountain building until the end of Older Precambrian time when great earth forces, directed essentially from south and southeast to the north and northwest, crumpled the geosynclinal rocks and formed mountain ranges trending northeast. Great intrusions of granitic and similar rocks accompanied the mountain building and locally metamorphosed the original sedimentary and volcanic rocks to schist, gneiss, and amphibolite.

This event, called the Mazatzal Revolution, was of such major importance that the structural pattern formed then has controlled almost all of the later geologic history of the state. Three major directions dominated this structural pattern. Folds, reverse faults, and schistosity of the rocks themselves trended mainly northeastward, along the axes of the mountain ranges. Other major structural lineaments, chiefly faults, along which large movements occurred, were oriented along north and northwest directions. A glance at the physiographic map of Arizona shows the importance of these directions in the modern topography and drainage patterns.

[93]

ERAS	PERIODS and EPOCHS			Years x 10^6	PLATEAU and TRANSITION ZONE	BASIN and RANGE PROVINCE	MAJOR EVENTS IN GEOLOGIC HISTORY
C E N O Z O I C	QUAT.	Recent			Alluvium	Alluvium	Volcanism and minor faulting
		Pleistocene		1	Pediment gravels	Pediment gravels	
						Alluvial basin deposits	
	Tertiary	U			Bidahochi fm. ? Hickey fm Chuska ss. ?	Pantano fm. and related beds	Basin and Range orogeny; Transition zone and Plateau uplift
		M					Volcanism Granitic intrusions Laramide Revolution
		L	70				
M E S O Z O I C	Cretaceous	U			Mesaverde ss. Mancos sh. Dakota ss.	Sonoita gp. Amole arkose ? Bisbee gp	
		L					Nevadan Revolution
	Jurassic				Morrison fm. San Rafael gp. Navajo ss. Kayenta fm. Moenave fm. ——?—	Sedimentary and volcanic rocks	Volcanism granitic intrusions
	Triassic		200		Wingate ss. Chinle fm. Shinarump fm. Moenkopi fm.		Mogollon Highlands in central Arizona
P A L E O Z O I C	Permian				Kaibab ls. Toroweap fm. Coconino ss. Hermit sh. Supai fm. ——— Naco fm.	Rainvalley fm. Concha ls. Scherrer fm. Epitaph dol. Colina ls. Earp fm. ——— Horquilla ls.	General uplift
	Pennsylvanian						
	Mississippian				Redwall ls.	Paradise fm. Escabrosa ls.	Uplift in central Arizona
	Devonian				Temple Butte ls.	Martin fm.	
	Silurian						General uplift
	Ordovician					El Paso ls.	
	Cambrian		550		Muav ls. Bright Angel sh. Tapeats ss.	Abrigo fm. Bolsa qtz.	
P R E C A M B R I A N	YOUNGER				Grand Canyon series | Apache gp.	Apache gp. { Mescal ls. Dripping Spring qtz. Barnes cg. Pioneer sh. Scanlan cg.	Grand Canyon disturbance; diabasic intrusions
	OLDER		2000+		Vishnu schist | Yavapai gp.	Pinal schist	Mazatzal Revolution; granitic intrusions

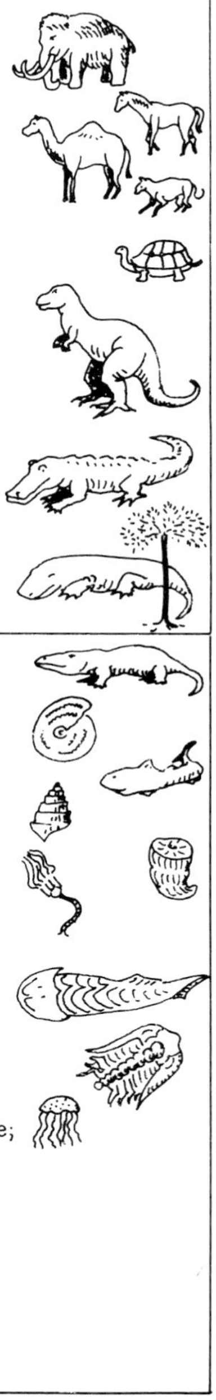

Fig. 7.1   Rock units in Arizona — oldest ones on the bottom — and associated animal life.

Following the Mazatzal Revolution, which must have produced mountain ranges of a size to rival the loftiest ones existing today, there was a long period of erosion, which beveled the ranges down to their very roots. Parts of the erosion surface or peneplain produced at this time are still preserved in the Grand Canyon and in central and southern Arizona, where they were buried beneath younger rocks. The surface is remarkably flat and uniform, having only a few feet of relief in tens of miles in most places where it can be traced.

YOUNGER PRECAMBRIAN ERA. The Grand Canyon Series in northern Arizona and the Apache Group of central and southern Arizona record the geologic events that followed the erosional truncation of the Older Precambrian rocks. A total of at least twelve thousand feet of sandstone, shale, limestone, and basalt flows was deposited on the old erosion surface in the Grand Canyon area. No more than fifteen hundred feet of similar rocks south of the Mogollon Rim occupy a similar position in the geologic column, and correlation of rocks and events between the northern and southern areas is uncertain, except that the Apache Group and the Grand Canyon Series both belong to the Younger Precambrian era.

The type of trough in which these rocks were laid down is not known. They were probably deposited by marine water spilling over from the continental margins. Algal structures and a few poorly preserved objects that resemble imprints of jellyfish or other primitive creatures serve only to suggest the type of life existing in the ancient seas.

Younger Precambrian time closed in Arizona with the Grand Canyon Disturbance, a mountain-building event that produced fault-block mountains trending generally northwest. There was extensive intrusion by diabase, but no granitic intrusion or intense crumpling or metamorphism of the rocks. This was a mild event compared to the Mazatzal Revolution, and the effects seem to have been pronounced only in the Grand Canyon area itself. The absence of any major structural disturbance in other parts of the state is shown by the fact that in central and southeastern Arizona, the Apache Group rocks were only slightly, if at all, tilted before the overlying Paleozoic strata were deposited. Some general uplift, however, is suggested by the fact that Apache Group rocks were locally beveled by erosion.

The erosion interval that followed the Grand Canyon Disturbance produced a surface that is not as remarkable for its flatness as the one above the Older Precambrian rocks, but which is, nevertheless, amazingly uniform over large areas. The block mountains of the Grand Canyon area were worn completely away, with only a few masses of resistant rocks projecting as much as several hundred feet above the surrounding plains. Erosion continued until the Cambrian seas advanced across the low surface, laying down beach sand and fossiliferous mud and lime that marked the advent of a new era in the history of Arizona and the first record of abundant life.

PALEOZOIC ERA. Arizona during Paleozoic time was a broad shelflike area, over which seas spread from deeper basins that lay to the northwest and to the south, depositing a blanket of sedimentary rocks a few thousand feet thick in most places. Irregularities of the shelf existed in the form of local swells and basins that modified the thickness and types of sediments deposited during different parts of the era. In particular, a large land mass in northeastern Arizona, the Defiance Positive area, remained above sea level during most of the Paleozoic. If it was submerged from time to time, it was later uplifted enough for erosion to strip off the deposits, because no Paleozoic sediments are left on the area except for a thin cover of red beds of late Paleozoic (Permian) age. A narrow ridge extending southwest from the Defiance area limited deposition in central Arizona during parts of Paleozoic time. This ridge, which probably appeared as an island archipelago at times, has been called Mazatzal Land. A large land mass that possibly existed in southwestern Arizona is called Enseñada Land.

The exact pattern of land and sea that existed at any one time is difficult to interpret, as many parts of central, and almost all of western and southwestern, Arizona do not now contain any Paleozoic rocks. However, a Paleozoic section a few thousand feet thick in the Harquahala Mountains, and a Mesozoic or Cenozoic conglomerate containing boulders of Paleozoic rocks in the New Water Mountains, support the belief that deposits once extensive over most of the state have been removed by erosion in post-Paleozoic time.

Sedimentation was not continuous during this era but was marked by repeated advances and withdrawals of seas. The Cambrian seas, for example, appear to have spread over the old erosion surface cut on Precambrian rocks from marine basins to the south and west, in a flood that slowly advanced eastward into New Mexico. A gentle uplift, with no appreciable tilting, resulted in erosion or nondeposition, or both, so that almost no record is left of the next two Paleozoic eras. Only a few exposures of Ordovician rocks are found in the extreme southeast and northwest portions of Arizona, and no Silurian rocks at all are known in the state.

Repeated flooding in Devonian, Mississippian, Pennsylvanian, and Permian times left several thousand feet of sandstone, shale, and limestone, presumably over most of the state (Fig. 7.2). Of particular interest is the blanket of Mississippian limestone, nearly a thousand feet thick, that forms the Redwall cliffs of the Grand Canyon and the Escabrosa cliffs of several

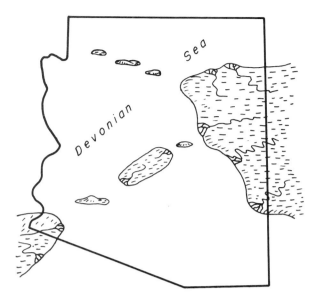

Fig. 7.2 Arizona in Devonian time.

ranges in southeastern Arizona. The Mississippian lime-stone thins and disappears in the northern Tonto area of central Arizona, giving evidence of uplift along the Mazatzal Land trend, probably following Redwall deposition.

During some parts of the Paleozoic, particularly in the Pennsylvanian and Permian, rocks formed as deltaic, floodplain, and sand dune deposits interfingered with marine sediments. Rocks of these types are particularly well displayed in the red bed sequences near the top of Grand Canyon, along the Mogollon Rim, on the Defiance Plateau, and in Monument Valley. A blanket of ancient wind-blown sand accumulated over much of northern Arizona to form the Coconino and DeChelly sandstone of the areas mentioned. These formations show, beautifully preserved, the cross-bedding typical of sand dunes that can now be observed in desert areas.

A final invasion of the Permian seas produced the Kaibab limestone that forms the rim of Grand Canyon and much of the thick, dark limestone of southern mountain ranges. The end of Paleozoic time in Arizona was not marked by any major mountain building such as the Appalachian Revolution of the eastern United States. Instead, a general uplift, local folding, and gentle erosion preceded the deposition of Mesozoic rocks. No igneous intrusive or volcanic activity left a record during any part of the Paleozoic Era in Arizona.

Life in Arizona during the Paleozoic Era was typical of that in other parts of the world. Shells and remains of marine animals such as brachiopods, mollusks, corals, sponges, and trilobites, are common enough in some places to furnish information for dating the rocks. Teeth and plates of bony armor of primitive fishes give evidence of vertebrate life in Devonian and younger beds. Reptiles and amphibians had appeared by the end of Paleozoic time, but their fossil record in Arizona is scanty.

MESOZOIC ERA. Rocks representing all three periods of the Mesozoic were deposited in northern Arizona, but in southern Arizona the Cretaceous strata rest directly on eroded Paleozoic rocks in many places. Most deposits of the era are continental, but invading seas left marine sediments in the northern, northwestern, and southeastern parts of the state. Isolated outcrops of deformed and metamorphosed strata in southwestern Arizona might belong to some part of the Mesozoic; however, fossil evidence is lacking.

Triassic and Jurassic rocks of northern Arizona are dominantly red beds, laid down along the margins of seas that existed to the north and northwest during most of the two periods. Streams flowing from highlands in central and southern Arizona deposited mud and sand that produced such spectacular formations as the Chinle, which contains the Painted Desert and Petrified Forest (Fig. 7.3). Great blankets of dune deposits such as the Navajo sandstone give evidence of arid, desert wastelands that occupied the area from time to time.

The shifting pattern of deposits attests to some crustal movements as well as to changing climates in Triassic and Jurassic time. A sharp uplift in central Arizona produced the Mogollon Highlands in middle Triassic time. This uplift followed approximately the trend of the present Mountain Highlands and is recorded

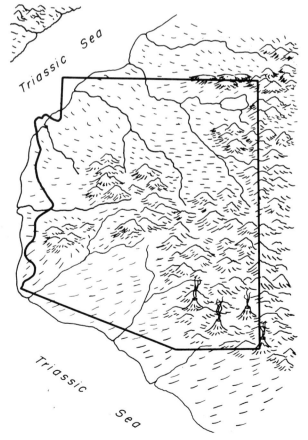

Fig. 7.3 Arizona in Triassic time.

by the great sheet of Shinarump conglomerate that was spread northward as far as southern Utah. Lava flows and granite intrusion in southern Arizona can be dated as belonging to the Triassic and Jurassic, and the late Jurassic Nevedan revolution, which affected much of western North America, is believed to be responsible for the ore deposits of the Bisbee area. Also, gentle folding in northern Arizona is indicated by the fact that the Upper Cretaceous Dakota sandstone was deposited on an erosion surface that bevels Jurassic and older beds.

Lower Cretaceous seas did not reach northern Arizona but entered the southeastern corner of the state in the Bisbee area. Deposits of both continental and marine origin were laid down over much of southeastern Arizona during most of the Cretaceous, but the time and spatial relationships of these rocks are not well understood because of Cenozoic deformation and erosion. Upper Cretaceous seas invaded northeastern Arizona and left alternating deposits of shale, sandstone, and coal beds. For the most part, remnants of the old Mogollon Highlands limited these deposits along the present area of the Mogollon Rim, but one advance of the seas carried the shoreline in an embayment as far south as Clifton and the Deer Creek coal basin east of Winkelman.

Toward the end of Cretaceous time began the great period of crustal disturbance and granitic intrusion, known as the Laramide Revolution, which extended well into early Cenozoic time. In northern Arizona, the Laramide was marked by sharp to gentle folding, which produced great monoclines, faults, basins, and domal upwarps. Many of these structural features are elongated on north or northwest axes. Except for a regional uplift in middle Cenozoic time, the Plateau Province of Arizona appears to have been relatively stable since Laramide time.

In southern Arizona, intense folding, faulting, and igneous activity of the Laramide initiated crustal unrest that lasted into middle and late Cenozoic time. The great porphyry copper deposits of the state were produced during the Laramide interval.

Mesozoic life left a record in Arizona in the form of some of the best-known fossil localities of the world. Armored amphibians and crocodile-like reptiles from the Chinle red beds are exhibited in major museums in North America and Europe, and yearly expeditions are still made to collect from the Chinle and other formations of northern Arizona. The Moenave formation near Cameron has produced skeletons of dinosaurs and of the most primitive crocodile known. The best specimens of early mammallike reptiles of North America were found in the Kayenta formation north of Black Mesa.

CENOZOIC ERA. The Laramide Revolution continued into early Cenozoic time with mountain building and general continental uplift. In southern Arizona, the crustal unrest seems to blend with the middle and late Cenozoic structural activity that blocked out the present Basin and Range topography.

Successive generations of mountains were built by orogenies that involved strong folding, thrust faulting, batholithic intrusions, and widespread eruption of acid to intermediate lava flows. The last major thrust-faulting in the southern part of the state can be dated by fossiliferous beds as being later than middle Tertiary (lower Miocene).

The present mountain ranges formed after the compressional activity had ceased, and valleys between the ranges hold locally great thicknesses of late Cenozoic sediments. In some places these sediments are warped and faulted, but Pliocene and Pleistocene displacements of great magnitude seem to be restricted to the boundary zone between the Sonoran Desert and Mountain Highlands regions.

The Laramide faults, monoclines, and warps of the Plateau Province were beveled by early and middle Cenozoic erosion, and the area appears to have remained relatively stable during most of Cenozoic time, except for regional uplift. Arching of the Mountain Highlands in Middle to late Cenozoic brought the Plateau to its present elevation, resulting in a gentle northerly tilting of the Plateau strata. Breaking occurred along the margins of the province, chiefly following Laramide structural zones.

Erosion throughout most of Cenozoic time stripped soft beds from much of the Plateau, leaving large surfaces floored with horizontal or slightly-dipping resistant formations such as the Kaibab limestone on the Coconino and Kaibab Plateaus, and the Navajo sandstone on the Kaibito Plateau. Lines of south-facing cliffs were formed by the retreating softer beds, following down the general northerly dip. North-south cliffs were formed by erosion along faults, monoclines, and the margins of major upwarps. Ponding of drainage in Pliocene time formed extensive lake deposits in the Hopi Buttes area, before the final stages of erosion that carved the Grand Canyon (Fig. 7.4).

Cenozoic volcanic activity was localized in several fields of intrusive centers and flows on the Plateau proper and along the margins. Early stages are recorded in the eroded flows and volcanic necks of the Hopi Buttes, the laccolithic Carrizo Mountains, and older flows along the Mogollon Rim and in the White Mountains. Later activity produced volcanic piles in the San Francisco, Trumbull, and White Mountains. Volcanism continued into very late geologic time, with basalt flows pouring into the Grand Canyon after the latter had been cut to within a few hundred feet of its present depth. Eruptions in the San Francisco field have been dated by tree rings as occurring in the eleventh century, A.D.

Cenozoic life in Arizona is known from Miocene and younger fossil localities. Plants, fish, birds, fresh water mollusks, and mammals indicate that the climate was generally similar to that of today, but somewhat

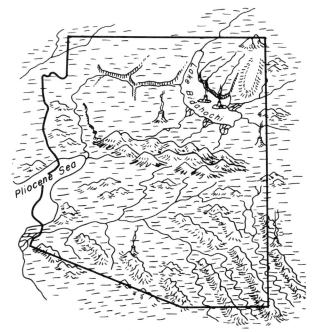

Fig. 7.4   Pliocene paleogeographic map.

more humid. The abundance of fossils in some localities shows that herds of several types of extinct camels, horses, rhinoceroses, and antelopes roamed the state at times, and were preyed upon by a variety of ancestral carnivores. In the late Pleistocene, more than ten thousand years ago, early man came to Arizona, where he found and hunted animals such as mammoths, ground sloths, tapirs, camels, bison, and horses.

Rock Units, Structure, and Physiography

PLATEAU PROVINCE. In Arizona the Plateau Province (Fig. 7.5) comprises several individually named plateaus together with valleys, buttes, and cliffy mesas; its general surface is surmounted in several localities by high volcanic mountains and is deeply incised by canyons of the Colorado River system. Except for canyons and valleys, the region as a whole lies above five thousand, much of it exceeds six thousand, and some areas attain more than nine thousand feet in altitude. The southwestern margin or "rim" of the plateau is marked by ruggedly indented cliffs from a few hundred to more than fifteen hundred feet high. In some places, such as areas north of Clifton and southeast of Camp Verde, the cliffs are concealed by younger lava flows.

The Plateau Province is a land of spectacular landscape that almost everywhere reveals the geologic framework and history with graphic clarity. The Grand Canyon, one of the great scenic wonders of the world, is essentially a textbook of geology in itself. Here a mile-deep slice, carved by the Colorado River into the Plateau rocks, exposes a complex history of all types of geologic events spanning the five eras of geologic time.

In a broad sense, the Plateau is a great slab of Paleozoic and Mesozoic sedimentary rocks lying on a relatively smooth Precambrian basement, capped locally by thin layers of Cenozoic sedimentary and volcanic rocks. The sedimentary beds are nearly horizontal over large areas but have been locally flexed by broad warps and sharp monoclinal folds and broken by faults. A gentle northward tilt carries the Arizona section beneath younger rocks of the high plateaus of the northern extension of the province in Utah. Erosion during most of the Cenozoic has etched out the major structural features in a remarkable way. Many of the sedimentary rocks are persistent units across the Plateau, but some are lenticular on a broad scale, or show marked lithologic changes laterally, indicating the effects of local basins and swells in the sedimentational history.

A convenient subdivision of the Plateau includes the Grand Canyon Region, the Mogollon Slope, and the Navajo country. The Grand Canyon area includes individual plateaus north and south of the canyon itself and the Marble Platform on the east. The Mogollon Slope is the uptilted southern edge of the Plateau, northward from the Mogollon Rim to the valley of the Little Colorado River. The Navajo country comprises the mesas, plateaus, buttes, and valleys of the northeast corner of the state and coincides approximately with the Navajo and Hopi Indian reservations.

Grand Canyon Region. The Grand Canyon Region consists largely of a series of terrace-like plateaus, elongated north and south, separated from each other by faults and monoclines. The highest of these is the Kaibab Plateau, which is a structurally uplifted area, with both the topography and geologic section stepped down to east and west. To the west, the successively lower steps, north of the Colorado River, are the Kanab, Uinkaret, and Shivwits plateaus. The Shivwits is bounded on the west by the Grand Wash Cliffs, a great structural break that overlooks the Basin and Range Province. Most of the land south of the river is included in the Coconino Plateau, with the San Francisco volcanic uplift on the east and a series of downdropped benches on the west. The surfaces of the Kaibab and Coconino plateaus descend to the east along the East Kaibab monocline to the Marble Platform.

The Colorado River flows westward across the area, locally turning to follow boundaries between the major and minor structural blocks (Fig. 7.6). Tributary canyons dissect the plateaus both north and south of the river. The high plateaus and the Marble Platform are floored with Kaibab limestone, locally surmounted by remnants of Mesozoic sedimentary and Cenozoic volcanic rocks, but the extreme southwestern corner has been stripped down to the Mississippian and Devonian limestones. North of the river, the plateau surfaces dip under a sheet of Mesozoic rocks, which form

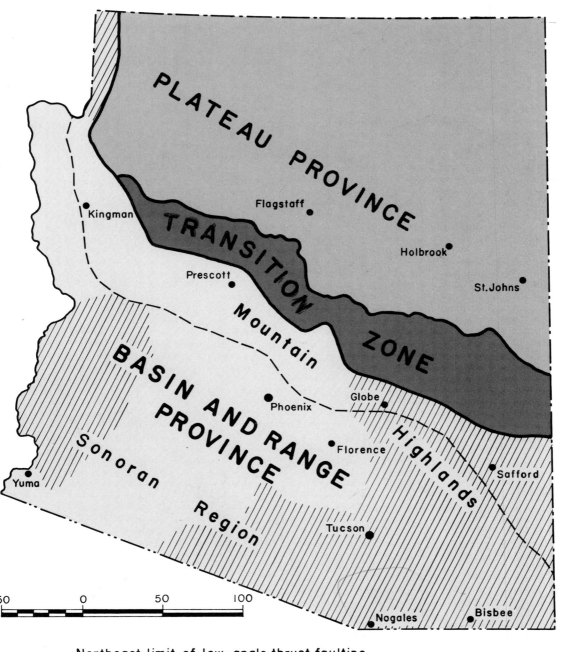

PLATEAU PROVINCE

TRANSITION ZONE

Kingman

Flagstaff

Holbrook

Prescott

St.Johns

BASIN AND RANGE
PROVINCE

Mountain

Phoenix

Globe

Florence

Highlands

Sonoran

Safford

Yuma

Region

Tucson

Nogales

Bisbee

50   0   50   100

— — — — Northeast limit of low-angle thrust faulting

Areas of Basin and Range Province containg
Paleozoic and Mesozoic sedementary rocks

Fig. 7.5   Basic geologic provinces of modern Arizona.

Fig. 7.7   Volcanic cinder cone crater and basalt flows, San Francisco volcanic field.

Tad Nichols

impressive escarpments, for example, along the Vermillion Cliffs.

Cenozoic volcanic fields cover large areas of the plateau on both sides of the river. Locally the great sheets of basalt are surmounted by cinder cones (Fig. 7.7) and stratovolcanoes. The San Francisco Mountains near Flagstaff include the highest point in the state. Its lofty peaks held glaciers at least twice during the Pleistocene. Relationship of the lava fields shows that most of the lavas were poured out after erosional stripping of the Plateau down to the surface of the

Manley

7.6   The Grand Canyon, near Toroweap Valley, looking upstream.

Kaibab limestone. Some flows pass unbroken across the major faults, showing that no renewed movement has occurred since the eruptions, but some flows have been broken by late Cenozoic faults.

Mogollon Slope. The Mogollon Slope is a convenient term for the area south of the Navajo country and north of the Plateau boundary. The Plateau strata dip gently north and northeast toward the Black Mesa basin. The western part of the Slope is underlain by Kaibab limestone, with patches of Mesozoic sedimentary rocks and Cenozoic lavas forming local prominences. The eastern edge contains a thick residual cover of Mesozoic rocks, including a few remnants of Cretaceous. Lake beds of the Bidahochi formation and Cenozoic gravels along the edge of the rim cover the older rocks in places. The White Mountains volcanic pile covers the edge of the Plateau on the southeast, and late Cenozoic flows extend in tongues northward toward the valley of the Little Colorado River.

A spectacular feature of the Slope area is Meteor Crater. This mile-wide, bowl-shaped depression is believed to have been formed either by the impact of a prehistoric meteorite or by a vapor explosion of volcanic source.

Navajo Country. The plateaus, buttes, mesas, and canyons of the Navajo country are in many ways similar to

those of the Grand Canyon Region but consist mostly of younger rocks and reflect different structural controls. Two major features dominate the area, the great downwarp of Black Mesa Basin and the upwarped Defiance Plateau.

From west to east across the area, the stratigraphic section descends from the Marble Platform by the Echo Monocline, flattens across the Kaibito Plateau, dips under Black Mesa, emerges on the east, and, after another flattening in Chinle and Beautiful valleys, arches over the Defiance Plateau and dips under the San Juan Basin in New Mexico. The structural relief is greater than the topographic relief across the area, so the rocks exposed at the surface reflect the underlying structure. Black Mesa consists of a large circular patch of Cretaceous rocks surrounded by rings of older rocks.

The situation is complicated by minor structural features, and by the fact that certain stratigraphic units are lenticular or wedge-shaped. In particular, the Paleozoic section of rocks thins notably from west to east. In the vicinity of Marble Platform lower Paleozoic Cambrian units rest on the Precambrian basement, whereas to the east, these units and other lower Paleozoic units wedge out, and in the region of the Defiance Uplift upper Paleozoic Permian rocks are resting directly on the Precambrian basement. Cenozoic lake beds and lava flows in the Hopi Buttes and southeast of the Defiance Plateau rest on eroded surfaces cut on the older rocks.

The dominant land forms of the area are plateaus, mesas, and buttes, largely carved from brightly colored beds. Deep canyons fringe the mesas. Spectacular pinnacles, arches, and natural bridges eroded in the crossbedded Paleozoic and Mesozoic sandstones form details of the landscape (Fig. 7.8). Canyon de Chelly cuts across the Defiance Uplift into the bright Permian red beds and rivals the Grand Canyon in scenic beauty, although not in size. Locally, particularly in the Hopi Buttes area, the landscape is dominated by volcanic necks which represent the congealed material solidified in the throats of Pliocene volcanoes now exposed by erosion.

Transition Zone. The Transition Zone (Fig. 7.5) has a somewhat arbitrary width of fifty miles in its southeastern segment but narrows out in northwestern Arizona near latitude 35° 30′. Topographically, it is more rugged than the Plateau, except for the area of the Grand Canyon. In general, the Transition Zone is lower in altitude than the Plateau, although some of its mountains rise as high as the Mogollon Rim.

The Transition Zone consists largely of Paleozoic and Precambrian rocks, overlain throughout extensive areas by Cenozoic lava flows.

Faulting since late Tertiary time has broken this zone in many places and has separated it from the

Western Ways Features

Fig. 7.8   Canyon de Chelly. The rock is De Chelly sandstone.

Fig. 7.9   Santa Rita Mountains, in the Mountain Region of the Basin and Range Province.

Western Ways Features

Plateau, which the zone resembles in that its strata lie essentially flat, except for local minor folding. Headward erosion by tributaries of the Gila, Salt, and Williams rivers has carved this zone into deep canyons or valleys and steep-sided mountains. In accord with their lithology and structure, these mountains are generally flat-topped or mesalike in the areas of sedimentary and volcanic rocks which prevail over most of this region; sharp and rugged in metamorphic terranes; and rugged to rounded in crystalline rocks. Three great valleys of central Arizona in this zone, the Chino, the Verde, and the Tonto, were formed as the result of relative down-faulting plus subsequent erosion.

BASIN AND RANGE PROVINCE. The Arizona portion of this province is characterized by numerous individual linear mountain ranges, which rise abruptly from broad plainlike valleys or basins (Fig. 7.9).

These mountain masses attain altitudes of a few hundred feet to more than ten thousand feet above sea level. They measure from a few miles to one hundred miles in length and from less than a mile to more than twenty miles in breadth. The widest and highest of the mountain ranges occur within an irregular, north-westward-trending belt ten to one hundred and fifty miles wide, which occupies the northeastern portion of the Province (Fig. 7.5); it is termed the Mountain Region and provisionally referred to as the Mountain Highlands. Its highest peak, Mt. Graham, is 10,713 feet above sea level or 7,790 feet above Safford, in the adjacent Gila Valley. Mt. Lemmon in the Santa Catalinas, Mt. Wrightson in the Santa Ritas, and Miller

Peak in the Huachucas rise to more than nine thousand feet, but most of its other peaks do not exceed eight thousand feet in altitude.

The portion of the Basin and Range Province that lies southwest of the Mountain Highlands is within the Sonoran Desert and may be referred to as the Sonoran Region (Fig. 7.5). Compared with the Mountain Highlands, its mountains characteristically are relatively low, rugged, and serrated (Fig. 7.10).

Only within particular areas are the mountain ranges approximately parallel to one another. For the Mountain Highlands, they follow somewhat the trend of the southwestern margin of the Plateau Province, except for a southward swing in southeastern Arizona. In the Sonoran Region, the mountains show sharp contrasts in alignment for various areas, and arcuate patterns predominate in them throughout an area of transverse ranges extending from Topock and Parker to Phoenix and Gila Bend.

Most of the intermontane valleys of the Basin and Range Province in Arizona are dissected by drainage systems tributary to the Colorado River, and only a few closed basins, bolsons, or playas ("dry lakes") are present. In many sections the valleys are wider than the mountains, and some are more than thirty miles across. The valley floors rise from approximately one hundred feet near Yuma to five thousand feet above sea level in the Sulphur Spring Valley of southeastern Arizona; many of them show maxima of twelve hundred to two thousand feet of relief between axis and margin.

The geologic structure and origin of the Basin and Range Province as a whole are complex and difficult

Fig. 7.10   Physiography of the Tinajas Altas Mountains.   *USAF Official Photo*

to unravel. Throughout large areas, the ages of its rocks have not been established positively, which makes geologic analysis provisional or doubtful. Owing to alluvial cover on the intermontane plains, numerous features of critical importance may not be traced or projected with certainty from one mountain range to another.

Although many data have been gathered and theories evolved during the past one hundred years, much additional research will be needed before this portion of Arizona can be thoroughly understood, or before its vast resources of minerals and groundwater may be adequately appraised.

Rocks of various ages from Older Precambrian to Recent make up the Basin and Range Province. Folding, faulting, igneous invasion, and volcanic eruption have afflicted the region at several intervals. As a rule, the structural deformation and igneous activity were governed by Older Precambrian features and therefore were most intense within particular areas or belts.

The general chronology, from oldest to youngest, is outlined in Figure 7.1.

The relationship of these periods of deformation and igneous activity to mineral deposits is discussed in Chapter 10.

Faulting and volcanism in Arizona are believed to be in a quiescent stage at present. No destructive earthquakes have occurred here during the twentieth century.

The present mountains represent blocks of the earth's crust, elevated by folding and faulting in refer-

ence to intervening relatively depressed blocks that underlie the basins or valleys. Displacement on the mountain-making faults of late Tertiary-Quaternary age may range from a few feet to sixteen thousand feet or more. This upheaval occurred intermittently from late Tertiary into Quaternary time, after a long history of folding, faulting, and igneous intrusion. Hence, the internal structure of the mountain ranges is complex in many places.

Between the mountain ranges, the basin or valley troughs are for the most part filled with loosely to firmly consolidated gravel, sand, and silt, from a few hundred to thousands of feet deep, of Tertiary and Quaternary ages. Part of this valley-fill material was derived from neighboring mountains, and part was transported by streams from distant areas. Erosion has fashioned the topography partly in keeping with the types and structure of the rock masses and partly under climatic influence. In this semiarid climate, erosion operates primarily through mechanical disintegration rather than chemical decay. The breaking-down process begins with differential expansion and contraction of the rock surfaces during repeated extreme changes in temperature. It acts most rapidly within zones of structural weakness. Meanwhile, torrential rains rapidly sweep the loosened rock fragments down slopes and outward onto the valley plains. As the stream channels become clogged through overloading, the floods spread sheet-like over the valley floors. Such sheet flooding is, through combined erosion and deposition, a primary factor in maintaining the plain-like surfaces of the valleys and mountain pediments. Winds are believed to cause only minor amounts of rock sculpture, but they transport much loose material, as proclaimed by extensive areas of dune sand in Yuma County.

Mountain Highlands Region. The Mountain Highlands Region (Fig. 7.5) is made up largely of Older Precambrian metamorphic and granitic rocks; Younger Precambrian quartzite, limestone and shale; Paleozoic and Mesozoic limestone, sandstone, shale, and conglomerate; Mesozoic and Tertiary intrusive masses and volcanic rocks; Tertiary and Quaternary valley-fill deposits; and Quaternary lava flows. Its southeastern, northwestern, and northernmost segments differ markedly from one another in rock components and structure.

The Paleozoic and Mesozoic strata attain maximum total thicknesses of six thousand and ten thosuand feet, respectively, in southeasternmost Arizona, but they thin out northwestward and are absent throughout the 230-mile segment of the Mountain Highlands from Roosevelt Lake to Lake Mead. Northwestward, the Paleozoic beds thicken again, to a total of nine thousand feet in Arizona, north of Lake Mead.

Thick piles of volcanic rocks extend over large areas in the Chiricahua, Peloncillo, Mule Creek, Gila, Galiuro, Tumacácori, Superstition, Turret, Mohon, and Aquarius mountain ranges. They were formed by eruptions from numerous local fissures and vents during Mesozoic and Cenozoic time.

Structurally, the Mountain Highlands Region in Arizona may be regarded as an anticlinorium, a complexly folded arch in the earth's crust, upon which complex faulting has been superimposed. Within this belt, Older Precambrian rocks lie at elevations thousands of feet higher than the Precambrian in the Plateau, and likewise higher than similar rocks in the neighboring Sonoran Region.

Overthrust faults, which dip at relatively low angles from horizonal, are common in the southern portion of the Region. Between Globe and Lake Mead, however, faults of this type younger than Precambrian are not known to occur within the Mountain Highlands Region, although they are common in the adjoining Sonoran Region. The thrust movement in general was from southwest towards northeast.

The principal folding and part of the faulting occurred during the Laramide or late Cretaceous-early Tertiary interval, and additional faulting has taken place since late Tertiary time.

Sonoran Region. Of the rock units which make up the Sonoran Region, some may be correlated definitely with those in the Mountain Highlands, and others are assigned to age groups upon uncertain bases of appearance or physical similarity. Metamorphic and granitic rocks of known or inferred Older Precambrian age occur widely distributed. Younger Precambrian strata are recognized in only a few small, isolated localities of southwestern Pinal County.

Sedimentary beds of Paleozoic and Mesozoic ages occupy widely scattered areas within the southeastern and western divisions of the region. In the western division, the Paleozoic succession is relatively thin, but the Mesozoic is very thick, and local features have been obscured by faulting, folding, or metamorphism. No Paleozoic or Mesozoic strata appear within a belt 65 to 150 miles wide, which lies between the southeastern and western divisions.

Granitic rocks, believed to be of Mesozoic age, constitute several mountain ranges in southern Yuma and southwestern Pima counties. Volcanic rocks of Mesozoic and Tertiary ages make up numerous mountain ranges, and sedimentary beds of those ages occur in many areas.

Loosely to firmly consolidated gravel, silt, and sand, of late Tertiary-early Quaternary age, form the intermontane valley plains which occupy from one-half to almost three-fourths of the Sonoran Region in Arizona. Marine limestone of late Tertiary age crops out in the lower Colorado River Valley north of latitude $33° 10'$.

Basaltic lava flows of Quaternary aspect appear prominently in numerous localities. The Sentinel basalt plain in southwestern Maricopa County, and the Pinacate in southeastern Yuma County are considered to be of historic or late prehistoric age.

Structurally, the Sonoran Region comprises numerous irregular fault blocks, among which relative uplift gave rise to the present mountains, and relative depression provided the intermontane valley troughs. This basin-and-range faulting of late Tertiary to Quaternary time was superimposed upon previous folding and locally complex faulting. Faults of the overthrust type are evident at many places, and they are particularly common throughout the northeastern portion of the Sonoran Region.

Fig. 8.1 A water reservoir on the southern Arizona desert.

Salt River Project

Hydrology and
Water Resources Faculty,
University of Arizona

Fig. 8.2 Water resources at the higher elevations.

8

WATER

WITHIN THE POLITICAL BOUNDARIES defining Arizona are many natural attributes that work together to provide a desirable environment for man. Thriving on the sunshine, enjoying the variety of choices for living and recreation offered by the differences in elevation between desert floor and mountain top, man has made great strides in learning to carry on his enormous complex of modern activities in an arid land. But his most urgent problem continues to be water.

In 1970 it was estimated that Arizonans each year use between 6 and 7 million acre-feet of water. Paradoxically, in an average year, Arizona captures for use only about 2 million of the 80 million acre-feet of water from rain or snow. The balance for use is obtained from underground water reserves. Water resources development and management in Arizona are becoming more critical than ever before to the welfare of the state, as demands for water increase and reserves of groundwater decrease.

Sources of Water in Arizona

Arizona may be divided into three principal water provinces: 1) the Plateau Uplands including the northern part of the state, 2) the Central Highlands, a mountainous area extending diagonally across the state, and 3) the Basin and Range Lowlands, or desert, which includes the heavily populated southern portion of Arizona (Fig. 8.3).

The Plateau Uplands are cool, semiarid, and receive only small amounts of precipitation. The aridity of the Uplands is seen in the flat desert plains, and most of the moisture from rainfall is dissipated by evapo-transpiration. Streams from the mountains fan out in broad, braided channels, where the water sinks into the soil and is soon pulled back into the atmosphere by evaporation. These intermittent streams yield very little water in proportion to the size of the drainage areas.

The Uplands include many mesas, buttes, and several gently sloping mountains. The altitude ranges from 4,000 to 10,000 feet above sea level. Water supplies in this scenic wonderland depend upon the availability of small amounts of surface water and the feasibility of drilling deep wells in sandstone aquifers. These water-bearing sandstones form a large natural underground storage reservoir, but not all the rocks yield water freely. Although the groundwater for the most part is undeveloped in the Uplands, full development may never occur because of the slow rates of movement and the difficulty of extraction.

The rugged, mountainous Central Highlands province receives the heaviest precipitation within Arizona. As precipitation ranges from ten to thirty-five inches annually, surface water from rainfall and snowmelt occur in relatively large amounts. This is the area of perennial water supply and is the source of streamflow to the lowlands provinces. The Highlands are composed of hard, dense rocks and some poorly consolidated rocks. As the hard rocks have few voids they cannot store large amounts of water except where they are broken by faults and other fractures. Even though many springs issue along faults, there are not large

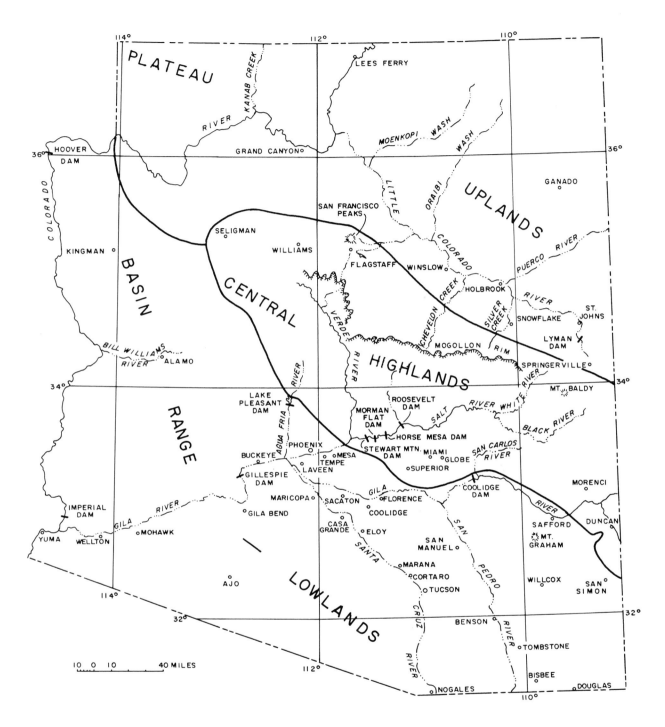

Fig. 8.3   The three major water provinces of Arizona.

amounts of groundwater stored in the mountainous area. The mountain slopes are steep, with a thin soil mantle which affords rapid runoff and decreases the amount of water lost by evaporation (Fig. 8.2).

A distinctive feature of grandeur and prominence in the Central Highlands is the Mogollon Rim. It extends more than 200 miles across the state and

ranges in height from several hundred to more than 2,000 feet. This brow forms the divide between the Little Colorado and Gila River drainage systems. Many springs occurring near the base of the Mogollon escarpment feed perennial water into the upper tributaries of the Gila, Salt and Verde rivers. Tonto Creek and Verde River join Salt River in a narrow gorge northeast of

Phoenix, and here is where the storage reservoirs have been built for use by agriculture, industry, and municipalities in the hot arid desert.

The Basin and Range Lowlands, which contain more than 80 percent of the state's population, consist of isolated mountain blocks jutting from alluvial sediments that form the broad desert basins. The arid basins range in altitude from about 100 feet above sea level at Yuma, to about 4,000 feet in the southeastern part of the state. The climate in the lowlands is hot and arid, and the rainfall is light, with precipitation averaging less than ten inches annually. Near the top of several of the high mountain blocks such as the Santa Catalinas, annual precipitation may amount to thirty inches. However, there are large desert areas which receive less than five inches annually. There are no large surface water reservoirs in this province as the runoff is very small. Average annual runoff from the driest 15,000 square miles in the lowlands is less than 0.1 inch. The headwaters of the San Pedro, Santa Cruz, and other large tributaries yield only about 0.5 inch per year. San Simon Creek, which joins the Gila near Safford, has a runoff of only 0.1 inch. Bill Williams River at Alamo in the west central part of the state has a runoff of one-fourth inch. Streams draining several of the higher mountain ranges — the Huachucas, Pinalenos, and Catalinas, for instance — yield moderate amounts of runoff along the base of the mountains. But when the water reaches the desert basin it evaporates quickly and thus only a small part remains to recharge the groundwater reservoir.

Streamflow in the lowlands occurs mostly as flash floods following thunderstorms. Storms originating in the Gulf of Mexico extend into the southeast corner of the state and drop their moisture in the mountainous areas. As floodwaters move downstream from the mountain areas, the volume of the flood decreases rapidly. Factors which contribute to this depletion include infiltration, evaporation, channel storage, and channel retention. All of these natural losses of water are important factors in appraising stream runoff. As an example, a flood in the Santa Cruz River in August, 1954, showed a loss of 2,000 acre-feet between Nogales and Cortaro, a distance of eighty-two miles, and none of this water reached the mouth of the Santa Cruz at Laveen. It is not known how much of this water seeps into the groundwater table and how much is lost by evaporation. Examination of water table fluctuations indicates that only a small fraction reaches the groundwater reservoir. There is much merit in the belief that most of the water loss is returned as vapor into the atmosphere. However, much research is needed to answer these questions quantitatively.

The sediments in the alluvial desert basins constitute large storage areas for groundwater, and the occurrence of these large water reserves has made it possible for man to live prosperously and comfortably in the desert. However, continued withdrawal of these underground water reserves has seriously depleted them. In the lower Santa Cruz basin and in several areas near Phoenix, the water level dropped as much as 360 feet in the 1923–1962 period. The amount of replenishment of natural recharge is a very small fraction of the amount withdrawn. Thus, the rate of pumping of groundwater was a depletion or mining process.

As the Central Highlands receive the largest amounts of precipitation, this province contributes the largest amount of surface water. However, runoff varies widely owing to differences in precipitation, temperature, and terrain. In the Mount Baldy area of the White Mountains, the average runoff is about four inches annually (one inch of runoff means a volume of water one inch deep over the entire watershed). The runoff in the upper Tonto Creek basin is more than two inches. The average runoff for the Salt River system above Roosevelt Lake was about 2.0 inches or about 600,000 acre-feet per year from 1946 to 1961. The streamflow in the Verde River basin in the western part of the Highlands is similar to the Salt River system. Oak and Granite creeks have an average runoff of four inches. The runoff at the Verde River where it enters the Salt River is 1.4 inches or 500,000 acre-feet. In the southern part of the Highlands province, San Francisco and San Carlos rivers and Eagle Creek are the main contributors of runoff to the Gila River. Their joint contribution into San Carlos Lake above Coolidge Dam is 0.6 inches annually, or about 210,000 acre-feet.

Most of the floods on the Central Highlands are caused by storms moving eastward from the Pacific Ocean, usually in winter or early spring. Large floods have occurred in the past, such as in February 1891, when the Salt River had a peak flow of 300,000 cubic feet per second (cfs). In November, 1905, the Verde River had a peak flow of 96,000 cfs. at its mouth. Other large floods occurred in 1937, 1941, 1952, 1958, 1960, and 1965. In addition, storms originating in the Gulf of Mexico have caused large floods, producing 45,000 cfs. in 1952 in Tonto Creek and 43,000 cfs. in 1954 in Queen Creek. Sixty percent of the annual runoff in the Salt River drainage occurs between January and April, compared to 15 percent between July and September. The minimum flows occur in June and early July just before the summer rains commence.

Water from spring flow at the base of the Mogollon Rim provides perennial flow in headward tributaries. The estimated total discharge from about 150 springs totals more than 180 cfs.

Except for the main stem of the Colorado River, almost all the perennial streams that flow across the Plateau Uplands originate in the Central Highlands. A ribbon of high precipitation extends along the Mogollon Rim westward to the Flagstaff area. Snowmelt and rainfall in this area drain northwest into the Little Colorado River system. However, owing to high rates of evaporation, the stream yields only small amounts of water. Also, small amounts of water seep into the subsurface, draining northward over the highly fractured Kaibab limestone. Runoff from the Plateau is generally less than 0.3 inch except in the headwaters near the Rim. The principal streams are Clear Creek, Chevelon Fork, Show Low Creek, and Greer Creek, the west fork of the Little Colorado. The runoff in these headward streams ranges from two to four inches annually.

Silver Creek, which flows through the Snowflake area, has a runoff of three inches, but about 6,000 acres are irrigated with the water and only 0.3 inch of runoff enters the Little Colorado. A similar situation exists on the upper Little Colorado near St. Johns where Lyman Dam impounds water for about 7,000 acres of land. The intermittent streams in the large expanse of arid lands to the north of the Little Colorado in the Navajo and Hopi Indian reservations yield only one-fourth inch of runoff annually. The low yield of stream-flow in this province is exemplified by the Little Colorado River, which is an intermittent stream although its drainage area is more than 26,000 square miles.

Many tributaries enter the Colorado River below Lees Ferry, the division point between the upper and lower basins, but they flow only during periods of heavy rainfall. However, several of these streams have a perennial flow from springs issuing from consolidated rocks. These include Blue Springs, Bright Angel Creek, Tapeats Creek (Thunder River), and several large springs in Havasu Creek near the west end of Grand Canyon Park. Their combined flow, plus that from other smaller springs, makes a total water contribution of about 300,000 acre feet per year to the Colorado River in the Uplands province. The average annual flow in the Colorado River at Lees Ferry is 13 million acre-feet for the period of record.

OCCURRENCE AND GEOLOGICAL ENVIRONMENT. In the Central Highlands the alluvial sediment mantle, for the most part, is only a few tens of feet thick, whereas in the Basin and Range lowlands, it is several hundred to thousands of feet thick. Water from the mountainous streams seeps through the sandy materials in the channels and moves downward by the force of gravity into the lowland basins. It forms the saturated zone overlying the impervious rock constituting the bottom of the basin. Over the past millennia, the groundwater has filled the large amount of pore space in the sediments. In fact, in places the basins were filled to overflowing, and groundwater returned to the surface at the lower ends. Thus, groundwater in the alluvial basins began as surface water and ended as surface water prior to entering the ocean. Such was the hydrologic balance prior to disturbance by man.

Water passing through pore spaces in sand and gravel moves very slowly, and a long time is required for groundwater to reach its own level in an aquifer. Actually, groundwater never stands still and seldom develops a horizontal water table. The table, under natural conditions, slopes away from the source of supply, and this slope is called the "hydraulic gradient." Before white men arrived in Arizona, the water system was in a dynamic hydrologic balance. Inflow equaled outflow. Outflow includes water leaving by evaporation, transpiration, streamflow, and groundwater underflow. Water used by man is obtained by diverting surface and groundwater from the system, and a large part of groundwater is drawn from the reserves in storage. Outflow may thus exceed inflow, as is the case in Arizona where man is removing large amounts of water from storage and converting it into vapor which leaves the region via the atmosphere. Today the amount of water seeping into the water table from mountain streams and rainfall is less than the amount pumped by man.

AQUIFERS. Geologists define an aquifer as a water-bearing bed or stratum of sand, gravel, or pervious rock. The distribution of these aquifers is of considerable economic importance. In the Basin and Range province, the water level in the upper part of the alluvial fill ranges from a few feet below the surface to several hundred feet. In places where the aquifer is overlain by nearly impervious silt and clay beds, the groundwater is under artesian pressure, but commonly groundwater occurs in unconfined aquifers where water table conditions prevail. In general, the unconfined water table aquifers have a greater permeability than the artesian aquifers and are capable of yielding large amounts of water to wells. The artesian aquifers commonly occur at greater depths ranging from about 500 to 1,500 feet below the surface.

The main aquifers in the Plateau Uplands are fine-grained sandstone with alternating layers of non-water-bearing siltstone and claystone (Fig. 8.4). Over most of the area the deepest formation yielding water to wells is the Supai formation, and it consists of sandstone, siltstone, and mudstone. Only the sandstone is of water-bearing importance; however, the siltstone and mudstone are important in that they retard the downward movement of water and in many places the Supai formation is an important confining layer. The Coconino sandstone of Permian age lies above the Supai formation and underlies nearly all of the area. It is about 600 feet thick near Holbrook but thins out northward. It is a fine-grained, well-sorted, highly cross-bedded sand, deposited by wind action. The next aquifer of importance is the Navajo sandstone of Jurassic age. It too is an ancient sand dune deposit and is the principal water-bearing unit in the western part of the Navajo Reservation.

The Mesaverde group of rocks of Cretaceous age consists of a series of sandstone and siltstone units. The sandstone units yield small amounts of water in the Black Mesa area and constitute the sole supply for many schools and trading posts. Tertiary sediments and

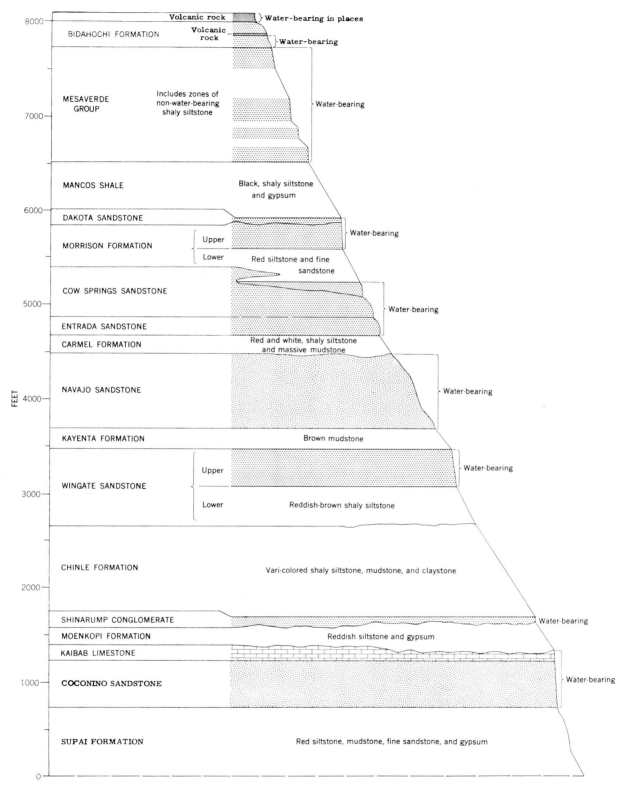

Fig. 8.4   Rock formations and water-bearing strata in northern Arizona.

volcanic rocks in the Springerville-St. Johns area are important aquifers, but storage capacity is small. A number of wells yield groundwater from the shallow alluvium along the Little Colorado River drainage system. The alluvium is not favorable for large yields because of its fine-grained character, but ample supplies are pumped for stock and domestic use.

Although the Coconino sandstone is widespread areally, it is several thousand feet below the land surface in many places. Further, in places the chemical quality of the water is unfavorable due to high chloride content and makes it necessary to develop supplies from other sources. As the Navajo sandstone and Mesaverde rocks are limited in areal extent, it is not possible to develop water from these aquifers everywhere in the Uplands.

In general, the Plateau Upland aquifers yield only small quantities of water to wells because of their low permeabilities. Yields range from a few gallons per minute (gpm) to less than 200 gpm. However, where the sandstones have been faulted, fractured, and jointed, additional storage space and greater permeability are created, and in such areas the yield is considerably more. Such conditions prevail near Flagstaff, St. Johns, and Snowflake. Wells in the Flagstaff area yield as much as 700 gpm, and near St. Johns a yield of 1800 gpm has been reported.

The fractured character of the rocks is also favorable for recharge from rainfall and snowmelt as it affords avenues for downward percolation into the water table. Thus, in areas of high precipitation, the rocks' character not only controls the groundwater supplies but also controls surface water in that the downward percolation reduces the amount of runoff of the area.

Uses of Water

The use of water may be separated into five categories: domestic and municipal, industrial and community, mining, livestock, and irrigation. Of these, the use for irrigation has been quantitatively, by far the most significant, since over 90 percent of the consumptive use of water in Arizona in the late 1960s was for this purpose.

DOMESTIC AND MUNICIPAL. Requirements for domestic water, supplied by municipal and private water companies or privately owned wells, are the most vital. The total use for this purpose may be approximated by using the average daily per capita consumption in the Tucson and Phoenix communities.

In the city of Tucson and the urban area supplied by the city water system, daily per capita deliverage has averaged 160 gallons per day over the period from 1955 to 1968. On this basis, an acre-foot of water is required to supply the needs of 5.6 persons for one year. It is believed that this figure may be applied to the approximately 325,000 population of the Tucson area.

The City of Phoenix Water Department reports a considerably higher use. In 1968 almost 225 gallons per capita per day were used by the 555,000 people in the service area. Smaller cities and towns and users supplied by private wells are believed to have a per capita use less than that of Tucson. Assuming that this use is around 150 gallons per capita per day, the computed use in the state, based upon a 1968 population of 1,634,000 amounts to about 245,000 acre-feet per year. Included in this estimate is water used by small industries with limited water requirements. It is estimated that only 50 percent of the deliverage is consumptively used.

INDUSTRIAL AND COMMUNITY. In all urban areas there are general community requirements. These include the water supply for golf courses, hospitals, school grounds, and other places. Army and Air Force bases in the state in most cases have their own water supplies, but personnel and their families are largely supplied with domestic water by municipal or private water companies.

Industrial water requirements are chiefly for cooling purposes. Although not to be compared with those of heavy industry in the East, these requirements cannot be ignored. Industrial users include ice plants, railroads, gas compressor stations, sand and gravel plants, cement plants, laundries, airports, and steam plants for the generation of electric power. Steam plants require water for condenser purposes. Where water is cooled by evaporation, the amount used is almost in direct proportion to the power generated; however, the amount does vary with the quality of the supply and the efficiency of its use.

No accurate figures are available for the consumptive use of water included under industrial and community use, but a survey in the Tucson area indicated that it amounts to between 20 and 25 percent of the domestic water requirements. Assuming that the same ratio is applicable to the state as a whole, it has been estimated that the water requirements for these purposes are about 50,000 acre-feet per year in the late 1960s.

MINING. The major water requirement for mining in Arizona is for the milling and concentrating of low-grade ores. Seemingly large quantities of water are required for this purpose with an average consumptive use of about 250 gallons per ton of ore treated. Total water consumptively used by the mining industry is approximately 50,000 acre-feet per year in the 1960s, which is equal to only about 1.0 percent of the consumptive use for irrigation. However, the gross value of products is approximately the same.

LIVESTOCK. Since earliest territorial days, the livestock industry has occupied a most prominent place in Arizona's agricultural economy. Consumption of water by livestock in summer is estimated at about ten gallons per day per large animal unit, with an annual water

Fig. 8.5 Irrigation with the use of siphons in central Arizona.

requirement of about one acre-foot per year for each 100 head of cattle or horses. For the livestock population of approximately 1,125,000, the annual requirement is about 12,000 acre-feet. Total requirements for the cattle industry are probably several times this, since much of the water is collected and stored for long periods in earth stock tanks from which evaporation losses may be as much as six feet in depth per year from the water surface area.

Estimates of the Soil Conservation Service place the number of these stock tanks at 12,000 in 1969, with an average water surface of less than .75 acres each. The computed evaporation loss from stock tanks, with combined evaporation and plant transpiration of six feet per year, will result in an annual loss of about 54,000 acre-feet, so the total use by the stock industry should equal about 66,000 acre-feet per year. The aggregate amount collected in stock tanks will be considerably in excess of this amount, but the losses by seepage may be considered as a direct contribution to the groundwater supply and not a loss.

IRRIGATION. Computations for determining the total amount of water used in Arizona each year for irrigation are intricate and complex. They involve the records of major water users such as the Salt River Valley Water Users' Association and others, and such records are often incomplete. Various other factors of evaporation, percolation, and transpiration affect such estimates.

Calculations suggest, however, that the consumptive use of water for irrigation in Arizona each year is around 3.75 acre-feet per acre. The best information available indicates that the total irrigated areas in the state in the late 1960s include 1,250,000 acres. Therefore, the net annual consumptive use for irrigation amounts to approximately 4,700,000 acre-feet of water each year (Fig. 8.5).

Thus, the total consumptive use of water in Arizona may be summarized as follows:

Domestic and municipal	122,000 acre-feet
Industrial and community	50,000 acre-feet
Mining	50,000 acre-feet
Livestock	66,000 acre-feet
Irrigation	4,700,000 acre-feet
Total Consumptive Use	4,988,000 acre-feet

Water Use Regulation

Even in those areas of the world where water is plentiful, it has been necessary to evolve a code of law concerning water use and ownership. In arid areas such as Arizona, water law is complex and varies in many respects from that of other states.

SURFACE WATER. Since earliest territorial days, rights to surface waters have been acquired under the doctrine of appropriation. This doctrine, so different from the riparian rights theory of most states, holds that the first person to use the water from a stream to improve a parcel of land has the right to continue to use that same amount of water indefinitely, and no subsequent owner of lands bounding the stream from which the water is taken can claim an equal or better right. The rights of the prior appropriator are superior to the rights of any later settler either along the borders of the stream or anywhere else, and these rights are in no way dependent upon where the water is used, provided it is used beneficially and not wasted.

The Bill of Rights adopted by the First Territorial Legislature in 1864 declared that all streams, ponds, and lakes capable of being used for navigation or irrigation are public and are available for use in mining or irrigation by appropriation. Waters so appropriated are subject to previously vested rights acquired from the Mexican government or impliedly as the result of local customs. The inference is rather clear that percolating groundwaters were not subject to appropriation.

Since 1919 the appropriation and use of surface waters has been in accordance with the provisions of the Arizona Water Code enacted by the state legislature in that year. The present statute provides:

> The water of all sources, flowing in streams, canyons, ravines, or other natural channels, or in definite underground channels, whether perennial or intermittent, flood, waste or surplus water, and of lakes, ponds and springs on the surface, belongs to the public, and is subject to appropriation and beneficial use, as herein provided. . . .

The inclusion of waters in definite underground channels has led to much confusion. However, the Arizona Supreme Court has placed the burden of proof upon the person making application for a water right from a definite underground channel to show that such an underground channel exists. The criteria for establishing said proof are exacting, and to date only a few certificates of water rights have been granted on this basis. One of these was presumably the result of a stipulated agreement between attorneys in a case before the Supreme Court. Prior to extensive development of groundwaters by pumping, there were numerous instances in which diversions from surface flow became diversions from underflow from the same stream during the dry seasons of the year. With general lowering of the groundwater table, this is now possible in but a limited number of locations, with underflow directly related to and a part of the surface flow of the same stream.

The 1919 Water Code vests in the state land commissioner the power to distribute water in accordance with respective priorities. Since most water rights, however, were acquired prior to the passage of the code, the major portion of the surface waters of the state are actually being distributed by court water commissioners appointed as the result of earlier court decisions, and not through the adjudication of water rights by the commissioner under provisions of the 1919 code.

GROUNDWATER. Water users in Arizona claim that their water rights are vested property rights under the English common-law doctrine as asserted repeatedly by the courts of Arizona. In the late 1960s the most recent dicta of the courts indicated that consideration of the principle of reasonable use might become a factor in determining the extent of these rights for landowners drawing water from a common source. The question of what constitutes reasonable beneficial use then becomes a matter of determination of the facts for each individual case. The American doctrine of reasonable use also differentiates between the rights of an overlying landowner placing water to beneficial use on this land, and the landowner transporting water to more distant lands either within or without the confines of the groundwater basin from which it is drawn.

Groundwaters are not subject to appropriation in Arizona, and therefore prior rights to the use of groundwater cannot be acquired nor could they have been acquired under the doctrine of prior appropriation. It would appear that rights to the use of percolating groundwater in Arizona have been acquired in accordance with the English or common-law rules with no assurance or protection as to the permanence of a future water supply.

A measure of protection is provided by the Groundwater Act of 1948. This act prohibits the drilling of additional wells for the irrigation of new lands in areas designated as critical groundwater areas. It should be noted that this prohibition applies only to irrigation wells. Wells for certain exempted uses or purposes are excluded from the provisions of the act. An exempted well is defined as a well used for domestic, industrial, or transportation purposes.

The 1948 act stated that it was enacted in the interest of general economy and welfare of the state and its citizens, to conserve and protect the water resources of the state from destruction and to provide reasonable regulation for the designation and establishment of critical groundwater areas. The act also provided that any groundwater basin, or portion thereof, not having sufficient water to provide a reasonable, safe supply for the irrigation of the cultivated land in the basin, should be designated as a critical groundwater area.

The act further provided for a system of permits for the construction and operation of all wells of over 100 gallons per minute capacity. Within critical groundwater areas, permits may not be issued for drilling new wells for the irrigation of lands not under irrigation at the time the area was declared critical, or within the previous five-year period. However, permits may be issued for deepening or replacing old wells. No new lands may be placed under irrigation within the critical areas. Permits shall be issued for drilling exempted wells for the withdrawal of groundwater for domestic, stock watering, water utility, industrial, and transportation uses. Wells may be constructed for any purpose outside of critical areas.

Pollution Control

Water pollution control is of paramount importance to Arizona. To control the quality of the state's water resources, Arizona has enacted comprehensive water pollution control legislation which became effective March 16, 1967. The law is administered by the State Department of Health, under the general direction of the State Board of Health and a newly created State Water Quality Control Council. The council is composed of thirteen members — six represent various state agencies and seven are citizens appointed by the governor. The council is directed to formulate reasonable standards of quality for state waters and enforcement of such standards. The State Board of Health is responsible for adopting rules and regulations necessary to minimize, prevent, control and abate existing or potential pollution from the discharge of wastes. The state legislation was stimulated by the enactment of the Federal Water Quality Act of 1965.

TYPES OF IRRIGATION ENTERPRISES. The ownership and operation of irrigation facilities, including dams, reservoirs, diversion structures, canals and distribution ditches, drainage structures, electric power and distribution lines, and pumping plants are found under various types of organizations. The more common types are: (1) private ownership, (2) corporate ownership, (3) corporate water companies, (4) mutual water companies, unincorporated, (5) mutual water companies, incorporated, (6) irrigation or other district forms, (7) water users' associations, and (8) federal projects.

1. Private ownership and control of water supplies predominate in Arizona where a major portion of the land is irrigated with pumped water from wells. Relatively few landowners have surface water rights with individual and separate diversions of gravity water. Pumping plants and other irrigation facilities are presumably on the tax rolls and are subject to the same local and state taxes as other property.

2. Corporate ownership of land and irrigation facilities is also common but is more prevalent in the large land holdings of several thousands of acres, with pumping from groundwater as the principal source of supply. A few enterprises of this type with water rights of early priority continue to operate with their own diversion structures and canal systems. Most of these are located near the headwaters of a stream and are subject to the same taxes as are private owners.

3. Water companies are incorporated under state law, and, subject to the rules and regulations of the Arizona Corporation Commission, were commonly formed as a subsidiary to a land development company. The primary purpose of the water company was to develop a water supply and to construct a distribution system for the delivery of water to purchasers of land during the development and sales period. The usual sales agreement provided for the purchase of shares of stock in the water company equal in number to the number of acres of land purchased. Delivery of the water company stock was contingent upon the final payment for the land or, in some cases, payment of a certain stated percentage of the purchase price. Control and management of the water company thus remained with the land company for a long period of years, and the price for the delivery of water, usually on an acre-foot basis, provided a continual source of disagreement.

Most of these water companies have since changed their form of organization to that of district or mutual companies to avail themselves of the benefits accruing to these organizations, especially property tax exemption. The Cortaro Water Users' Association of Marana, Arizona, is one of the few remaining corporations of this type. As of 1971, there was both an Association and a District with board members in common.

4. Mutual water companies, unincorporated, cooperative in nature, were one of the earliest forms of irrigation enterprise in the state. Some date back almost to the 1850s, and their water supplies from surface streams have highest priority. Only in recent years have these supplies been augmented by pumped water from wells owned either by individual farmers or water companies.

The mutual water companies are an association of private individuals for the purpose of providing an irrigation water supply, usually from a common source, on a nonprofit basis for shareholders. These companies are not subject to local or state taxes. Disadvantages are the difficulty of enforcing regulations and collecting assessments from members. Such companies are adapted only to situations where the irrigation problems are of a simple nature.

5. Mutual water companies, incorporated, are similar in many respects to the unincorporated companies and have the same objectives. However, because of their corporate character mutual companies are better adapted to the operation of large and complicated forms of irrigation projects. Shares in the company are usually on the basis of one share for each acre of land. The business of the company is conducted by a board of directors, and individual land owners are not liable for debts of the company. Assessments may be levied against shareholders and their stock sold for nonpayment of assessments. Tolls may be collected for delivery of water and if not paid, water may be withheld. Mutual water companies have the right to issue bonds — the interest on which is tax exempt — and the property of the company is not subject to ordinary property taxes. The property of the company may be mortgaged to insure payments of loans.

6. The irrigation district organized under state law has become the most popular form of irrigation organization. It is defined as a public or quasi-municipal corporation much the same as a city, with definite boundaries, but it is formed for a different purpose. It is a political subdivision of the state. The statutes

provide for electrical, power, drainage, agricultural improvement, conservation, and flood control districts, which are similar in character to irrigation districts and differ but slightly from them in operation.

The irrigation district is created by the county board of supervisors after petition by the landholders, notification and public hearing, and a public election with the usual requirements for such elections. Electors must be landowners within the district boundaries and residents of the county in which the district is located. Each elector has but one vote whether he owns a great or small amount of land. In this respect it differs from other forms of irrigation organizations. It is a self-governing, cooperative form of enterprise, operated and managed by the landholders through an elected board of directors, subject to supervision by a board of state officials as specified by law with respect to the issuance and sale of bonds for the construction of irrigation facilities and for other purposes. The district as a public corporation is exempt from both state and federal income taxes.

Revenue for bond service and other purposes is obtained by assessments on an acreage basis, based upon an annual budget prepared by the board of directors and approved by the county board of supervisors. Upon order of the latter, the assessments or taxes are placed on the county tax rolls and are collected by the county treasurer in the same manner as state and other county taxes. Assessments become liens against the lands and the lands may be sold for nonpayment the same as for other taxes. The county treasurer is ex-officio treasurer of the district. The budget must provide for operation and maintenance expense, interest, a sinking fund for bond redemption or repayment of money borrowed, deficiencies incurred in the previous year's operation, and may include a fund for the purchase at tax sale of the lands of delinquent landowners.

7. Water users' associations are a special form of corporate organization with some of the features of incorporated mutual water companies — they are exempt from the payment of local taxes, and shares are held and voted on an acreage basis. They are designed to meet specifically the requirements of the Reclamation Act of 1902 in providing a legal entity to represent a large number of water users with various size landholdings, water rights of different priority, and water delivery from different canal systems and other facilities. The Salt River Valley Water Users' Association was the first of this form of corporate organization and has since been the pattern for many others in the West. It is stated that the basis and underlying reasons for the formation of the association were these:

1. To establish, both for the benefit of the United States Government and the water users themselves, a central organization which could represent the individual water users in dealing with the Secretary of the Interior.

2. To establish and maintain a central organization which could be in position to guarantee payment of the construction costs of the Project to the government and to enforce collection of each installment of the construction costs from the individual landowners.

3. To establish a central organization which could assume at a future date the responsibility for operation and management of the irrigation works, and distribution of water to the landowners in accordance with their rights.

4. To insure that the right to waters stored by Roosevelt Dam would be equally available to all participants in the Association.

5. To insure that the cost of construction would be distributed equally among the members of the Association and that assessments should likewise be equitably distributed, notwithstanding use or non-use of water.

In 1937 the Salt River Agricultural Improvement and Power District was formed with identical boundaries and interests in order to secure for the association lands the added exemptions and immunities granted to public corporations. All association property was transferred to the district, but the association continues to operate the irrigation system as agent of the district.

8. Federal participation in project construction has been largely through the Bureau of Reclamation under the Reclamation Act of 1902, supplemented by later acts of Congress. Contracts for repayment of construction costs must be executed by water users' associations before delivery of water, but the terms are most liberal. They may permit a ten-year development period in which no payments are required and thereafter a fifty-year term for repayment of construction cost without interest. Multiple purpose projects embracing power, navigation, fish and wild life preservation, flood control, and irrigation may now be included with reclamation. The construction costs payable by water users are limited to that part allocated to irrigation works.

During the period of operation by the Bureau, the water users' organization is responsible for the collection of all charges from the individual water users for operation and maintenance of the project works. The water users' organization is expected to take over the operation and management of project facilities when repayment of construction costs has been made on the major part of project lands. However, it may assume this responsibility at an earlier date through special arrangements with the Secretary of the Interior.

Federal funds have also been available through the Bureau of Indian Affairs for the construction, operation, and maintenance of project works and for the subjugation of land for irrigation in Indian reservations. Hydroelectric or other types of power plants with transmission lines and substations have been included in some project works. Indian landowners or white farmers benefitting from the construction of Indian irrigation projects must repay construction costs under contracts similar to those in Bureau of Reclamation projects.

Development of Water Reserves

The principal areas of groundwater development are in the Basin and Range Lowlands. Large agricultural areas in the Salt River Valley and in the lower Santa Cruz basin are irrigated with groundwater. In about 1920 a startling situation developed in the Salt River Valley area. Surface water was used for irrigation and excess water caused the groundwater table to rise to the land surface, causing waterlogging of the land. Wells were drilled and pumped to drain the land and the water was transported for irrigation to the west of the waterlogged area. This was the beginning of the large well construction which led to the expansion of developing groundwater for irrigation that we find in Arizona today.

Since 1960 about 2.25 million acre-feet per year in the Salt River Valley and about 1.5 million acre-feet yearly in the lower Santa Cruz have been withdrawn. The annual withdrawal in these areas constitutes about 70 percent of the total groundwater pumped in the entire state. Figure 8.3 shows the location of the basins where groundwater has been developed for irri-

gation, and the bar graph (Fig. 8.6) shows the totals of water pumped and surface water diverted by years.

In 1957 there were about 3,500 active irrigation wells in the Salt River Valley and lower Santa Cruz basin, and the discharge from these ranged from 100 to 5,000 gallons per minute. Approximately 5,000 irrigation wells in the state deliver more than four million acre-feet per year. The depth of wells ranges from about 100 feet to over 2,000 feet deep. In recent years it has been necessary to deepen old wells or drill new deep wells in order to maintain large yields.

The entire water supplies for the Tucson metropolitan area come from groundwater reserves. Phoenix obtains its supply by pumping groundwater and also from surface water from the Verde River. Since the communities in the northern part of the state are small and have no large industrial water demands, only a few thousand acre-feet are withdrawn.

DECLINE OF WATER LEVELS. Groundwater table declines occur in areas where wells continually withdraw water from the subsurface reservoir in excess of local replenish-

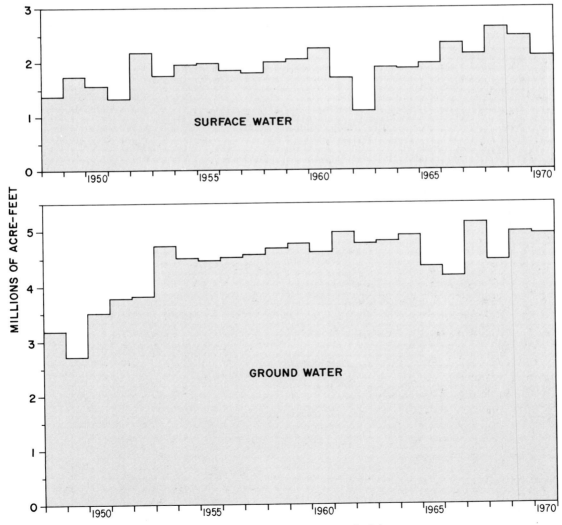

Fig. 8.6 Surface water diversion and groundwater pumpage in Arizona.

ment. The water table declines in the form of an inverted cone referred to as the cone of depression. When large quantities of water are pumped from closely spaced wells, the depression cones of such wells soon overlap and result in an irregular depression of the water table. As pumping continues in excess of recharge or replenishment, the depression continues in depth and extends outward with time, and eventually results in a depletion of the groundwater reserves. Many of the alluvial groundwater basins in southern Arizona are now in advance stages of this depletion process.

The areas experiencing the greatest water level decline coincide with areas of large withdrawals. Records show that the water table dropped as much as 300 feet in several places in the Salt River Valley in the 1923–1964 period. In Deer Valley north of Phoenix, the area of maximum decline was as much as 300 feet in the 1963–1964 period.

The lower Santa Cruz basin in Pinal County has the second largest amount of water withdrawn in the state (Fig. 8.6). In the Maricopa-Stanfield area the total drop from the original static level, i.e., prior to disturbance by man, is as much as 300 feet. Again most of this drop has taken place since World War II. Recent field observations have revealed that a lowering of the land is taking place due to the large amounts of groundwater removal in the basin between Picacho and Casa Grande mountains.

In nearly all the groundwater basins the decline is related to the magnitude of agricultural development. There have been rapid declines in recent years in several areas where large-scale vegetable cultivation has been carried on.

Safford Valley is one of the few fortunate agricultural areas that receives annual recharge or replenishment of water to the subsurface reservoir. Here the Gila River constitutes a source of water both for surface water diversion for crops and for recharge to the groundwater reservoir. Consequently, the water table fluctuates; the fluctuation is related to the annual amount of rainfall and runoff.

With the water-starved Basin and Range lowlands, a unique situation exists in the Yuma-Wellton-Mohawk area. Here, surface water from the Colorado River is diverted for irrigation. As large amounts of water are needed to maintain good soil conditions, excess water has seeped into the subsurface. Within a period of several years, this downward seepage has caused the water table to rise to the surface and has caused unfavorable conditions. Paradoxically, in the driest part of Arizona, water has become a nuisance, and federal funds have been appropriated to construct drainage ways to transport excess irrigation water from the land.

GROUNDWATER RESERVES AND ULTIMATE WITHDRAWAL. The amount of groundwater stored in the desert alluvial basins of southern Arizona and in the fine-grained con-

Fig. 8.7 Experimental studies on the desert, pertaining to water use.

solidated rocks in northern Arizona is directly related to the porosity of the rocks. Porosity is not a measure of how much water can be removed. Rocks may have high porosity but yield very little water as the small pores hold onto the water tenaciously. In the alluvial basins the porosity ranges from a few to 40 percent, with the average about 25 percent. In the Plateau Uplands the sandstone aquifers have about 30 percent porosity.

The amount of water that can be withdrawn from aquifers is referred to as specific yield, which is the volume of water that can be drained from a unit volume of rock. It is expressed as a percentage to the total rock volume quantitatively. A certain amount of water is held in the rocks by molecular attraction and adhesive forces. The specific yield of an aquifer is of prime importance in the production of groundwater, as the ultimate amount of water that can be withdrawn is related to this characteristic. The alluvial basin aquifers have specific yields ranging from several percent to 30 percent. The sandstone aquifers in the Plateau Uplands have very low specific yields, and tests indicate that, generally, the specific yield is less than one-half of 1 percent.

FUTURE TRENDS. Large-scale water development in Arizona is one of the basic factors contributing to the state's wealth today. The personal income of Arizonans has passed the two-billion-dollar mark, largely due to development of water. The federal taxes collected in one year amount to more than fifty times the original cost of Roosevelt Dam. However, of greater importance is the fact that the availability of water has stabilized a diverse and well-rounded arid-land economy in Arizona.

Population experts advise that Arizona will have about four million persons by 2000. Most of these people will be supported by an increase in industrial and mining activities. The additional population will create a demand on recreational activities, and the demand for water in places will be keenly competitive. Owing to a higher dollar return, water for recreational use may come from that used for agriculture today.

Economics will continue to influence trends in water use. In the West, water for domestic use and livestock enjoys the highest priority. Agriculture ranks next, while industry and mining hold a poor third in position. An important trend taking place in Arizona is the transposition of industry and mining to the second position and agriculture to third. As the population is supported mostly by industry, the trend is natural, but a reallocation of water supplies is not an easy matter, for legal codes, priority of rights, and availability of water all affect allocation. Further, all surface waters are already appropriated, mostly for agriculture, and the remaining source is from water reserves.

Agriculturists have recognized the shortage of water supply for maintaining continued irrigation. Research studies have paid handsomely, for today larger crop yields are being produced with the same amounts of water (Fig. 8.7). The use of conservation practices, particularly the lining of canals and ditches, has also reduced the amount of water needed for crop growth. Cultivated acreage attained a near record high in 1959 without any increase in water use. Agricultural experts believe they will grow even greater crop yields in the future without an increase of water demand and even hope to decrease the amount of water used in the 1960s.

Many farmers believe they cannot pay more than twenty dollars for an acre-foot of water for low-value crops and make a reasonable profit. As industry and domestic water users can afford to pay a price several times this amount, economics in future water use are an important factor.

SOURCES OF WATER FOR FUTURE SUPPLIES. The vital need for additional water in Arizona is recognized by many leading citizens. Multiple-purpose planning for use of water and conservation is essential to assure adequate supplies for future years. Many suggestions and proposals have been made, but most do not realistically consider factors of the physical and economic conditions. Several possible sources and methods of future water development include: (1) transport of water into areas of high demand and use, (2) development of groundwater at greater depths in alluvial basins, (3) capture of surface water for artificial recharge, (4) conversion of brackish water, (5) increased runoff from vegetation and soil modification (Fig. 8.8).

Water transport. The concept of transporting water into areas that have a high demand and use is not new.

Fig. 8.8   A site for the study of evaporation suppression.

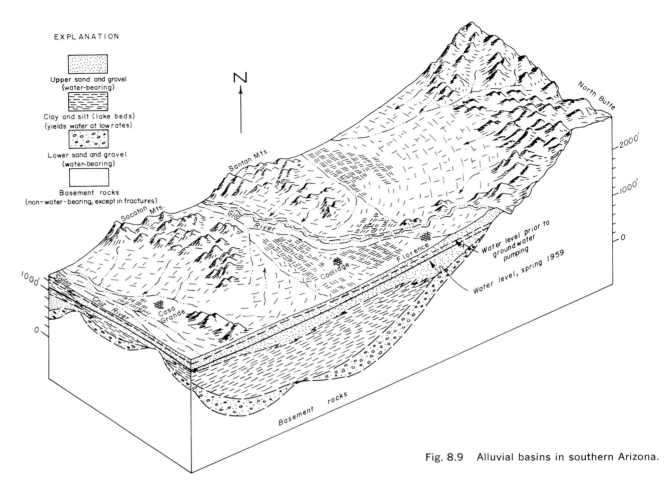

EXPLANATION

Upper sand and gravel
(water-bearing)

Clay and silt (lake beds)
(yields water at low rates)

Lower sand and gravel
(water-bearing)

Basement rocks
(non-water-bearing, except in fractures)

Fig. 8.9   Alluvial basins in southern Arizona.

The basic factors are cost and allocation of water rights, permitting water transport. There are several sources of water in Arizona which are available for transport from an engineering and hydrologic viewpoint. However, the problems of obtaining necessary funds and the right to use the water owned by others must be resolved. The flow from springs at the base of the Mogollon Rim and other areas in the Central Highlands constitutes a possible source. Most of this water is lost to evaporation and transpiration on its route to the lowlands so that its contribution to surface water storage is quite small. Transporting such water to areas of high demand and use would provide man with more water for beneficial use.

Groundwater development. The depth of the alluvial deposits in the desert basins is unknown, but the occurrence of alluvium at 3,000 to 5,000 feet has been reported from oil well tests in several places. Complete saturation of alluvial materials would provide a tremendous volume of water, but the chemical quality and quantities of water the sediments would yield have not been determined. However, detailed knowledge of the geologic fabric and subsequent electronic computations may provide realistic estimates on the amount and rate at which groundwater could be withdrawn. The cost of pumping water is an important factor, and thus the

depth of the water level is paramount. Removal of water at rates that do not cause rapid decline is the keynote for successful exploitation.

In areas of intensive groundwater development and where local interests can pay the price, it is believed that additional groundwater can be produced by secondary recovery methods. The principles of reservoir mechanics have been used successfully by the petroleum industry in recent years. Secondary fracturing by hydraulic methods should be quite successful in fine-grained aquifers. Application of high pressure on artesian aquifers would maintain the water level close to the surface for economical pumping lift. The limits of modern technology are not known in the science of hydrogeology; indeed much is still to be learned.

Artificial recharge. One of the most practical measures to increase the availability of water supplies is the capturing of surface water and putting it in the subsurface. Artificial recharge methods have been practiced for nearly a hundred years in several parts of the world. In recent years much attention has been given to these methods in the western states, and successful operations have been established in Texas, California, Oregon, Washington, and other states. In Arizona, several small experiments have been conducted successfully in the Salt River Valley area. Water stored in the subsurface suffers no loss by evaporation and can be recovered when needed. The capture of floodwaters in the lowlands and the transport of water to areas suffering from large water table decline provide ideal conditions for successful operation. After the water is desilted and treated, it can be recharged into the dewatered sediments via wells. The specific retention or the wetting of rock material in dewatered areas is already satisfied, and it is possible to recover nearly 100 percent of the water recharged. There are still many economic, legal, and engineering problems that need to be solved. However, as the need for additional water increases, there is little doubt that artificial recharge will prove to be an important method for increasing water supplies in specific areas.

Conversion of brackish water. The desalting of sea water for freshwater use has been demonstrated to be economically feasible. Costs of conversion in the late 1960s were about one and one-half times the cost of municipal water in Arizona. However, the large industrial and municipal areas are more than 100 miles from the nearest seacoast, and Tucson is 2500 feet above sea level. The cost of transport would be around 300 dollars per acre-foot compared to water at eighty dollars per acre-foot in the late 1960s. The possibility of converting the brackish or saline waters in the groundwater basins for municipal use is greater than the possibility of conversion of sea water. Certain zones in the subsurface reservoirs contain salty water that is blocked from entering wells. The amounts and distribution of these waters are not well known, but when costs become comparable the brackish groundwater reserves will offer a potential source for future years.

Vegetation modification. Some experts believe that more water can be obtained by eradication of juniper and piñon, by thinning ponderosa pine, and by strip-cutting in spruce-fir areas. At the lower altitudes, chemical treatment is used to eradicate chaparral and other vegetation with the hope of increasing runoff from the land surface. State and federal agencies are conducting many experiments to test the practicability of these measures. Preliminary estimates indicate that it might be possible to increase the runoff in the Salt River watershed by about 280,000 acre-feet of water annually. This is an appreciable quantity of water, but the cost of production must also be equated.

Many of the stream channels in Arizona are choked with willow, salt cedar, sycamore, and other water-loving vegetation. These plants consume large quantities of water from the shallow groundwater table and convert it into vapor. Salvage of this water would provide large supplies for beneficial use. The eradication of these non-beneficial plants is not an easy matter. Many methods have been tried, but the plants come back in more vigorous growth. One of the most efficient methods of destroying salt cedar is to lower the water table quickly beyond the root system. Multipurpose planning for the best interests of all is necessary to obtain maximum benefit from water in Arizona. Otherwise much water will continue to be lost to the atmosphere.

Arizona's history has been and will be closely associated with water development. The continuing growth of population and industry will demand ever-increasing quantities of water. Fortunately, water to meet this demand is available from several sources. The choice of selection will be based on many economic and legal factors. The physical conditions relating to water table decline by groundwater withdrawal are not well known. However, such knowledge is increasing rapidly, and scientific regulation and management can be utilized when the demand is sufficiently urgent. With proper conservation and intelligent exploitation of Arizona's water supplies, the citizens of Arizona could prepare for a long and prosperous future.

Irrigation Projects and Irrigated Areas

THE SALT RIVER PROJECT. As in most parts of the world, early water development in Arizona was from surface water supplies. Although irrigation has been practiced by white men in Arizona for nearly a hundred years, the Indians irrigated land in the Salt River Valley more than a thousand years ago. Extensive Indian irrigation ended around A.D. 1400, possibly due to prolonged drought conditions. Tribes such as the Pima, however, were using irrigation on a small scale, by diverting water directly from streams onto their fields, at the time the Spanish entered the state.

Most of the farmers who migrated westward in the early territorial days in search of gold or other quick riches found nothing more profitable than a job working for wages. But they noted the thousands of acres of fertile soil in the flat, wide floodplains of the Salt River Valley near the village of Phoenix and realized that only water was needed to make the land productive. Apparently sufficient water was available from the river. All that seemed to be needed was to go upriver far enough to develop the elevation necessary for gravity flow, improvise a headgate, construct a canal, and lead the water out onto the land. The first canal company was organized in 1867 and the project was a success. By 1880 nine additional canals had been built, and 55,000 acres were under cultivation. The area prospered, despite the occasional floods which washed out the flimsy diversion dams and deposited silt in the canals. But in 1897 a drought descended upon the valley. There was no rain in the mountains, and the flow of water dwindled to a trickle. The drought continued through 1898–99. What had been a growing and prosperous community all but faded into oblivion. The drought was broken early in 1900 by a flash flood which washed out all of the diversion dams and with them the prospect of a spring crop.

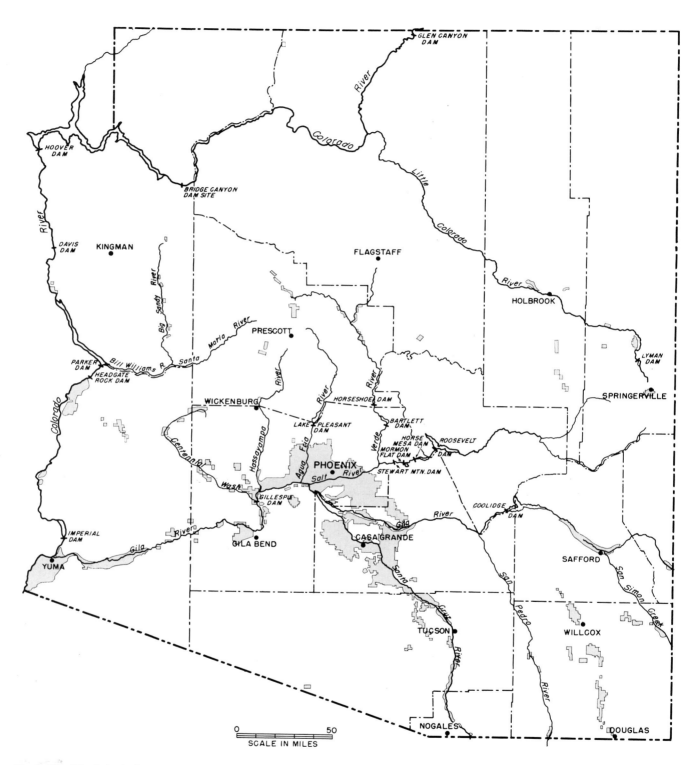

Fig. 8.10   The irrigated areas of the state.

The farmers of the area realized that more adequate methods would have to be devised to control the river. The answer seemed to be a large dam to store the water and to regulate its flow. A good site for a storage dam was found, about eighty miles east of the area, at the confluence of the Salt River and Tonto Creek. But the cost of construction of such a dam was too great for local financing, so emissaries were sent to Washington to appeal to Congress. Persuading Congress to act was not easy, but with help from President Theodore Roosevelt, the first reclamation act was passed by Congress in 1902. Before any funds would be spent upon this Salt River project, however, it was necessary for the land owners in the valley to settle all disputes, to reconcile water rights, and to form some sort of an association with which the Bureau of Reclamation could deal. Eventually this was accomplished by the formation of the Salt River Valley Water Users' Association — the first of its kind.

Under the Bureau of Reclamation, construction of Roosevelt Dam started in 1905 (Fig. 8.11). It opened for delivery of water in 1911 and was completed the following year. Its reservoir, Roosevelt Lake, is 17,500 acres in area and has a storage capacity of 1,420,000 acre-feet. Following completion of the dam, a power plant was constructed at its base. The final cost of the dam and power plant was $5,560,000, but this was not the entire cost of the project, for an adequate diversion dam had also to be built. This was located at Granite Reef, thirty-two miles east of Phoenix, and cost $627,000. Much additional work had to be done on the distribution system. This included three small hydroelectric power plants in the main canal system. The Bureau of Reclamation operated the project for some years, but not to the satisfaction of the water users. A dispute arose about the allocation of the power generated. As the Bureau of Reclamation was anxious to rid itself of the problems of project operation, in 1917 the whole project was turned over to the Salt River Valley Water Users' Association, it being agreed that the association owed the bureau $10,166,021.97. This was paid off in 1955. To operate the project, officially

Fig. 8.11 Roosevelt Dam, the first to be built on the Salt River.

Fig. 8.12   Horse Mesa Dam provided additional storage and hydropower.

known as the Salt River Project, a subsidiary group called the Salt River Agricultural Improvement and Power District was formed.

By 1920 Roosevelt Dam had overflowed four times, and precious water had been lost. To provide additional storage facilities and hydropower, Horse Mesa, Mormon Flat, and Stewart Mountain dams were constructed on the Salt River below Roosevelt Dam at a total cost of $10,584,000 (Fig. 8.12). The storage capacity of the reservoirs created by these dams is 374,755 acre-feet. The association has one diesel plant and several large steamplants for power generation and in addition is a large purchaser of Colorado River power. Storage has been increased by the construction of the Bartlett and Horseshoe dams on the Verde River. The association now has the most completely integrated irrigation and power system in the West with almost 100 percent utilization of the flood waters of the Salt and Verde rivers. Not since 1941 has there been any waste of water over the spillways of this system of dams. The association in 1969 owned 239,000 acres of irrigable land, and had available a total of about 2,077,000 acre-feet of storage capacity.

Water users in the project have three types of water rights as follows: (1) normal flow rights with priorities from 1869 to 1909 on 151,000 acres; (2) stored and developed water rights with equal rights for project lands; (3) special pump-water rights on about 155,000 acres which have been acquired through contract with the association. For the past ten years the association has had available for project use an average of about 800,000 acre-feet of gravity water for diversion at Granite Reef and about 400,000 acre-feet of pumped water per year. Water was delivered to 169,000 acres within the project in 1958.

Lands remain in the project whether they are under cultivation or have been subdivided. However, the city of Phoenix has taken over the distribution of domestic water in many areas which have been annexed. By contract with the association, the city of Phoenix now pays the assessments levied against those subdivision lots on which irrigation service has been discontinued. In return, the project delivers the water which formerly went to these lands to the city filtration plant on the Arizona Canal. In May of 1967 the project was furnishing about 60 percent of the total water supplied to the city's population.

The association was obligated also to deliver annually up to 40,000 acre-feet to United States Indian lands and water for a few thousand acres under contract to small irrigation enterprises. In addition, through contract and court decrees, 6.9 percent of the diversions at Granite Reef were being delivered to the Roosevelt Conservation District and the Buckeye Irrigation District.

Water costs in the project are very low compared with most other areas in the state. This is due primarily to the increasingly large revenue received from the sale of power which has been used in part to pay for construction of irrigation facilities and to reduce operation charges to water users. Charges for water in 1958 and 1959 were $1.25 per acre-foot for the first two acre-feet, $3.50 for the next acre-foot of developed or normal flow water, and $7.50 per acre-foot of water from pump rights.

OTHER PROJECTS IN THE SALT RIVER VALLEY. The irrigated area in Maricopa County in 1965 is estimated at 481,000 acres. Over 90 percent of this acreage is in the Salt River Valley. The irrigated area in the valley has extended far beyond the boundaries of the original Salt River Project. Much of this expansion occurred in the 1920s under the district form of irrigation enterprise. The more recent developments have been entirely pumped water from wells and have been mainly under private ownership.

The Roosevelt Water Conservation District containing approximately 37,000 acres was organized in 1920. It is located immediately east of the Salt River Project, and its principal source of water supply is from wells located within the district boundaries. The district also has available gravity water from storage and flood waters of the Salt River amounting to about 40,000 acre-feet per year on the average. The major portion of this water requires a pump lift of approximately fifty-five feet.

Farther to the southeast is located the Queen Creek Irrigation District securing its entire water supply from wells. The irrigated area has been extended in this same direction, under private ownership with water from wells, to within a few miles of the town of Florence on the Gila River.

South of the Salt River Project boundary and extending to the Gila River Indian Reservation, practically all of the irrigable lands have been placed under irrigation with pumped water.

Northwest of Phoenix and near the edge of the Salt River Valley is located the Maricopa County Municipal Water Conservation District No. 1, organized in 1925, with over 39,000 acres within its boundaries. The district obtains about one-quarter of its delivered water supply from the Carl Pleasant Dam and Reservoir on the Agua Fria River. The remainder is supplied by water from deep wells, supplemented by pumped water from privately owned wells.

The Roosevelt Irrigation District containing 38,000 acres was organized in 1923. It occupies a strip about three miles in width and twenty-four in length, extending from the Agua Fria River on the east to the Hassayampa River on the west. The district obtains its water from wells, forty-six of which are located within its boundaries and fifty-five in the lower end of the Salt River Project. The project wells were originally drilled for drainage purposes. They are now operated by the district under contract with the Salt River Valley Water Users' Association to supply water to district lands. Water from Salt River Project wells is conveyed to the Agua Fria River in concrete-lined canals to a flume across the river and thence in a concrete-lined main canal for twenty-six miles to the lower end of the area.

About three-quarters of the water supply is from project wells, and the balance is from wells within the district.

The Buckeye Irrigation District of over 18,000 acres lies along the Gila River south of the Roosevelt Irrigation District. Its water supply is obtained partly under court decree from the Salt River Valley Water Users and the balance by pumping from about forty-five district-owned wells.

Immediately above the Gillespie diversion dam are located the lands under the Arlington Canal, comprising several thousand acres irrigated with return flow from the Buckeye District and with water from a few large-capacity wells.

Practically all the irrigable land between the organized irrigation projects and extending northward into Deer Valley and along the Agua Fria and New rivers has been developed with pumped water supplies. In some instances the development has been under corporate ownership of several thousands of acres such as that of the Goodyear Cotton Company at Litchfield Park and the Boswell Cotton Company near Marinette.

THE UPPER GILA RIVER VALLEY. The irrigated area along the Upper Gila River is concentrated principally in the Safford Valley with 32,500 acres, and in the Duncan Valley with about 5,200 acres. Crop irrigation in the former area was begun about 1872 and in the latter area in 1879. These areas have water rights to gravity flow from the river established in accordance with the federal court decree of 1935, with priorities on a small percentage of the lands dating back to the early 1870s. Diversions from the Gila River in 1958 were made by eleven canal companies in the Safford area and by five canal companies in the Duncan area, the total amounting to 165,000 acre-feet. The various canal companies are organized as mutual water companies with each maintaining and operating its own irrigation system. However, when joint action of all the water users is desirable they function as the Gila Valley Irrigation District in the Safford area and as the Franklin Irrigation District in the Duncan area. The actual apportionment and distribution of waters to the water companies is made by the federal water commissioner.

The lands are dependent upon the unregulated flow of the river for gravity water. Recurring shortages of water supply during the summer months led to the drilling of wells by private individuals and by many of the canal companies to augment the supply of natural flow waters. Most of the well water is high in total soluble salts and is inferior to the gravity water for irrigation. Even a limited amount of storage on the Gila River above the irrigated lands would be of immense value to these areas.

In addition to the lands having gravity water rights there is a small area near Artesia of about 1,000 acres obtaining its water supply from artesian wells. Pumps are required in most of the wells.

CASA GRANDE VALLEY AND ADJACENT AREAS. Irrigation in the Casa Grande Valley centers about the San Carlos Project of 100,000 acres for which construction was completed in 1928. This is an Indian Service project providing for the irrigation of 50,000 acres of land on the Gila River Indian Reservation at Sacaton and 50,000 acres of non-Indian land in the vicinity of Coolidge, Florence, Eloy, and Casa Grande, but the total acreage has never been placed under irrigation. The non-Indian lands are all included in the San Carlos Irrigation and Drainage District and, through contract with the U.S. Bureau of Indian Affairs, water users secure water from the San Carlos Project. Water is obtained from three sources: stored water, pumped water, and normal flow water.

To control the flow of water for this project, Coolidge Dam was built on the Gila River some twenty-five miles southeast of Globe at a cost of $5,500,000. The reservoir which it formed is known as San Carlos Lake and has a capacity of 1,300,000 acre-feet, but the maximum storage attained has been only a little more than 800,000 acre-feet in 1942. The Ashurst-Hayden diversion dam was built about ten miles above Florence. The gravity water supply, which varies from year to year, has been supplemented with an average of 90,000 acre-feet of pumped water per year. Crop acreage is adjusted to the water supply and has varied from a minimum of 26,000 to a maximum of 46,000 acres on non-Indian or white lands. The average irrigated acreage of Indian lands on the project in the past ten years has been 20,000 acres per year and on the whites' lands approximately 30,000 acres.

In 1933 a small hydroelectric plant was constructed at Coolidge Dam, and power lines were run to Hayden, Mammoth, and the irrigation project at Coolidge. A diesel standby plant was also constructed at the town of Coolidge.

The most urgent need of the San Carlos Project in 1969 was additional storage below the mouth of the San Pedro River so that the wasted flood waters of this stream could be salvaged. The construction of a high dam at the Buttes site, advocated by the water users for many years, would provide storage, flood protection, and silt control.

The San Carlos Irrigation and Drainage District occupies areas adjacent to Coolidge and Casa Grande, and the Indian lands located along the Gila River. Practically all of the irrigable land between the designated project areas and extending southward through the Eloy district to the Pinal-Pima county line has been developed with pump water supplies. West of Casa Grande, and including the Maricopa and Stanfield district as far south as the Papago Indian Reservation, irrigation development has been entirely with pumped water. It is estimated that the irrigated area included within the Casa Grande Valley contains approximately 230,000 acres wholly dependent upon groundwater supplies.

COCHISE COUNTY LANDS AND THE SAN PEDRO VALLEY. The irrigation water supply is obtained almost entirely from privately owned wells which, compared with those in other major pump areas in the state, are of small capacity — less than 1,000 gallons per minute, except in the Kansas Settlement and Bowie areas. A survey by the Soil Conservation Service indicates an irrigable acreage in the county of about 120,000 acres of which approximately 76,000 acres were irrigated in 1959. It is estimated that about one-half of the irrigated acreage is concentrated in the Kansas Settlement areas and south of Cochise Dry Lake. The other important irrigated areas are northwest of Willcox, along Whitewater Draw in the southern end of the Sulphur Spring Valley, and in the Bowie-San Simon district. There are scattered small areas between the Mexican boundary and Redington. The Benson and the St. David Canal companies furnish a limited water supply of gravity water by diversion from the San Pedro River for several hundreds of acres adjacent to the towns of the same name. However, most of the land along the San Pedro is irrigated with pumped water.

Between Redington and the mouth of the river at Winkelman there are small scattered areas on the bottomland irrigated with pumped water from shallow drilled wells. A few small gravity ditches diverting water from the San Pedro River are still in existence, but the supply is supplemented with pumped water. The irrigated acreage can be only roughly estimated and probably does not total more than 5,000 acres.

SANTA CRUZ VALLEY. Irrigation development from Tucson south to the Mexican boundary has been confined primarily to the narrow strip of bottomland on both sides of the Santa Cruz River. Pumped water from wells averaging between 200 and 300 feet in depth with capacities usually of less than 1,000 gallons per minute is used almost exclusively. A crop survey along the Santa Cruz River in Santa Cruz County showed 4,650 acres under irrigation in 1959; most of this has been under irrigation for many years. This portion of the Santa Cruz Valley is one of the few pump areas in the state in which the groundwater has not been seriously lowered as the result of pump draft. Opportunities for recharge from flood flows in the river are excellent, and the irrigable acreage is limited to the narrow bottomland. The largest concentration of land under irrigation is in the Sahuarita-Continental district south of Tucson where the bottomland is more than a mile in width.

Urban development in the vicinity of Tucson has replaced agriculture, and there is little pumping for irrigation for a distance of seven or eight miles above and below the city. The acreage under pump irrigation in the Cortaro area has also decreased but is still being pumped to augment the supply in the Marana district.

The largest area under irrigation in Pima County is located in the Marana-Avra Valley region where the Santa Cruz Valley widens out and is joined by the Avra

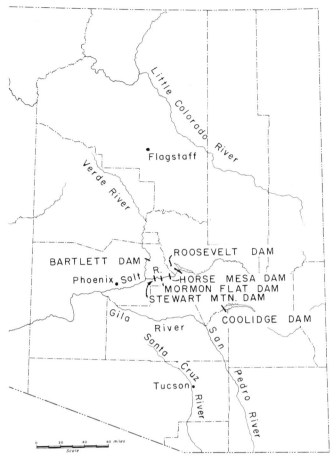

Fig. 8.13   Dams on the Salt, Gila, and Verde rivers.

Valley near Marana. Pump capacities of wells in the district may exceed 5,000 gallons per minute. The total irrigated acreage in 1968 in the district was about 32,000 acres, of which 12,590 acres received water from the Cortaro Water Users' Association.

This association is organized as a nonprofit corporation under the laws of the state, with each water user holding one share of stock for each acre of land within the association boundaries. The association operates and owns the wells and the distribution system of canals and laterals. Water costs in 1959 were $8.00 per acre-foot.

The total irrigated acreage in Pima County in 1965 was estimated at about 50,000 acres.

IRRIGATED AREAS IN CENTRAL AND WESTERN ARIZONA. The expansion of irrigated acreage in recent years has taken place largely through the development of groundwater supplies in the central and western semidesert valleys of the state. The area under irrigation may vary considerably from year to year in any one region, but in general there has been an increase. The approximate acreages in the various districts in 1959 were as follows:

Rainbow Valley and Waterman Wash. These districts are adjacent and are located just south of the lower end of the Salt River Valley and the Gila River.

The estimated acreage under irrigation in Rainbow Valley, which drains west into the Gila River, was about 6,000 acres in 1959. The Waterman Wash area drains into the Gila River and had an irrigated average in 1959 of about 12,000 acres. Both districts are entirely dependent upon wells.

Gila River Valley, Gillespie Dam to Painted Rock Dam. This district includes some lands adjacent to the Gila River with gravity water rights, but because of inadequate water supply has been dependent upon supplemental pump water for many years. The two largest areas with gravity water are the lands under the Enterprise Canal and those in the Old Gillespie Project. The number of acres under irrigation in the latter has varied greatly since 1940. Development has been mainly on the bottomlands on both sides of the Gila River and on the mesa lands west of Gila Bend. The total acreage under irrigation in this district in 1959 has been estimated at 65,000 acres.

Gila River Valley, Painted Rock Dam to Wellton-Mohawk Project. Scattered areas on both sides of the river have been developed in this district but are concentrated principally south of the river below the Painted Rock Dam and north of the river in the lower end of the Palomas Plain. This district, as well as most of the area along the lower Gila River, has waters with a higher soluble salt content than is desirable for irrigation. The irrigated acreage in 1959 was estimated at approximately 17,000 acres, all dependent upon well water.

Tonopah and area west of Hassayampa River. This district has developed rapidly since 1952 and was reported in 1969 to have an irrigated area of almost 25,000 acres. It is entirely pump irrigated with depths to water ranging from less than 15 feet near the Hassayampa River to almost 250 feet northwest of Tonopah.

McMullen Valley. About 14,000 acres are reported under pump irrigation in this district which extends from above Aguila in the east end of the valley to Salome at the west end. Development has been concentrated principally in the area north of Aguila in the last few years. Depths to water range from less than 100 feet to about 400 feet on the valley slopes in the upper end of the valley in irrigation wells.

Harquahala Plains, Centennial Wash. The irrigated lands are located in two principal areas, the Harquahala Plains in the northwest end of the valley and along Centennial Wash above the Gila River. The irrigated area has almost doubled in the last few years in the upper end of the valley and is estimated to be about 25,000 acres in the entire district. There is a wide range in depths to water in each of these two areas, between 25 and 225 feet in lower Centennial Wash and between 30 and 375 feet in Harquahala Plains.

Yavapai County areas. The irrigated areas are located in the small valleys in the mountain section of central Arizona. The main areas are Skull Valley and Kirkland Creek, Chino Valley, Big Chino Valley, and the upper Verde River Valley. The total irrigated acreage in 1959 was less than 20,000 acres.

Skull Valley occupies a small area on a tributary of Kirkland Creek about fifteen miles west of Prescott. The irrigated area in Skull Valley, with that along Kirkland Creek, does not exceed a couple of thousand acres. Most of the farming in this area is combined with cattle ranching. Water supply is obtained from wells which are relatively shallow and of low capacity.

Chino Valley is located about twenty miles north of Prescott with part of the irrigated area in the Chino Valley Irrigation District, which obtains its water supply from two small storage reservoirs on Willow Creek and Granite Creek located just north of the city of Prescott. The district contains slightly over 2,500 acres and over a period of years has had an inadequate supply for its irrigation requirements except in unusually wet years. Probably less than half of the district acreage on the average is in crop. The remainder of this area obtains its water from wells in the Chino Valley artesian basin. Except for a small area in the north end of the basin, the wells are nonflowing and must be pumped. The area is unique in that the artesian water is found in buried, fractured lava flows. The acreage irrigated from pumped and flowing wells has remained nearly constant since the mid-1950s at approximately 4,000 acres.

Big Chino Valley which begins about twenty-four miles north of Prescott and extends northwestward along Chino Creek for a distance of about twenty-five miles is irrigated entirely from wells. Chino Creek may be considered as the beginning of the Verde River since it is known by that name from the lower end of the valley. This area has developed rapidly in the last few years in comparatively large units that were formerly cattle ranches. The area is not intensively farmed, and large parts of the irrigated acreage are still in the development stage. The total acreage under irrigation in this district was about 8,000 acres in 1959.

The upper Verde River Valley District consists of small acreages located principally on both sides of the Verde River and along Oak Creek, Beaver Creek, and Clear Creek. The district extends from a few miles north of Clarkdale for a distance of about twenty-five miles down the Verde River. Irrigation water supplies are primarily from gravity diversion from the Verde River and tributary creeks. The individual farms in this district are comparatively small with numerous individual diversion headings with old established water rights. Along the Verde River alone there are twenty-five small ditches for the irrigation of lands having water rights on an area of little over 3,000 acres. Established water rights are held for a little over 1,600 acres in Oak Creek and for about 1,000 acres on Beaver and Clear creeks.

In addition to the areas listed above, there are irrigated areas on Date Creek, on the Hassayampa River near Wagner, and on the Agua Fria River near Dewey. The aggregate acreage under irrigation is probably not over 1,400 acres, almost entirely from pump water supplies.

Little Colorado River areas. The irrigated lands in Coconino, Apache, and Navajo counties are located principally along the Little Colorado River, Silver Creek, and Show Low Creek. The total acreage under irrigation in 1959 was reported to have been less than 27,000 acres. The water supply is principally by direct diversion from stream channels or from storage in small reservoirs near the headwaters. However, there has been some increase in recent years in the use of pumped water from wells in the Taylor-Snowflake and Hunt districts and also along the Little Colorado River in the vicinity of Holbrook. Most of the irrigated lands are located fairly close to the drainage divide with limited drainage area above them, and storage is confined to reservoirs of small size. During wet years the reservoir capacity is insufficient for the storage of spring runoff, and in dry years the water supply is inadequate for the irrigable lands. Most of the water users are organized as mutual water companies which operate and maintain their own storage reservoirs, diversion structures, and distribution systems.

The largest area of irrigated land is located near St. Johns and obtains water in part from the Lyman Dam on the Little Colorado River. Water stored above this dam is used on about 3,000 acres of the Lyman Water Company land. The company also supplies part of the water used on 3,300 acres of the St. Johns Irrigation Company, which obtains additional water by direct diversion. About 4,900 acres are under irrigation in the Springerville-Eagar district with water from three small storage reservoirs and diversions from the Little Colorado River. Between Lakeside and Show Low on Show Low Creek and between Shumway and Snowflake on Silver Creek, additional lands are under irrigation with water primarily from gravity diversions and stored water from the Daggs Reservoir on Silver Creek. There is also a small area of between 300 and 400 acres near Concho, which obtains water from Concho Reservoir. The principal irrigated areas along the Little Colorado River are in the vicinity of Hunt with pump water from nonflowing artesian wells, near Woodruff by diversion from the river, and in the Holbrook-St. Joseph district with water from wells, and a limited amount obtained there by diversion from the Little Colorado River.

In addition to the larger impounds of surface water, there are a number of small dams and lakes which collect flood waters for municipal and stock purposes. The city of Flagstaff reservoirs on Walnut Creek have a total storage of 35,000 acre-feet. The city of

Williams and several other communities depend on surface water for their sole supply. Ranchers and stockmen have long employed the construction of small earthen dams and tanks to provide water for their livestock. These structures help conserve the land from erosion and arroyo-cutting in addition to supplying water. Unfortunately, much of this impounded water is lost to evaporation and may contribute to the decrease in overall runoff observed in recent years.

COLORADO RIVER LANDS. The lands irrigated with Colorado River water constitute the largest and almost the only area of any size in the state deriving its entire water supply from gravity sources. Development has been mainly by the Bureau of Reclamation through the construction of the Yuma Project, authorized in 1904, and the Gila Project, as reauthorized in 1947. The construction of Hoover Dam and the later construction of the Davis and Parker dams has insured the lands along the lower Colorado River of flood protection and an ample water supply. In the late 1960s, surplus water from the Upper Colorado River Basin states was available and was wasted into the Gulf of California.

The irrigated areas are located on the bottomlands adjacent to the Colorado and Gila rivers and also on the higher mesa lands. The bottom lands with shallow water tables have to contend with drainage problems. These lands comprise the only irrigated areas of any size in Arizona in which drainage may be considered a major problem. The mesa lands, except in a few isolated cases with perched water tables, do not have drainage problems. The larger irrigation enterprises along the Colorado River include the following:

Yuma Project. The Arizona water users in this project were organized as the Yuma County Water Users' Association in 1903 to contract with the Bureau of Reclamation for their part of the construction of the Laguna diversion dam, irrigation, and drainage facilities. Yuma Valley has one of the oldest water rights on the Colorado. By 1904 about 10,000 acre-feet were diverted by pumps and gravity flow through more than fifty miles of canals but were dependent on unregulated flow. Upon completion of Hoover Dam in 1935, the impoundment of flood waters in Lake Mead assured constant flow and nearly sediment-free water.

The Yuma Project occupies the bottomlands between Yuma and the Mexican boundary. Since 1941 water has been diverted at the Imperial Dam and carried through the All-American Canal, and thence by canal to the siphon crossing the Colorado River to the Yuma Valley. The association has for many years maintained and operated the irrigation and drainage system for the 52,000 acres within its boundaries, of which 45,000 are under irrigation. The operation and maintenance costs are obtained by water charges which, on most of the lands, amount to $12.50 for the first five acre-feet and additional amounts at $1.50 per acre-foot.

Most of the land is now exempt from repayment charges for construction costs, which have largely been repaid. Total water costs on the major portion of the lands are thus about $13.00 per year per acre.

Yuma-Mesa Division of the Gila Project. Under the Re-authorization Act of 1947 this part of the original Gila Project was reduced to 40,000 acres to be irrigated from Colorado River water diverted at the Arizona heading at Imperial Dam. It is comprised of three units, the North Gila and the South Gila units of 15,000 acres and the Yuma-Mesa Unit of 25,000 acres.

Most of the irrigated lands in the North Gila Unit are within the North Gila Valley Irrigation District, which operates and maintains the irrigation system and drainage facilities. The district is comprised of 7,050 acres located in the Y between the Gila and Colorado rivers. Several hundred additional acres secure water directly from the Gila Gravity Main Canal through contract with the Bureau of Reclamation. Water charges are $8.50 per irrigated acre, quantity unlimited.

The Yuma Irrigation District, organized in 1919, is located on the bottomlands south of the Gila River just east of Yuma. There are about 11,000 acres within the district boundaries of which about 10,000 acres were irrigated in 1958. The district is primarily an electric district supplying power to landowners for the operation of private wells. The district owns and operates the substations and transmission lines. The water supply is from large-capacity drilled wells of between 150 and 200 foot depth. The water costs are comparable with those in the North Gila Valley Irrigation District with district assessments only $1.00 per acre in 1958 and power costs three-fourths of a cent per kilowatt hour. The district has no contract for water from the Bureau of Reclamation, although its lands are included with those designated as part of the Yuma-Mesa Division of the Gila Project. Two problems confront the water users: the increasingly high salt content of the well waters and seepage from irrigation of the mesa lands to the south.

The Yuma-Mesa Unit is under the operation of the Bureau of Reclamation with the Yuma-Mesa Irrigation and Drainage District representing the water users with over 19,500 acres under irrigation in 1967. The unit occupies the mesa extending from Yuma to the Mexican boundary. The construction costs were high for this unit, and the contract for repayment extends over a period of sixty years, with only nominal payments during the development period of the first ten years. Water is diverted from the Imperial Dam in the Gila Gravity Main Canal and delivered to Mesa Unit through a fifty-two-foot pump lift at the Yuma-Mesa pumping plant. Water requirements on the sandy mesa land are greater than for most areas. Charges in 1967 were $12.15 per irrigated acre.

The Unit B Irrigation and Drainage District, organized in 1947, consists of 3,000 acres of mesa land south of Yuma, designated as the Yuma Auxiliary Project. Between 1922 and 1953 its water supply was obtained from the Yuma Project main canal with a pump lift to the mesa and since 1953, from the canal system of the Yuma-Mesa Unit. The Bureau of Reclamation reports 2,992 acres irrigated in 1958 with water charges of $13.50 for the first four and one-half acre-feet and $2.25 for each additional acre-foot. The district assessments were $5.04 per acre including annual payments on rehabilitation and construction costs.

Wellton-Mohawk Division of the Gila Project. The 75,000 acres of this division are located on both sides of the Gila River, beginning about 15 miles east of Yuma and extending almost fifty miles up the river. About 60,000 acres are bottomland and 15,000 acres are on the mesa. The distribution system is operated and maintained by the Wellton-Mohawk Irrigation and Drainage District with approximately 45,000 acres under irrigation in 1967. Water is delivered to the District canals from Gila Gravity Main Canal in three pump lifts of thirty-one, sixty-four, and fifty-five feet. District assessments are $2.00 per acre per year in addition to water charges for a minimum of $10.60 for four acre-feet of water, plus payments on construction costs which are small during the development period. Additional quantities vary in price with maximum charge of $3.40 per acre-foot. The district has drainage problems at the lower end of the area near Dome and in some locations on the bottomland at the edge of the mesa escarpment.

Colorado River Indian Reservation. This is a U.S. Indian Service project constructed and operated by this agency. Water is diverted at the Headgate Rock Dam for the irrigation of approximately 31,000 acres of bottomland, located south of Parker. About 11,500 acres are farmed by Indian owners or leasers and the remainder by white leasers. The water charges in the late 1960s were very low — $6.00 for the first five acre-feet on average soil and $8.00 for the first eight acre-feet on sandy soil with excess water at $1.50 per acre-foot. The drainage problems in this area are serious, and construction of additional drainage facilities and the concrete-lining of canals are continuing. Future expansion to an irrigated area of 100,000 acres of bottomland and 25,000 acres of mesa land is possible.

Other Colorado River lands. Pumping from the Colorado River or from wells provides a water supply for several thousand acres of scattered, privately owned lands along the river. Two of the larger areas are 1,600 acres below Ehrenberg and 6,500 acres in Cibola Valley. Some of the lands now under irrigation on the bottomland adjacent to the river have been acquired under squatters rights, and title to them is in controversy.

Control and Use of the Colorado River

The Colorado River, with its main tributary, the Green, is 2,700 miles long and drains an area of about 244,000 square miles, including practically all of Arizona. About 43 percent of the drainage area is within the boundaries of Arizona, and about 700 miles of the river's stream bed are wholly within Arizona or along its western boundary.

In the early territorial days the river was navigated north of the mouth of the Bill Williams River. But navigation was difficult due to stream velocity and the vagaries of the uncontrolled river. Stream-flow on the lower reaches varied from a trickle to devastating floods. In the 1960s, except for a few small boats, navigation was of no importance, but the United States Supreme Court has declared the river navigable. Consequently, its main stream is subject to federal control and can only be distributed in accordance with federal law.

Along the boundary which the Colorado forms between Arizona and California, much of the land on the Arizona side is high, that on the California side low. This topography makes it difficult for Arizona, but easy for California, to acquire prior rights by putting the water to beneficial consumptive use. There are thousands of tillable acres in California's Imperial Valley immediately west of the lower reaches of the river.

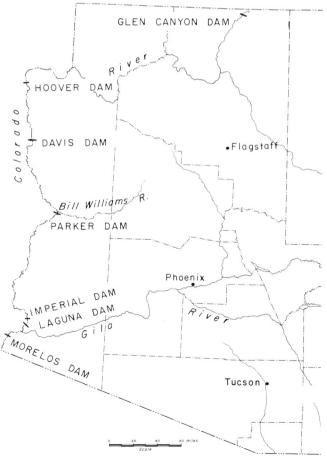

Fig. 8.14 Dams on the Colorado River.

Much of this land is below sea level. This makes the delivery of water for irrigation easy, but danger of floods great. The river carries enormous amounts of delta-building silts. As the delta forms and blocks the exit channels, the river bed rises, thus increasing the danger of overflowing. In 1890–91 the river broke its west bank, flowed into the Imperial Valley and formed the Salton Sea. In 1900–1902 a canal was constructed and irrigation begun in the Imperial Valley. Against the advice of engineers, the landowners made a breach in the west bank of the river for convenience in getting a larger supply of water. The engineers were right; for a flood came and quickly eroded a large channel through this breach. For some sixteen months the whole flow of the Colorado emptied into the Imperial Valley, causing damage amounting to about $3 million. This was before the days of federal disaster aid, and had it not been for the work of the Southern Pacific Railroad the whole of the Imperial Valley would probably be a sea today, through which the waters of the Colorado would flow to the Gulf of California. At a cost of between $2-3 million, the Southern Pacific transported and dumped trainload after trainload of stone and gravel into the breach. Eventually, the breach was closed and a dike built along the west bank strong enough to contain the river in its old channel. Later the Southern Pacific received a partial payment from the federal government for its work.

In 1903 the Yuma County Water Users' Association was formed, and the use of water was authorized. But only a small area could be irrigated on the Arizona side of the river. In 1905–09 the Laguna Diversion Dam was built a few miles above Yuma and the Imperial Canal constructed on the California side at a total cost of $21.1 million. Laguna was a low, wedge-shaped dam, which spanned the river and raised the level of the water on the upstream side high enough to divert water through the headgate into the canal. The dam was designed to prevent erosion of the riverbanks during floods. In 1912, at a cost of $667,648, a siphon was constructed to carry water from the Imperial Canal to irrigate by gravity an area just south of Yuma. Thus was born the Yuma Valley Project.

The Boulder Canyon Project. In 1918 the Bureau of Reclamation proposed the construction of a large dam in Boulder Canyon on the Colorado as the best means of preventing floods, storing water for irrigation, controlling the flow, and developing power. This proposal caused much controversy among the Colorado River basin states. Bill after bill was introduced into Congress requesting studies and appropriations for developments. Most of these proposals were introduced by California for its benefit and were not supported by Arizona. Congress was reluctant to appropriate funds for the Boulder Canyon Project unless and until six of the seven basin states, including California,

reached some sort of agreement as to the allocation of water. After several attempts, representatives of the seven states (Arizona, California, Colorado, Nevada, New Mexico, Utah, and Wyoming) drew up a compact in 1922 which designated the drainage area of the river above Lees Ferry in northeastern Arizona as the upper basin, and that below as the lower basin, and allocated half of the river's anticipated annual flow of 15,000,000 acre-feet to the upper basin and the other half to the three lower basin states — Arizona, California, and Nevada. All of the states ratified the Colorado River Compact except Arizona.

With the ratification of the compact, Congress passed the Boulder Canyon Project Act which appropriated funds for the project and authorized the Secretary of the Interior to make contracts for water and power with any state that had ratified the compact. Limits were set of 4,400,000 acre-feet of water for California, 2,800,000 for Arizona, and 300,000 for Nevada. This did not meet with the approval of Arizona, but California went right ahead making contracts for water and power and putting both to use. The California legislature did, however, have to pass an act limiting its use of water to the allotted 4,400,000 acre-feet in order to obtain approval of its contracts. Arizona tried to halt California's appropriation of water by recourse to the courts but found it had no standing due to its failure to sign the 1922 Compact. In 1944, Arizona finally signed.

Following the initial Boulder Canyon proposal, full engineering and geologic studies were made of the proposed dam and reservoir sites. A nearly perfect dam site was found in the Black Canyon, immediately below Boulder Canyon, and plans were made to locate the dam in this canyon. Here the canyon was narrow, the walls high and almost vertical, and the rock of the walls hard and solid. There were, however, many problems to be solved, and many competent engineers were skeptical of the entire project. Their doubts were unfounded, for the dam was completed without incident.

Construction of the dam, a gravity arch type, was begun in 1931 and completed in 1936. Originally called Boulder, and later named Hoover, the dam was the largest and tallest ever built up to that time. It is 730 feet high, 650 feet thick at its base, 1,180 feet wide at the top, and contains 3,500,000 cubic yards of concrete. Lake Mead, the reservoir formed by the dam, is 115 miles long, eight miles wide at its widest point, and has storage capacity of 30,500,000 acre-feet of water.

The tremendous heat generated by the hydration of cement is one of the problems encountered in the pouring of massive concrete structures. To solve this problem at Hoover Dam, 662 miles of steel pipe were embedded in the concrete as it was poured, and refrigerated water was circulated through this pipe to cool the concrete. Building the dam in small blocks and waiting for atmospheric cooling, in order to prevent formation of cracks, would have required 125 years.

Fig. 8.15   Hoover Dam in Boulder Canyon on the Colorado River.

Before construction could start on the dam, roads had to be built; a town — Boulder City, Nevada — located and built to house the workers and provide offices; a spur rail-line built out from Las Vegas, Nevada; four large diversion tunnels bored to carry the water while construction was underway; coffer dams constructed; the site cleared of all rubble and loose rock; and the foundation and walls grouted. The contract price for the dam and the construction of a building to house the generating units was just above $50 million, but changes and extras ran the cost above this figure.

The prevention of floods and the storage and control of irrigation water was not enough to justify the cost of building such a monumental structure. Hydroelectric power had to be developed, not only to fill a need for power, but also to pay the major portion of the cost of construction. To supply such power, fifteen generating units of 115,000 H.P. each, and two 55,000 H.P. units were installed. Contracts for the purchase of this power were signed before the generators were installed. Most of this power goes to California, but Arizona gets a certain portion. It is estimated that the sale of this power will, by 1985, pay the $108.8 million total cost of construction and generators, as well as the accumulated interest of $11.2 million.

To complete the control of the river, it was necessary to construct a diversion dam and desilting works above the now inadequate Laguna Dam on the lower section of the river. Provision for this was made in the Boulder Canyon Project. Construction of the Imperial Dam and desilting basin was started in 1936. This dam, located about eighteen miles north of Yuma, is of the slab and buttress type, supported and anchored by long concrete piles. It is forty-five feet high, 3,430 feet long, and equipped with roller and radial gates for control of water discharge. Its main purpose is diversion of water into the old Imperial Canal, part of which is in Mexico, into the All-American Canal, and the Gila Canal on the Arizona side of the river. However, it also acts as a storage dam for the drainage area between it and Parker Dam, the next storage dam upstream. The desilting works consist of three basins

500 by 800 feet, in which the heavy silt load of the water can be removed, thus saving the large annual cost of removing silt from the canals. It was estimated that the entire cost of the desilting works, $1.5 million, would be saved in two years. These works were not put into operation for several years after the All-American Canal was constructed as some silt was needed to seal the sandy bottom and sides of this canal. The original contract for the construction of the Imperial Dam and desilting works was $4,374,240. All of this was a part of the Boulder Project.

Other Dams on the Lower Colorado. Parker Dam, with its power plant, is located about twelve miles above Parker, Arizona, and just below the confluence of the Bill Williams River with the Colorado. It was constructed in 1937–41, primarily to serve the needs of the Metropolitan Water District for domestic and commercial water and power. The five southern California counties which form this district in 1931 voted an issue of $220 million for the construction of this

dam, power plant, and an aqueduct to carry the water to the district. This dam is unusual because of the fact that an excavation 235 feet below the stream bed had to be made to reach a satisfactory foundation. This makes it the deepest dam in the world. Its power plant has a capacity of 120,000 kilowatts. About half this power is necessary to lift the water in the aqueducts over the summits which had to be transversed to reach the West Coast area. Lake Havasu, formed by the dam, has an area of thirty-nine square miles and a capacity of 619,000 acre-feet.

Davis Dam was constructed in Pyramid Canyon, which is eighty-eight miles upstream from Parker Dam and sixty-seven miles downstream from Hoover. It is an earth and rock fill embankment with concrete spillway, intake structure, and powerhouse. It forms the long and narrow Lake Mohave, which has an area of forty-five square miles and a storage capacity of 1,818,300 acre-feet. This lake, like Mead and Havasu, is important as a recreation and fish and wildlife preserve. The power plant has a capacity of 225,000 kilo-

Fig. 8.16   Davis Dam and power plant, downstream from Hoover Dam.   *U.S. Bureau of Reclamation*

Fig. 8.17   Glen Canyon Dam, just below the Arizona-Utah border on the Colorado River.

U.S. Bureau of Reclamation

watts. Built by the Bureau of Reclamation at a cost of $67 million for dam and power plant, Davis Dam acts as a forebay for the control of water made available for irrigation of lands in Mexico, in accordance with the United States treaty with that country in 1945. The cost of this facility eventually will be paid for by the sale of power developed at the dam.

Also on the lower Colorado is Headgate Rock Dam, a diversion dam located just below the town of Parker, Arizona, for the purpose of diverting water for the irrigation of about 37,900 acres of land on the Arizona side of the river in the Colorado River Indian Reservation. Another diversion dam, Palo Verde, located just north of Blythe, California, diverts water for the irrigation of 72,000 acres of California land in the vicinity of Blythe. Below the Mexican border, Morelos Dam diverts water for irrigation of Mexican farm land.

THE GLEN CANYON DAM PROJECT. The last of the great dams to become operative in the 1960s and one of the largest in the nation, the huge, gray concrete monolith of Glen Canyon Dam is wedged between the nearly perpendicular red cliffs of the canyon walls below the Arizona-Utah border on the Colorado River.

Eight years in the building, (1956 to 1964) the crest of the dam is 710 feet above bedrock and 583 feet above the original river channel. It has a storage capacity of 28,040,000 acre-feet.

A multi-purpose dam, Glen Canyon becomes the key unit of the entire Colorado River Storage Project, making possible the distribution of the waters of the Upper Basin among the participating states, and controlling the allotments of water to the lower basin area. Its nine massive power units, which went into full service in February, 1966, furnish 75 percent of the power of the entire CRSP. Its 900,000 KW, distributed and sold in 1969–70 was sufficient to provide all of the electrical energy for a city of a million people.

Glen Canyon Dam combined with four other units, to provide the joint output of the CRSP feeding electrical energy into 1800 miles of transmission lines to deliver power to the marketing area in seven states — Wyoming, Utah, Colorado, Nevada, Arizona, New Mexico and a small portion of southern California.

In 1964 the power generated by the units of the CRSP was fed into a grid linking the Pacific Northwest and Pacific Southwest, and in 1967 the electrical energy so created was tied into a national power network, permitting exchange of power beyond the project.

Glen Canyon Dam thus becomes a "cash register" dam, its income from power sales being earmarked for the repayment to the federal government of more than 95 percent of the $1.5 billion cost of the CRSP. The remainder of the reimbursable cost of the entire project will be paid to the U.S. Treasury by irrigation, municipal and industrial water users who benefit from the water storage facilities involved.

There are 28 participating programs in the CRSP, the main purpose of which is to provide irrigation water to lands not now farmed and to older farms which have been short of water. A total of 1,448,300 acres will be benefitted and 835,000 acres of that amount will be lands which are presently irrigated. Here again Glen Canyon Dam becomes the key to the problem, since 80 percent of the water storage will be in Lake Powell, created by Glen Canyon Dam.

The country along the Colorado in Glen Canyon area seems ageless. The first people who left traces of their habitations there were agriculturists, similar to the Pueblo people, but they left about A.D. 1200 after facing a destructive drought. The first white man to record the beauty of Glen Canyon was Father Escalante, who with Father Domínguez, of the Franciscan Order, set out from Santa Fe, seeking a route to California. In his journal, written in 1776, Father Escalante records the story of the return trip from Utah, the discovery of what was to become known as the Crossing of the Fathers, and the wild beauty of the canyon.

Approximately 100 years later, Maj. John Wesley Powell, explorer scientist, traveled through the canyon where the lake now bears his name, and mapped the nearly 200 miles of quiet river and the multitude of side canyon tributaries which fed into it, calling it Glen Canyon because of the numerous wooded glens in the mouths of the feeder streams and along the sandy banks of the river.

After another century, in 1970, a lake nearly 186 miles long, with a shoreline of 1,960 miles was filled with clear, blue-green waters as runoff from the high mountain country pours down into the Colorado river and is stored behind the dam.

The waters of the Green River, the Yampa, the Strawberry and the White joined with those of the Gunnison, the Dolores, the San Juan and the Escalante to form on the Colorado the great lake which is a part of the Glen Canyon recreation project, administered by the U.S. Park Service. Nationally known (though in 1969–70 it was not completely filled), Lake Powell and the huge dam which created it, had already become a mecca for tourists and outdoor sportsmen. In 1968–69 there were 750,000 visitors registered in the area; boating, fishing, camping and photographing against a backdrop of scenery unsurpassed in the western world.

Page, Arizona, a modern community which grew as the dam grew, is the hub for the recreation area which spreads in all directions. Located 275 miles north of Phoenix, the town is 389 miles south of Salt Lake City, a bustling community in what was one of America's remote areas.

THE CENTRAL ARIZONA PROJECT. The water supply of central Arizona will be increased when the Central Arizona Project becomes a reality. With the President's signature on September 30, 1968, the Colorado River Basin Project bill became law. The Central Arizona

Project (CAP) is by far the largest project authorized by the passage of the bill. The authorized CAP will bring water from Lake Havasu on the Colorado River to the Phoenix and Tucson areas (Fig. 8.18). The actual amount to be delivered will vary depending upon the schedule of development of authorized projects in the Upper Basin states and the flow of the river.

A pumping station near Parker Dam will lift the water to the Granite Reef aqueduct in which it will be transported to a storage facility behind proposed Orme Dam northeast of Phoenix. In addition to providing storage, Orme Dam will alleviate flooding problems in the Phoenix area and provide recreational opportunities in the population center of the state. The reservoir would be integrated with the present Salt River Project storage system that serves Phoenix and the surrounding areas.

The proposed Salt-Gila aqueduct would carry releases from Orme reservoir to the San Carlos Project and adjacent districts and to the Tucson aqueduct. The Tucson aqueduct, a pipeline capable of carrying 100,000 acre-feet of water annually, will deliver water to the Tucson metropolitan area for municipal and industrial uses.

Two other dams in Arizona were authorized as a part of the CAP, namely, Buttes Dam on the Gila and Charleston Dam on the San Pedro. These dams are for water conservation, sediment and flood control, and recreation. A pipeline from the Charleston Dam would provide additional water for the Tucson area.

Hooker Dam and reservoir in New Mexico would be built on the Upper Gila River. Its function would be to provide river regulation, water conservation, sediment detention, and substantial recreation and fish and wildlife benefits.

Provisions for wise and efficient use of water have been made an integral part of the project planning, such as water salvage along the Colorado River and ground water recovery in the Yuma area.

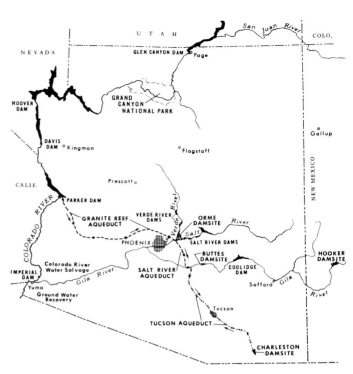

Fig. 8.18   The Central Arizona Project — a program intended to increase the water supply for the state.

The schedule for the development of the project will depend upon appropriations by the federal government. The minimum time for completion is considered to be ten years from the date of authorization.

To assure adequate water of suitable quality in the future, Arizona needs to develop an overall water plan based on projected demands into the next century or longer. Alternative sources of water for the future include more efficient use of presently available water, reuse of reclaimed water, shifting of water uses to gain greater economic benefits, importation of water from water surplus regions, and the desalinization of brackish and sea water.

Wallace H. Fuller
Agricultural Chemist

9

SOILS

IN THE MIDST of Arizona's fertile soils, favorable temperatures, and abundant sunlight, modern agricultural management practices have done much toward creating ideal growing conditions for plants and crops. Potentially one of the world's most productive regions, with irrigation, Arizona has long been in the lead in yield per acre of alfalfa and barley, and except for an occasional year in the 1960s led the nation in yield per acre of cotton. The benign conditions of growth under maximum sunlight have also made it possible for specialty and exotic fruits and vegetables to thrive in Arizona.

Even highly productive soils, however, have deficiencies in their composition and are often deteriorated by man's poor management. It is the job of the soil scientist to find ways to improve soil by adding to or altering its basic elements. As his knowledge about soil increases, the scientist's experimental techniques become more sophisticated. He is able to reclaim saline and alkali soil, correcting deficiencies and working always toward achieving a satisfactory nutrient balance.

Most Arizona soils are well equipped with native phosphate. A small portion of this has been found in the organic form. Not all of the native soil phosphorus, however, is available for plant use.

Calcium has been found to unite with soil phosphates to form slowly soluble forms. If the combined elements are slow to go into solution, the plant is unable to obtain enough phosphorus. Thus, soil scientists have found that when the readily available amount of phosphorus is low, it becomes necessary to provide this plant nutritional element as a fertilizer. As a result of the long Arizona growing season and the double-cropping of intensified farming, growers do add this available nutrient to certain crops.

The soils of Arizona appear to be well supplied with available potassium. The same is usually true of micronutrients — those elements required by plants only in minute amounts. A notable exception, however, is available iron, which must be added for some plants to have healthy, vigorous growth.

There have been indications that zinc, too, is becoming important as a micronutrient in certain Arizona soils. This element is especially necessary where citrus and nut trees are grown.

The last of the three main elements needed by plants is nitrogen, the nutrient most limiting to plant growth. Nitrogen must be added to all Arizona soils to obtain high crop-production levels.

With respect to natural factors of influence, the soils of Arizona are widely diversified in their responses to variations in four major soil-formation factors: climate, parent rock material, relief, and vegetation.

The climate in Arizona ranges from arid to subhumid. Great temperature and precipitation differences, caused by rapid changes in elevation over short distances, combine to play an important role in the formation of a host of different soil types.

The parent rock material from which soils are formed also varies considerably within short distances, often in response to abrupt change in elevation. Geological materials of Arizona are characterized by the presence of many types of rocks. The volcanic rocks include acid igneous, basic igneous, cinders, ash, and tuff. The sedimentary rocks include a wide variety of limestone, sandstones, siltstones, shales, claystones, and conglomerates of different geological ages and physical and chemical characteristics. Many types of acid igneous (molten-formed) rocks are distributed in the area as are a variety of metamorphic rocks. These rocks also occur in various proportions in different alluvial (waterborne) deposits.

The more common types of Arizona topography are desert floors or flats, undulating to gently rolling plains, nearly level to moderately sloping alluvial fans, outwashes, basins, valley plains, dissected rolling plateaus, moderate to steep hills, mountain footslopes, and steep mountains. Complex patterns of soil result from sharp changes in terrain. In such cases each soil series may occupy only a small acreage, and considerable progress has been made in classifying these soils.

Vegetation influences the nature of soil, particularly with respect to the accumulation of organic matter and lime. In general, those soils having a high proportion of grass to trees and shrubs are higher in organic matter, and lime often accumulates nearer the surface.

Time markedly affects soil characteristics. Some soils in Arizona show evidence of weathering under a climate different from that of today. Such soils are old on the basis of both time and maturity. At the other extreme is the very young alluvial soil which shows little or no influence of weathering.

By 1969 about two percent of the land in the Southwest was under cultivation, the bulk of this area being irrigated, the remainder dry-farmed. Most survey work in Arizona has been concentrated on cultivated soils. Classification has progressed only to a limited extent on cattle ranges and forest lands, but interest in an intensive classification of range and forest soils is increasing. Arizona soils are often described as being alkaline, salty, limy, dry, sandy, and low in organic matter — decayed plant residues or humus. Although these terms do not fully describe all the soils of Arizona, the more level desert land, which has been in high demand for crop production, industry, and the development of municipalities, does have some of these characteristics. Hills and mountains in general are more highly leached of these alkaline properties and support a denser vegetation. Certain soluble salts and lime accumulations are

Fig. 9.1   Leveling and preparation of borders with land plane and caterpillar for planting in desert soil.   *Ray Manley*

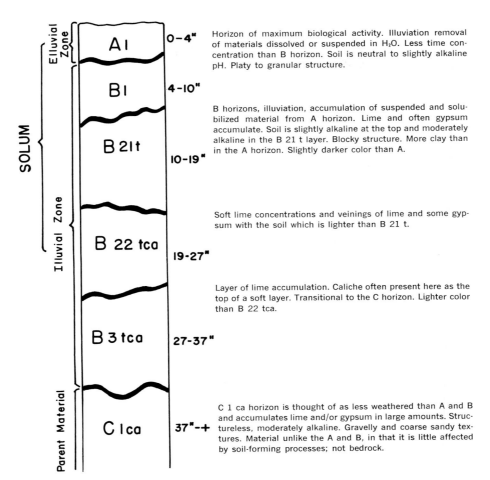

SOLUM

Elluvial Zone

Illuvial Zone

Parent Material

| A 1 | 0-4" | Horizon of maximum biological activity. Illuviation removal of materials dissolved or suspended in H₂O. Less time concentration than B horizon. Soil is neutral to slightly alkaline pH. Platy to granular structure. |

A 1 — 0-4"

Horizon of maximum biological activity. Illuviation removal of materials dissolved or suspended in H_2O. Less time concentration than B horizon. Soil is neutral to slightly alkaline pH. Platy to granular structure.

B 1 — 4-10"

B 21 t — 10-19"

B horizons, illuviation, accumulation of suspended and solubilized material from A horizon. Lime and often gypsum accumulate. Soil is slightly alkaline at the top and moderately alkaline in the B 21 t layer. Blocky structure. More clay than in the A horizon. Slightly darker color than A.

B 22 tca — 19-27"

Soft lime concentrations and veinings of lime and some gypsum with the soil which is lighter than B 21 t.

B 3 tca — 27-37"

Layer of lime accumulation. Caliche often present here as the top of a soft layer. Transitional to the C horizon. Lighter color than B 22 tca.

C 1 ca — 37"-+

C 1 ca horizon is thought of as less weathered than A and B and accumulates lime and/or gypsum in large amounts. Structureless, moderately alkaline. Gravelly and coarse sandy textures. Material unlike the A and B, in that it is little affected by soil-forming processes; not bedrock.

Fig. 9.2 Diagrammatic profile of soil.

found within the root zone of plants in the valley floors under the arid and semiarid climatic conditions where irrigated agriculture flourishes. Lime occurs as nodules, mottlings, or layers ranging in thickness from a few millimeters to several feet. This lime accumulation is known to gardeners and farmers as "caliche."

Arid soils in Arizona, for the most part, have not developed sharp or distinct profile characteristics as have the soils of more humid areas. The soils in narrow valleys as well as those of steep mountains and mountain footslopes appear to be little more developed than they were when deposited by stream or erosion action. They are often characterized as stratified gravel, sand, silt, or clay materials with rocks prevalent on the footslopes.

Soils of Arizona are characteristically low in organic matter and are therefore low in reserve nitrogen. This is the reason that nitrogen fertilizers are used so widely. With the practices of continuous cropping, this natural reserve has often been further depleted. Other than nitrogen, no plant nutrient is so universally required by the soil to support the latter-day demand for high crop yields. The recognition of nitrogen's importance has created a large commercial fertilizer industry in Arizona. More than 203,000 tons of nitrogen-carrying fertilizers were used in the state during 1967. Among the various sources used were ammonium sulfate, sixteen thousand tons; ammonia (anhydrous) fifty-eight thousand tons;

urea, twenty-six thousand tons; calcium nitrate, five thousand tons; ammonia solutions (20-0-0), eleven thousand tons; and ammonium nitrate, three thousand tons. Included in the nitrogen-carrying materials were sixty-five thousand tons of mixed fertilizers containing one or more of the above forms of nitrogen. Quantities of ammonia, ammonium nitrate solutions, calcium cyanamid, sodium nitrate, and liquid nitrogen fertilizers also have been applied annually. Nitrogen from all sources must be used efficiently if high production levels are to be sustained despite limited water resources.

By 1968 the great soil resources of Arizona were still only partly utilized, with large areas of potentially fertile land in their virgin state. These areas, naturally, depend upon the availability of water for their development. The estimated area of land in Arizona suitable for cultivation, if water were available, is about ten to eleven million acres. In 1968, about one and one-quarter million acres were under irrigation. About four million acres of arable land were judged excellent in quality and sufficiently level to permit them to be put into production with little or no treatment. About two to three million acres were said to require some leveling before irrigation could be applied properly. An estimated two million acres were not well suited to flood irrigation but could be irrigated by the sprinkler system, a fast-developing agricultural technique.

Great Soil Groups

To give readers a perspective on Arizona soils, let us look at the association of Great Soil Groups, considered to be a logical generalization helpful in the preparation of broad soil maps of Arizona. Figure 9.3 shows nine different associations of Great Soil Groups that occur in Arizona.

Since topography plays a dominant role in soil characteristics, a topography map, orienting the nine different associations of Great Soil Groups, is included. In 1966 the soil survey personnel of the University of Arizona and the USDA Soil Conservation Service collaborated in preparing a generalized soil map of Arizona (Fig. 9.4).

Caliscol-Alluvial-Rock Land Association, Area 1

Location: the extremely hot and dry lower Colorado River basin.

Topography: flat to slightly undulating desert floor interspersed with occasional steep stony uplift peaks and low, rocky mountain ranges.

Annual Rainfall: 3 to 6 inches.

Vegetation: short grass and singly-growing shrubs.

Surface Soil: light gray to grayish brown.

Subsoil: becomes slightly darker with depth until visible lime appears.

Fertility: highly productive on flat desert floors under irrigation.

The low annual rainfall and the high prevailing temperatures in this area are not conducive to complete removal of lime from surface soil. Consequently, there is

Fig. 9.3   Topographic map of Arizona, showing the nine associations of Great Soil Groups.

Fig. 9.4   A generalized map of the various Arizona soils occurring in areas of 25 square miles or more.

A — STEEP UPLAND AREAS

A1 — Shallow soils on granite and schist parent rock in the thermic region.

A2 — Shallow soils on granite and schist parent rock in the mesic region.

A3 — Shallow soils on limestone parent rock in the mesic region.

A4 — Shallow and skeletal soils on granite and schist parent rock in the frigid region.

A5 — Soils on volcanic parent material in the frigid region.

A6 — Soils on sandstone parent material in the mesic region.

A7 — Shallow soils on basalt parent rock in the mesic region.

A8 — Soils on Tertiary and Quaternary sands and gravels in the mesic region.

B — DEEP SOILS OF THE ALLUVIAL FLOOD PLAINS

B1 — Deep soils of the thermic region.

B1a — Deep sandy soils of the thermic region.

B2 — Deep soils of the mesic region.

C — SOILS OF THE THERMIC REGION

C1 — Developed soils from acid igneous alluvium on nearly level topography.

C2 — Developed soils from acid igneous alluvium on gently rolling to hilly topography.

D — SOILS OF THE MESIC REGION

D1 — Developed soils from basalt parent material.

D2 — Developed soils from mixed alluvium.

D3 — Developed soils from sandstone and associated sandy parent material.

D4 — Soils on limestone parent material.

D5 — Developed soils from granite and schist.

D6 — Soils on clay and shale parent material.

E — SOILS DEVELOPED UNDER THE CONIFER FORESTS

E1 — Forested soils developed on basalt and cinders.

E2 — Forested soils developed on limestone.

E3 — Forested soils developed on sandstone.

E4 — Forested soils developed on alluvium.

F — SWELLING AND CRACKING CLAYEY SOILS

G — MEADOW SOILS IN THE FRIGID REGION

H — SALINE-ALKALI SOILS

I — NON-SOIL AREAS

I1 — Dune lands.

I2 — Badlands.

I3 — Grand Canyon.

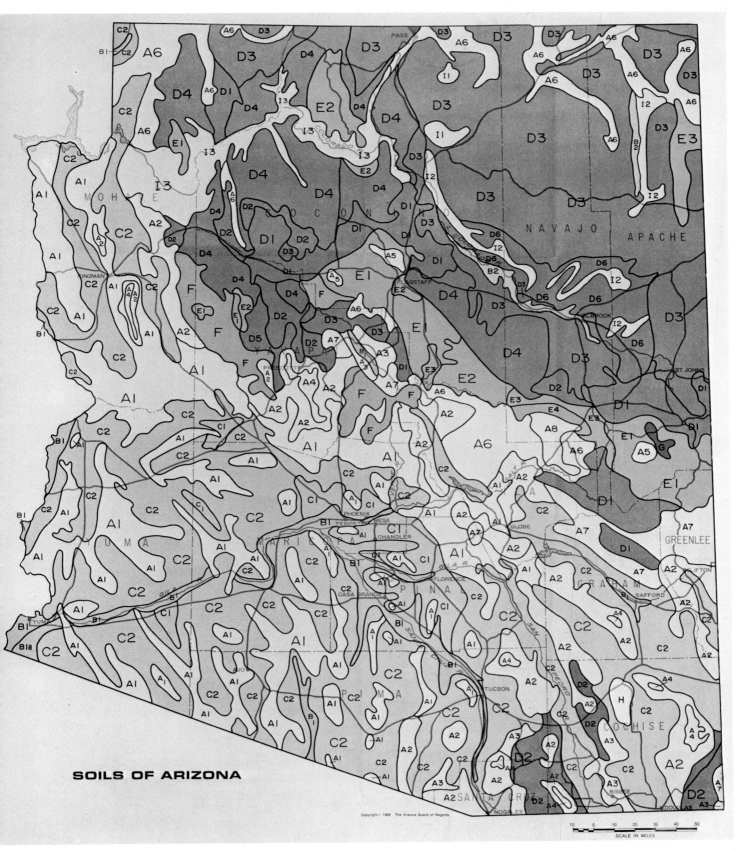

SOILS OF ARIZONA

Copyright © 1966 The Arizona Board of Regents

SCALE IN MILES

S. W. Buol, Arizona Experiment Station Technical Bulletin 171

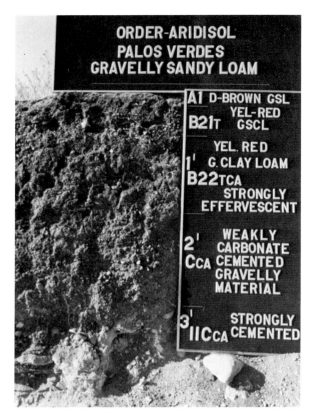

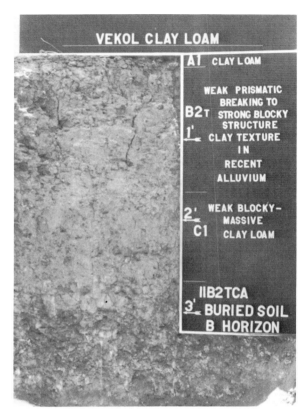

Fig. 9.5   Some typical desert soils of Arizona, with and without horizon differentiation.

an accumulation of lime throughout the soil profile. Calcisols form on highly limy parent material, developing where leaching is limited. Although the surface of only a few of these basin soils is gravelly, usually the limy zone is underlain with coarse gravel and stones. Chemical changes are limited, but accumulations of salts, sand, and debris from higher, more humid elevations have taken place.

Red Desert-Calcisol-Rock Land Association, Area 2

Location: desert of Southwest Arizona.

Topography: mostly flat desert floor interspersed with rock outcrops and small mountain ranges of steep slopes.

Annual Rainfall: between 6 and 7 inches.

Surface Soil: ranges from light pinkish-gray to reddish brown or red.

Subsoil: upper — often deeper red than the surface and compact.
     lower — pink to light gray, rich in lime and mineral nutrients.

Fertility: soil on valley floors under irrigation among most productive in the world.

Land Types: rockland predominant in the small, scattered mountain ranges.

Rainfall in this area has either been effective in removing lime from the upper part of the solum or has maintained the condition that developed under a previous wetter climate. Red Desert soils are the only significant zonal soils that occur within this area. Calcisols occur widely, and the valley floors are used intensively for agriculture.

Reddish Brown-Grumusol-Lithosol Association, Area 3

Location: transition zone between Sonoran Desert and Colorado Plateau.

Topography: variable, transition zone between the desert and the high Colorado Plateau. This is rough, rocky, mountainous land, cliffs and escarpments interspersed with narrow strips of alluvial-colluvial debris.

Fertility: inherently high, containing no appreciable soluble salts or alkali.

Soil Types: 1. Reddish Brown
            Surface: reddish brown to red; mellow consistency.
            Subsoils: pink or white and very limy
            Vegetation: short grass at elevations above lower valleys.
       2. Grumusols
            Surface: reddish-brown clay weathered on volcanic rocks.
       3. Lithosols
            Surface: shallow soils over stones with no appreciable profile development, dark colors.

Other Great Soil Groups: Noncalcic Brown and Alluvial; small areas of Reddish Brunizem, Reddish Chestnut, and Brunzems.

This area is extremely variable as to parent material, vegetation, topography, and climate. Lack of soil surveys here precludes an accurate appraisal of Great Soil Groups which constitute the predominant association, but Reddish Brown soils are the most abundant zonal soils. Most of this area is in livestock, ranches, and public ranges. Because of the high clay content of an expanding lattice type in the Grumusols, the soils shrink severely during the dry season and swell during the rainy season. They have the unique property of churning to a depth of 20 to 48 inches, a phenomenon resulting from soil granules sloughing down the shrinkage cracks. When rains occur, water fills the cracks first, causing expansion in the vicinity of the crack and bringing about strong pressures which extend the expansion in a lateral direction. This sequence of forces results in a churning or turning motion of the whole soil mass. A few lime nodules are found throughout the profile, and a weak to moderate lime horizon appears immediately above the bedrock. The surface may be hummocky or somewhat undulating. Lithosols are noted for their shallow depth over rock and for lack of profile development.

Gray Desert Sierozem-Reddish Brown Association, Area 4

Location: western edge of Colorado Plateau in northern Arizona.
Topography: gently to moderately rolling with scattered hills and mountains; canyons and escarpments common.
Vegetation: desert shrubs.
Surface Soil: light grayish-brown to gray; low in organic matter.
Subsoil: lighter in color, limy, and slightly leached.
Fertility: very productive when irrigated.
Other Great Soil Groups: Grumusols, Lithosols, Regosols.
Land Types: rock land extensive in area of escarpments, canyons, and mountains.

The Gray Desert Sierozem soils are considered the counterpart of the Red Desert soils because they are formed under similar circumstances, although temperature conditions are cold rather than hot. Small areas are found to be salty.

Mixture of Many Great Soil Groups under Conifer Forest Vegetation, Area 5

Location: the most mountainous area in Arizona, north of Areas 3 and 4, in a strip running northwest to southwest and including Flagstaff.
Topography: most mountainous of the Southwest, high mountains and steep slopes.
Land Types: mostly rockland with shallow soils of no to slight development, on the one hand, and well-developed soils on the other.
Vegetation: predominantly conifers with small islands of juniper and grassland.

No particular soil association is given because information concerning the area is still too limited to permit naming an association with accuracy. The pattern of Great Soil Groups in this area is quite irregular. The recognized groups are Reddish Chestnut, Reddish Brown, Lithosols, Brumusols, Reddish Brunizem, Grey Wooded, Planosols, and Western Brown Forest.

Reddish-Brown-Calcisol-Red-Desert Association, Area 6

Location: southeastern Arizona.
Topography: sloping and gently to moderately rolling valley basins, hills, and mountains.
Other Great Soil Groups: Reddish Chestnut, Solonetz, Lithosols.

Land Types: rockland, sand, gypsum dunes.
Vegetation: grass on the more deep and level soils, trees and shrubs on rougher rock land.

Information on the soils in the mountain area is limited because of the lack of soil surveys. Most of the area has a semiarid climate or an arid climate in the lower elevation. Several mountain ranges, although small, add to the complexity of the soil pattern. A few of the basins have closed drainages with intermittent lakes or playas.

Gray Desert-Calcisol-Lithosol Association, Area 7

Location: Colorado Plateau in northeastern Arizona.
Topography: neither hilly nor mountainous, but appears so because of many escarpments, breaks, mesas, buttes, and canyons.
Other Great Soil Groups: Alluvial soils and small areas of Reddish Brown Soils.
Land Types: rockland, sand dunes, and "badlands" or "Painted Desert."
Vegetation: predominantly grass, shrubs and scattered trees on roughest topography.

Area 7 is the highest portion of the plateau. Most of the area lies at an elevation of between five thousand and seven thousand feet.

Reddish Brown-Calcisol Association, Area 8

Location: a strip north of Area 5, on the Colorado plateau from north of Flagstaff to Springerville.
Topography: neither hilly nor mountainous, rolling land with occasional mountains and escarpments.
Subsoil: red, with lime at a greater depth where it accumulates in the lower subsoil.
Vegetation: variable, grassland, trees, and scattered shrubs.
Other Great Soil Groups: Reddish Chestnut and Lithosols.
Land Types: small amount of rock outcrops, buttes in rolling land.

The most important differences between this area and the true desert are the greater amounts of rainfall and the higher mean annual temperature. These differences have significant effects on soil formation.

Reddish Chestnut-Reddish Brown Association, Area 9

Location: southeastern portion of Colorado Plateau.
Topography: nearly-level to rolling plains with hills, mountains, escarpments, and mesas.
Vegetation: juniper and grass predominating.
Other Great Soil Groups: Reddish Brunizem, Grumusols, Lithosols, and Alluvial soils.
Land Types: small areas of rockland throughout the rolling plains.

Low Sr-90 Level

Arizona has a small blessing in disguise in its low rainfall. Research sponsored by the U.S. Atomic Energy Commission on the concentration of radioactive fallout from nuclear testing programs in the 1960s indicated that soils of the Southwest were lower in Strontium-90 than soils of any other region in the continental United States. Because rain scavenges tropospheric nuclear debris, those areas having the lowest precipitation have the lowest Sr-90. Radiostrontium levels in Arizona soils were among the lowest in the United States (range from 20-30 mCi per Km^2) according to analyses taken at the Tucson site.

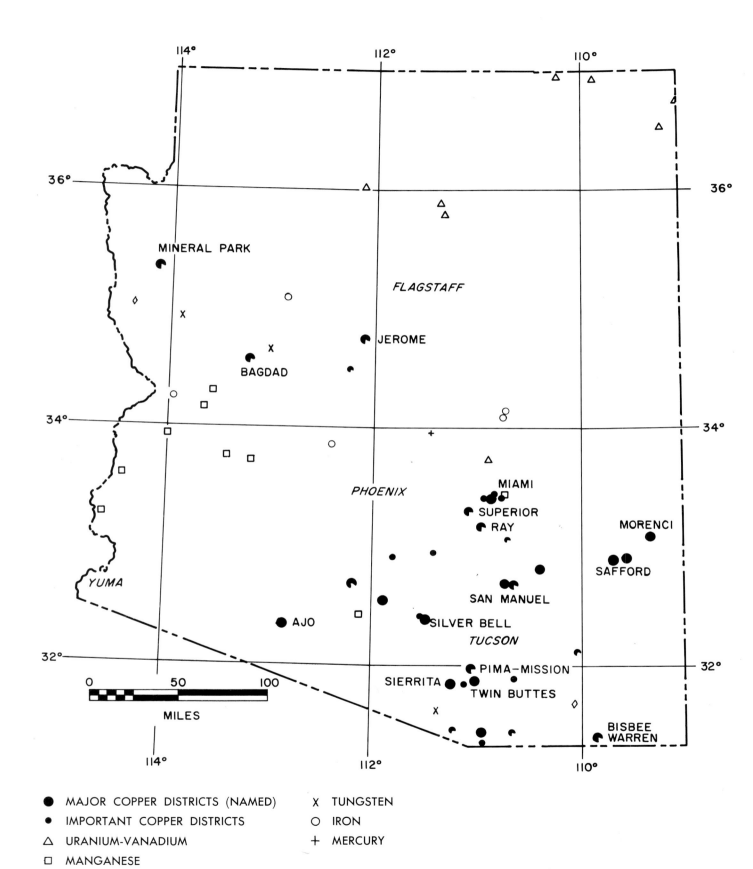

MINERAL PARK

FLAGSTAFF

JEROME

BAGDAD

PHOENIX

MIAMI
SUPERIOR
RAY

MORENCI

SAFFORD

SAN MANUEL

YUMA

AJO

SILVER BELL
TUCSON

PIMA-MISSION

SIERRITA

TWIN BUTTES

BISBEE
WARREN

```
0        50        100
████████████████████████
         MILES
```

● MAJOR COPPER DISTRICTS (NAMED)   X TUNGSTEN
• IMPORTANT COPPER DISTRICTS   O IRON
△ URANIUM-VANADIUM   + MERCURY
□ MANGANESE
◇ GOLD, SILVER

*(Important zinc and lead deposits
indicated by blank sectors in symbols)*

Fig. 10.1   Significant metallic mineral deposits in Arizona.

College of Mines Faculty,
University of Arizona

10

MINERALS AND FUELS

ARIZONA IS PARTICULARLY WELL ENDOWED with metallic and nonmetallic minerals. Scientific and technological advances, as well as improvements in transportation during the past hundred years, have augmented discovery and development of these metal resources. The discovery rate since 1950 has been outstanding, and a brilliant future for continued discovery is anticipated.

Metal resources of Arizona are varied. The important ones are copper, molybdenum, uranium-vanadium, gold, silver, zinc, and lead. Others which are noteworthy are manganese, tungsten, iron, titanium, and mercury. Minerals of many other metals are found in Arizona, but these are not recognized as resources, judging from present knowledge of their occurrences and from predictable economics.

Metallic Ores

DISTRIBUTION OF METAL DEPOSITS. Distribution of significant metallic mineral deposits is shown on Figure 10.1. This map presents a "miner's view" of Arizona's metal resources. Generally, only the most important deposits are shown for each mineral known to be present in significant concentrations and quantities. Past production and future potential are the bases for selection of districts and deposits. Neither the known nor potential deposits of some selected areas were considered to be economically important under conditions in the late 1960s. These deposits, however, were expected to become profitable with minor favorable changes of present conditions — technological, economic, and political.

Metal deposits have been divided into two main types in Figure 10.1: copper-zinc-lead, and other types, with deposits of copper, zinc, and lead considered as one type. Ore bodies of any one of these three metals either contain significant amounts of one or both of the other

two or are found in very close proximity to ore bodies of one of the other metals.

From the early 1900s, Arizona has been the leading copper-producing state. In 1969 its relative position was increasing, and the state was producing more copper than all other states combined. Since 1940 Arizona had lost some of its large copper mines by depletion of reserves. However, record discovery and development had more than replaced these losses by the late 1960s.

The important copper resources are in the Mountain and Basin and Range provinces of the state. Outside the important districts, copper deposits are widely scattered over these areas of the state. Small, scattered, and less significant copper occurrences are found within the Colorado Plateau portion of the state.

Although copper is found throughout all parts of Arizona in many types and forms of deposits and occurrences, the major resources are concentrated in the southern and western sections.

GENESIS. Southern and southwestern Arizona comprise a metal province of major importance, mainly because the province is one of extensive and complex igneous activity. The major activities took place during the Precambrian era and the Tertiary period, although activity in other periods is recognized.

The periods of igneous activity were the results of fracturing, broad-scale shattering, displacement, and deformation of rocks, caused by enormous differential stresses in the crust of the earth. The molten igneous rocks intruded the fractured and deformed crust and flowed out on old surfaces in the form of extensive lava flows. These events occurred repeatedly in many localities.

Hot, metal-bearing solutions accompanied or followed the cooling intrusions, and most of Arizona's metal-bearing (ore) deposits were emplaced originally in fractured rocks by these solutions. In the case of many deposits, the metal-bearing solutions dissolved rock-forming minerals in the vicinity of fractures and replaced them with metallic minerals. Later weathering and erosion have caused some change in the characteristics of the original ore deposits.

THE SEARCH FOR UNKNOWN ORE DEPOSITS. The southern and western parts of Arizona form the nation's best copper province, largely because of the heritage of the great crustal forces and the igneous intrusions that occurred in that area. It was the hub of America's copper exploration effort in the 1960s. Arizona, past and present, has attracted a large percentage of the best mining geologists in the world. This, too, is Arizona's heritage.

As of 1970 many major metal mining companies, as well as a number of small organizations, had exploration offices in Arizona. The discovery record demonstrates that, on the average, these exploration efforts have been successful. However, the risks are high, and many expensive efforts go for years with no reward. Hidden wealth is not easily won from Arizona's rugged face. Scarred and wrinkled in antiquity, it presents complex puzzles. Some organizations spend millions of dollars, only to be forced into retreat empty-handed. Others receive smiles of fortune, reaping fabulous rewards. Many discoveries are made annually near known ore bodies, and occasionally discoveries are made in isolated areas.

The challenging problems occupy the attention of both prospectors and geologists — not only practicing mining geologists but geological scientists, such as those of the U.S. Geological Survey and of the University of Arizona. The most basic problems have been reconstruction of geologic events and the relative timing of those events.

AGE OF METAL DEPOSITS. Geologists have focused a great deal of their attention on the age of metal deposits in the state. While the ages of some deposits are fairly well established, the ages of the majority of deposits are matters of geologic speculation, based on indirect evidence. As Arizona entered the 1970s, much research was needed to solve problems of time relationships.

Age classification is attempted here subject to the above qualifications. Arizona metal deposits can be classified, in time of formation, as follows: Precambrian, Jurassic, Laramide, Late Tertiary, and Quaternary. The first three categories are of major importance. Laramide, a period of widespread rock deformation and mineralization in the western states, is approximately equivalent to early Tertiary in Arizona.

Metals deposited in Arizona during Precambrian time are copper, gold, silver, zinc, lead, tungsten, titanium, iron, and possibly mercury and molybdenum. In the 1960s the most important known Precambrian deposits were those located at Jerome (copper, gold, silver, zinc) and Humboldt (zinc, lead, gold, silver, copper) in Yavapai County. Most of the Precambrian deposits were in Yavapai County. One important exception was the iron deposits near the Mogollon Rim in Gila and Navajo counties.

The only metal deposits which are assigned approximately to the Jurassic period are some of those in Cochise County, the major Bisbee-Warren district being the only district clearly in this category. Metals of these deposits are copper, zinc, gold, silver, lead, and manganese.

Most of the important metal deposits in Arizona were deposited during Laramide time. The majority of these important deposits are copper-gold-silver, zinc-lead-copper-gold-silver, or combinations of the two types. Copper deposits have been by far the most important, and these provide the main source of molybdenum. Ores from these deposits commonly contain more iron than copper, zinc, or lead, and this is also true of the Jerome ores. The iron, in the form of sulfides, has not been used in making steel, but it is an important resource. All of the significant uranium and vanadium deposits of Arizona are probably Laramide, as are many of the gold-vein deposits. Some of the manganese deposits also originated during this time. Iron deposits in northern Yavapai County are probably Laramide, and the numerous small copper deposits scattered over the Colorado Plateau also are probably placed in this category.

The only important metal deposits assigned to late Tertiary are those of manganese, such as those of the Artillery Peaks area. Some minor concentrations of uranium were formed in Tertiary alluvial beds during late Tertiary time.

Many older metal deposits were considerably altered by weathering during late Tertiary and during Quaternary times. Arizona's semiarid climate was much the same then as it is now. Under such climatic conditions, copper deposits tend to become enriched to produce greater copper content per unit volume. This process has been so important in Arizona that the state's high position as a copper producer can be attributed, in part, to its climate. The soluble copper salts, resulting from weathering, were moved by groundwater, not only causing enrichment but, in some cases, forming new copper deposits. Such deposits, as some of those north of Miami, can be dated as late Tertiary or early Quaternary.

With the possible exception of the secondary copper deposits described above, Quaternary metal deposits are mainly limited to gold placers, gold in sand and gravel of washes. The placers are scattered over the southern and western portions of Arizona.

THE PORPHYRY-COPPER STORY. Copper, the red metal, has been an important part of Arizona's history. Major, high-grade ore bodies have been discovered and mined at Bisbee, Jerome, Globe, Superior, and Morenci. These ore bodies are of various shapes and forms, such as those called "oreshoots" (in veins) and "blankets," and they are often found in close proximity, occurring in clusters — chests of hidden treasure, million-dollar jewel boxes. Copper in Arizona has not been limited to high-grade ore bodies, however. It is found also as large low-grade disseminations, seemingly "soaked" into large masses of rock. Copper minerals of such deposits are both intergranular with the rock itself and in small cavities or veinlets.

Copper deposits of large volume but small copper content per unit volume comprise a type generally known as porphyry-copper deposits. A porphyry is a fine-grained igneous rock with scattered larger grains. The name is applied to this type of copper deposit because the type is commonly associated with porphyries.

The southern and southwestern section of Arizona is a classical locality for porphyry coppers, and most of the porphyry-copper deposits of the world in the 1960s could be found here. At that time the important known porphyry coppers of Arizona were Miami, Inspiration, Castle Dome, Copper Cities (all in the Miami district), and Morenci, Ajo, Ray, San Manuel, Kalamazoo, Bisbee, Silver Bell, Bagdad, Safford, Mineral Park, Sierrita, and Esperanza. The major Mission, Twin Buttes, and Pima deposits of the Pima district, south of Tucson, could also be added to the list, although technical reasons can be cited as to why these should not be classified as porphyry coppers. Including these, a total of eighteen Arizona porphyry coppers are listed.

By 1970 it was probable that most of the sparkling jewel boxes had been found and opened and their contents exploited. Arizona's elevated copper position has not been dependent on rich, high-grade ore bodies, which, in nature's balance, are relatively small. The position has been based instead on the large to enormous low-grade ore bodies — the porphyry coppers.

In most fields of research, the slowly expanding frontiers of knowledge are marked, on rare occasions, by major breakthroughs — mileposts of man's efforts to rise above abysmal ignorance. One of the main mileposts in the mineral-exploration area of knowledge applies directly to porphyry coppers and concerns the interpretation of leached outcrops.

Augustus Locke and Roland Blanchard were the two men who led the leached outcrop effort and were most responsible for the breakthrough. They were commercial mining geologists and scientists as well, combining the incentive of the prospector with the scientific inspiration of the knowledge frontier.

An outcrop is the surface exposure of a rock or mineral body. Weathering, at and near the surface, often causes changes in the minerals comprising rocks or mineral deposits. In the case of copper deposits, the copper sulfide minerals, as originally deposited, are oxidized, and resulting copper salts are often carried into solution, usually downward as rain waters seep into the ground. Thus, copper values are often removed from the outcropping or upper portions of copper deposits.

Through the weathering process, the exposed, outcropping portions of copper deposits can become essentially barren of copper. The extracted copper values would percolate downward to the water table, being dispersed and lost. Under the correct conditions of geology and climate, however, the dissolved copper values are not altogether lost. Below the water table, sulfide minerals are protected from oxidation by water saturation, and there, in the absence of free oxygen, copper tends to be precipitated from solution. Thus, at the water table, the copper content of the deposit tends to increase, being built up by values swept from above. The copper is precipitated from solution in the form of chalcocite, a sulfide of copper.

Through the process of oxidation, solution, and precipitation, an enriched zone is formed at the water table. This zone is called a "chalcocite blanket," although such a blanket is not always present. Whether or not a chalcocite blanket can be found below a given outcrop depends on many factors. These include recognition and interpretation of the leached outcrop, original alteration of the mineralized ground and its original mineral content, conditions of geologic structure, geologic history, and paleoclimate. The copper content of some porphyry coppers was sufficiently high, before subjection to the weathering process, so that a chalcocite blanket is not needed to make the deposit economic. Without a chalcocite blanket, however, the copper content of many porphyry-copper deposits would be too low for economic interest.

A unique set of favorable conditions forms the ideal environment for a porphyry-copper deposit. Igneous history should be intense and complex, and breccia pipes should occur in the vicinity. The water table should be deep for a prolonged period, and erosion should be deep and slow.

Rates of erosion and weathering should be in approximate balance, the rate of weathering slightly exceeding that of erosion. Rocks in the immediate vicinity should be nonreactive to acid solutions. The right combinations of these and other conditions are likely to be found in the southern and southwestern section of Arizona. For example, the antiquity of Arizona's present semiarid climate is favorable to the weathering, erosion, and water-table conditions expressed above.

All of Arizona's porphyry-copper mines which were in operation in the 1930s were among the "laboratories" used in leached-outcrop studies. The leached-outcrop concepts, summarized in a classical paper by Blanchard, have given man understanding of the porphyry copper and its genetic processes. With this knowledge, the porphyry copper has been discovered, developed, and exploited more intelligently and more economically.

Of the eighteen Arizona porphyry coppers, thirteen have been discovered, developed or both, since the full development of the leached-outcrop concepts. Also, much additional ore has been discovered at old porphyry-copper mines since that time. In order of magnitude, the value of these newly developed ore bodies is at least several billion dollars. The impact of these concepts on Arizona — the role that the concepts have played in most of the new discoveries and developments — is immeasurable. It is sufficient to say that the leached-outcrop concepts rank high among the most important events in porphyry-copper history, and Arizona owes much to the men who developed them.

Industrial Rock and Mineral Resources

Industrial rock and mineral resources include those non-metallic minerals or mineral aggregates which are neither organic fuels nor sources of metals. Their development has lacked the glamour of the metallic deposits since these commodities are almost always low in unit value and generally consist of common rock materials — there for the taking. Their value generally is dependent upon development of local markets, interest in these resources rising with population growth.

The rapid population increase in the Southwest with accompanying expansion of highway and building construction has stimulated interest in Arizona's industrial rocks and minerals. In 1966 these constituted 6.8 percent of the total value of mineral production in the state, as compared to a 2.5 percent average till then. Most of the products have been used locally, but a few of the products with higher unit value, such as asbestos, quartz, feldspar, and beryl, columbite, and tantalite by-products were in 1969 being marketed outside of the state.

INDUSTRIAL ROCKS. The complex geological history in Arizona has resulted in a wide variety of industrial rocks. These include low-unit-value rock materials of sedimentary, igneous, and metamorphic origin which have widespread distribution, are mined and utilized in bulk, and require only simple processing, such as sand and gravel, building stone, volcanic cinders and pumice, perlite, clay, limestone, and gypsum deposits.

Relatively recent uplift of mountain ranges and their erosion in southwestern Arizona have produced vast resources of sand and gravel filling the broad intermontane valleys. These cover approximately one-half of the total land area in southern Arizona. Mountain streams emerging from the narrow canyons deposited their load of sediment as alluvial fans, and these were modified and reworked by the more leisurely flowing valley streams to produce imperfectly stratified sand and gravel with silty clay lenses. In northern Arizona the sand and gravel deposits are limited to narrow streambeds or to remnant terraces.

Explosive volcanic activity from Early Tertiary to Recent time has yielded a variety of industrial rock

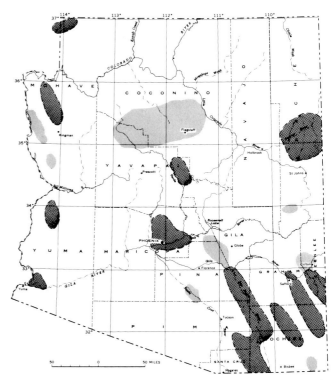

Fig. 10.2   Principal areas of volcanic industrial rocks (light) and potential Tertiary lake bed accumulations (dark).

materials. Volcanic cinders (scoria), pumice and pumicite, and pozzolan materials occur in widely separated areas throughout the state (Fig. 10.2). Cinder cones of geologically recent volcanoes abound north and west of Flagstaff in Coconino County, in the Show Low-Springerville area of Apache County. They occur also as isolated cones east of Douglas in Cochise County. Pumice is found west, east, and northeast of Flagstaff and east of Safford in Graham and Greenlee counties. Pumicite, volcanic ash or tuff, and pozzolan materials are widespread through the Tertiary and Quaternary volcanics that cap much of the state and are interbedded with the lake deposits. These beds are particularly well developed in the Tertiary Bidihochi formation near Chambers in Apache County. Perlite, a glassy siliceous rock which expands many times in volume when heated to the proper temperature, abounds in the area northwest, west, and southwest of Superior in Pinal County. Less extensive deposits of good quality occur south of Casa Grande in Pinal County and west and northwest of Yucca in Mohave County.

Outpourings of volcanic flows and uplift of mountain ranges during Tertiary time dammed valleys and impounded lakes which received clastic sediments and volcanic ash and were fed by hot springs of volcanic origin. A wide variety of industrial rock materials resulted: structural, ceramic, and bloating clays, bentonite, bleaching clays, diatomite, pozzolan materials, chalk, gypsum, salt, sodium, sulphate, zeolites, and possibly boron salts. Extensive Tertiary lake deposits are found, or may be disclosed by further search, in the

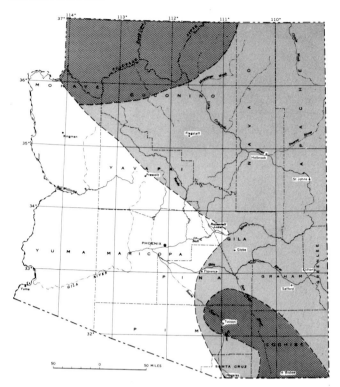

Fig. 10.3 Paleozoic limestones with potential as cement materials (light), and chemical line (dark).

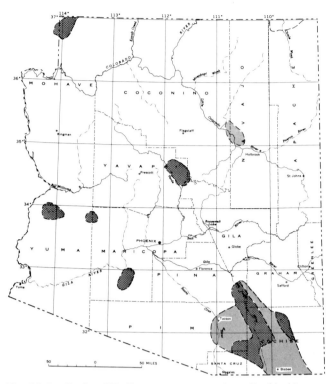

Fig. 10.4 Basis of Tertiary age gypsum deposits (dark) and of Permian and Triassic age (light).

Salt River, San Simon, Sulphur Spring, San Pedro, and Santa Cruz valleys in southeastern Arizona and in the Verde Valley in central Arizona (Fig. 10.2), in the valley of Red Lake north of Kingman in Mohave County, and in the vicinity of Chambers in Apache County.

Mesozoic and early Tertiary rocks of Arizona consist of marine, near-shore, and continental deposits containing a variety of industrial rock materials. Cretaceous Mesaverde and Mancos formations and the Jurassic Morrison formation in north central Arizona contain illitic and kaolinitic clays suitable for structural, ceramic, and possible refractory products. High-swelling bentonite occurs in the Triassic Chinle formation, and restricted lenses of gypsum are found in the Triassic Moenkopi formation in Coconino County. Lime is produced from the Cretaceous Mural formation in the southeastern portion of the state.

Paleozoic rocks, consisting of limestone, shale, sandstone, quartzite, and gypsum are distributed through eastern and northern portions of Arizona and yield a wide variety of industrial rock products. Cement materials occur throughout the entire area (Fig. 10.3). High-quality limestone is restricted to the Mississippian Escabrosa and Redwall formations in the northwest and southeast corners of the state, and gypsum to the Permian Andrada formation in the southeast portion of the state (Fig. 10.4). Suitable ganister materials may be found in Cambrian and Permian quartzites.

Dimension stone is available in all parts of the state in rocks ranging from Precambrian gneiss and granite to Quaternary volcanics. Special quality dimension stone

and flagstone is quarried from the Permian DeChelly, Coconino, and Triassic Moenkopi formations in north central Arizona.

INDUSTRIAL MINERALS. Igneous, hydrothermal, and metamorphic processes have resulted in the formation and concentration of various industrial minerals in pegmatites, veins, or metamorphic aureoles. Contrasted with the industrial rocks these deposits are more restricted in distribution, generally of small bulk, have a higher unit value, and generally entail more complex beneficiation processes. They include such minerals as asbestos, feldspar, mica, lithium minerals, beryl, fluorspar, and barite.

Deposits of pegmatite concentrations are known in many parts of Arizona; however, most of the largest and best-known deposits lie within a belt some thirty to eighty miles wide and extending south-southeast from Lake Mead, across the state through parts of Mohave, Yavapai, Yuma, and Maricopa counties, and tailing out southeast of Phoenix (Fig. 10.5). These deposits have produced feldspar (perthite), ceramic grade quartz, scrap and sheet mica, lithium minerals, beryl, tantalite, and columbite. The pegmatites occur typically as lenticular dikes, sills, pods, or irregular branching masses, often in groups or swarms. They average less than forty feet in width and four hundred feet in length and generally show zonal structure with siliceous cores which commonly carry the unusual industrial minerals.

Veins of fluorite and barite are almost entirely restricted in their distribution to two belts trending west

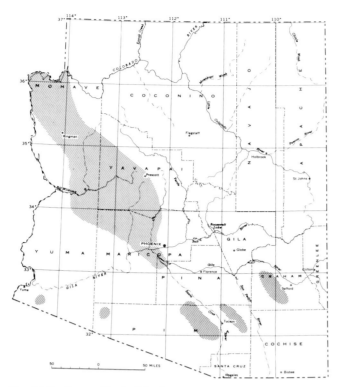

Fig. 10.5   Pegmatite belt in Arizona.

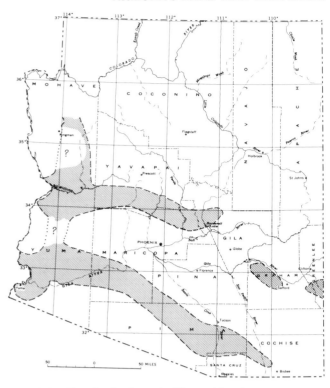

Fig. 10.6   Fluorite, barite, celestite, and beryl areas.

to west-northwest across the southern part of the state (Fig. 10.6). Both are common gangue minerals for lead veins and may occur either together or separately. There appears to be a close relationship of the distribution of beryl and celestite to these same distinct mineralized belts.

Arizona's chrysotile asbestos has been valued highly because of its low iron content and soft, spinnable fibers. The most important deposits in the 1960s could be found in the late Precambrian rocks in central Gila County in the vicinity of Globe (Fig. 10.7). Some small deposits have been found in the Grand Canyon area of Coconino County. The asbestos occurs with serpentine in the Precambrian Mescal or Bass dolomite near the contacts of diabase dikes and sills.

OUTLOOK. The outlook for industrial rocks and minerals in Arizona is exceedingly bright. Population growth, with expansion of construction programs, and development of chemical and ceramic industries will utilize known deposits, develop new requirements, and stimulate renewed search and discovery.

Mineral Fuels

The industrial development of any nation or state is to a large extent controlled by its sources of energy. The principal sources available to Arizona have been water power, solar energy, radioactive minerals, and the mineral fuels. Mineral fuels in this section include coal, gas, and oil.

Water power, solar energy, and radioactive min-

erals are discussed elsewhere in this volume. Wood as a source of energy has only limited use because it furnishes neither the volume nor the intensity of heat needed for industrial purposes.

The mineral fuels may be regarded as solar energy which was stored by plants or animals during past ages. This energy is released through the combustion of these residual, modified organic remains.

OIL AND GAS. If oil or gas is to be discovered in commercial quantities, at least four fundamental requirements must be met. If any one of these factors is missing, no commercial production can be expected. The first requirement is the presence of source beds from which oil and gas have been derived. These source beds generally are black, organic-rich shale or limestone rocks.

The second requirement is an adequate reservoir in which oil and gas that has been derived from the source beds can be stored. Reservoir beds may be any porous rock, but they are generally either sandstone or carbonate formations. In rare instances nonporous formations such as shales, volcanic, and crystalline rocks may be sufficiently fractured to serve as reservoirs.

The third requirement is a trap to catch migrating oil and gas and to allow them to concentrate in sufficient quantities to form a commercial accumulation. Broadly speaking, most traps are either (1) folded structures, such as anticlines, domes, terraces, or noses, (2) faulted or broken rock structures, or (3) stratigraphic traps. The latter are traps related to changes in porosity and permeability of the rocks and are caused by unconformities, intrusions, litification, solution, cementation, recrystallization, wedgeouts, reefs and related organic growths, changing conditions of sedimentation, and other geologic factors.

Finally, the fourth requirement is adequate cover to prevent the oil and gas which may have accumulated in the trap from escaping. Such cover is generally of some impervious sedimentary rock such as shale.

The presence of all four of these requirements does not assure the discovery of oil or gas, since other factors influence the possibilities, but without these four requirements the chances of finding commercial accumulation are essentially nil.

Therefore, in evaluating the petroleum-bearing potential of any given region, it is prudent to examine the stratigraphic section in detail in order to determine the presence of any source beds, reservoir beds, and traps.

Because of these fundamental requirements, it is obvious that sedimentary rocks are the usual habitat of oil and gas, and in particular, marine sediments are most favorable, although small amounts of oil and gas have been discovered in nonmarine rocks.

Furthermore, in general, the thicker the stratigraphic section the greater is its oil or gas potential. Conversely, if the section is thin or is largely composed of redbeds and nonmarine beds, the probabilities of finding oil or gas in it are poor.

In general, the most favorable areas for oil and gas accumulation are those that have had gentle structural deformation such as occur when rocks are folded into anticlines, domes, and noses. Where the beds have been much broken and fractured, oil and gas which might have accumulated in a reservoir may have since escaped.

Although small igneous or volcanic intrusions may produce traps, a small intrusive implies additional igneous activity at depth. The heat accompanying extensive igneous activity probably will have destroyed any adjacent petroliferous possibilities, unless the intrusion occurred prior to the time of accumulation.

History of Exploration. According to Philip Johnson of the U. S. Geological Survey, the earliest known oil test well in Arizona was drilled during 1906, by A. C. Alexander in section 17, T5S, R24E, Graham County. It was abandoned as a dry hole at fourteen hundred feet. Between the years 1906 and 1948, about ninety additional oil test wells were drilled. Many of the data on these older wells are lacking, although in a few cases logs and other information have been secured. Most of these holes were shallow and were located without benefit of geology or geophysics, and had little relationship to fundamentals controlling the occurrence of petroleum. Some logs report "shows" of oil or gas or both, but quantitative data on these shows are lacking. Altogether about six hundred wells had been drilled by 1969. For most

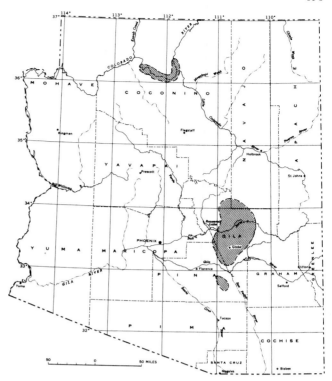

Fig. 10.7   Areas containing deposits of asbestos.

of them some kind of record has been preserved. In many cases cuttings, cores or core chips, records of testing, and other pertinent data are on file.

Information on these wells has been assembled in the Department of Geology and the Bureau of Mines, both of which are located at the University of Arizona in Tucson, and in the office of the Oil and Gas Commission in Phoenix. Various offices of the U.S. Geological Survey have records of holes in their areas of jurisdiction. Records of deep water wells and some recent stratigraphic mineral borings, both of which may give important geological information, are on file with the above agencies. Samples of Arizona well cuttings are available at the Arizona Bureau of Mines. Records and samples of wells drilled in the northern part of the state are on file at the Museum of Northern Arizona in Flagstaff.

As Figure 10.8 shows, the drilling in Arizona has been concentrated particularly in the northeastern and southeastern parts of the state.

The Dineh bi-Keyah oil field, Apache County, was discovered in early 1967. Its great interest to the petroleum industry is that it produces from a Tertiary igneous rock intruded into Pennsylvania sandstones and shales. The wells are three thousand to four thousand feet deep, and the oil is sulphur-free and of high gravity. It occurs in pores within the porous and permeable igneous rock as well as in fractures. Initial production from some of the wells was as high as three thousand barrels per day. As of midsummer, 1969, the field covered some six square miles.

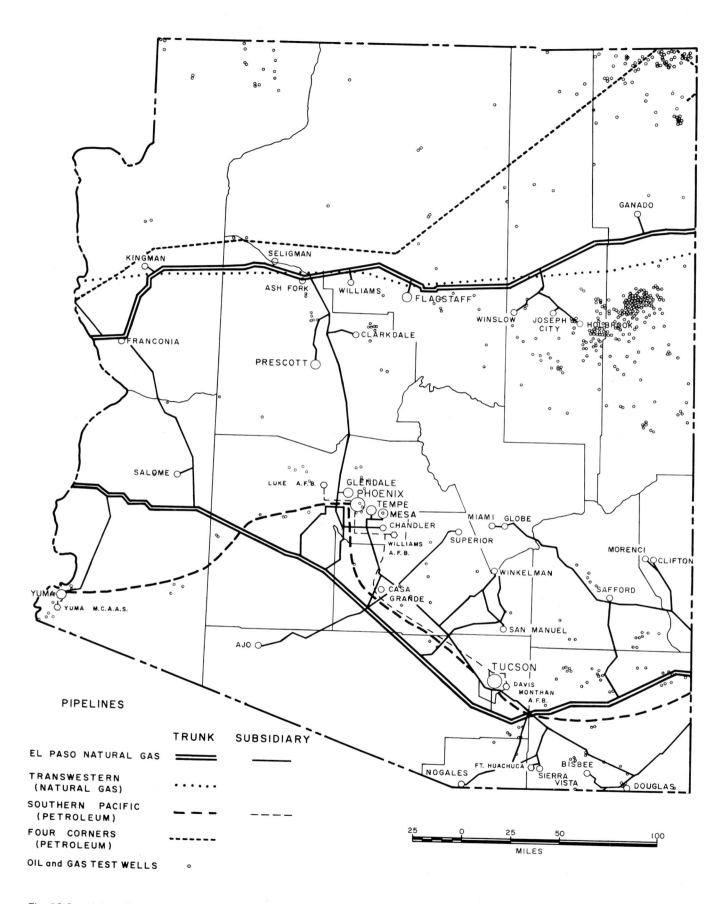

PIPELINES

	TRUNK	SUBSIDIARY
EL PASO NATURAL GAS	══════	────────
TRANSWESTERN (NATURAL GAS)	••••••	
SOUTHERN PACIFIC (PETROLEUM)	── ── ──	── ──
FOUR CORNERS (PETROLEUM)	------	
OIL and GAS TEST WELLS	∘	

Fig. 10.8   Major oil and gas pipelines and test wells.

The depth range of most wells has been only a few thousand feet, but by 1969 several holes in Apache, Cochise, Coconino, and Navajo counties had reached depths of over seven thousand feet.

Although shows of oil and gas had been recorded for several wells, the only commercial production found by 1969 was in the Four Corners region. It was obtained first in 1954 when the Shell Oil Company No. 2 Boundary Butte well in Sec. 3, T41N, R28E, was completed for an initial yield of two million two hundred thousand cubic feet of gas per day. This well is considered the discovery well of the East Boundary Butte pool. In 1958 the Humble Oil Company, No. 1E Navajo, was drilled in the same pool and came in as the first oil well of Arizona, with initial production of 562 barrels of oil per day from the Hermosa formation. Subsequent production showed increasing gas, and in 1969 it was considered a gas well.

In addition, in various parts of northeastern Arizona, certain wells in the Coconino formation were found to have gas containing as high as eight percent of helium. The rest of the gas is mainly nitrogen. The helium content makes these wells important as a source of that gas.

As of midsummer, 1968, Arizona had six producing oil fields, all located in northeastern Arizona on the Navajo Indian Reservation. Total cumulative production was in excess of five million barrels of oil, the majority of which came from the Dineh bi-Keyah field. In addition there were five fields producing natural gas. These were also on the reservation and had produced in excess of eight million seven hundred and fifty thousand cubic feet of gas by midsummer, 1968.

Petroleum Possibilities of Arizona. Arizona may be divided into northwestern, northeastern, southeastern, and southwestern regions. The northwestern and northeastern regions comprise, in general, the Plateau portion of Arizona. The southeastern region includes that part of Arizona east of Tucson and south of the Plateau, and the southern and western parts of Arizona comprise that portion west of Tucson and south of the Plateau.

Northwestern Arizona. In northwestern Arizona a thick marine section is present which should be favorable for the occurrence of oil and gas. However, locally deep canyons have cut entirely through the section, and the oil and gas may have escaped. Nevertheless, there are structures which may have served as traps for some local accumulation. Oil shows have been reported from a number of formations and some production has been secured across the line in Utah.

Volcanic rocks between Flagstaff and Seligman cover much of the area, but presumably the underlying sedimentary rocks are similar to those exposed farther north, east, and west. The intrusives which fed the volcanoes in the area locally might have destroyed any oil present. Also, the volcanic flows mask the structure.

Northeastern Arizona. In northeastern Arizona, Paleozoic rocks are overlain by Triassic and Jurassic nonmarine redbeds and sandstones. These in turn are overlain by Cretaceous marine beds. The Paleozoic section may be thin or almost absent, as on the Defiance Uplift. In other areas the section may be relatively thick. Rocks of Cretaceous age are limited largely to the Black Mesa Basin, and because of erosion, are relatively thin. Some of the extensive Cretaceous sandstones which produce in New Mexico are present in the Black Mesa Basin, but because of thin cover or exposure probably have lost any oil or gas they might have contained. Triassic and Jurassic sandstone beds serve as reservoirs for natural gas which may carry small percentages of helium.

The Hermosa-Paradox formation complex occurs in the extreme northeastern corner of the state. These interfingering Permo-Pennsylvanian limestone, redbed, evaporite, and shale facies have yielded oil and gas in the Four Corners. The oil and gas potential of the pre-Pennsylvanian beds was not known in the 1960s, although they are largely of marine origin. The discovery of oil, however, from the Mississippian section in the Texas Pacific Coal and Oil Company No. 1 Navajo-138 well is significant because of the widespread distribution of Mississippian rocks in the state. Indications of oil have been found in rocks of Devonian age over wide areas of Arizona, and in north central Arizona an "oil seep" has been exposed along a road cut. The Fort Apache member of the Supai Formation (Permian) has had shows of gas in wells and smells of hydrocarbon on the outcrop.

The Hopi Buttes volcanic field and other volcanic intrusives present in northeastern Arizona might have done no vital damage to the oil potential, but subsurface volcanic alteration must be expected. Likewise, the extensive volcanic fields in the Greenlee and southern Apache County areas mask all of the subsurface and volcanic intrusions, and alterations have probably destroyed any oil and gas potential which might have been present.

Southeastern Arizona. East of Tucson and south of the Plateau, a thick section of Paleozoic marine limestone, sandstone, and shale occurs. This rock section has all of the attributes necessary for an oil province. The rocks, however, show considerable faulting and locally are extensively intruded and mineralized. Mountain blocks are relatively narrow, and any oil that might have been present in these tilted blocks will have escaped. Within the basins the same Paleozoic section may be present; however, thick sections of sand, gravel, and clay mask the character of the older section and conceal its structure. The San Simon well penetrated more than seven thousand feet of this alluvial fill without passing into the underlying bedrock. Also, since the basins are narrow, in most cases the area available for oil drainage into a pool is limited.

The post-Paleozoic rocks exposed are largely continental redbeds of Upper Cretaceous age. These are overlain by Tertiary rocks which in many places include extensive volcanics. In the extreme southeastern portion of the state, the Lower Cretaceous rocks become marine in character. Under proper conditions, these marine Cretaceous beds might carry oil.

The most likely rocks in which oil or gas may be found in southeastern Arizona are the Devonian, Mississippian, Pennsylvanian, and Permian marine beds. The tongue of Ordovician limestone present in extreme eastern Arizona was also a potential oil horizon in the late 1960s.

Southwestern Arizona. Southwestern Arizona consists essentially of mountains of crystalline and volcanic rocks separated by basins which are covered with alluvium. There are a few local exposures of Paleozoic rocks in this area, but where exposed in the mountains the rocks usually have been metamorphosed, altered, and badly deformed. However, southward in Mexico a thick, unaltered marine limestone Paleozoic section ranging from Cambrian through Permian is present. If this section can be found in western Arizona underlying some of the basins, and if it is not metamorphosed, it could carry good production. Unfortunately, the basins are too deeply covered with alluvium to allow adequate evaluation of their geology. The mountain blocks of western Arizona appear to have essentially no potential oil section. In general it was believed in the 1960s, on the basis of waterwells and other information, that in southern and southwestern Arizona the oil potential was slight.

Possible Petroliferous Regions in Arizona. The petroleum potentiality of Arizona as controlled by stratigraphic relationships is summarized in Figure 10.9. The areas occupied by crystalline rocks have no potentiality and are indicated. Areas masked by volcanic rocks are also depicted. Southern and western Arizona as a whole are largely masked by Tertiary cover and are difficult to assess. In general it was considered in 1969 that the western part had limited possibilities, and the southeastern part had some possibilities for oil production. The areas around the canyons may have lost their oil potentiality through drainage. This leaves a region in northeastern Arizona which probably is the most favorable in the state for the occurrence of oil and gas.

SOME OIL ECONOMICS. The future production and development of oil and gas in Arizona are closely tied to the problem of marketing. Gas is difficult to market without a pipeline. If no gas pipeline exists, the well must remain shut in, or if gas is produced in association with oil, it must be burned or pumped back into the ground. In the case of oil, production may be stored temporarily in tanks but then must be transported to market by pipeline, rail, or truck. Oil and gas pipelines usually are not built until substantial oil and gas reserves have been developed.

No rail connections extended into the Four Corners area in 1969. Some highways and roads were present, but wide areas had none. Several transcontinental gas and oil pipelines crossed the region. If sufficient reserves are proved, pipelines may be built to connect the fields with these major pipelines.

The nearest refineries for Arizona crude in 1969 were in northwestern New Mexico, and until pipelines are established, crude will be transported by truck to them or to a rail or pipeline head. Following the discovery of the Dineh bi-Keyah field a spur pipeline was constructed in 1967 to connect this field with the Four Corners Pipeline which transported the crude oil to the Pacific Coast market. The ultimate market for oil and gas is expected to be Arizona and the Pacific Coast states.

With the exception of the Dineh bi-Keyah spur line, the oil and gas pipelines existing in 1969 throughout the state were for transcontinental transportation and for distribution within the state of natural gas and refined oil products. Figure 10.8 indicates the position of the major trunk lines.

COAL. Coal is derived from vegetable material. In the coalification process, the woody material of plants passes successively into peat, lignite, bituminous coal, and anthracite. In rare instances where hot liquid intrusive rocks have come close to a coal seam, the coal may be baked and changed into a natural coke.

The change from wood to peat occurs early in the process and is essentially a decaying and hydration step. Withdrawal of swamp water and gradual burial and compaction due to weight of overlying sediments change peat to a lignite which commonly carries up to about thirty percent water. Lignite has a relatively low heating value, in the range of eight thousand B.T.U. (A British Thermal Unit is the amount of heat necessary to raise one cubic foot of water 1° Fahrenheit.)

The change from lignite through sub-bituminous coal also is primarily dehydration, together with some loss of volatile materials. Bituminous coal normally has only about five percent moisture. Heating value may increase to over fifteen thousand B.T.U. These are the main coking coals, or coals which can be converted to coke for industrial purposes. This change to bituminous coal is primarily the result of compaction due to overburden and to other stresses in the earth. Length of burial of the coal does not seem to be very significant, although in general the older the coal, the higher the rank. Rank designates in part the quality of coal and is indicated by the terms lignite, bituminous, or anthracite.

The change from bituminous through super-bituminous, sub-anthracite, and anthracite is primarily a loss of volatile materials such as hydrogen compounds. Moisture content on an ash-free basis has dropped to about three percent, volatile material to about five percent, and there has been a corresponding increase to about 92 percent fixed carbon. The heating value, because of the loss of volatile material, has dropped, but still is in the vicinity of fourteen thousand B.T.U.

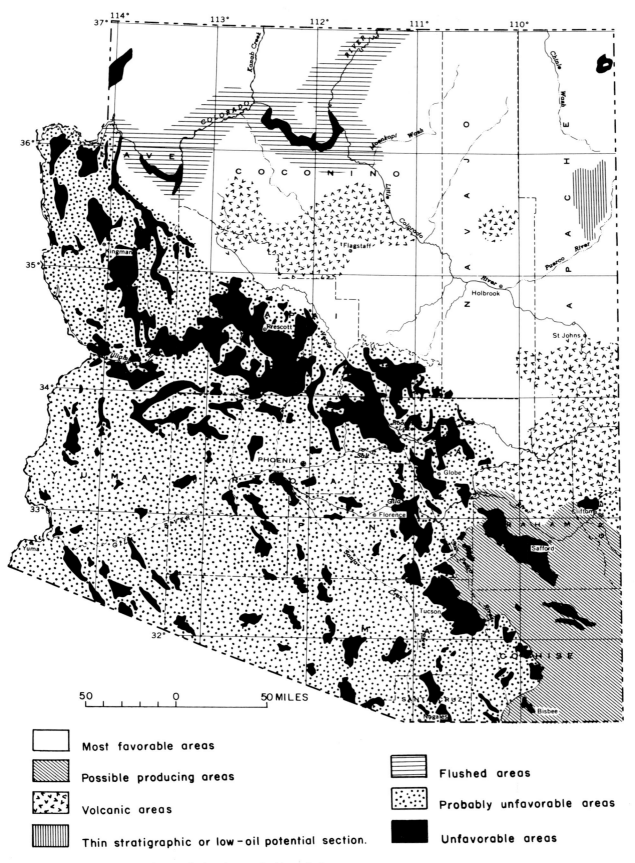

Fig. 10.9 Arizona's areas favorable for the production of oil.

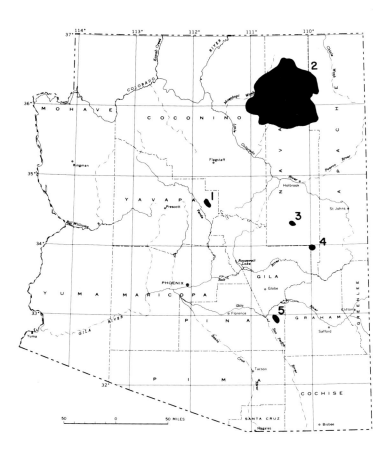

Fig. 10.10   The Black Mesa Basin to the northeast contains the state's most extensive deposits of coal.

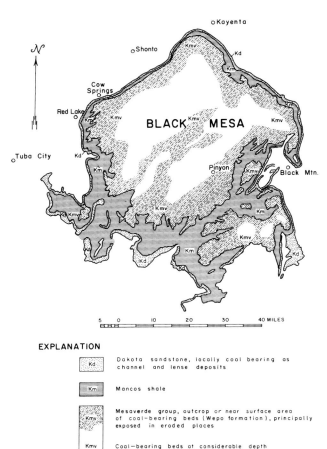

Fig. 10.11   Dakota and Mesa Verde coal beds in the Black Mesa Basin area.

Most of the coals of Arizona fall in the sub-bituminous to bituminous range. The age of the Arizona coals are Pennsylvanian and Cretaceous.

Pennsylvanian Coals. Coal occurs in the Supai redbeds in the vicinity of Fossil Creek, southeast of Clarkdale, Arizona (Fig. 10.10). Details of the geology had not been determined in the 1960s, but apparently there were several seams which thickened back from the outcrop. The extent of the field and volume of coal were also unknown.

A proximate analysis determines the percentage of moisture, volatile matter, fixed carbon, and ash present in coal. It reveals important characteristics of coal and permits its classification as to rank and use. A proximate analysis of this Supai coal shows its contents to be 5 percent moisture, 35 percent volatile matter, 44.4 percent fixed carbon, and 15.6 percent ash. The samples used for this analysis were taken from the outcrop and, therefore, tend to show higher ash, higher water, and lower volatile content than may be true for more deeply buried coal.

The samples indicate poor coking properties; however, the quality may improve in fresh samples. No sulphur determination was made, but the outcrop

samples did not appear to contain much pyrite or marcasite. The ash is reported to contain copper.

Cretaceous Coals. The largest coal field in Arizona in 1969 was in the Black Mesa Basin (Fig. 10.11). This field is adjacent to and closely related to the Gallup coal field in northwestern New Mexico. The coal seams are of Cretaceous age and are confined to the Dakota formation and Mesa Verde group of beds. These seams were being developed in the late 1960s for large-scale open-pit mining to supply a thermal power plant on the Colorado River.

The Dakota coal occurs above the massive sandstone of the Dakota formation and consists of two-to-four-foot beds, although some lenses up to nine feet thick are present. The beds are highly lenticular. The coal is of low bituminous rank and contains substantial ash. The coal can be utilized locally but probably is unsuitable for large-scale developments.

The Mesa Verde coal has been confined to the Wepo formation, which occurs in the middle of the Mesa Verde group. The coal beds are usually over four feet thick and may reach thicknesses in excess of ten feet. They are lenticular, although the coal-bearing portion of the section is fairly continuous. The coal ranges from high grade lignite to medium grade bituminous. It contains a moderate amount of ash and in places substantial sulphur in the form of pyrite and marcasite. Coking properties are poor. Its main use is expected to be in steam plants and other power generation installations.

Most of the Black Mesa coal is produced by underground mining. In 1969 a number of mines were operating, furnishing coal for local use. In a number of areas overburden is not excessive, and strip mining methods can be utilized. The dip of the coal is gentle. Campbell and Gregory estimated eight billion tons of mineable coal in the Black Mesa Basin; Kiersch estimates about two billion tons.

The Upper Cretaceous coal outcrop in the Pinedale-Show Low area is limited in extent. It is an erosional remnant of the more extensive Mesaverde coal areas to the north and east. The character of the coal is similar. Two coal seams are present about fifteen feet apart. The upper one is about ten feet thick and is very dirty; the lower one is about three feet thick and is good subbituminous rank. Because of its distribution it will be limited to local use.

The coal in T7N, R23E, west of Whiteriver, is a low-grade, thin-bedded coal in shale, and is probably a continuation of the Pinedale-Show Low field. Its age is Upper Cretaceous. It was mined until about 1930.

The Deer and Ash Creek basins near Hayden contain coal of Upper Cretaceous age. Surface exposures indicate several thin seams, none over three feet thick. The coal is dirty and frequently has shale and sand partings; sulphur and ash content are high. The coal may be badly crushed, although in places it is hard. The area is limited, and there are structural complexities. Dips of the coal in places are steep, and topography is rugged. The coal is of such poor quality that little work has been done on its distribution and economics. It is regarded as suitable for local use only. An estimate of thirty million tons has been given for the area, but this is probably high.

The areas discussed above contain the only large-scale coal deposits known in Arizona late in the 1960s. Detailed work may locate other occurrences of coal in the state, but probably no extensive high-grade coal deposits remain undiscovered.

SUMMARY. Northeastern Arizona by 1970 was most plentifully supplied with energy available from coal, oil, and gas deposits, and transcontinental railroads and pipelines connect northern Arizona with major out-of-state producing areas.

Southern Arizona has not had extensive coal deposits, and any oil and gas fields discovered were expected to be limited in extent. The area is not easily connected directly by railroad with major coal deposits, and distances to them, for economic reasons in the 1960s, precluded extensive industrial utilization of coal as a source of energy. Natural gas and oil pipelines connect southern Arizona with out-of-state sources, and these mineral fuels can economically be imported to supply necessary industrial energy. Direct connection with northeastern Arizona and Four Corners oil and gas fields might develop as demand for the products increases and as known oil and gas reserves are developed.

In northern Arizona helium gas has been found in a number of wells both on the Navajo Indian Reservation and south of it. The helium occurs in combination with other gases such as hydrocarbons (natural gas) and nitrogen. On the reservation the wells produce helium with the petroleum gases; south of the reservation, near Pinta and Navajo, the helium occurs with nitrogen. Associated with the helium are other rare gases such as argon and neon.

Helium content of the gases in the Pinta Dome area usually is about 8½ percent with the balance (approximately ninety percent) being nitrogen; elsewhere, the helium content may range down to one or two percent.

All of the helium being produced from Arizona in the late 1960s came from the Coconino Sandstone of Permian age, but the Shinarump member of the Chinle Formation (Triassic) reported good shows of gas, as did other Mesozoic and Paleozoic formations. A number of wells, especially in the Pinta Dome-Navajo Springs area, were shut in awaiting connection to a processing plant.

Pinta Dome and Navajo Springs fields were the only actively producing fields in Arizona in 1969. These fields are adjacent to each other. The raw gas is processed at Navajo, and most of the extracted helium is shipped to California as compressed helium gas or as liquid helium. In 1969 only one extraction plant was operating, but a second one was under construction, also at Navajo.

Helium produced from the reservation wells was not being processed in 1969. Predictions were that it would go to Shiprock if that government plant should be reactivated, or piped to Navajo, or that a new plant might be constructed on the reservation near the wells.

Editor: Charles Mason
Botanist

11

VEGETATION

MUCH IS HEARD of "the good old days," "grass as high as a man," and "miles and miles of good grazing for animals." It is usually man who has been responsible for the change for the worse — whether through overgrazing by livestock, carelessness with fire, or overcultivation. Occasionally one hears also that Arizona is drying up and that rainfall is not "what it used to be."

The desert of southern Arizona and northwestern Sonora has undergone many changes — some obvious, some less noticeable — since the 1880s.

Such recent changes as the spread of mesquite, affecting the range economy in southern Arizona, and the spread of water-stealing piñon and juniper in the north, are simply part of local cycles. On the whole, Arizona's present vegetation is much the same as it was when the white man first arrived, and it promises to be better in the future with new concepts of management.

Changes that have been brought about by man, climate, cattle, fire, and other factors, are the subject of *The Changing Mile,* by James R. Hastings and Raymond M. Turner (University of Arizona Press, 1965). The authors used historical records to recreate the climate and vegetation of the past, along with ninety-seven pairs of matched photographs. Each set of pictures of the same ground was taken from the same vantage point — but decades apart in time — to show changes over intervening years.

Vegetation is, after all, a product of its environment. Including extremely diverse topography and soils, the conditions encountered throughout Arizona make varying habitats available to plants representing north, east, south, and west.

Ecological Setting

Arizona divides roughly but neatly into a northern half, on the Colorado Plateau, and a southern half, with basin and range topography. The separation between these two diverse areas is the escarpment creating the Mogollon Rim, a well-defined landmark along the northern boundary of the Tonto Basin north of Payson. The northern plateau area slopes gently downward to the north and is dissected by the Colorado River and the Little Colorado, as well as by many smaller streams. Characteristic of the area are the flat-top mesas. This plateau is penetrated in places by volcanic activities resulting in such features as San Francisco Peaks at Flagstaff, or the extensive, less well-defined lava flows in the White Mountains of Apache County. The southern half of the state contains the basin and range area and is in general lower in altitude, consisting of numerous mountain ranges separated by alluvial valleys.

At Yuma, in the southwest corner of Arizona, where the Colorado River leaves the state, the elevation is about 100 feet above sea level, while only slightly more than 250 miles northeast, the lofty San Francisco Peaks rise to an elevation of over 12,600 feet. The ecologist recognizes a rule of thumb, which states that every thousand-foot rise in altitude is the equivalent of about 300 miles' distance north. Thus, while Yuma and the San Francisco Peaks are only some 200 miles apart geographically, they are some 3,600 miles apart ecologically. Yuma basks in a sub-tropical climate, while at the other extreme, on top of San Francisco Peaks, is a climate similar to that of the Northern realms of Canada and Alaska.

Altitude is not the only variable. The distribution of plant life is dependent upon a number of environmental factors, all interacting, which, on the broad scale, establish the type of vegetation encountered. Temperature, rainfall, slope, soil — man himself — all contribute to the vast complex of interacting conditions some of which tend to extremes in the Southwest. Often these maximums and minimums are decisive in determining vegetation types.

In general, forests occur where the soil is moist throughout the year and especially during the growing season. Grasslands are found where an extremely dry

Fig. 11.1 The southern Arizona desert offers conditions that are singularly favorable to the growth of the saguaro cactus.

period occurs during the year, or where the soil does not remain moist because of low rainfall. Deserts — regions of sparse vegetation — are found in combination with warm temperatures and scanty rainfall that seldom moistens the soil to a depth of more than a few inches.

The layman regards deserts as areas of no vegetation. If this were the case, deserts would be rare, because some plant life can exist, even under the most extreme climatic conditions. Areas of shifting sand dunes — the popular conception of a desert — are barren simply *because* of shifting sands rather than from lack of moisture. The so-called desert areas of the Southwest, for example Arizona, are better thought of as semideserts or semiarid areas. Growth of vegetation in such areas is sparse when compared to growth in the eastern areas of United States, but Arizona's kind of desert is rarely devoid of vegetation.

Since forests, grasslands, and deserts exist mainly because of variations in rainfall and temperature, to understand the plant cover found in Arizona, it is neces-

sary to recognize rainfall patterns and temperature variations which are closely allied to general topography and larger climatic patterns. Western Arizona receives its moisture from winter storms and summer thunderstorms in about equal proportions. On the eastern side of the state the rainfall comes mostly from summer thunderstorms, and winter rains are less important in shaping the vegetation pattern. The physiographic features that shape rainfall patterns so strikingly and the temperature variations that result from elevation and slopes are discussed elsewhere in this book and should be consulted in connection with vegetational patterns.

The plan of vegetation within Arizona can perhaps be best understood through knowledge of vegetation patterns within larger surrounding areas, since elements of Arizona's plant life come from all points of the compass. Regions to the north contribute two main vegetational types: the coniferous forests and the cold desert. From the circumpolar belt of coniferous forests, Arizona has coniferous elements, found higher and higher on the plateaus and mountains. This forest region culminates along the high rim of the escarpment forming the southern limit of the Colorado Plateau, stretching from the New Mexico boundary to the vicinity of Williams, Arizona. Similar areas on the higher regions north and south of the Mogollon Rim country are often the isolated forested regions that claim the attention of the plant geographer. In addition to the southern extensions of the northern coniferous forest on this plateau, there is also an extension of the Great Basin desert around Great Salt Lake. This cold, winter desert, which follows the low-lying land of the eroded river valleys in northern Arizona, is very striking along the northern portion of the Colorado River and its main Arizona tributary — the Little Colorado.

A large area of grassland in northern Arizona is closely related to the Great Plains. This vegetation is usually thought of as a western extension of the short grass plains, lying just east of the Rocky Mountains.

The region south of Arizona contributes another grassland, as well as desert species. In southeastern Arizona, there is an extension of the Sonoran grassland. The desert of the southwestern part of Arizona represents a continuation of the desert of Sonora. Along the Colorado River in western Arizona are regions representing extensions of southern California deserts. Also related to the vegetation of California is chaparral, a curious mixture of grasses and low shrubs forming margins along the southern desert and the Sonoran grassland.

Vegetation Types

Depending on the authority consulted, Arizona's vegetation is divided into different types — from three to twelve. These extremely diverse units make Arizona's plant life among the most varied in the United States. For the purpose of this study, Arizona's vegetation can be divided into four main categories: alpine, forest, grassland, and desert, with some subdivisions.

ALPINE. Typical alpine vegetation is very limited in Arizona, occurring only on San Francisco Peaks, which go above tree line to 12,655 feet. Vegetation at the summit of Baldy Peak (11,500 feet) in the White Mountains comes close to being alpine in character. Such areas are interesting to the botanist because the alpine plants often represent the southernmost limit of some plants that are common farther north. Such outlying stations of alpine species connect this type of vegetation with the alpine and arctic flora of circumpolar regions. The following figures show the clear relationship of this vegetation with the north:

	Number of Species	Percent
Arctic-alpine circumpolar species	15	30.6
North American arctic-alpine species	5	10.2
Rocky Mountain alpine species	24	49.0
Southwestern species	3	6.1
Endemic species	2	4.1

Fig. 11.2   Desert grassland, with the Santa Rita Mountains of southern Arizona in the background.

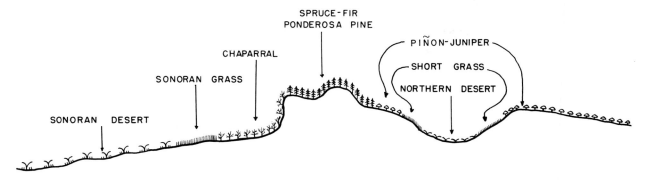

Fig. 11.3 Typical profile of Arizona from south to north showing relationships of various vegetation units. Below is a summary of principal vegetation types in Arizona (adapted from Little, 1950).

Name of Vegetation type	Characteristic plants	Elevation (feet)	Rainfall (inches)	Percentages of Total Vegetation	Location in Arizona
Alpine tundra (Arctic-Alpine Life Zone).	Mountain avens, alpine sedges, and grasses.	11,500-13,306	30-35	—	Above timber line on summit of San Francisco Mountain.
FORESTS					
Spruce-fir forest (subalpine forest, Hudsonian and Canadian Life Zone).	Engelmann spruce, alpine fir, corkbark fir.	8,500-12,000	30-35	1	High elevations, White Mountains, San Francisco Peaks, and Kaibab.
Douglas-fir forest (montane forest, Canadian Life Zone).	Douglas fir, white fir, quaking aspens, limber pine.	8,000- 9,500	25-30	2	High mountains in eastern and northern parts.
Ponderosa pine forest (Transition Life Zone).	Ponderosa pine, Arizona pine.	5,500- 8,500	19-25	6	Mountains and plateaus in northeastern half.
Piñon-juniper wood-land (Upper Sonoran Life Zone).	Piñon pines and various junipers.	4,500- 7,500	12-20	17	Plateaus and mountains in northern half.
Chaparral-Oak wood-land (Upper Sonoran Life Zone).	Shrub live oak, manza-nitas, sumacs, cliff-rose, ceanothuses.	4,000- 6,000	13-25	8	Mountains in central part.
GRASSLANDS					
Short grass (plains grassland, Upper Sonoran Life Zone).	Blue grama, hairy grama, galleta, buffalograss.	4,500- 6,500	9-20	15	Plains and plateaus in northern part.
Desert grass (semi-desert grassland, Lower Sonoran Life Zone).	Black grama, tobosa, dropseeds.	3,000- 5,000	9-18	10	Plains in southeastern part.
DESERTS					
Sagebrush (northern desert, Upper Sono-ran Life Zone).	Big sagebrush, black brush.	2,500- 6,000	7-17	6	Lower portions of northern area. Little Colorado River drainage.
Desert (semidesert shrub, Lower Sono-ran Life Zone).	Creosote bush, mesquite, tarbush, acacias, palo verdes, bur sages, cacti, saltbush.	100- 4,500	3-15	35	Southwestern half of the state and bottom of Grand Canyon.

Fig. 11.4   Subalpine grass meadows are interspersed in the forests at elevations just below the tree line.

FOREST. The subalpine, spruce-fir forest in Arizona occurs at elevations just below the tree line. San Francisco Peaks, the White Mountains, the highest parts of the Mogollon Rim, and the Kaibab Plateau support stands of this forest-type. Probably the best developed stands are those of the White Mountains. Open meadows of grass used extensively for summer grazing are interspersed in these forests along the streams. Engelmann's spruce and the two closely related firs, corkbark and alpine, are the dominant trees, with scattered broad-leaved trees, mainly aspen. In the Apache National Forest the Phelps Botanical Area on the east fork of the Little Colorado at the base of Baldy Peak has been set aside as a study area for the spruce-fir forest. The flora is rich in subalpine species. A disjunct area of this forest is found on the top of the Pinaleno Mountains of Graham County. Some of Arizona's most delightful camping areas are found in such forests.

Ponderosa Pine. The most extensive forest type in Arizona — and the most valuable economically — is the ponderosa pine. Only about six percent of Arizona in 1969 was occupied by trees of sawtimber quality, and ponderosa pine constituted almost all of it.

Pure stands of ponderosa pine occur in areas below the spruce-fir forests, merging on the north with piñon-juniper forest and on the south with the chaparral at lower elevations. The largest area of this forest occurs along the Colorado Plateau north of the Mogollon Rim from New Mexico to Williams, Arizona. Other stands

are found on the Kaibab Plateau of the North Rim of the Grand Canyon and in the high mountains of northeastern Arizona. There are many isolated patches at high elevations in other such locations as the vicinity of Prescott, Jerome, and on some peaks in southern Arizona.

These forests of ponderosa pine are often quite open, and the discontinuous canopy provides clear space where grasses form excellent grazing areas. In some of the finer stands, the grasses of the forest floor, along with the ponderosa pines, make up the entire vegetation. In some areas an understory of broad-leaved shrubby species is developed. The place of these shrubby species in the ecology of the ponderosa pine forests has been debated for a number of years, and researchers are still looking for a definitive explanation.

Not well developed in Arizona but often recognized is the Douglas fir forest-type, found at the upper limits of the ponderosa pine forest and merging with the spruce-fir forest of the higher altitudes.

Piñon-Juniper. Dropping to lower elevations from the high country of the ponderosa pine, trees become smaller and spaced more widely, with the ponderosa pine eventually giving way to smaller and more shrubby conifers — piñon pines and junipers. The phenomenon of the replacement of ponderosa pine by the piñon pine and juniper shows clearly on the road north from Flagstaff to Cameron (U.S. 89). Descending into the Little Colorado Basin, the rainfall drops from twenty inches

Fig. 11.5 Mountain meadows are ideal for grazing.

Fig. 11.6 Conifers and aspen in subalpine forests.

per year at Flagstaff to only six inches per year at Cameron at the Little Colorado crossing. Large ponderosa pines of the Flagstaff area eventually are replaced by piñons and junipers, which in turn are replaced by grasses, in a gradual transition that is complete at Cameron where the northern desert takes over.

The piñon-juniper is a distinctive type covering large areas in the northern half of the state at elevations between forty-five hundred and seventy-five hundred feet. When the trees of this forest are not too close together, a good grass covering is interspersed. This forest is a transition type between forests and grasslands, forming a variable boundary between the two vegetation types.

Chaparral-Oak Woodland. South of the ponderosa pine country of the Mogollon Rim, one encounters the same dwarfing of the trees that occurs to the north. However, the trees and shrubs that take over where rainfall becomes more sparse are not piñons and junipers but a variety of broad-leaved sclerophyllous shrubs. This type of vegetation — called chaparral — is as characteristic of the lower country south of the Rim as piñon-juniper is of the lower country north of the Rim. However, the limits of the chaparral are not as sharp or as easily defined as the limits of the piñon-juniper. The vegetation consists of shrubby oaks, sumacs, manzanitas, cliff rose, ceanothus, algerita, and buckthorns. At lower altitudes to the south these are gradually replaced by typical desert species of southwestern Arizona. Farther to the southeast at altitudes of four thousand to five thousand feet, the chaparral takes on the aspects of an oak woodland. This extension of the chaparral results in larger species of oaks and gives the grassland an appearance of an open park, again a transitional vegetation between forest and grasslands.

GRASSLAND

Northern Grassland. In the lower altitudes with lower annual rainfall, trees get smaller and more scattered until finally nothing but grass remains. Such areas in northern Arizona, below the piñon-juniper country and merging with it, constitute one of the important grasslands areas in the state. Generally conceded to be a western extension of the Great Plains of the central United States, these grasslands are continuous with the Great Plains through the low passes of the mountains of New Mexico. In addition to the grasses there are shrubs *(winter fat and chamiso)* in this type that yield excellent browse.

Sonoran Grasslands. In the southeastern part of Arizona, the chaparral is replaced at lower elevations by a grassland which represents an extension of the Sonoran Highlands grass-type found in Mexico. Included in this area are isolated mountain ranges which are covered with the chaparral-type vegetation. A few of these ranges are high enough to intercept rains that will support ponderosa pine forests, which are curious combinations of plants from the more northern coniferous forests and plants from the Sonoran Highlands to the south. Because of the milder winters, this grassland provides one of the best grazing areas in Arizona. It is where this grassland fringes the southern desert areas that mesquite has developed into a problem plant for ranchers.

Fig. 11.7   Shrubs of the southern chaparral take over.

DESERT

Northern Desert. Along the Little Colorado River basin at the lower levels in northern Arizona, there is a desert type of vegetation which is a southern extension of the Great Basin Desert of the intermontane area in Utah. Small xerophytic shrubs characterize this desert and include the salt bushes, mormon tea, blackbush, and shadscale. Big sagebrush occupies some of the higher parts of this desert and is very prominent in the Strip Country of northwestern Arizona.

Fig. 11.8   At lower elevations with less rainfall annually, ponderosa pine gives way to piñon pine and juniper.

Sonoran Desert. More than a third of Arizona is covered by the desert vegetation for which Arizona is famed in story and picture. This is the land of the stately saguaro and other cacti, as well as of many plants with small, hard leaves. This region has been called the *microphyllous desert* (referring to the small leaves), the *succulent desert* (referring to the water-storing habits of some of its plants), but is probably best known as the Sonoran Desert. It is mainly a northward extension of the desert of Sonora, Mexico.

This region is characterized by typical basin and range country. The desert mountain ranges, reaching altitudes of 3,000 to 4,000 feet, are separated by the broad, alluvial-filled valleys. The vegetation of the region is very closely related to the topography. The rough, eroding slopes of the many ranges are covered with palo verde, bur sage, cholla, prickly pear, yucca, and agave. Below the steep slopes are the outwash plains, here called *bajadas*. Here are found the most spectacular displays of cacti, including the saguaro.

As the bajadas level out to form alluvial plains, creosote bush makes its appearance. In the southwestern desert area, there are thousands of square miles covered with this well-known plant. In areas where drainage is not efficient, salt accumulations in the soil give rise to *playa* vegetation, and the salt bushes take over. Stream beds, dry in this area for much of the year, are lined with thickets of large trees and shrubs including mesquite, catclaw, wolf berry, desert willow, and the introduced tamarisk. The range of diurnal temperatures is great. Daytime temperatures in the summer are high, and nights, especially in the winter, are cool but frosts

Chuck Abbott

Fig. 11.9 The century plant is a Sonoran Desert landmark.

Fig. 11.10 The most striking displays of cactus and other unique plant life are in the alluvial-filled desert valleys.

Fig. 11.11   The pale green cottonwood tree announces spring along the desert streambeds.

are minimal. Rainfall is low and spotty. Torrential thunderstorms are the rule in summer, and flash floods are common.

The vegetation of the region between Congress Junction and Kingman and westward in the valley of the Colorado River and its tributaries north of Parker Dam is an extension of the Mohave Desert of California. One of the outstanding plants is the Joshua tree.

The region along the Colorado River south of Parker Dam is sometimes called the Colorado Desert. This desert type of vegetation is centered in the Salton Sea basin of California. The area in general is relatively frost-free, providing a habitat for some of our most frost-sensitive plants, such as ironwood and smoke trees. This is also the best citrus-growing area of the state.

A General View

THE ABUNDANCE. Kearney and Peebles' *Arizona Flora* lists 3,438 species of plants known from Arizona. These species are classified in 921 genera and 133 families. The richness of Arizona's flora is equaled by very few other regions of the United States. Composites, grasses, and legumes constitute the three largest families. In 1969 Texas and California were the only states in this country with more than the 385 grass species recorded for Arizona. The cactus family, especially well represented in Arizona, has 71 native species. Arizona is rich also in members of the fern family and fern allies, with nearly one hundred species.

THE VALUE. The vegetation of Arizona is as varied as its topography, which makes it an impossible task to place a monetary value on the plant life of a state used by over one and one-half million residents and hundreds of thousands of tourists. Some Arizonans are involved in businesses which utilize the vegetation through a removal of plants and plant parts, for example, lumbermen and cattlemen; many others utilize the vegetation, knowingly or unknowingly, for its value in protecting watersheds; still others are directly or indirectly interested in the vegetation for its aesthetic value.

Many people are surprised to find that a "desert state" such as Arizona has a lumbering industry. Ponderosa pine forests of the higher elevations have supplied raw material for the lumbermills around which cities like Flagstaff and McNary have developed. It has been estimated that in the late 1960s Arizona had about 16 million board feet of timber. This amount represented only a small portion of the annual demand in the United States, but by careful harvesting similar to that practiced on the Apache Indian Reservation, Arizona's lumbering industry is expected to be on a sustaining basis.

A prime user of Arizona's vegetation is the cattle industry. Although the principal areas for cattle raising are centered in the northern and southern grasslands, cattle can be grazed on any vegetation type. Desert areas with their sparse grasses and predominant shrubs furnish browse and in a wet year good forage; however, these areas are easily over-grazed, and the carrying capacity of the vegetation varies with the rainfall.

Fig. 11.12 Northern Arizona grasslands frequently include shrubs of a kind that are excellent browsing for livestock.

Arizona's forests likewise supply grazing areas with a grass cover determined by the spacing of the trees. The grasses are likely to be sparse in the denser shade, but the open meadows scattered through the forested areas supply abundant grasses during the summer growing season. The grasslands also can and have been overgrazed, but careful management of this valuable vegetation should make possible the continuation of cattle raising as one of Arizona's most important industries.

To evaluate in monetary terms the vegetation on Arizona's watershed is difficult, if not impossible. Water is one of Arizona's critical natural resources, as well as one of life's necessities. Man attempts therefore to do anything and everything possible to make more water available.

Water is needed by plants, as it is by most living things. Water is taken in by plant roots, transported through the plant and utilized in part in various processes; however, much of the water taken in by the plants is returned to the atmosphere by the evaporation process termed transpiration. It is the transpired water which causes difficulty with the water-users for man anticipates this as water he could use to irrigate crops or support more people in the cities. Various proposals have been made to save this water for man's use, from the most drastic one of denuding the mountain slopes to the plan for selective thinning. The first of these proposals met with storms of protest from many directions.

Plants on a watershed have a great value in return for which the water they use is but a small price. Their roots hold the soil and prevent erosion which would fill the reservoirs with silt; at the same time the roots keep the soil loose and porous so water can soak into the ground to be released slowly, thereby preventing flash floods. Plants also shade the ground and prevent the loss of much water through evaporation of snow and water. Trees on the high-mountain watersheds slow the melting of snow packs, thus extending the water supply over a longer period of the year to provide perpetual streams and to reduce the risk of floods. Finally, the less tangible aesthetic value of plants on a watershed and the value of the vegetation to the sportsman as a protection for game should be considered.

Value of vegetation to the sportsman should not, however, be limited to the watershed, because game of one form or another is adapted to each type of plant association: deer and elk to the chaparral and mountain forests; quail to the grasslands; doves to desert river bottoms. Lakes and streams, cool and refreshing, provide fishing areas made possible in part by the surrounding vegetation.

The aesthetic value of Arizona's vegetation is attested to in part by the number of picnickers and campers. In the winter many parties can be found coming to the warm, sunny desert; in the summer the desert dwellers move to the cool, shaded forests of the mountain areas.

Tourists are also indicators, in part, of the value of the vegetation. Arizona is well endowed with national parks and monuments. Two of the monuments have been established exclusively for the vegetation they contain. Saguaro National Monument represents many species of desert vegetation including a magnificent stand of the giant cactus. The saguaro, more than any other single plant, represents Arizona and the desert in the minds of most people. Symbolizing sun and warmth to people of cooler climes, it is probably Arizona's best advertisement. Organ Pipe Cactus National Monument likewise contains an outstanding display of desert vegetation, including the only abundant stand of organ pipe and senita cacti in the United States. Both of these sites attract many tourists each year. Grand Canyon National Park and Chiricahua National Monument were established because of their topographic features, but each has a vegetation of considerable interest to the visitor.

Cities and counties have also established parks and recreation areas that exploit the natural vegetation to attract visitors. Tucson Mountain Park has an outstanding example of desert vegetation, and the Arizona-Sonora Desert Museum has assembled a large collection of plants labeled in enlightening detail. The Desert Botanical Garden at Papago Park near Phoenix has noteworthy collection of labeled cacti.

The ultimate value of Arizona's vegetation is based on multiple-use principles. One use must be set against another until a balance suitable to nature is reached. Only when it is possible to see all factors in relationship will the value of the vegetative resource be known.

Howard K. Gloyd
Biologist

Lyle Sowls
Wildlife Management

Charles H. Lowe
Biologist

Floyd Werner
Entomologist

12

ANIMAL LIFE

THE ANIMAL LIFE of Arizona, like its plant life, is extremely diversified. This diversity results from the vast differences in climate, physiography, and vegetation which occur within the state. Accordingly, a large number of different types of animal habitats — or life zones — exist in Arizona, ranging from the hot, arid, low desert in southern Yuma County, through rich upland deserts, grasslands, and woodlands to moist, cold, high montane and alpine habitats such as those in the San Francisco and White mountains.

In many places these habitats merge so gradually that, as one travels along the highway, it is practically impossible to determine where the dividing line is between two adjacent life zones. In other areas, particularly where the elevation rises abruptly, the lines between different habitats are quite distinct. In fact, it was in the San Francisco Mountain region of central Arizona that C. Hart Merriam, in 1889, made the first observations of distinct zones of plant and animal life which he later developed into the Life-Zone System for classifying habitats. Merriam's system has been widely used by biologists in North America studying the distribution and evolution of North American animals and plants.

The fauna or animal life of the state is made up of three major elements: Mexican, Rocky Mountain, and Grassland. In general the Rocky Mountain forms occur at higher elevations in the northern and central part of the state, and also as isolated populations on various of the higher mountains in the southern part. The Grassland forms occur mainly in the eastern half of the state, both north and south of the high Mogollon Rim. The highly diversified Mexican forms occur primarily in the southern half of the state and at all elevations from desert to over 10,000 feet in the Graham Mountains.

In the recent past man has played an important part in changing the composition of the fauna and influencing the ranges of the various kinds of animals present in Arizona. With the damming of major rivers such as the Gila and Salt, and minor rivers, and the pumping of the groundwater for irrigation, drastic changes have been imposed upon the animal life. The great Gila River, whose waters once traversed the entire state of Arizona from New Mexico to California, in modern times has been dry most of the year throughout much of its length. This and similar losses of natural heritage affect not only such forms as fish and beaver but all kinds of animal life — invertebrates, fishes, amphibians, reptiles, birds, and mammals — which depend in some part on the habitats afforded by intermittent or permanent streams.

The large carnivores in Arizona, such as the wolf and grizzly bear, have been exterminated or extremely reduced in numbers, and many of the large herbivores, such as the antelope, have also been greatly diminished in population and in their distribution within the state. Many of the grassland species, including the prairie dog, have also become more scarce. At least one, the black-tailed prairie dog which formerly occurred throughout the southwestern part of the state, seems to have been exterminated.

Since the 1850s naturalists from all over the world have visited Arizona to study its unique fauna. Many scientists have returned to Arizona to live and to study problems of arid lands which will probably take many lifetimes to solve completely.

Invertebrates

Arizona's geographic position, varied topography, and climate have given it one of the most interesting faunas of land invertebrates in the United States, dominated by the arthropods. The phylum Arthropoda, which includes the classes Insecta, Arachnida, Crustacea, and Chilopoda, consists of invertebrate animals with articulated bodies and limbs.

Marvin H. Frost Jr.

Fig. 12.1   The hairy scorpion, the tarantula, and the centipede are venomous but not extremely dangerous to man.

Arizona is visited annually by many zoologists, who sometimes travel for thousands of miles to study animals that are found in this area and nowhere else in the United States. Despite intensive study for some years, kinds previously completely unknown are still being discovered, even in areas that are now urban. Only a few kinds can be included in the brief summary here. Over twenty thousand kinds are estimated to exist in the state. The kinds discussed here are arranged according to general habitat, since those in the various areas differ greatly from each other.

DESERT ARTHROPODS. The arthropods that live in the desert have many problems. They are cold-blooded animals of small size and very soon reach the temperature of their immediate environment; if this temperature rises too high, they die. Most of the desert arthropods can be classed as "desert-evaders." They spend the day underground, inside plants, or in other places where they are protected from the full impact of the sun. In the hottest areas, most of them are underground. At night they come out, move around, feed, mate, and carry on other normal animal functions. A desert area that appears to be completely free of animal life during the day may become very active at night. A few arthropods, particularly some of the insects, seem to be better adapted to the desert and are active during the day. Somehow they keep their body temperatures down, although the way they do it is not well understood. Some have reflecting layers of white hair or other special modifications. A very few are opaque black, and one would suppose that these get very hot. *Phodaga alticeps,* a black blister beetle, runs around on the sand in the Yuma area during the hottest time of the day and the hottest months. Certainly it is not evading the heat. Most of the diurnal flying insects observe the siesta, hanging up under leaves or retiring to their burrows around noon and becoming active only in the morning and late afternoon. Even the introduced honeybee stays at home during the hottest part of very hot days.

Perhaps of greatest interest to the person who lives or travels in the desert are the various venomous arthropods found there. They form a distinctive segment of the desert, ranking with the spiny plants and rattlesnakes. They are almost always present, but the danger of being hurt by them is not great, and reasonable precaution prevents trouble. Of top rank are the scorpions. These are primarily nocturnal animals, related to spiders but placed in a separate order. They have four pairs of walking legs, a pair of slender, crab-like pincers and a long, slender tail, which ends in a stinger. All scorpions are provided with venom, and they all will use it if they are disturbed. The normal function of the stinger and the venom is one of getting food, for scorpions live by killing and devouring insects and other arthropods. When the stinger is being brought to use, the abdomen is curved up over the body so that the tip points forward over the head. Most scorpions are quite aggressive, and the stinger can be inserted with great accuracy. The old admonition to shake out shoes and clothing in the morning should be observed wherever scorpions are present, and particularly if one has been using an abandoned building as a campsite. Only one group of scorpions has a deadly venom. This is the genus *Centruroides.* Members of this genus measure up to about two and one-half inches in length and are pale, with slender tails. The stinger has a small spine at its base, on the underside, on the bulbous last abdominal segment. Anyone stung by a scorpion of this genus should seek medical attention at once. The sting may not be very painful at first, but a systemic reaction follows. It is well to capture the offender, so that it can be identified by the attending physician. Even smashed remains may help him to decide on the proper course of treatment. Some other scorpions are much larger, up to six inches long and are dark brown in color. These are relatively harmless. Should scorpions become abundant around a residence, they can be controlled by the application of residual insecticides. Particular attention should be paid to woodpiles, the undersides of large stones, and trash, because the scorpions return to daytime hiding places there after foraging for food at night. Premises free of piled material rarely are scorpion-infested.

A related group, the solpugids or sun spiders, is almost as universally feared as scorpions, but without reason. These animals are about an inch long, with eight legs and a pair of strong pincers and a stubby abdomen. They are pale in color and often congregate around outside lights, where they run down and eat the insects that are found there. For some reason they are known locally as *vinegaroons,* a name correctly applied to the harmless whip scorpion of higher elevations.

Spiders are more feared than their actual reputation warrants. Tarantulas, Arizona's largest spiders, are often seen along roads in the evening. They live in holes in the ground and come out in search of insects at dusk. The largest individuals are females, and they may have a body-length of three inches, with four pairs of rather heavy legs making them look much larger. Most individuals are brown, but some have reddish hair that makes them look quite striking. The venom of the tarantula is not dangerous, and because of their sluggishness there is little chance of being bitten. The only truly dangerous spider in the region is the black widow. Females are usually shiny black, with a red-hourglass marking on the underside of their pea-sized abdomens. Young females, all adult males, and a few females have diagonal white markings on the upperside of the abdomen. They spin loose webs of very tough silk in protected places and are very likely to move into houses and outbuildings, even in urban areas. Spraying with a residual insecticide is effective in their control. Few people are bitten by these spiders, even in areas where they are much more abundant than they are in Arizona. The species is found all the way across the southern United States and well into Mexico. The brown recluse spider of the midwest and southeast does not range into Arizona although a closely related species, the Arizona brown spider, is native to the state. The normal habitat of the Arizona brown spider is under pieces of wood, dead cacti, and similar objects in the desert, but it does occasionally move into dark places in buildings in desert locations. The Arizona brown spider has undoubtedly been in contact with man for a long time and there is no reason for alarm at its presence in the state. But it would be only prudent to eliminate any household infestation, rather than take the risk of a bite.

Centipedes, or hundred-leggers, are also venomous but not deadly. *Scolopendra heros,* Arizona's largest species, reaches a length of more than six inches and is straw-colored, with the front and hind ends black. Centipedes have the first pair of legs modified into fangs, which lie just under the head. The legs at the end of the body have no venom, though by the layman they are usually reputed to have. Even large centipedes occasionally find their way into houses. They can be controlled by the use of the same insecticides that are used against scorpions and the black widow spider. The venom produces violent pain, but the chances of being bitten are not great unless one attempts to pick the centipede up.

The foregoing venomous arthropods have probably received more than their share of popular interest. The person who lives in the desert should be aware of their presence and should know what to do about them. Children should be taught not to turn over logs and stones without looking to see what might be underneath. But their presence should not deter anyone from enjoying the desert with its many beauties, free from most of the pesky biting insects he finds in the out-of-doors in many other regions.

There are no truly venomous insects in Arizona, in the sense that they carry a deadly poison. In fact, most of them have no poison at all. A few individuals are so sensitive — or allergic — to bee and wasp stings that they must avoid them at any cost, but for most people the few insects that bite or sting cause little more than minor local pain. Insects are six-legged arthropods that usually have wings in the adult stage. The immature stages may be very much like the adult, as with grasshoppers, or they may be larvae of very different appearance, as with butterflies, flies, beetles, and wasps. The larva transforms to an immobile pupa, from which the adult emerges. Once an insect has reached the adult stage and has wings, it grows no more. A little fly does not develop into a big fly or a little beetle into a big beetle. Some kinds increase in size as the eggs and fat bodies fill out the abdomen, but the wings and the rest of the body remain the same. Although the adults of insects are usually rather short-lived, their immature stages may last as long as several years.

A great many of the desert insects are nocturnal. This is the case with one of the few distinctively desert forms that actively seeks a blood-meal from man — the cone-nose bug, known locally as Hualapai tiger, Texas bed bug, and other names. This insect has sucking mouthparts and is about an inch long in the adult stage. The immature individuals are similar to the adult and live in the burrows of native rodents, especially of the pack rat. They feed on the blood of their rodent hosts. The adults fly around at night and move toward light. If a house in the desert is well lighted, some of the adult bugs may end up inside, and they then seek out a blood-meal from man, rather than from the normal host. The bite they inflict on a sleeping man is quite painful, but the pain does not develop until after the insect has fed. Well-screened houses are rarely invaded, and the insects are not often seen far from undisturbed desert areas. However, they do sometimes become a problem in suburban areas around Tucson and Phoenix.

In the same areas, a stinging caterpillar sometimes becomes very abundant on palo verde trees. This is the caterpillar of the palo verde buck moth, which reaches a length of about an inch and a half and is covered with numerous branching spines. These spines have poison inside them and are capable of causing painful wounds if one is so unfortunate as to brush against them. The caterpillars develop in later summer; they form loose cocoons, pupate, and emerge in the middle of the winter as gray and white moths with reddish abdomens. The adults mate then, and the females lay masses of eggs on palo verde, these hatching into caterpillars the following summer.

Another caterpillar also becomes a problem in similar areas. This one may be as much as three inches long, smooth, with a harmless spine on the end of the body. The color varies from green to black, through spots and strips. This is the caterpillar of the white-lined sphinx moth. It feeds on various native relatives of the garden four-o'clock plant. Great numbers may be produced in favorable years, and they migrate from their feeding grounds by the thousands, overrunning the yards and patios in their way. They eventually dig into the ground, pupate, and emerge as adult moths about two inches long, with narrow wings. These moths are often abundant around lights at night and may also be seen at dusk, hovering over flowers like hummingbirds.

Of the beetles, one of the largest to appear in Arizona is the rhinoceros beetle, up to two inches long, shiny brown, and heavy bodied. The males have three blunt horns on the front of the body. The larvae live in rotten wood. Both adults and larvae are harmless. Another large brown beetle, up to three inches long and with long antennae or "feelers" is the adult of the palo verde root-borer. The beetles fly from late afternoon to early evening. The females lay their eggs in holes under palo verde trees, and the larvae bore down until they reach roots. In the course of their development they may hollow the roots out completely. The Mexican palo verde is extremely susceptible to damage, large trees sometimes dying suddenly. The white larvae may be as much as five or six inches long. Active black beetles about an inch long, found running under street lights, are ground beetles. These are protected by a vile-smelling secretion and are known in most areas as "stink bugs." They should not be confused with the stink bugs that damage crops; these are usually green, are much smaller, and have sucking mouth parts. The ground beetles are beneficial to the balance of nature, feeding on caterpillars in both adult and larval stages.

The most abundant of the day-flying beetles in the cities is the fig or green June beetle. This insect is heavy bodied, about an inch long, opaque green with yellow margins above and metallic green below. The adults arrive at just about the time that figs, grapes, peaches, and other fruits are ripening in dooryard plantings. The adults may devour most of the fruit in some areas. Covering the plants with paper bags or cloth is the only practical protection. The larvae live in compost and in old manure, and the only permanent way of eliminating the beetles is to get rid of their larval habitat. This is difficult in most urban areas but is feasible in commercial plantings of fruit trees and vines.

Of the grasshoppers, the desert grasshopper *(Trimerotropis)* is the most abundant. The adults are up to two inches long, grayish with black markings and with hind wings mostly yellow. Enormous numbers sometimes fly to street lights in early summer. The desert race of the common field cricket often comes to lights also, particularly in the region from Yuma to Phoenix, as well as in the deserts of southern California. This race develops long wings and flies readily. Other races in Arizona have short wings.

Ants are numerous in the desert, but two kinds are spectacular. One is the harvester ant group, of which there are several species, varying in color from reddish-brown to black. These large ants have simple nest openings but clear all vegetation for several feet around them. Their food consists largely of seeds. The visitor who has never encountered stinging ants before is likely to get quite a surprise if he lingers too long close to the nest. The other conspicuous ant is the leaf-cutter ant, which makes large mounds at its nest entrances, often in the form of a hollowed cone. This species cuts green leaves from many plants, carrying them back to the nest, where they are used in raising a fungus serving the ants as food.

Desert shrubs in bloom may attract a swarming mass of flying insects that are there to obtain nectar and pollen. Many kinds of beetles, flies, bees, wasps, and butterflies may be found on a single bush. In size they are dominated by the huge tarantula-hawk wasps, up to two and one-half inches long, blue-black, with black or orange wings. The female stings and paralyzes tarantulas, carries them to a burrow, and lays an egg on each. The tarantula serves as food for her larva. The wasps have a formidable stinger. They are not often really abundant but they are so large that they form a conspicuous part of the fauna.

GRASSLAND ARTHROPODS. Since there is a gradual transition from desert to grassland, many of the arthropods of the desert are also found where grass is the dominant plant. But the grass as richer plant cover provides a habitat for additional varieties. The grasshoppers, in particular, are more diversified. Several kinds become abundant enough in some years to warrant insecticidal control. Perhaps the showiest grasshopper is the horse lubber, up to two and one-half inches long, heavy bodied, and black with yellow markings. The wings are too short to be used for flying, and the hind wings are mostly pink. These grasshoppers and the much more drab plains lubber are sometimes numerous along roads. While many kinds of grasshoppers damage the range, some of them are really beneficial to man, since they do not eat grass, but other plants that are undesirable on the range. For this reason careful checks are made of the species present before any control measures are started, even in outbreak years.

Among the more abundant beetles of the grassland are certain of the blister beetles. These are tied in with grasshoppers rather directly. The young larvae of the beetles seek out the egg-pods of the grasshoppers, which are laid in the ground. There, a single larva soon eats up all the eggs in one pod. Then it withdraws from the egg-pod, goes into a resting stage, and emerges as a beetle the following year. Blister beetles and certain flies do such an effective job of destroying grasshopper eggs that outbreaks are infrequent. The adult blister beetles themselves sometimes cause damage, particularly in cultivated areas, but they must be counted as beneficial on the range.

OAK-ZONE ARTHROPODS. Some of the most unusual insects in Arizona are found principally or entirely in the oak zone. Entomologists who visit the state usually spend much of their time in the lower canyons in this zone, and such sites as Ramsey, Madera, and Oak Creek canyons have become famous for their insect fauna. The oak zone is more or less continuous with a similar one in northwestern Mexico but is much more accessible in Arizona than it is there. Many insects in the oak zone are known in the United States only in Arizona. The richest portion extends from Cochise and Santa Cruz counties northwestward along the Mogollon Rim.

Butterflies, moths, and beetles make up a large portion of this interesting fauna, depending on the varied oak-zone flora for their food supply. The climate is not as extreme as it is on the desert, and most of the insects have no special adaptations to withstand intense heat. Very few of them would be classed as pests, for the simple reason that there are few cultivated or valuable wild plants in this zone. One of the very few poisonous arthropods found here is the puss caterpillar. This is about an inch in length when full-sized, brown, and very soft-looking. Under the soft covering of hairs, however, are some erect poison spines, which stick into the hands of a person handling them, causing intense pain. The caterpillar is most likely to be found on oaks. It makes a tight cocoon, which opens by a sort of lid at one end when the adult moth emerges.

Among the beetles of the oak zone, several kinds of scarabs are especially noteworthy. The most famous is *Plusiotis gloriosa,* a pale green beetle about an inch long, with metallic silver stripes. The adults are most often seen around lights at night but apparently feed mainly on juniper and have been seen covering single trees to produce a summer Christmas tree without equal. The larvae live underground. A related species, *Plusiotis beyeri,* is slightly larger and pale green with lavender legs. Both species are avidly sought by amateur collectors.

Of the arthropods other than insects, perhaps the best known is the whip scorpion. This animal is up to three inches long, with a heavy brown body and an extremely slender, whiplike tail. Because it looks something like a scorpion, it is almost universally feared. It is harmless. A strong vinegarlike odor gives it the local name of vinegaroon, a name indiscriminately applied to the solpugids or sun spiders and to one wingless subterranean relative of grasshoppers. Whip scorpions are much more abundant in the area to the east of Arizona, but they have been found in most of the southeastern mountains in this state.

CONIFEROUS FOREST ARTHROPODS. At higher elevations, at least wherever moisture is adequate, the coniferous forest is dominant, and the arthropods associated with it are generally different from those at lower elevations. Most of them are the same as the ones found in the Rocky Mountains and even in southern Canada and the northeastern United States. Arizona shares with the Rockies a number of kinds that attack standing trees either by burrowing under the bark or into the wood, or by stripping the tree of its foliage. A caterpillar, the Great Basin tent caterpillar, often defoliates cottonwoods and aspens in this zone. The insects that damage forest trees are capable of causing great loss in marketable wood products and are under constant scrutiny. Outbreaks are often treated chemically.

Aside from the tree-killing or defoliating forest pests, which are conspicuous because of the damage they cause, the most obvious single kind of insect in the mountains is the convergent lady beetle. Great numbers of this small black and orange beetle congregate on certain peaks every summer. The areas covered are so uniform that one might think that the beetles were permanent residents. They are not, however. For some reason, generation after generation of beetles select the same spots. The beetles breed in the lowlands, where they are important predators on aphids or plant lice. In early summer, part of them move to the mountains and remain there the rest of the summer and the following winter, leaving again the following spring.

The permanent streams of the higher elevations have a diverse aquatic insect fauna that is quite different from that of the intermittent streams and ponds lower down, and from that of the Colorado River. As a source of food for fish, this fauna has some indirect economic significance.

Of particular biological interest are the populations of *Scaphinotus,* a group of flightless, snail-eating, ground beetles. The populations on the isolated mountain ranges of southeastern Arizona are mostly different from each other, the differences being great enough that they are classed as separate species. They seem to have evolved in these mountains from an ancient stock which must have been able to get from mountain to mountain at some time in the past when the climate was more favorable for forests in the lowlands.

SUMMARY. The arthropods of the several climatic and vegetational zones of Arizona are generally quite different from each other. Those of the desert are largely nocturnal, and some of the diurnal ones have special adaptations to reflect the strong sunlight. Most of the kinds that are provided with venom are restricted to the desert. In the oak zone more are diurnal, and there is great diversity of kinds, many being shared with similar areas in northwestern Mexico, but not with the rest of the United States. In the zone of the coniferous forest most of the arthropods are like those of the Rocky Mountains and other forested areas in northern North America.

Vertebrates

The vertebrate animals occurring within the state of Arizona fall into the five major classes of vertebrate: namely, fishes, amphibians, reptiles, birds, mammals.

FISHES. Of the total of sixty-one species of fish now inhabiting Arizona waters, twenty-eight are natives, and thirty-three are introduced. The introductions from other states include, in addition to game species, several small bait fish which are mostly minnows and large, rough fish which are mainly carp.

A single native game fish, the Arizona native trout *(Salmo gilae)* occurs in the headwaters of the Gila River. It has now hybridized in large part with the planted rainbow trout. This beautiful yellow-golden native trout reaches a length of about sixteen inches and a weight of about two pounds. It remains in pure form in Greenlee County in the headwaters of Eagle Creek, a tributary of the Gila River.

Arizona's waters are well stocked with trout and warmwater sport fishes including panfish and catfish. The primary warmwater fishing areas are rivers and lakes in the central part of the state, from the Colorado River on the west across Arizona to Lyman Reservoir in Greenlee County on the east. The warmwater game fishes are channel catfish, yellow bass (or striped bass), smallmouth bass, largemouth bass, green sunfish, bluegill, white crappie, black crappie, and yellow perch.

Primary trout fishing waters are in the central and northern parts of the state from the Colorado River on the west and Grand Canyon on the north to Coolidge Dam on the Gila River at the south and eastward to the Blue River. In addition to the Arizona native trout there are four principal introduced trout species: rainbow, brown, cutthroat, and eastern brook.

Howard K. Gloyd

Fig. 12.2   The venomous Gila monster (top) and the harmless horned lizard (horny toad) are both native to Arizona.

Although surprising, it is nonetheless true that a remarkable and highly diversified native fish fauna is a recreational resource and scientifically important part of Arizona's heritage. Moreover, the native Arizona fishes are among the most interesting found in the United States. Some are rare and much sought after, others are isolated relics also of scientific importance, and others are of value because of their interesting peculiarities.

One of Arizona's fishes is among the world's largest minnows. This is the Colorado River Squawfish *(Ptychocheilus lucius)* which reaches a length of approximately five feet and a weight of about one hundred pounds. In sharp contrast, two other species occurring in Arizona are among the smallest of North American fishes. These are the Gila Topminnow *(Poeciliopsis occidentalis)*, which is a live-bearer from one to two inches in length, and the Desert Pupfish *(Cyprinodon macularius)*, which reaches a length of from two to three inches.

The Colorado River that courses through the Grand Canyon of Arizona is the home of several remarkable native species. For example, in addition to the one-hundred-pound Squawfish there occur two striking humpbacked species. One is a huge humpbacked sucker *(Xyrauchen texanus)*, and the other is a large humpbacked minnow *(Gila cypha)*. The adaptive significance of humpbackedness in fishes is unknown.

In the Colorado, Salt, Gila, and Verde rivers, and in other rivers and streams in many parts of the state there occurs the "Verde trout" or "Gila trout" which is a large minnow also known as the Bonytail *(Gila robusta)*. This native species reaches a length of sixteen inches and a weight of about two pounds. It readily takes a fly and, to some people at least, superficially resembles a trout. While not officially considered a game fish and rather bony to eat, it is a hardy native that can be fun to catch.

Of Arizona's native fish fauna with its immense interest and scientific importance, it is inevitable that we must also record that it is rapidly disappearing.

AMPHIBIANS. The amphibians in Arizona as elsewhere are represented by salamanders, frogs, and toads. The salamanders, however, are represented by only a single widespread species, the tiger salamander *(Ambystoma tigrinum)*. It is common in northern Arizona where it is represented by two subspecies, the Utah tiger salamander *(Ambystoma tigrinum utahense)* and the Arizona tiger salamander *(Ambystoma tigrinum nebulosum)*. In southern Arizona the salamander is of only infrequent occurrence south of the Gila River; here the subspecies is the Sonora tiger salamander *(Ambystoma tigrinum stebbinsi)*.

The greenish gilled larvae called water dogs or mud puppies are sold for bait-fishing and prove an excellent bass bait. Unfortunately, such activity leads to accidental mixings of population and is, of course, detrimental to the study of the natural distribution and geographic variation of the tiger salamander.

Fig. 12.3 Unlike the Gila monster, who is a carnivore, the chuckwalla is a harmless, plant-eating lizard.

There are twenty-one species of frogs and toads in Arizona. One of these, the bullfrog *(Rana catesbeiana)* is an introduced species from the southeastern United States. It is now the largest western frog, reaching a body-length of eight inches.

The majority of the remaining twenty species are primarily Mexican in distribution. Several are grassland species. Some of the toads *(Bufo, Scaphiopus)* are especially well adapted amphibians for life in open, semiarid lands, while most of the frogs *(Rana, Pseudacris, Hyla, Pternohyla)* are more restricted to the nearness of permanent or semipermanent streams or ponds.

Some species, notably the spadefoot toads *(Scaphiopus),* begin their seasonal activity with the onset of summer rains in July. They virtually "explode" out of the ground at this time, and several hundred males and females may constitute the breeding congregation at a single temporary, rain-formed pond.

The Colorado River toad *(Bufo alvarius)* of southern Arizona and northern Mexico is the largest western toad and reaches a body-length of about six inches. It is also the most poisonous species in Arizona. While the skin and skin secretions of most frogs and toads are poisonous to some degree, those of the Colorado River toad are especially toxic and have proved lethal to small dogs which have mouthed them.

Taken as a whole, the amphibian component of Arizona fauna is neither large in number or species, nor is it particularly well known. During the summer rainfall period (July-September), however, frogs and toads are often found in great abundance. The species which do occur here are remarkably well adapted for life in some of the harshest environments occupied by amphibians in North America. With respect to these animals, scientists would like to know more about the mechanisms of the adaptations that permit their successful life.

REPTILES. Arizona is a paradise for herpetologists and other students of reptilian biology. The state's fauna includes forty-eight species of snakes, forty-four species of lizards, and five species of turtles.

The turtles include the well-known desert tortoise *(Gopherus agassizi)* which is strictly land-living, the lesser known box turtle *(Terrapene ornata)* of the grassland, two mud turtles *(Kinosternon sonoriense* and *Kinosternon flavescens),* all of which are semiaquatic, and the introduced soft-shelled turtle *(Trionyx spinifera)* from the eastern United States. The last is aquatic except for the moment of egg-laying on stream and river banks.

Among the lizards, one of the best known but most poorly understood is the Gila monster *(Heloderma suspectum). Heloderma* is the only poisonous lizard in the United States, and this genus includes one other member equally poisonous, the Mexican beaded lizard *(Heloderma horridum).* The venom of the Gila monster is but mildly toxic compared to that of deadly spiders, scorpions, rattlesnakes, and coral snakes. In fact, it remains questionable that the bite of a Gila monster alone can kill a healthy human being. While the animal is potentially dangerous to man, its deadliness is greatly overrated. When confronted by man the Gila monster's only desire is to escape and be left alone.

Howard K. Gloyd

Fig. 12.4   The diamondback is one of eleven rattlesnake species in Arizona. The Sonoran coral snake (right) and the rattler are the only snakes in Arizona potentially dangerous to man.

The Gila monster also occurs in extreme southwestern Utah, extreme southwestern New Mexico, and in Sonora, Mexico. Two other lizards are confused with the Gila monster. The adult banded gecko *(Coleonyx variegatus)* of the desert reaches a length of three inches and is thought by many people to be a baby Gila monster. The chuckwalla *(Sauromalus obesus)* is a large, rock-dwelling lizard reaching a length of eight inches, and this harmless desert species also is often mistaken for an adult Gila monster.

Arizona is the headquarters in the United States for horned lizards *(Phrynosoma),* or horny toads. Six of the seven species of the United States occur here. Five of the six are desert or grassland species, or both. One, the short-horned lizard, is primarily a mountain species, found at elevations up to ten thousand feet. It bears its young alive as an adaptation to a colder climate.

Many other kinds of lizards are adapted to desert habitats as varied as shifting dune sand (the fringe-toed lizard), desert shrubs and trees (the brush and tree lizards), and rocky hills (the collared lizard). Others live in the grasslands of eastern Arizona (the prairie lizard and the little striped whiptail), and some live in woodlands and forests (the plateau lizard, the alligator lizard, and the plateau whiptail).

In addition to the banded gecko *(Coleonyx)* two other lizards *(Xantusia)* are also nocturnal species. During the heat of the summer the Gila monster is also frequently active at night. Most lizards, however, are diurnal, and all but the Gila monster are harmless. None should be needlessly destroyed. Most are "insect feeders" and include such animals as grasshoppers, spiders, scorpions, and centipedes in their diets. The chuckwalla *(Sauromalus)* and the desert iguana *(Dipsosaurus)* are vegetarians. The Gila monster is a carnivore and eats birds and bird eggs, mammals, and lizards.

In Arizona the horned lizards and the Gila monster are protected by law. Eleven species of rattlesnakes *(Crotalus)* occur in Arizona, and when the subspecies are also counted the total of kinds of rattlesnakes is fifteen. They occur from one hundred feet (Yuma County) to more than ten thousand feet elevation in the Graham Mountains of Graham County. They occur almost everywhere in Arizona, from shifting desert sands to high coniferous forest habitats. All rattlesnakes are potentially dangerous to man from the time they are born.

One other kind of snake that is potentially dangerous to man occurs in Arizona. This is the Sonoran coral snake *(Micruroides euryxanthus)*. While containing a lethal neurotoxic venom for small animals, this small snake of a maximum twenty-inch length has not been known to bite human beings even when it has been carelessly picked up and handled. It occurs in the southern half of Arizona where several other small, brightly colored snakes are frequently confused with it. The Sonoran coral snake has a black snout which readily distinguishes it from the harmless species.

In addition to the rattlesnakes and the coral snake, there are four other poisonous kinds of snakes in Arizona, none of which is dangerous to man. These are the lyre snake *(Trimorphodon),* the night snake *(Hypsiglena),* the vine snake *(Oxbelis),* and the black-headed snake *(Tantilla)*. Their distribution is primarily in the southern half of the state.

A true member of the boa family occurs in Arizona. This is the desert boa *(Lichanura),* a small group of species and subspecies which occurs in the Sonoran and Mohave deserts of Arizona, Sonora, California, and Baja California.

Snakes of the Southwest are highly diversified and, as in the case of the lizards, those occurring in Arizona are found primarily either in the desert, in grassland, or in woodland and forest habitats. The bull snake *(Pituophis)* is an example of a species that lives in all of these situations rather than being more or less restricted to one or two of them.

Snake habits are as varied as their habitats. The variety of environments in Arizona has led to a great number of different ways in which reptiles live. There are burrowers, climbers, racers, wormlike crawlers, and sidewinders. There are bird and mammal eaters, and lizard eaters. Some lay eggs, and others bear living young (rattlesnakes and garter snakes). The males of some species fight one another. More is unknown than is actually known. The study of Arizona's herpetofauna has little more than just begun.

GAME BIRDS. Arizona's largest resident game bird is the Merriam wild turkey *(Meleagris gallopavo merriami).* These birds probably once inhabited all of the higher country in Arizona including the desert mountain ranges and, according to early newspaper accounts, were once common in the valleys of the San Pedro and Santa Cruz rivers of southern Arizona. At an early date the wild turkey disappeared from the southern desert mountain ranges and from the river valleys. It continued to persist in the pine and spruce forests of central and northern Arizona, however, and today, under careful protection and management, has been restored to abundance. The depleted southern desert mountain ranges have been repopulated with turkeys from areas to the north by transplanting operations of the Arizona Game and Fish Department. Today these transplanted populations are thriving in the Santa Catalina, Chiricahua, Graham, and Huachuca mountains.

In the higher country the turkey is migratory, going to the spruce and pine forests to spend the summer and retreating to lower country with the first cold weather and storms, about the first of October. These birds are

Lewis Wayne Walker

Fig. 12.5 Scott's oriole and the cactus wren.

highly gregarious, and seldom are they found in small groups. The nesting season begins in May and lasts into August. Normally from eight to twelve eggs are laid in well-concealed nests. After an incubation period of about twenty-eight days, the young, referred to as "poults," are hatched.

Five species of quail were once native inhabitants of Arizona. Two of these — Benson's quail and the masked bobwhite — are now extinct. Of the three remaining, the most abundant today is the Gambel's quail *(Lophortyx gambeli).* This bird inhabits most of Arizona below an elevation of four thousand feet. Its favorite haunts are brushy arroyos, the timbered bottomlands, and the chaparral areas. During most of the year it is

Arizona Game & Fish Department

Fig. 12.6 The wild turkey, Arizona's largest resident game bird, has been restored by careful wildlife management.

Fig. 12.7   The white-winged dove and the Palmer thrusher.   *Lewis Wayne Walker*

gregarious, living in large coveys. Each year in March, however, the whistling of lone cocks signals the beginning of the nesting season. Pairs break away from the coveys, and for the nesting season monogamy is the rule. The female lays her eggs, usually numbering twelve to fifteen, in well-concealed places. After an incubation period of twenty-three days, the young are hatched. From the first few hours they are able to run about, and the male joins the mother and young. Many times, however, nests are destroyed, and new attempts at renesting are necessary before a brood is hatched. In the fall the covey is again the rule. During very dry years, few young are hatched, and sometimes during extreme drought conditions the birds remain in coveys and do not form pairs. The annual production of young birds varies greatly between years. In years of high winter rainfall and abundant green vegetation, large numbers of young are hatched. These quail, like all ground-nesting birds, have many natural enemies, and their own lives are short. About sixty percent of all quail alive in October die of natural causes before another year has passed. A very few of these quail live more than four years.

The scaled quail *(Callipepla squamata pallida)* inhabits more open country than does the Gambel's quail. This gray bird is slightly larger than the Gambel's quail. It moves about in coveys and has a similar chronology of nesting; though it is most abundant in Cochise County, it is also present in parts of Pinal and Santa Cruz counties. It is considered an extremely fine game bird; however it is not pursued by hunters to the extent that the Gambel's quail is.

The third species of quail now living in Arizona is the Mearn's quail *(Cyrtonyx montezumae mearnsi).* It is sometimes called the fool's quail because of its apparent lack of fear. This quail inhabits the live-oak areas where openings with high grasses are dominant. Its numbers vary over the range, and it is abundant only in years of good rainfall on grassy areas.

There are many migratory species in addition to the residential game birds that inhabit Arizona. Of the migratory game species the doves are the most important. Among the doves there are five native to Arizona: the mourning dove, the white-winged dove, the band-tailed pigeon, the Inca dove, and the Mexican ground dove. The first three of these can be considered game birds, while the last two are non-game species.

By far the most abundant of these is the mourning dove which is well known to everyone. In Arizona it is a year-round resident but must be classed as a migratory bird because the wintering birds represent populations different from the nesting birds. These birds arrive in Arizona in late fall and leave in the spring. Their nesting areas are far to the north in the western United States and southern Canada.

The larger white-winged dove is also hunted extensively in Arizona at waterholes and near grain fields. This dove, however, is in Arizona for only a short period each year. Very rarely does one see a white-winged dove in Arizona after the first of October. Arriving from Mexico about the last week in April, the white-winged dove begins its first southward movement out of the state about the third week in August, and only a few remain as late as October. Its nesting habits are quite similar to those of the mourning dove. Its nest is also a flimsy structure of twigs, but this species is generally not as widely scattered over the country as is the mourning dove. It seems to prefer such areas as heavy mesquite bosques, citrus groves, salt cedar thickets, and palo verde trees as nesting sites. Destruction of salt cedar and mesquite thickets has reduced the nesting cover of this bird.

The white-winged dove does not nest in any state

north of Arizona, and even in Arizona its range covers not more than about one-half of the state. It is largely restricted to the lower desert, the river bottoms, and the agricultural lands.

This dove is a favorite game bird of hunters, generally favored over the mourning dove because of its larger size. Methods and places for hunting the white-winged and the mourning dove are similar, and generally the two are taken together. The biggest difference between the two is the very short time that the white-winged dove is available to hunters. Dove-hunting season in Arizona begins on the first of September. By this date, however, many of the white-wings have migrated from the state.

One of Arizona's most interesting game birds is the band-tailed pigeon. This bird nests in the high pine, fir, and spruce forests, and in piñon areas. The nests are located on the lower branches of trees about twenty feet above the ground. The usual number of eggs in the nest is one and, occasionally, two. Both sexes help incubate the eggs. A wide variety of seeds and fruits comprise the diet of the band-tailed pigeon. In late summer it is gregarious and bands in great flocks, which dwell in the canyons and live-oak areas where acorns are abundant. During this period the band-tailed pigeon is more frequently seen by travelers than in the summer.

MAMMALS. In all, a total of 290 different kinds (species and subspecies) of mammals are known in Arizona. These represent 135 species belonging to 63 different genera, 23 different families, and 7 different orders.

The marsupials (Order Marsupialia) are represented in Arizona by a single species, the Virginia opossum *(Didelphis marsupialis),* and this species is extremely rare in the state. At least part of the opossums that exist in the state today result from the release of individuals brought into Arizona from the Midwest and the East, and all may be the result of such introductions.

The insectivores (Order Insectivora) are represented in Arizona by only five species, all shrews. Moles, so evident in certain other parts of the United States, are absent from our fauna. In general, shrews are restricted to the higher mountainous areas, but one species, the desert shrew *(Notiosorex crawfordi)* is widely distributed at lower elevations in the state. Individuals of this species occur along the Colorado River near Yuma, an unusual habitat for any shrew.

The bats (Order Chiroptera), represented by 28 species of 14 different genera, are much more common and diverse than in most parts of the United States. Some species, such as the Mexican freetailed bat *(Tadarida brasiliensis),* congregate during the summer months in maternity colonies estimated to contain as many as 20 million individuals.

The rabbits and hares (Order Lagomorpha) are some of the most common and best-known forms of wildlife in the state. Arizona has three different species of cottontail rabbit and two species of jackrabbit.

One species — the California jackrabbit *(Lepus californicus)* — is found in almost every part of the state. The Allen's jackrabbit *(Lepus alleni)* is found only in isolated areas in southern Arizona. In many places the two are found together. They differ considerably in appearance. The California jackrabbit is predominantly gray, while the Allen's jackrabbit has very conspicuous white patches on the rump. Both are rather prolific, bearing several litters of young per year. Their food consists of a great variety of grasses and other green vegetation. At times of abundance these animals do great damage to field crops in Arizona, especially to alfalfa, grain crops, and gardens.

The rodents (Order Rodentia) are probably the most numerous and diverse of all of the mammalian groups in the state. This order contains 70 species, representing 22 different genera and 8 different families. Some of the more obvious kinds are tree squirrels, ground squirrels, chipmunks, beavers, and muskrats. The nocturnal kangaroo rats are also widely known, as are the wood rats or pack rats.

The most plentiful tree squirrel in Arizona is the Abert's squirrel *(Sciurius aberti aberti).* This is the large gray squirrel with the tassel-ears which travelers see in all of the pine country of northern and central Arizona. North of the Grand Canyon in the spruce and pine forest of the Kaibab Plateau is another large, gray, tassel-eared squirrel. This is the Kaibab squirrel, now considered not a separate species, but only a subspecies of the same group to which the Abert's squirrel belongs. His habits are very similar to the typical Abert's, but rather than having white undersides, he is black along all ventral parts. The Abert's squirrel has a black tail, while the Kaibab squirrel has a white tail.

The Abert's squirrel is the only Arizona squirrel that is considered a game animal. All of the tree squirrels

Fig. 12.8   The California jackrabbit.

Arizona Game & Fish Department

are protected by law, but each year there are open hunting seasons on the Abert. There are two other less common large tree squirrels in Arizona — the Nayarit fox squirrel, *Sciurius nayaritensis,* and the Arizona gray squirrel, *Sciurius arizonicus.* The first of these is very similar in appearance to the large eastern fox squirrel and is found in Arizona only in the Chiricahua Mountains. The Arizona gray squirrel occurs in the wooded mountain canyons of most southern Arizona mountain ranges. Neither of these squirrels is very abundant, and travelers seldom see either one. No detailed studies of these animals have been made, and why their numbers remain low is not known.

The carnivores (Order Carnivora) are represented by 22 species of 16 different genera and 5 different families. In the dog family (Family Canidae) the coyotes and gray foxes are still common; the swift fox is becoming relatively rare, and the wolf is now almost extinct, although a few wolves are still seen in some of the more remote parts of the state each year.

In the bear family (Family Ursidae) Arizona once had two native species, the black bear *(Euarctos americanus)* and the grizzly bear *(Ursus horribilis).* The grizzly bear is now entirely gone from Arizona. Just how extensive its early range was will never be known, and it was probably never abundant. According to Bill Casto, an early government hunter, the last grizzly bear to be killed in Arizona was taken by Ben Lilly on Horton Creek in the White Mountains in the spring of 1916.

The black bear is still common in Arizona and is protected by the game laws. Only a few are present today in the southeastern mountain ranges — the Chiricahuas, the Huachucas, the Rincons, the Santa Catalinas, the Santa Ritas, and a few other isolated ranges. In some of these areas it is illegal at any time to kill a black bear. In the Graham Mountains and in the parts of Arizona north of the Mogollon Rim, especially in the White Mountains, larger numbers are present and are still legal game for properly licensed hunters under regular open seasons.

In the raccoon family (Family Procyonidae) Arizona has the raccoon, the coati-mundi, and the ringtailed cat. In the Family Mustelidae are skunks of four different species, weasel, badger, otter rarely, and at least formerly, the black-footed ferret. In the cat family (Felidae) the bobcat is still common throughout the state. The mountain lion is found regularly in remote regions, and occasional reports of other species, such as the ocelot and margay cat, still occur.

The Order Artiodactyla, with six species of five different genera and four different families, includes the large game mammals of the state. These are: Family Tayassuidae, the javelina or "wild pig"; Family Antilocapridae, the pronghorn antelope; Family Cervidae, the elk and two species of deer; and Family Bovidae, the bighorn sheep.

The story of Arizona's antelope herds, like that of the elk, is a tale of early depletion and a later spectacular recovery under management. When the first white settlers came to Arizona, much of the open grassy country was range for large herds of antelope, not only in the north and central parts of the states where the largest herds are found today, but also in southern Arizona. Some mammalogists have recognized three separate subspecies as originally occurring in the state, one in the north and central, one in the extreme southeast, and another in the southwestern corner. The one in the southwestern part of the state — *Antilocapra americana sonoriensis* — is occasionally seen on the Cabeza Prieta Game Range near Ajo and in surrounding country near the Mexico boundary. The antelope generally inhabits open, grassy country. In Arizona, however, travelers will often find herds of antelope in fairly heavily wooded areas in central Arizona. The cienegas and other open areas within these forested regions are heavily used by antelope. Being primarily social animals, they are found in herds throughout the year, except that bucks are often found alone or in small groups in spring. The antelope does, at the time the young are born, generally seek isolation. The breeding season is in August and September. After a gestation period of from 230 to 240 days, the young, referred to as kids, are born in May and June. During the more severe weather in winter all sexes and ages are found together in groups.

Arizona's largest game mammal is the elk or wapiti *(Cervus canadensis).* Native to Arizona, he became extinct about 1900. Our present elk herds are descendants of animals brought from Wyoming in several releases, beginning in 1913.

Little reliable information exists on the early Arizona elk. Only part of one skull is present in America's museums. From the small amount of information, it seems likely that the elk was not abundant in early Arizona. It ranged principally in the White Mountains.

Fig. 12.9   The javelina — a large game mammal.

Arizona Game & Fish Department

Fig. 12.10   Antelope herds, depleted early in Arizona's history, have been restored.

Tad Nichols

The reintroduction of elk into Arizona and its re-establishment as an important game animal form an exciting chapter in the annals of Arizona game conservation. By the 1960s, under careful management and control by the Arizona Game and Fish Department, the elk was thriving in Coconino National Forest, Sitgreaves National Forest, Tonto National Forest, and Apache National Forest.

The elk, like the deer, must be annually reduced in numbers so that the herd does not overbalance the available food. Since 1950 the annual harvest of elk by hunters has averaged 877 animals. The kill varies considerably between years, depending mostly upon weather conditions. In times of drought little food is available; fewer calves are born, and fewer survive. The highest kill since 1950 was 1,693 elk, taken by hunters in 1951. Naturally many more people want to hunt elk than can be allowed to do so. To manage the herds under this condition, the Arizona Game & Fish department allows a prescribed number of permits each year, and the hunters are selected by a drawing system.

Arizona has two species of deer, the mule deer *(Odocoileus hemionus)* and the white-tailed deer *(Odocoileus virginianus)*. A handsome game animal, the mule deer is found over most of the state. He is abundant in the pine, fir, and spruce forest areas, in the canyons, juniper country, and chaparral areas of central and northern Arizona. In this country he is called the Rocky Mountain mule deer. In the southern part of the state he dwells in the low desert areas and rarely invades the higher forests of pine and spruce. To the local people he is known as the desert mule deer; however, though of the same species, the two mule deer probably represent what are commonly called two different subspecies.

In the high country the Rocky Mountain mule deer

is often migratory, coming down from the spruce and pine forests with the first heavy storms of later autumn into the lower canyons, the "juniper breaks," the chaparral areas, the sagebrush flats, and similar places to spend the winter. Here in early December the bucks gather together their harems, and the breeding season begins. This breeding season or rut lasts about two months.

With the beginning of the first spring thaws in the mountains, these animals migrate upward in May to their summer homes. Soon after their arrival in the higher country the fawns are born. The normal number of fawns born to a healthy well-fed female is two. When the food is poor or there are too many deer for the

Fig. 12.11   The desert mule deer is a southern subspecies.

Norman Simmons

Norman Simmons

Fig. 12.12 The desert bighorn sheep is maintained on two large refuges, one near Yuma, the other near Ajo.

food supply, fewer young are born, and they have less chance of survival. In about March the bucks shed their antlers, and slowly a new set is grown.

In southern Arizona the chronology of events in the life of the desert mule deer lags somewhat behind that of his cousin in northern Arizona. In mating season, period of fawn drop, antler drop, and antler replacement, the southern subspecies lags behind the northern subspecies by about three to four weeks.

Arizona's white-tailed deer *(Odocoileus virginianus couesi),* a subspecies of the eastern white-tail, is found principally in the higher elevations of the desert mountain ranges of southeastern Arizona. It ranges from an elevation of about three thousand to about ten thousand feet above sea level.

The Arizona white-tail is generally considered non-migratory, living the entire year in the same area without altitudinal migrations. Its breeding season begins in mid-December and lasts until February. The young are born in July and August. The period of birth corresponds to the summer rainy season in this area and occurs during the period of abundant food.

Though not as small as its tiny and rare relative, the Florida white-tail, this Arizona species is much smaller than its eastern and northern cousin. Hunters experienced with the larger white-tailed deer may be surprised to learn that any Arizona white-tail, field-dressed over 110 to 120 pounds (live weight 140 to 160 pounds) would be considered large, with field-

dressed deer over 125 pounds very rare. Though deer weights vary greatly with food conditions, most adult white-tailed bucks shot in Arizona have a field-dressed weight under one hundred pounds.

In Arizona one often hears reference to the fan-tailed deer, the little red deer, the Sinaloa deer, and other names which hunters use sometimes to describe what they believe to be a different species. All of these are actually the same little Arizona white-tail. No other kinds of deer except those already mentioned live in Arizona. The differences encountered are only those of size — especially of antler dimensions.

Though Arizona has very large areas of deer range, probably the most famous is the Kaibab Plateau in the Kaibab National Forest in northwestern Arizona, north of the Grand Canyon. Much of the fame of the Kaibab derives from the large and beautiful antlers which are developed by bucks there, and trophy hunters from many parts of the country come to the Kaibab to hunt. The Kaibab herd became well known in past years, however, in a less fortunate way, because of the heavy mortality of deer from winter starvation which occurred in the herd before World War II.

These tragic, large-scale die-offs of deer are fortunately far less common today because of the greatly improved management of the deer herds. Better management has been achieved partly through better law enforcement and better protection.

Arizona still has thriving populations of the desert bighorn sheep *(Ovis candensis mexicana).* These are found principally in the dry desert mountain ranges of Yuma and Mohave counties. Small remnants still exist precariously on Pusch Ridge of the Santa Catalina Mountains just a few miles from the city of Tucson, in the Silverbell Mountains about fifty miles west of Tucson, and in other areas.

The chronology of events in the life of the desert bighorn does not coincide with that of other Arizona game animals. These animals do not have seasonal altitudinal migrations as do the northern mule deer and elk; the mating season is in the summer, the gestation period is from 157 to 165 days, and the young are born in January, February, and March.

Investigations in recent years by the Arizona Game and Fish Department and the U.S. Bureau of Sport Fisheries and Wildlife have determined the numbers, needs, and general conditions of these remaining herds. The latter bureau in 1969 was maintaining two large refuges for the sheep, the Kofa Desert Game Range of 660,000 acres of desert near Yuma, and the Cabeza Prieta area of 860,000 acres near Ajo. The principal improvement on the range for desert bighorn sheep has been the development of permanent sources of water. Even in these dry mountain ranges where but three inches of rain fall each year, natural water areas are present. These are few and far between, but man has been able to provide water with tanks, runoff aprons, and catchments.

ARIZONA'S GOVERNMENT
AND SOCIAL SERVICES

Fig. 13.1   Members of the first state constitutional convention held in 1910.

David A. Bingham
Political Scientist

13

THE ARIZONA CONSTITUTION

IN THE SENSE OF BASIC LAW and practices, the Constitution of the State of Arizona consists not only of the written document which bears the title of constitution, but also important statutes enacted by the legislature, judicial decisions, and customs and conventions. The power of judicial review, one of the most significant of those belonging to the state courts, is based upon judicial precedent, not upon specific provision of the written constitution. Party control of the two houses of the legislature finds its authorization in custom rather than in written article. The written document, however, is the core of the Arizona constitutional system, and other parts of the constitution cannot be in conflict with it.

The written constitution drafted in 1910 was a significant step in the orderly development of law and governmental institutions that had been going on in Arizona since the organization of territorial government in 1863 and in other states for an even longer period. The constitution provided for the continuance, with some changes, of the pattern of local government which had grown up in the Territory, of the system of private and public law, and of numerous other procedures and institutions. The constitution's distinctive quality was derived, however, not from the familiar, but from the innovations, the departures from the customary way of doing things, which it contains. These innovations caused friends of the constitution to praise it as "progressive" and critics to label it as "socialistic."

As a consequence of its "liberal" constitution, Arizona has the initiative, referendum, and recall, workers are protected against many of the hazards of employment by the workmen's compensation system, the state has a voter-registration system and a direct primary, and a number of municipalities have home-rule charters. In contrast to the constitution, the government in general since 1912 has been conservative, and if anything,

became more so in the 1950s and 1960s, probably as a result of the growing number of Republican voters among newcomers to the state, the conservative temper of the times in Arizona, and public reaction to the excesses of some segments of organized labor. The conservatism of the government has tended to give the constitution a similar conservative quality, since the character of a constitution is determined to a great extent by the manner in which it is interpreted and applied. However, with the continued urbanization of the state and the diversification of industry, which may weaken some of the traditional clusters of political and economic power, there is some possibility that the contrast between government and written constitution may tend to disappear.

To understand why the Arizona constitution contains a number of "liberal" or "progressive" provisions, in contrast to the conventional constitution framed by New Mexico at approximately the same time, one must examine certain forces at work in the nation at large and in Arizona in the early part of the century. The innovations of the constitution were the product of two forces — the determination of liberal groups within the Territory to create a government which would be more responsive to popular will and which would place various restraints upon the power of the large corporations; and the nationwide progressive movement, which created a climate of public opinion favorable to the objectives of Arizona liberals, probably contributing to the objectives themselves. The Arizona liberals, although concerned with checking the power of the large corporations, were also interested in other changes as well, a fact which is amply supported by numerous sections of the constitution.

The Territory of Arizona, as well as that of New Mexico, was authorized by Congress in the Enabling Act of June 20, 1910, to draft a proposed state constitution. The act fixed the number of convention delegates at fifty-two, directed territorial officials to apportion the delegates among the counties on the basis of their 1908 vote turnout for the territorial delegate to Congress, and appropriated $100,000 to underwrite the election of delegates, the costs of the convention, and the popular vote on the proposed state constitution.

Labor's Role

Organized labor played an important role in the campaign for the election of convention delegates and in the writing of the constitution. Its influence was out of all proportion to its membership, which embraced only a minority of the workers, because its demands coincided with the objectives of the contemporary progressive movement and, what is probably more important, were in the main acceptable to the dominant liberal wing of the Democratic party.

A section of organized labor, led by the Bisbee Miner's Union, organized a labor party at a conference at Phoenix in July, 1910, in an attempt to elect labor delegates to the convention; they disbanded the organization, however, after reaching an understanding with the leaders of the Democratic party. The new party had failed to win the support of all sections of organized labor and feared, moreover, that its activities might contribute to a Republican victory by splitting up the Democratic vote. In the accord with the Democratic party, labor agreed to disband its party and work for the election of Democratic delegates, while Democratic leaders promised to support labor objectives. George W. P. Hunt, who was to become president of the constitutional convention, is credited with the negotiation of the agreement.

In the campaign for the election of delegates, the initiative, referendum, and recall as proposed provisions of the constitution excited the most controversy. The Democratic county conventions supported these objectives, while the Republican county platforms either ignored or denounced them. During the campaign, however, numerous Republican candidates endorsed direct legislation. In terms which have a contemporary ring, the charge was made during the election campaign that the initiative, referendum, and recall were designed by the socialists to destroy the American form of government. Democratic platforms also contained proposals for employer's liability, an income tax, direct election of United States senators, and corrupt practices legislation.

Delegates were elected on September 12, 1910, the voters choosing forty-one Democrats and eleven Republicans. A majority of the Democrats was aligned with the progressive wing of the party. The constitutional convention opened on October 10 and closed on December 9, 1910. The Enabling Act had stipulated that members would be paid for every day the convention was in session, up to a total of sixty. Sessions were held in the chamber of the Territorial House of Representatives in Phoenix.

George Hunt, who later became Arizona's first state governor, an office to which he was elected seven times in all, was chosen president of the convention. He is credited with exercising more influence upon the work of the convention than any other delegate. At the time, labor groups regarded Hunt as a particular friend.

Names of Delegates

Other delegates whose names are well-known in Arizona include Dr. B. B. Moeur and Sidney Osborn, both of Maricopa County, who became governors of the state. Mitt Simms, a farmer from Graham County, served as secretary of state, state treasurer, and as a member of the State Corporation Commission. Dr. A. M. Tuthill of Graham became Adjutant General and later director of selective service, and Mulford Winsor was named the first land commissioner and later the director of the State Department of Library and Archives, a post he held until his death in the late 1950s. Carlos C. Jacome of Pima County, Morris Goldwater of Yavapai County, and E. A. Tovrea of Cochise County were prominent in the economic life of Arizona, as were Tom Feeney of Cochise County, one of the principal spokesmen at the convention for mining interests, A. C. Baker and Alfred Franklin of Maricopa County, and Jacob Weinberger of Gila County.

The work of the convention was distributed among twenty-four committees, three for "conducting the convention," and twenty-one for "constitution making." Chairmanships went to members of the liberal wing of the Democratic party. A verbatim record of convention proceedings was kept, which today constitutes an invaluable guide to the work of the convention. The record suffers, however, from the failure of the convention to appropriate funds to hire trained stenographers. Numerous speeches made in the course of debate are included in the record. In the preparation of official copies of the verbatim report, speeches were lifted from the stenographic record and sent to members for editing. Many were not returned.

In writing the constitution, the delegates studied not only the institutions and practices of government developed during territorial days, but also various state constitutions. Special attention was paid to the constitutions of Oregon and Oklahoma. As might be expected in a numerous assemblage, the work of the convention was marked by controversy and compromise. The dispute over the recall provision was more heated than that over direct legislation because of the proposal to apply the recall to judges. Conservative delegates, as well as outsiders, warned their colleagues that President Taft was certain to reject the constitution if the recall did not omit the judiciary. Some delegates feared that a recall provision which included judicial office might delay statehood indefinitely. This fear was reflected in several of the invocations of Chaplain Crutchfield of the convention, who on the morning of November 28 prayed, "O Lord, we are not willing to believe President Taft will turn down our constitution on account of such a small matter as the Recall, Initiative, and Referendum. . . ."

When the document was drafted and submitted to the delegates for signature, eleven delegates, including one Democrat, refused to sign. The dissidents, doubtless with an eye to posterity, proposed that they be permitted to sign and place the words, "We disapprove" under their names, but the majority rejected the idea. On February 2, 1911, the constitution was referred to the voters, a large majority of whom voted in favor of the document.

The proposed state constitution was acceptable to Congress, but not to President Taft, who, as predicted because of his opposition to the application of the recall to judges, vetoed the joint resolution which Congress had passed on August 10 providing for the admission of Arizona. In conformity with the suggestions of Congress in its joint resolution of August 21, Arizona amended the constitution on December 12, 1911, to remove judges from the recall, and President Taft on February 14, 1912, proclaimed the admission of Arizona to statehood. The voters of Arizona on November 5, 1912, endorsed an amendment to restore the original wording to the recall provision.

When it went into effect in 1912, the constitution was a relatively short document of approximately twenty-five thousand words. It is still comparatively brief. Similar to other state constitutions, it contains a preamble and a bill of rights; it provides a framework of government based upon the familiar doctrine of separation of powers and its corollary, checks and balances; it embodies provisions dealing with the popular control of government, public finance, education, local government, private corporations, water rights, and labor; and it contains an amending clause.

Although the constitution was in general liberal or progressive, in the sense that a number of its provisions represented deviations from traditional institutions and ways, its liberal character did not extend to the legislature and executive articles. The reform movement of the early twentieth century tended to neglect such matters as legislative councils and unicameralism, and apparently did not understand that an efficient, well-organized executive branch was just as essential to good government as honest officials. The merit system was an objective of the general political reform movement of the day, but it was not an issue in Arizona. Serious proposals for reform in these areas were not raised in Arizona until sometime later.

The initiative, referendum, and recall were the best known, but not the only progressive features of the constitution. Labor regarded others as being of equal importance. With respect to the liability of employers for injuries suffered by their employees, the constitution abolished the fellow-servant doctrine of the common law and narrowed the protection offered by the doctrines of contributory negligence and assumption of risk by stating that these defenses in accident cases were questions of fact, subject to jury determination. The legislature was directed to enact employer's liability and workmen's compensation laws. The constitution reserved to workers the privilege of electing to sue for damages in the event of injury, with the amount involved in the suit, or in any other damage suit, not subject to statutory limitation. Employers were forbidden to require employees, as a condition of employment, to release them from liability for personal injuries received through the negligence of employer or agent.

Blacklists were outlawed by the constitution, and the office of state mine inspector was created. The constitution fixed an eight-hour day for employees of state and local government and forbade the employment of children under fourteen during school hours and children under sixteen in underground mines or other hazardous occupations or in work injurious to health or morals.

Sections of the constitution which limit or control the activities and powers of business corporations also indicate the progressive nature of the document. The constitution forbids the enactment of any law granting an irrevocable privilege or franchise, and empowers the legislature, without impairing the obligation of contract, to change or repeal laws pertaining to corporations at any time, and to impose conditions other than those given in the constitution. Municipal corporations cannot grant, extend, or renew a franchise for a term of more than twenty-five years, and action taken is subject to a popular referendum. "Monopolies and trusts shall never be allowed in this State," and business concerns and other associations are forbidden to enter into contracts or other schemes to fix prices, limit output, or regulate the transportation of any product.

The constitution states that the resources of public service corporations, state banks, building and loan associations, trust, insurance, and guaranty companies "shall be at all times liable and subject to the full visitorial and inquisitorial powers of the State" and gives to the Corporation Commission the power to investigate any corporation whose stock is offered for sale to the public. Corporations are forbidden to contribute money or anything else of value "for the purpose of influencing any election or official action." The Corporation Commission, which developed from the railroad commission of territorial government, was established to regulate public service corporations.

Although the constitution protects persons accused of crime from compulsory self-incrimination, it does not extend this guarantee to persons "having knowledge or possession of facts that tend to establish the guilt of any other person or corporation charged with bribery or illegal rebating." A person with such knowledge cannot escape giving testimony or producing evidence on the ground that he might incriminate himself. However, he cannot be prosecuted or penalized because of his testimony or evidence.

Undoubtedly the desire of the liberal majority of the convention delegates to permit the greater taxation of personal and corporate income was an important factor behind the section authorizing the legislature to levy not only uniform income, inheritance, and legacy taxes, but also "graduated income taxes, graduated collateral and direct inheritance taxes, graduated legacy and succession taxes, stamp, registration, production or other specific taxes."

Forward-Looking Provisions

The constitution also included other provisions which were relatively advanced for the times. It authorized the legislature to provide for juries of fewer than twelve in courts not of record, for a verdict by nine or more jurors in civil cases in courts of record, and for waiving a jury in civil cases with the consent of the interested parties. Persons could be brought to trial on criminal charges by information, as well as by the traditional grand jury indictment. Salaries rather than fees were required for all state and county officers and all justices of the peace whose precincts included a city or town. The constitution directed the legislature to enact direct primary and registration laws. The legislature was also directed to adopt rules and enact laws prohibiting the practice of lobbying on the floor of the two houses and further regulating lobbying. The latter part of the injunction has not been heeded. Under the home-rule section of the constitution, cities having a population of more than thirty-five hundred were given permission to frame, adopt, and amend their own charters rather than to operate on the basis of a ready-made charter written into state law.

The constitution has been changed by formal amendments, statutory elaboration, and judicial decision. Because of the tendency of state courts to construe the powers of the legislature narrowly, the role of the legislature in constitutional change, while important, has been of a lesser order than that of Congress with respect to the federal Constitution.

Amendments may be proposed to the Arizona constitution by any one of three methods but ratified by only one method, popular action. The legislature may propose amendments by a majority vote of the members elected to each house, and groups of voters may offer them by initiative petition signed by voters equivalent in number to at least 15 percent of the total votes cast for all candidates for governor at the last general election. Amendments may also be put forward by a convention called by the legislature, provided that the laws for convoking the convention are first approved by the voters in a referendum election. The last method has not been used to date. If the voters approve, the legislature also may call a convention to revise the constitution or draft a new one. As the methods used to date for proposing amendments have worked satisfactorily, the legislature likely would have revision or a new constitution in mind if it should call a convention.

Amendments Proposed

One hundred and fourteen amendments had been formally proposed as of the end of 1968 and sixty-four adopted. The legislature proposed seventy-six and groups of voters, using the initiative process, forty-seven. Forty-six of the former and eighteen of the latter became part of the constitution.

Amendments of note since the close of World War II include the so-called "right-to-work amendment" of 1946 which forbids the closed and union shops (although both exist on a *de facto* basis); the amendment of 1949 which excepts city managers from the requirement that persons elected or appointed to state or local office must be qualified electors of the political division of which the office is a part; and the amendment of 1950 which replaced biennial regular sessions of the state legislature with annual sessions. Others include the legislative reapportionment amendment of 1953 (now superseded by a federal court decision on the "one man-one vote" principle); the 1960 modern courts amendment; and the 1968 amendments which provided for a four-year term for governor, secretary of state, and attorney general, abolished the elective offices of state auditor and state examiner, established the appointive position of auditor general, and increased the annual pay of state legislators from $1,800 to $6,000.

David A. Bingham
Political Scientist

14

THE EXECUTIVE AND LEGISLATIVE BRANCHES

THE CONSTITUTION of the state of Arizona disperses executive power and responsibility by creating a plural executive consisting of governor, secretary of state, treasurer, attorney general, and superintendent of public instruction. Prior to 1969, there was also an elected state auditor. These five officials, according to the constitution, make up the executive department; but, in reality, they head an executive branch consisting of numerous other administrative officers, boards, commissions and agencies established by statute. The constitution also provides specifically for an elective corporation commission of three members, an elective mine inspector, and a state board of education and a board of regents which are partly ex officio and partly appointive. By statute a three-member tax commission is also elected.

The constitution fixes four-year terms for the five officers who head the executive branch. All are eligible for re-election for an indefinite number of terms, with the exception of the treasurer, who cannot "succeed himself . . . for the succeeding four years after the expiration of the term for which he shall have been elected." In view of the scanty discretionary power lodged in the treasurer, this ban upon two consecutive terms seems unrealistic.

Constitutional qualifications are the same for governor and the other four officers. Each must be at least twenty-five years of age, a citizen of the United States for ten years and of Arizona for five years preceding election, a qualified voter of the state, and proficient in the use of the English language. The attorney general is required by statute to have been eligible for practice before the state Supreme Court during the five-year period immediately before his election. Since most Arizona residents, if they live long enough, are able to meet constitutional requirements, such other qualifications as political skill, experience, and associations are at least of equal importance.

Aside from resignation, death, or defeat at the polls, means by which the governor and other executive officials may be removed from office include the electoral process of recall or the legislative process of impeachment, with the latter being limited to cases involving "high crimes, misdemeanors, or malfeasance in office. . . ." No one in Arizona has been removed by either method. By statute, the legislature has ruled that a vacancy exists in an office where the incumbent has been found guilty of a felony or adjudged insane, or when he has been absent from the state for more than three months without legislative permission, or fails to perform the duties of his office for a period of more than three consecutive months.

Succession to Office

In the event of death, resignation, removal from office, or permanent disability of the governor, the secretary of state, if holding office by election, becomes governor, both in fact and in name. Next in line of succession are the attorney general, state treasurer, and superintendent of public instruction.

The Governor

The governor is by implication the chief executive, although the constitution nowhere uses the title. As chief executive, he has the nominal responsibility for seeing that laws are administered or enforced, exercising some legislative leadership, performing certain judicial functions, and serving as the social and ceremonial head of state government.

In his capacity as chief administrator, the governor "shall transact all executive business with the officers of the Government, civil and military, and may require information in writing from the officers in the Executive

Department upon any subject relating to the duties of their respective offices" and "he shall take care that the laws be faithfully executed." The governor, furthermore, is directed by law to supervise the official conduct of all executive and ministerial officials, and he is vested with the authority to require any officer or board to make a special report to him. He has some opportunity to influence administration through his appointive power, since he names nearly 400 persons to boards, commissions, and other agencies. Senatorial confirmation is required in approximately half of the gubernatorial appointments. The governor's removal power is much narrower than his appointive power, in cases of appointments for definite terms. He has a fairly free hand, however, in removing officers whom he has appointed for indefinite terms.

In recent years the office of governor has shown some tendency to develop into an important center of legislative leadership. The growth of state government as a positive force in the economic and social life of Arizona has contributed to the need for legislative leadership which has not always been met from within the legislature. There is some inclination, moreover, for the people of Arizona to look to the governor for leadership because he, in contrast to members of the legislature, is elected by the voters of the entire state.

The governor has the opportunity to submit a legislative program to the legislature, and to the state at large, when he obeys the constitutional mandate "to communicate, by message, to the Legislature at every session the condition of the state, and recommend such matters as he shall deem expedient." He may veto bills passed by the legislature, which in turn may repass those bills by a two-thirds majority or — if the bills are emergency measures — three-fourths. In addition, he may veto items of appropriation laws. The governor may call the legislature into special session, and the legislature can consider only the proposals listed by the governor in his call. The governor may supplement his constitutional powers for influencing policy-making by bidding for public support of his program or of special measures through press conferences, radio and TV addresses, and from the public platform. He may use his influence as a party leader, when his party also controls the legislature, and he may employ persuasion and cajolery in informal conferences with legislative leaders.

In his capacity as social and ceremonial head of the state, the governor welcomes distinguished visitors, makes numerous public addresses and appearances, eats hundreds of free meals, proclaims special days and weeks, and officiates at dedication ceremonies for public and private works. Judicial powers of the governor include the granting of reprieves, commutations, and pardons, subject to rules laid down by the legislature, except where treason is involved.

GUBERNATORIAL POST DIFFICULT. The Governor of Arizona is essentially a weak chief executive in comparison to the President of the United States or to governors of states which have undergone extensive administrative reorganization. The constitution, in dispersing executive power among the five elective executives, puts the governor in a difficult central position. In addition, the governor has little control, save through the budget formulation process, over the other elected officers who are primarily answerable only to the voters. He does not have effective supervisory authority over the numerous boards and commissions, many of whose members have been appointed by his predecessors in office. Even if his administrative authority were greater, he would have great difficulty in directing and coordinating the activities of an executive branch containing more than one hundred separate administrative agencies. Some improvement in this situation may occur in the future, however, through (1) the recent statutory creation of a department of finance, the commissioner of which is appointed by the governor and the organization of which includes a budget office and a purchasing office; and (2) the statutory creation of a five-member state personnel commission, the members of which are appointed by the governor, with the commission having the authority to appoint a personnel director who in turn recommends position classifications and pay plans for state employees.

Proposals to change the office of chief executive include comprehensive plans for the complete overhauling of the administrative structure. Griffenhagen and Associates of Chicago, in their study of Arizona state government in 1949 for a special committee of the legislature, recommended the creation of a strong governor through the consolidation of the many separate administrative agencies into fifteen major departments, which would be subject to the direction and control of the governor. The governor, the only elective officer, would appoint department heads, who would be answerable to him. Collectively, the department heads would constitute the governor's cabinet. A modern system of personnel management was also recommended.

Activity in this area continues, especially since the Republican party gained control of both houses of the state legislature in 1966 — for the first time in the history of statehood — and retained control in the elections of 1968. In 1967 the legislature created the Council on Organization of Arizona State Government, a commission composed of twelve members whose assigned task was to study the executive branch and make recommendations to the legislature for organizational and procedural changes. The Council's activities have resulted in a number of administrative changes, including the 1968 voter approval on referenda abolishing the elective office of state auditor, abolishing the appointive office of state examiner, and approving four-year terms for the five elective officers of the executive department. A third referendum, calling for the abolishment of the elective offices of the Corporation Commission, was defeated at the polls by a narrow margin. Allied bills passed by the legislature and signed by the governor in 1968 included the creation of an auditor general, appointed and controlled by the joint legislative budget committee as a legislative agency to which the functions of the state examiner were transferred; and the transferring of functions previously performed by the state auditor to the Commissioner of Finance.

In defense of reorganization, it is argued that a strong governor would serve the ends of efficiency by providing the opportunity for better administered state laws, and the ends of democracy by providing for a more responsible executive in whom both power and responsibility are centered. Demands for improvements undoubtedly will be stimulated further by the growing volume, technical difficulty, and increasing costs of state administration.

The Legislature

The primary responsibility for making laws is vested in the state legislature. Like all but one of its counterparts in other states, the Arizona legislature is bicameral, consisting of the House of Representatives and the Senate. As a consequence of a 1965-66 decision handed down by a three-member federal court panel, the legislature is now apportioned on a population basis, with sixty members in the House and thirty in the Senate. Half of the members of each house come from the state's most populous county, Maricopa, in which is located the Phoenix metropolitan area. Pima County, the Tucson metropolitan area, has twelve members of the House and six in the Senate. The remaining twelve counties, organized into six legislative districts, share nine senators and eighteen representatives.

Prior to the 1966 elections each of Arizona's fourteen counties had two members in the Senate, with the eighty-member House being apportioned among the counties on the basis of their vote turnout for governor in the previous election. Reapportionment of the House occurred every four years. Since World War II, political conflict in the legislature has reflected more of a metropolitan vs. nonmetropolitan split, rather than the traditional urban vs. rural division found in other states. Hence, federal court imposition of the "one man-one vote" principle is expected to have a decided effect on future legislative behavior, already visibly reflected in (1) the centralization of legislative power in the Phoenix area; (2) Republican control, for the first time in statehood, of both the House and Senate; (3) state organizational and administrative reforms; and (4) tax policy changes.

There are no differences in the qualifications for membership in the House and Senate, each requiring citizenship, minimum age of twenty-five years, residence of three years in Arizona, residence of one year in the legislative district from which elected, and ability to

read and write English. The terms of office for both House and Senate are two years.

Membership in the state legislature is not considered a full-time occupation. The legislature met biennially before 1950, but in that year a constitutional amendment was adopted providing for annual sessions. The legislators are paid an annual salary of $6,000 regardless of the length of regular sessions, or the number of special sessions.

The powers of the legislature are very broad, generally subsumed under what are known as the "police powers" — the power to protect the health, welfare, safety, and morals of the community. The legislature, exclusive of those powers delegated to the national government by the United States Constitution, may enact laws on any matters not prescribed by the Arizona Constitution. The state constitution prohibits the passage of special or local laws relating to the granting of divorce, location of county seats, granting of special privileges to corporations, and numerous other matters. The Declaration of Rights, which is comparable to the Bill of Rights in the Constitution, also limits the legislature.

IMPORTANCE OF PARTIES. Although political parties are nowhere mentioned directly in the state constitution, it would be impossible to understand the operation of the legislature without an awareness of the important roles parties play. The parties are the basis for organizing the legislative chambers, and are the means of making the legislative process work.

SHIFT IN POLITICAL PRIMACY. While Arizona traditionally has been a Democratic state, since World War II the Republicans have not only gained in the percentage of total registered voters, but have captured state-wide offices as well. Even though the Democrats retain a voter registration edge, the conservative wing of that party often defects to Republican candidates. Republican party strength is concentrated mostly in the Phoenix and Tucson metropolitan areas. An example of their muscle flexing — the 1968 elections — resulted in capturing control of both legislative houses, the offices of governor, attorney general, treasurer, and superintendent of public instruction, and control of the courthouses in Maricopa and Graham counties. Republicans also hold the state's two U.S. Senate seats, and two of the state's three congressmen.

The importance of the party in the operation of the legislature is found in the election of the presiding and other officers, the choice of committee chairmen and members, and the control over the agenda of the chambers. The two presiding officers, Speaker of the House and President of the Senate, make all committee assignments (agreed upon in caucus), assign bills to committees, and recognize members on the floor for legislative discussions and speeches. Their conduct in part determines the direction of legislative behavior.

The committee system is an extremely important element in the legislative process. All bills introduced into either house are referred to committees having jurisdiction over particular subjects, such as public lands, counties or highways and bridges. These bills are considered in detail by the committees, which may suppress the bills, report them out favorably or unfavorably, or report them without recommendation. Any one bill may be referred to as many as four different committees, each having the power to dispose of the bill as it wishes. In theory, each house may discharge a committee from further consideration of a bill after a certain period of deliberation, but this procedure is seldom used. The influence of the leadership, however, is usually sufficiently strong so that most bills supported by the leadership are reported out of committees. In 1970 there were fourteen committees in each house, along with several joint and special committees.

In deliberating, the committees may take testimony and evidence from representatives of executive departments, from private interest groups, other legislative members, or others interested in the legislation, but are not required to do so. Such hearings may be conducted either in public or executive (closed) sessions. Seldom is a verbatim record kept of hearings, and the committees rarely make formal written reports to the chambers at the conclusion of their deliberations.

Each house adopts its own rules of procedure, with certain restrictions imposed by the constitution. Normally, after committee consideration, a bill is placed on the calendar and then brought up for debate in the house in question when it is sitting as the Committee of the Whole. At the conclusion of debate and after all amendments have been disposed of, the bill is then brought before the house for final consideration and vote. It is necessary for a majority to be present to conduct business; every bill must be read in its entirety at least once; votes on final passage must be by roll call; bills may be passed only by the approving vote of a majority of the entire membership of each house. This latter provision means that absentees may count as automatic negative votes when the legislature is closely divided. If attached to a bill is an emergency clause which waives the normal requirement that acts remain inoperative for 90 days after enactment, two-thirds of the entire membership of each house must approve the bill. Frequently the emergency clause is attached to routine legislation in which no emergency, in fact, exists.

If the two houses fail to agree on all features of a particular bill, the disagreement may be removed by one of the two houses accepting the other's views, or by the convening of a conference committee consisting of members of both houses appointed by their respective presiding officers. If the conference committee can resolve the differences, the bill is then returned to each chamber for final passage. Approved bills are then sent to the governor for his signature.

The state legislature has availed itself of professional assistance through the Legislative Council, established in 1953. The Council is composed of the Senate President and five senators appointed by him, and the House Speaker and five representatives appointed by him. The Council meets periodically and is responsible for legislative research, maintenance of a legislative library, and bill drafting. It also plays a strong role in the development of legislative issues to be considered during regular and special sessions, and cares for legislative matters when the legislature is not in session. Professional staff members are employed on a fulltime basis by the Council to provide assistance in research and bill-drafting areas.

LEGISLATIVE RECORD-KEEPING. The two other permanent legislative agencies are the Department of Library and Archives, which maintains the library facilities for the Council, and the newly created Auditor General, who functions under the joint legislative budget committee. The Auditor General's activities center on audits of counties, school districts and state agencies; responsibilities transferred to his office and formerly lodged in the offices of Post Auditor and State Examiner.

In theory and sometimes in fact, the legislature is the "law-making" branch of government. But a large number of proposals considered by the legislature have their origin elsewhere. The governor is one of the most important sources of bills. Executive agencies are frequent contributors of proposed legislation. Private interest groups and individuals, working with and through their elected representatives, and local governmental units and their associations provide a great deal of the grist for the legislative mill.

Article XXII, section 19 of the state constitution, requires that the legislature pass laws prohibiting lobbying on the floor of either house and further regulating the practice of lobbying. While this obligation has not been totally fulfilled, the legislature has passed strong bribery and corruption and conflict-of-interest laws, governing not only members of the legislature, but also all public officials and employees at the state and local level. Lobbyists engage in considerable activity during each legislative session, many organizations maintaining full-time representation in Phoenix during the sessions. Their ability to present information and points of view make them potent though informal participants in the legislative process.

Not all legislative power is lodged in the legislature. The voters, through the initiative and referendum, have reserved the prerogative of considering legislation which the legislature has refused to enact, or of reconsidering certain enactments. Through the initiative, ten percent of the qualified electors may, by petition, require any measure they desire to be submitted to the voters. Fifteen percent may require a constitutional amendment to be submitted. The Secretary of State presents these proposals to the voters after ascertaining the validity of the petitions. In each case, a majority of the votes cast is required for approval. An example of the initiative function was the 1958 name change of Arizona State University.

Under the referendum procedure, the legislature must refer approved constitutional amendments to the people. It also may refer acts or parts of acts to the voters. Five percent of those voting for governor in the last election may require that there be submitted to the people any acts not carrying the emergency clause. Again, a majority vote is required for passage. If initiated or referred measures receive a majority of the votes cast, but less than a majority of votes from all registered voters, the legislature may amend or repeal such legislation. An example of the five percent referendum process was the 1968 passage of a state legislative reapportionment plan, which was later ruled unconstitutional by a three-judge federal court panel.

John D. Lyons
Professor of Law

15

THE JUDICIAL BRANCH

THE JUDICIAL BRANCH is composed of the courts; its function, to interpret the law and administer justice.

Robert Traver, American judge and novelist, describes the courts as "society's safety valve." "Every trial in the land," one of his characters reminds us, "is a small miracle of man's triumph over passion, a celebration of his escape from his ancient bondage to violence."

This chapter, then, will summarize briefly the development, structure, and procedure of the Arizona courts.

The Federal District

Within the territorial limits of Arizona there are both state and federal courts. And since our concern is with the state courts, we ought to begin by distinguishing them from the federal courts.

The federal constitution vests the judicial power of the United States in one supreme court and such inferior courts as Congress may establish. The principal courts which Congress established are the federal district courts, which are trial courts, and the federal courts of appeal, which are intermediate appellate courts.

For organizational purposes Congress presently divides the nation into some ninety judicial districts, in each of which there is a federal district court, and into eleven judicial circuits, in each of which there is a federal court of appeal. Arizona constitutes one of the judicial districts, and with eight other states and Guam it constitutes the ninth judicial circuit.

The jurisdiction of the federal courts is limited to matters arising under the constitution and laws of the United States. All other justiciable matters fall to the jurisdiction of the state courts. One might conclude, therefore, that although physically mingled, the two systems would operate independently. And so they do, in the main. But there are two important exceptions.

The first concerns state cases involving the federal constitution. The Constitution of the United States provides that "the judges in every state shall be bound thereby." It also provides that the judicial power of the United States "shall extend to all cases . . . arising under this constitution." Thus it happens that the United States Supreme Court may review state court judgments on federal constitutional questions. In this way, and for this limited purpose, the Supreme Court of the United States becomes, in effect, the final court of appeal in the Arizona judicial system.

The second important exception to the general rule that state and federal courts operate independently, is in so-called diversity cases. The jurisdiction of Arizona courts is not limited to Arizona citizens; it often embraces citizens of other states. But the federal constitution extends the judicial power of the federal courts to all controversies "between citizens of different states." It follows that, in what would otherwise be purely state cases, if there is diversity of citizenship between adverse parties, the federal courts have jurisdiction, too. In such case the federal court applies state law, and in the language of Justice Frankfurter, becomes "only another court of the state."

With these exceptions — which are of rather frequent occurrence — the state and federal courts in Arizona operate independently.

The Territorial Courts

For several years after becoming part of the United States, the region which is now Arizona was virtually without legal process. Although officially part of the Territory of New Mexico, it was so far from the seats of territorial government, and the roads between were so infested with hostiles, both red and white, that it was effectively a land without courts.

Thus, Arizona can hardly be said to have inherited a judicial system. Rather, its judicial system was launched new, on February 24, 1863, when President Lincoln signed the Act creating the separate Territory of Arizona. It provided that "The judicial power shall be vested in a supreme court, to consist of three judges, and such inferior courts as the legislative council may by law prescribe." The next year the first territorial legislature prescribed a complete court system.

A complete system requires only three kinds of courts: 1) *A trial court of general jurisdiction,* where most cases of consequence are first heard, where witnesses testify and juries render verdicts; 2) An *appellate court,* with power to review the judgments of the general trial court; and 3) *local courts,* which are trial courts of limited jurisdiction, designed to try lesser offenses and smaller claims more expeditiously and less expensively than the general trial court.

But this classic court structure was often complicated in earlier days by numbers of *special courts,* to each of which was assigned some part of the total territorial or subject-matter jurisdiction of the general court. One eastern jurisdiction, for example, could boast fourteen kinds of courts. Fortunately for Arizona its first territorial legislature avoided this bad example. It simply enacted that "The following shall be the courts of justice for this Territory: 1) the supreme court, 2) the district court, 3) the probate court, 4) the justices' courts, and 5) such other courts of a police character as may be established by law." This provided Arizona, in the order listed, with an appellate court, a trial court of general jurisdiction, one special court, and the local courts.

One may wonder why the special probate court was thought necessary for a population of only six thousand five hundred. But considering the customs of the day, it was a small transgression. And to insure that the probate judge would not be idle the Legislature assigned him from time to time some extra duties, including assessing and collecting property taxes, issuing commercial licenses, settling the accounts of the treasurer, sheriff, and all constables, clerks, and collectors, appointing the county treasurer and election judges, issuing election proclamations, superintending roads, disposing of vagrants, examining into Indian depredations, apprehending fugitives, serving as ex-officio Chairman of the Board of Supervisors, and punishing disobedient children.

The probate judges were elected by counties, and the justices of the peace by election precincts. As for the appointive judges, it was said that they wore three hats. By authority of the Act of Congress, they were appointed by the President to four-year terms as appellate justices of the territorial supreme court. Then by authority of the territorial legislature, each of them was designated as the trial judge of one of the three divisions of the territorial district court, to try cases arising under the laws of the territory. Finally, for the first six days of each trial term, each one performed the functions of a federal judge, in matters arising under the constitution and laws of the United States.

This combination of trial and appellate functions raised the question whether trial judges ought to sit in review of their own judgments. At first it was permitted, and records show that the judges sometimes voted to reverse themselves. Later the territorial legislature prohibited the practice, but that law was repealed after two years, probably because it resulted in a supreme court with only two eligible members. Finally, Congress resolved the matter by increasing the number of territorial judges and judicial districts, and disqualifying a trial judge from sitting on appeals from his own trial court.

Arizona is indebted to its first territorial legislators, not only for a streamlined court structure, but also for an enlightened system of pleading. The word pleading, in this sense, refers to the written averments and counteraverments with which a lawsuit begins, and by which the parties formulate the issues to be tried.

Most American jurisdictions, including our parent territory of New Mexico, were then using what was called *common law pleading.* Common law pleading was characterized by rigid "forms of action." If the plaintiff could squeeze his fact situation into one of these predetermined forms he had a remedy, otherwise not. This obvious injustice had given rise to a second judicial system, called *equity,* which functioned parallel to the older law courts, and had its own system of pleading. What with two systems of pleading, and the technicalities of the forms of action, common law pleading had become more an intricate game than an aid to justice.

Still, the easier course for Arizona would have been to retain the established style of pleading of New Mexico. Instead, it chose a new and controversial system which had recently been introduced into a minority of states. Known as *code pleading,* it abolished the forms of action, and the distinctions in pleading between common law and equity, and required the pleadings to state simply the facts giving rise to the cause of action or defense. All American jurisdictions have since adopted code pleading, but in being among the first to adopt it, Arizona's territorial legislators gave further evidence of their progressive spirit.

Statehood

The coming of statehood, momentous as it was for Arizona, did not produce any radical changes in the structure or procedure of her courts. The name of the trial court of general jurisdiction was changed from District Court to Superior Court and the special probate court was eliminated, and its functions transferred to the Superior Court.

Arizona has never since had a special court in the sense of a separate court, exercising a specified part of the total subject-matter jurisdiction. Statutes as late as the 1960s refer to the "Juvenile Court" and the "Conciliation Court," but these were only formally organized departments of the Superior Court, having no separate existence apart from that court. The only new court added in Arizona from statehood through the sixties was the Court of Appeals, not a special court, as we shall see a little later, but an intermediate appellate court.

Also, statehood put an end to the three-hat era for Arizona judges. A separate United States District Court for the District of Arizona was established by Congress for federal trials. And Arizona judges no longer sat regularly in both trial and appellate courts.

The final stages of Arizona's struggle for statehood did, however, involve her judicial branch in a collateral way. The voters of the territory had adopted a proposed state constitution which included a provision for the popular recall of all elective officials. The fact that judges were not exempt conflicted with President Taft's convictions about an independent judiciary, and he promptly vetoed the joint congressional resolution for Arizona's admission. Congress then passed a second resolution conditioned upon Arizona's amending her proposed constitution so as to exempt judges from its recall provisions. Such an amendment was adopted by the voters of the territory on December 12, 1911, and the President approved admission as a state on February 14, 1912.

Once admitted, however, the now state of Arizona, at an election on November 5, 1912, amended the state constitution again, repealing the exemption, and restoring the liability of judges to recall. And so it remained as the 1970s began — Arizona being one of only eight states which permitted the popular recall of judges. But this remnant of the old populist movement has been resorted to but once, and then under circumstances which did not really compromise the principle of judicial independence.

The Procedural Reform of 1940

A practical set of rules for the conduct of litigation is essential to any court system. Such *rules of procedure,* as they are called, concern "pleading" (noted above) and "practice" (the manner of conducting the actual trial).

In 1913, the year after Arizona was admitted to statehood, the American Bar Association established a committee to encourage procedural reform by preparing a proposed uniform code of civil procedure. This committee quickly decided that the best way to promulgate such a code would be to have Congress empower the United States Supreme Court to make uniform rules of procedure for all federal district courts.

There was opposition to this plan in Congress, and it was 1934 before this power was granted, and 1938 before the Uniform Rules of Civil Procedure for the United States District Courts went into effect. Similar authority was then granted by the Arizona Legislature to the Supreme Court of Arizona, and effective January 1, 1940, Arizona became the first state to adopt these uniform rules, substantially unchanged, as the rules of civil procedure for its own courts.

The uniform rules covered both pleading and prac-

tice. As to pleading they followed the principles of code pleading, which, as already noted, were adopted by the Arizona Territory upon its organization. The full effect of the code pleading reforms had been postponed to a considerable extent through its strict construction by reluctant judges. This was especially true of the fact pleading provisions, where over-elaborate distinctions between ultimate facts, evidentiary facts and legal conclusions had given rise to a confusing mass of finespun constructions. But a new generation of judges, trained in the theory of code pleading, had amended the language of the pleading rules to conform to their intent, and this improved language was made available to the Arizona courts when they adopted the 1940 rules. Nevertheless, since Arizona already had code pleading, the chief importance of the uniform rules here was in practice, rather than pleading.

The underlying concept of these new rules of practice, which distinguishes them from older rules, is that the trial of lawsuits is not a game, in which one party should be free to surprise the other with artfully concealed evidence, but that it is, rather, a method of arriving at the truth. For the latter purpose it is desirable that each side be able to learn the other side's case at an early stage of the proceedings. And to this end the new rules are replete with provisions for deposition and discovery, summary judgment, and pretrial hearing.

DEPOSITION AND DISCOVERY. At any time after suit commenced and before trial the testimony of any person under the reformed practice may be taken and recorded by any party, either for later use as evidence, or for the purpose of discovery. The witness in such case may be examined regarding any matter relevant to any phase of the case, including the existence and whereabouts of other evidence, and of persons having knowledge of relevant facts. Similarly, the court may at the request of a party order another party to produce any tangible evidence for inspection, measuring, or photographing any object or operation.

SUMMARY JUDGMENT. Also before trial, any party may move for summary judgment, without trial, based on the pleadings, depositions, and admissions on file, together with affidavits, and counter affidavits, if these show no material issue, or that the movent is entitled to a judgment as a matter of law. Or the court may make an order reducing the matters to be tried, and the remaining matters only shall then be tried accordingly.

PRETRIAL HEARING. This authorizes the court to order opposing counsel to appear for a conference before trial to consider face to face any matters that may aid in the disposition of the case, such as the possibility of obtaining admissions of fact or documents which will avoid the introduction of unnecessary proof at the trial. Thereafter the court shall issue an order which sets out the agreements and limits the issues for trial to those not disposed of at the pretrial conference. A pretrial conference may result in greatly reducing the issues to be tried, with consequent shortening of the trial, and sometimes in a settlement without trial.

The uniform rules discussed apply to civil actions, but the same year — on April 1, 1940 — the Supreme Court of Arizona also issued a new code of criminal procedure. Patterned largely on a model code prepared by the American Law Institute, it had the same aims as the uniform civil code, i.e., to eliminate useless technicalities from criminal pleading and practice, and to make criminal trials less of a game by putting the cards on the table before trial.

As to the first of these objectives the most important rules, perhaps, were those authorizing the short form of information or indictment. One or the other of these is the foundation of a criminal action, somewhat as the complaint is the foundation of a civil action. Like the old common-law complaints, their language had become technical and prolix, so that criminal actions were frequently dismissed, without regard to the merits, because of some failure of allegation in this initial document. The short forms served a purpose similar to the simplified complaint in code pleading, and to the extent that they might provide inadequate notice to the defendant of the details of the charge against him, the remedy was, not to dismiss the action, but to correct the inadequacy by demanding a bill of particulars.

As for reducing the opportunities for gamesmanship in criminal trials, an important new rule required the county attorney to endorse on the indictment or information the names of the witnesses he proposed to call. There was no other provision for discovery, in the 1940 criminal rules, but in 1955 the Arizona Supreme Court adopted a rule giving the defendant a limited right of discovery as to papers and tangible objects material to the preparation of his defense.

The Modern Courts Amendment of 1960

The ancient problem of "the law's delay" was acute in most of the United States in 1960, and Arizona was no exception. Although free of the outmoded and cumbersome court structure which contributed so largely to the plight of older states, Arizona had grown so phenomenally since statehood that it had outdistanced its own judicial structure.

Population had quintupled, and business and litigation had increased at an even faster rate. Meantime, the number of judges of courts of record had scarcely doubled, and judicial administrative machinery — or more accurately, the absence of judicial administrative machinery — had remained essentially as it had been half a century before. As a result, the Supreme Court's calendar had fallen two and a half years behind, and in the Superior Courts, serious calendar delay existed in Maricopa County, and was imminent in Pima.

In this condition of affairs, the State Bar of Arizona

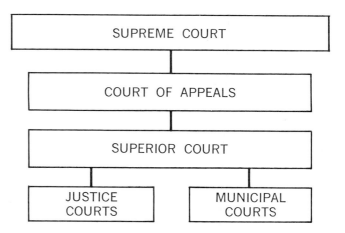

Fig. 15.1 Interrelation of the Arizona courts and the principal United States courts.

prepared and sponsored a new judicial article for the state constitution. This "Modern Courts Amendment," as it came to be known, was submitted to the voters as an initiative measure at the general election in 1960. It was approved, and became effective on December 9 of that year.

The most significant change brought about by the new judicial article was the drawing together of the Arizona courts into an integrated judicial department. Previously, each court, and each judge of a multi-judge court, had been essentially independent. It is true that the old judicial article had provided the Supreme Court with a chief justice, authorized to preside at its sessions, and that the Supreme Court had at least statutory authority to make rules of procedure for the superior courts. But with these small exceptions, the Arizona court system was an uncoordinated lot of independently elected and functioning officials, without administrative machinery to draw it into an efficient operational unit.

The Modern Court Amendment sought to correct this situation by giving the Supreme Court administrative supervision over all the other courts of the state. It provided that this new supervisory power should be exercised by the court through its chief justice, and that the court should appoint an administrative director and staff to assist the chief justice in discharging his administrative duties.

One of the important functions of the administrative director has proved to be the compiling of statistics concerning the business of the courts. How many cases filed? Where? What kinds? How many decided? Is the number of filings increasing or decreasing? Are the dispositions keeping up with them? This sort of information is invaluable to the chief justice in deciding when and where to assign judges and to take other steps to keep the business of the courts moving as speedily as may be consistent with a fair hearing.

In addition, the administrative director has, of course, many other duties connected with the new function of the Supreme Court as the administrative center for the judicial branch. For example, the very successful annual conferences, instituted by the Supreme Court for superior court judges, and for justices of the peace, would be impossible without the availability of the administrative director to manage the logistics.

To eliminate any suggestion that the Supreme Court's power to make rules of procedure for the superior courts existed by grace of the legislative branch, and to extend its rule-making power to other courts as well, the amendment provided, for the first time expressly, that the court's constitutional powers include the power to make rules of procedure for all state courts.

In 1948 the old judicial article had been amended by adding the provision that the superior courts, formerly treated as fourteen separate courts, were declared to be a single court, composed of all the duly elected or appointed and qualified judges of the superior court in each and all of the counties of the state. This same language was carried over into the new judicial article, but with this difference in result: that whereas in the old judicial article the courts seemed inclined to interpret this language narrowly, (in view of a limited purpose for which it had been originally enacted), in the new amendment, where it appears as part and parcel of an overall plan for judicial integration, they have applied it broadly, in the light of the overall purpose of the voters in adopting the amendment.

To provide local administrative supervision for the courts, and to perform other duties as required by law or supreme court rule, the amendment further provides for each county a *presiding* judge of the superior court. Where, as in most counties, there is only one superior court judge, he is automatically the presiding judge for that county. But in multi-judge counties, the Supreme Court appoints one.

An important result of fusing the separate superior courts into a single court, and of integrating all the courts of the state into one judicial department, is the increased and more orderly interchange of judges, so that their services may be employed where the case load makes them most valuable. Even before the recent amendment it was possible for a superior court judge to serve in another county, upon invitation of the judge in that county; but he was not required to do so, except upon order of the governor — obviously an emergency, and not a regular administrative procedure. But now, the chief justice, in the exercise of his administrative powers, may assign any judge to serve in other courts and counties as the exigencies of the calendars require.

Second in importance only to court integration was the authorization, by the new judicial article, of intermediate appellate courts, with such jurisdiction, power, and duties as should be provided by law. Before implementing this authority, however, the legislature chose to test the effect of other devices provided by the amendment for accelerating the disposition of appeals. For example, the Supreme Court, which had been increased from the original three to five members in 1947, was authorized by the amendment to sit in divisions of three. And by using this means, and others, it was able, by 1963, to double its annual disposition of cases. Unfortunately, however, the new cases filed increased at an even faster rate, so that the backlog, instead of shrinking, continued to grow.

Consequently, the 1964 Legislature created the Court of Appeals, an intermediate appellate court, divided into two divisions of three judges each. Division 1 consists of the counties of Maricopa, Yuma, Mohave, Coconino, Yavapai, Navajo, and Apache; division 2, of Pima, Pinal, Cochise, Santa Cruz, Greenlee, Graham, and Gila. In 1969 the number of judges in division 1 was increased to six.

The jurisdiction of the Court of Appeals includes all matters appealable from the Superior Court, except crimes punishable by death or life imprisonment. Also, the Supreme Court is authorized to transfer to the Court of Appeals any pending appeals which are within the newer court's jurisdiction. A party who is unsuccessful in the Court of Appeals may request a review by the Supreme Court, which may grant or deny the request at its discretion.

The question soon arose whether litigants appealing from the Superior Court were obliged to take their appeals to the new Court of Appeals, or whether they retained the right to appeal directly to the Supreme Court. It was argued that the statute, by vesting certain appellate jurisdiction in the Court of Appeals, implied revocation of their right to appeal directly to the Supreme Court in cases within that jurisdiction. But in a 1966 case the Supreme Court held that the right to appeal directly to the Supreme Court was a constitutional right, which could not be restricted by legislation, and that litigants had the option, therefore, to appeal to either the Supreme Court or, as to matters within its jurisdiction, to the new Court of Appeals. Having thus preserved the right of direct appeal to the Supreme Court, that court, however, promptly transferred the very appeal in question to the Court of Appeals for disposition, stating that this would be its ordinary policy so long as the state of its calendar required.

Although overlapping appellate jurisdiction may be unusual, the power of the Supreme Court to transfer appeals from its docket to that of the Court of Appeals has made it workable, and has even further enhanced the flexibility of the system.

There were other provisions of the Modern Courts Amendment to increase the efficiency of the judicial process and avoid unnecessary delay. Retired judges of courts of record were authorized to serve as needed; judges pro tempore may be appointed as provided by the legislature; court commissioners, masters, and referees could be appointed by superior court judges, "to exercise . . . powers conferred by supreme court rule." The minimum jurisdictional amount in the superior court was raised from $200 to $500, thus shifting about 10 percent of the superior court's civil litigation to the

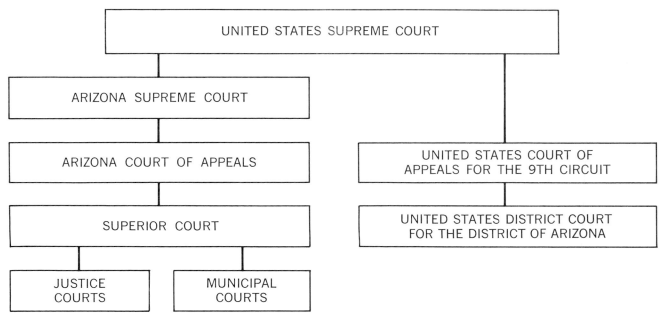

Fig. 15.2 The courts of Arizona.

Justice Courts. Trial by jury could be waived by the parties, with the consent of the court, in criminal cases. The Supreme Court could by rule put teeth in the old requirement that all submitted matters must be decided by superior court judges within sixty days of submission. And population determinations, for arriving at the proper number of superior court judges for a county, could be made, not only from the decennial census enumeration, as previously, but also "by such other method as may be provided by law." The Legislature has left the determination of population to the boards of supervisors, "based on, but not limited to," recent estimates issued by the bureau of the census, auto registrations, nonagricultural employment, gross utility revenues, and retail sales. This innovation was important in a state whose population increased 50 percent between the 1940 and 1950 census enumerations, and 74 percent between those of 1950 and 1960.

As a result of these constitutional changes, and their legislative implementation, the problems of calendar delay have been largely controlled. Assuming one year, after the matter is at issue, as a reasonable time for disposing of a case in courts of record, and six months in local courts, then only two out of nearly a hundred and fifty courts and divisions of courts in Arizona were in arrears on the eve of 1970. While such near-perfection is not to be expected as a permanent condition, it did appear that these aims of the Modern Courts Amendment had been achieved to a remarkable degree.

Conclusion

It should be apparent that Arizona's judicial branch is by no means static. As population has increased, the number and size of courts has increased. As the more leisurely living style of 1863 has given way to the modern emphasis on efficiency and dispatch, the administrative structure of the judicial branch has been altered. As the society has refined its concept of equal justice, the rules of pleading and practice have been modified to accommodate the changes.

So far Arizona has had a relatively progressive attitude toward its courts. Although not always abreast of changing times, Arizona has more often been in the van of the states than in the rear. That was easier for a young state, however, and as the seventies began it remained to be seen whether Arizona would sustain that record when encumbered with the impedimenta of a longer legal history.

David Shirley
Economist

16

PUBLIC FINANCE

As NATIONAL INCOME HAS GROWN in the state of Arizona and in the nation, citizens have thrust greater and greater responsibilities on government. To meet these responsibilities Arizona has found it necessary to expand the size of the public purse almost yearly. The fiscal year 1912-13 was the first full year of Arizona's statehood, and the state spent slightly in excess of $1.6 million exclusive of refunding of about $1.5 million of territorial bonds. In that year the cost of what is now identified as general government accounted for more than 30 percent of the total, and interest on the state's debts took another 10 percent. By 1967-68 the state had assumed a variety of new activities, and the state auditor reported that the two activities noted accounted for less than 3 percent of the state's direct expenditures of more than $403 million.

Education, highways, health, and welfare have become the dominant state activities. These functions in the late 1960s were absorbing more than 85 percent of the direct expenditures of Arizona, whereas in 1913 they accounted for only 40 percent of a much smaller total. As in other states, a substantial portion of highway, health, and welfare costs were being met by grants-in-aid from the federal government.

Conservative Growth

Throughout this period of growth the state of Arizona followed what must be identified as a conservative financial posture. The authors of the state's constitution provided the framework for conservatism, most obvious in the sections of the constitution related to the use of the state's credit. One provision which applies to the state and all its political subdivisions prohibits the use of public credit to support any private company or corporation. Another limits the aggregate general obligation debt of the state of Arizona to $350,000. Even though

this amount represented less than one-tenth of one percent of the state's annual expenditure in 1969, efforts to have the debt limit increased have failed. One further limitation specifies that the legislature shall levy taxes sufficient to liquidate any debt within twenty-five years of the passage of the law authorizing such debt. In view of these limitations, and prices in the late sixties, it was little wonder that the U.S. Bureau of the Census listed Arizona as one of the seven states which had no long-term full faith and credit debt outstanding. The only significant debt was $84 million of revenue bonds sold primarily to finance dormitories on the state's three university campuses.

No similar restrictions on the state's taxing powers were written into the state constitution. There were the usual restrictions that taxes "shall be levied and collected for public purposes only" and that taxes "shall be uniform upon the same class of property." There were no rate limits specified, nor was any specific type of tax outlawed. However, a constitutional amendment approved in 1950 specifically exempted manufacturers' inventories from taxation. Also, one rather unusual limitation has reflected the aforementioned conservatism. The constitution provided that "Every law which imposes, continues, or revives a tax shall distinctly state the tax and the objects for which it shall be applied." This provision was clearly intended to insure clarity, but has also contributed to a complex fund structure apparent in the state's financial reporting. A court interpretation that this constitutional provision does not apply to excise taxes has made it possible to maintain a workable fund structure.

From the beginning of statehood, Arizona has made extensive use of property taxation. In 1912, the general property tax was the state's principal source of revenue. It was supplemented by a gross earnings tax imposed on railroad companies in lieu of property taxes and an inheritance tax which was not very productive. The general procedure for determining the state property tax rate each year was still in use in the late 1960s, the rate being determined by what may best be described as the residual method. The estimated revenue from non-property tax sources is subtracted from the budgeted expenditures to determine the amount of property tax revenue needed. This needed amount is then divided by the assessed value of the state to determine the actual state tax rate. County treasurers collect the state property tax along with the property taxes of counties, school districts and municipalities, and then forward the state's share to the state treasurer.

Responsibility Increased

The state in the late 1960s assumed much greater responsibility for the determination of assessed value, the base of the property tax. Originally the determination of assessments was left largely to county assessors with only "general supervision" of these local officials assigned to the elected State Tax Commission. Over the years rather wide intracounty as well as intercounty discrepancies developed, and in 1963 the state legislature ordered a specially created division of the State Tax Commission to do a statewide revaluation. The revaluation was completed and a Department of Valuation created as an "independent agency of state government." In order to insure continued statewide uniformity, this new department was given considerable authority over the fourteen elected county assessors. This authority was reinforced by the power of the department to contest in its own name any proposed valuation "before any county board of equalization or before the state board of equalization," and to request the state attorney general to issue a mandamus action if a local assessor "fails to follow any regulation, rules, order or direction" of the director of the Department of Valuation. He may request a similar action if he determines "that an assessor or a county board of equalization has practiced discrimination in the valuation of property." Clearly the state had determined, as of the late 1960s, to reform rather than abandon the property tax.

Diversification of Arizona's revenue structure began shortly after statehood. In the years immediately following World War I, the growing use of automobiles gave rise to the demand for improved roads. In this large but sparsely settled state, the cost of meeting this demand was substantial and the state passed legislation taxing motor fuels for the first time in 1921. Revenue from this source, as well as from other sources directly related to vehicular movement, have from the beginning been administered by the State Highway Commission rather than the Tax Commission. Continuation of the practice of earmarking funds from these sources was written into the constitution in 1952.

The depressed economic conditions of the early 1930s resulted in a precipitous drop in property tax receipts, and for a short period the state was forced to pay its current bills in interest-bearing warrants which were not immediately redeemable. The search for additional — and more dependable — sources of revenue resulted in the adoption of three new broadbased taxes. The privilege sales tax, originally the most productive of the three, is a tax on the privilege of doing business in the state as measured by gross receipts or gross proceeds of sales. To the consumer this tax has appeared to be identical with the retail sales taxes found in other states, but it has a substantially broader base since it has not been limited to final transactions. The effective rate of this tax was increased in 1959 when the state legislature adopted an Education Excise Tax utilizing the privilege tax base and a tax rate equal to 50 percent of the rate imposed under the privilege tax legislation. The combination of these two taxes produced almost 30 percent of the state's total tax revenue in 1967-68.

The financial crisis of the 1930s also contributed income taxation, both corporate and individual, to the state's revenue structure. As in most states this tax in Arizona is patterned after that imposed by the federal government but allows higher personal exemptions and applies a lower rate structure. As of 1969, the maximum tax rate for both individuals and corporations was eight percent. In 1967-68 when a slightly lower rate schedule applied, income taxes yielded 20 percent of the state's total tax revenue.

A luxury privilege tax was the third tax introduced under the pressure of this earlier financial crisis. This tax still applies only to tobacco products and alcoholic beverages, although the law specifies that a luxury is "any article, object or device upon which a tax is imposed under the provisions of this article." There have been numerous rate adjustments since its introduction, and the tax in 1967-68 yielded almost 10 percent of the state's tax revenue.

The pattern established in this much earlier period has persisted: in the late 1960s Arizona was deriving 90 percent of its tax revenue from five sources: a privilege sales tax, an income tax on both individuals and corporations, a general property tax, fuel taxes, and luxury taxes. Rate adjustments during the intervening years shifted the relative importance among these five, but they remained as the backbone of tax support for state activity.

Government Aid

Supplementing the state tax revenues has been a substantial flow of funds from the federal government. Because of the vast acreage of federally owned land in Arizona and the large area affecting its entitlement to federal highway funds, the state has always enjoyed considerable financial aid from the national government. For 1967-68 the state auditor reported that Arizona received

$119 million which represented 28.9 percent of its revenue in the form of "contributions, grants and aids." The Highway Fund, which received slightly more than $59 million from the federal government, was the chief benefactor. Arizona has also benefited from increased federal aid to education, but less than half of these funds have been reported in the state's figures, since the amounts going directly to the school districts are not included.

Revenue from the payroll tax for unemployment insurance in the late sixties went into a trust fund held for the federal government, and benefits were paid from this fund to eligible claimants. In 1967-68 benefit payments totaled $11.94 million. Income for the fund from payroll taxes and interest on the fund balance totaled more than $20 million so that the fund balance stood at an all-time high of $84.7 million at the end of the fiscal year. Regarding this fund Arizona was in an excellent financial position.

The state government began sharing its financial strength with units of local governments during the 1930s. The original privilege sales tax law provided that a portion of its yield — approximately 40 percent — be divided among the fourteen counties for the express purpose of lessening the burden of the county property tax. Later this law was amended so that counties received 33.6 percent and the municipalities 25 percent of privilege sales tax revenue. Individual county shares were determined by a formula which included both county assessed valuation and the source of sales tax collection; under this formula, Maricopa County — the most densely populated area of the state in 1969 — received approximately 50 percent of the total county distribution and cities within that county received slightly more than 60 percent of the city funds. Cities and counties were also sharing in revenue received from the motor vehicle fuel tax, the vehicle license tax, and the bank and savings and loan income tax. The alcoholic beverage license tax was being shared only with counties.

The costs of education, the most expensive of the services provided by state and local government, have been shared by the state, county, school district, and federal government. The report of the state superintendent of public instruction indicated that the tax levies of the local school districts provided 45 percent of

school district receipts in 1967-68. A variety of state programs contributed 37 percent, federal programs 10 percent, and counties plus other local receipts 8 percent. The 1968 session of the state legislature provided additional state support, and it is assumed that both state and federal assistance to local school districts will be increased in the years ahead.

While the sources of public revenues are necessarily subject to annual scrutiny and frequent adjustment to meet the changing needs of the state, the management of the state's public finances have tended to be more stable. Arizona's period of stability, despite frequent efforts to institute change, extended from statehood until the early 1960s. The constitution and early legislation reflected the belief that the best defense against malfeasance in the handling of public moneys was the diffusion of financial responsibility among numerous elected and appointed officials. Arizona's constitution provides for an elected state auditor, an elected state treasurer, who cannot succeed himself, and a state examiner appointed for a two-year term by the governor. Nothing has been said, however, about the governor's financial powers except that he does have item veto power over appropriation bills. Legislation has provided for a three-man state tax commission to serve as the state's chief revenue collection agency, and for a post auditor to be appointed by the legislature. Efforts to simplify and clarify this complex structure prior to the 1960s ran afoul of one or more of the established financial offices and were unsuccessful. The first successful reorganization effort was the previously noted statewide revaluation authorized in 1963, and the creation of a Department of Valuation as an independent state agency. In 1966 legislation was approved, making the governor responsible for the preparation and submission of an executive budget. This same legislation authorized the creation of an executive department, the Department of Finance, with three divisions: State Planning, Budget and Systems, and Purchasing. The legislature in 1968 approved bills which would further simplify and clarify the financial management of the state and these bills became effective in 1969 following electoral approval of the necessary constitutional amendments.

Conrad Joyner
Political Scientist

17

LOCAL GOVERNMENT

BECAUSE ARIZONA is one of the fastest-growing states in the union and one of the most highly urbanized, its local governments are facing problems which were once thought to be unique to larger metropolitan areas. It is a gross exaggeration to argue that Arizonans confront difficulties of the magnitude existing in Los Angeles, Detroit, New York, or Chicago, but local governments all over America are in trouble. In fact, problems in Arizona with regard to cities, school districts, counties, and special districts are merely of lesser degree as compared with other larger jurisdictions.

One of the most serious and nagging problems facing local governments is that of adequate revenues, particularly in the Phoenix and Tucson metropolitan areas. In part, the revenue crisis has been generated by continued population growth during the 1960s. The over 300,000 increase in Maricopa (663,510 in 1960 to 967,522 in 1970) and the nearly 100,000 addition in Pima (265,660 in 1960 to 351,667 in 1970) have served to make the revenue squeeze tighter. The saying that people create problems certainly holds correct. And it is equally correct that with more people and more problems, more money is needed.

Local governments require funds for education, protection, health, sanitation, public works, and other related activities. To these traditional responsibilities have been added others stemming from social and economic problems. Such matters as control of drug abuse and alcoholism, welfare of many types, recreation, and manpower training have increasingly appeared on the agendas of local jurisdictions. Many new and expanded programs which deal with human problems have been initiated at the national level. In order for cities, counties, school districts, and other units to take advantage of these nationally inspired programs there is generally required some type of cash outlay by local governments prior to the input of federal funds.

Funding of both old and new activities has been through two major sources of taxation — property and excise (sales). The state does share in financing certain programs through grants of monies. As examples, the Arizona legislature established formulae for distribution of funds to school districts for education, and to county and city governments for the construction of streets and highways. The distribution schemes were the subject of much haggling during the decade of the sixties, particularly concerning primary and secondary education. At virtually each session of the legislature the battle over "revenue sharing" between the state and local governments has appeared in some form or other. There is every reason to believe that in the 1970s, the struggles over financing will continue, although there exists some hope that satisfactory arrangements between the state and its major subdivisions can be reached.

Not only have additional people caused traditional problems to become more pressing, but new difficulties have come to beset Phoenix and Tucson. A major concern in recent years has been the quality of the environment. This problem encompasses more than just air and water pollution, serious and growing as both of these are. Urban dwellers and their rural counterparts are troubled also by sight and sound pollution. Measures to deal with billboards, litter, and disposal of such solid waste as non-returnable containers became manifestations of Arizona's increasing anxieties about the quality of life.

The state in mid-twentieth century developed a thriving tourism industry which became threatened by the "newer" forms of environment despoilation. Tourists represent dollars for Arizonans — an ample justification for concern over pollution. Of equal importance, both old and new citizens have enjoyed the benefits of one of the country's most pleasant environments. If pollution continues, the very factors which make life agreeable will

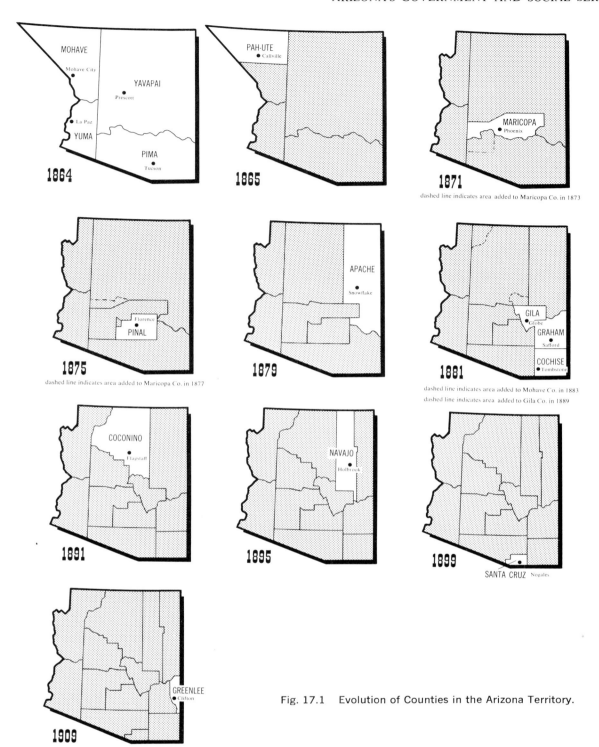

Fig. 17.1 Evolution of Counties in the Arizona Territory.

be threatened. In fact, there are those who predict that the Phoenix-Tucson corridor could become another Los Angeles. Although few Arizonans want this kind of growth, it may become a reality if adequate planning and preventive measures are not undertaken.

In both Phoenix and Tucson, fairly large and vocal groups came forward at the beginning of the 1970s to protest extensive freeway development. But from the vantage point of other groups equally seriously concerned, blocking freeways was no solution to Arizona's

growth problems, nor were the existing freeways that skirted the city an answer to increasing internal problems of urban traffic. As of 1970, Phoenix and Tucson planners had not come up with any workable alternative for moving people. Although mass transit systems were under discussion, the current form of public transportation — antiquated bus systems — did not inspire much confidence in the future. Given the superabundance of private cars and the wide open spaces of the state, it was argued that the Arizona public would not readily agree to leave cars at home and use mass transit in any of its present viable forms.

At the opening of the 1970s then, it was felt that Arizonans, while rejecting massive freeway projects, may have retarded growth of another megalopolis but had not stopped it. Predictions were frequent that in all probability it would be only a matter of time until Tucson and Phoenix, separated by a distance of approximately 100 miles, would be linked by a series of communities. The question of how these communities would relate to one another was regarded as one of the more vexing problems facing Arizonans up to the year 2000.

By 1970 the legislature had made various attempts to solve the problems of urban sprawl versus quality living, including the passage of a "model cities" bill setting criteria for the development of new cities. While providing some safeguards, this legislation did not satisfy everyone in its confrontation of the complexity of issues involved in urban growth.

Also during the 1970s, county governing bodies were already confronted with what for Arizona was a new problem — wholesale land speculation. Large national corporations purchased some of Arizona's oldest ranches and were engaging in nationwide sales campaigns to get people to buy lots and land for living, retirement, and speculation. Actualities and plans ranged from elaborate leisure-oriented communities, well-adapted to use and enjoyment of the environment by the affluent and retired, to trailer court and low-cost housing, deploying Arizona land in a helter-skelter kind of growth.

A problem here pinpointed in relation to the growth of lower-income population is Arizona's insufficiently diversified economic base. This is seen as serious because people continue to come to Arizona in large numbers despite the vociferousness of groups desiring to retard both economic and population expansion. Although the goal of these groups arouses general admiration — to preserve and enhance the Arizona environment — yet the very factors making Arizona a desirable place to live outweigh the efforts of those who want to slow down the state's growth. On such a view, local governments in conjunction with the state have undertaken programs to attract industry. The Phoenix metropolitan area has enjoyed greater success in these efforts than Tucson. Jobs in both metropolitan centers, however, are a growing problem.

The battle between those who want industry for present and future Arizonans and those who oppose it will probably become more intense. One point of view finds it grossly unfair to spend money to attract tourists while not striving to bring in industry compatible with the Arizona environment. Another position regards the target tourist as someone who comes to Arizona with money to spend rather than a need to earn, thus minimizing the need to open more jobs. A still different stand is taken by those determined not to increase either the population or the industrial base.

As of the 1970s, however, Arizona's major cities already contained many unemployed or underemployed people, notably among the minority groups — black, Mexican-American, and Indian. Ethnic group leaders have tended to be suspicious of those opposed to industrial development, viewing this opposition as another effort to keep minorities in their place and make Arizona a middle-class state in which the white majority dominates and exploits the poor. Unfair as it may be to most Arizonans who are relatively affluent, this accusation points up a potential source of conflict between the economic and social haves and have-nots in the state.

Although the battle over industry has certain racial and ethnic overtones, thus far the state has escaped the more serious forms of racial problem which have been present elsewhere. This probably results from several factors. First, blacks comprise only about three percent of the total population. Second, most Arizona Indians live on reservations. Third, even though approximately thirty percent of the state's population have Spanish surnames, Mexican Americans have been able to achieve both upward social and economic mobility. Despite these factors, there have been some racial and ethnic tensions in both Tucson and Phoenix.

During the latter half of the 1960s and early 1970s charges of racial discrimination were made against school districts. In Phoenix one high school was struck by Mexican-American students. In Tucson young blacks and Mexican Americans have staged sporadic and short-lived walkouts. There have been other kinds of minor eruptions from these two ethnic groups. For example, in Tucson, there was an effort to turn a municipal golf course into a park. The movement was led by Mexican Americans who objected to what they regarded a symbol of middle-class affluence — a golf course in the midst of a predominantly brown and poor neighborhood.

It is difficult to forecast where such minor manifestations of ethnic and racial unrest will lead. Tucson has been trying to head off these and other more serious difficulties through the massive Model Cities program. Through federal assistance, the city government has developed a whole range of programs, including a regional public health facility, day-care centers, manpower training programs, and the like, designed to improve the lot of the poor, and particularly the blacks and browns. Both Phoenix and Tucson have undertaken new starts in public housing. The success of these activities, together with such already existing efforts as local wars on poverty, can do much to integrate minorities into the larger society and provide them with realistic chances to improve their economic and social lot.

In this same connection it should be noted that many school districts have developed programs directed towards providing greater opportunities for the disadvantaged. School districts have not engaged in so-called "busing" to achieve racial and ethnic balance, but they have adopted open enrollment programs which permit students, mainly at the high-school level, to select schools of their choice. There also exist programs to improve the quality of education in poorer areas together with efforts to employ more black and Mexican-American teachers.

Thus, it is fair to say that on several levels local governments have not been unresponsive to the needs of the disadvantaged. But a discussion of problems confronting cities, counties, and school districts comes almost full circle. That is, if ethnic and racial difficulties as well as other problems are to be solved, it will require more than good intentions. Put simply, money is needed to sponsor tangible programs which will improve the quality of life for all Arizonans, particularly the ethnic and racial minorities.

Although solutions to such specific problems will come through efforts of national, state, and local governments, it is the latter institutions which are closer to the people and are in large part responsible for the delivery of many services which touch people's lives most intimately. To know "where the action is," one need look no farther than the local school districts, city governments, county supervisors, and certain other special districts. For this reason, citizens need at least a general understanding of the governments which are closest to them.

Despite its large land area, Arizona has only fourteen counties. Only two, Maricopa and Pima, have more than 100,000 people. The population total for these two counties as of 1970 was 1,319,189, while the remaining twelve counties had a combined total of 434,086. In fact, no county other than Pima and Maricopa had achieved the 70,000 population level. Nonetheless all counties generally elect the same officers regardless of size. These include board of supervisors, sheriff, superintendent of schools, attorney, assessor, treasurer, clerk of the court, and recorder. With the exception of Maricopa and Pima counties, the boards of supervisors are composed of three members elected from geographical districts. As a result of pressures from the metropolitan areas for greater representation, five supervisors were to be elected in Pima and Maricopa counties beginning in 1972.

The fact that various officers are elected whose functions are largely administrative, e.g., clerk of the court, means that county governmental and administrative organization is decentralized. This leads at times to duplication of effort and disagreement among officials. In the two larger counties, these problems have been overcome to a degree by establishing offices to coordinate the activities of various officers. Beginning in 1952, Maricopa County created the position of county manager while more recently Pima County established the office of administrative assistant to the board of supervisors. It is likely that sometime in the 1970s this latter official will be given greater powers, corresponding to those of a county manager.

There have been various proposals to eliminate certain elective county offices and make them appoint-ive. One reason offered for such proposals is that most citizens, being unfamiliar with tasks performed by lesser county officials, are not able to make intelligent judgments concerning the relative qualifications of those seeking office. Another argument in favor of reducing the number of elective offices is that with fewer officials, lines of responsibility could be more readily identified. Thus, citizens would more readily get an answer to the question: "Who is in charge here?" Countering these arguments, there are strong pressures, mainly from those with vested interest — incumbent officials and others planning to seek election — to keep things as they are.

As the 1970s opened, one fairly major change had been made in county elective officials — choosing them for four instead of two years. There was criticism of this change because county elections now occur in presidential election years. It was argued that since Arizona normally votes Republican in presidential contests, the change favors Republicans.

Not only does Arizona have a limited number of counties, but the state has not experienced the proliferation of municipalities which is generally typical in periods of rapid population growth. One of the principal reasons for this is that Arizona has a fairly stringent law regarding incorporation of cities and towns. No new municipality may be established within three miles of an existing city or town with less than 5,000 people, while no incorporation may occur within six miles of cities with more than a population of 5,000. This law has fostered annexation by existing municipalities rather than the creation of satellite or "bedroom" communities.

From a legal standpoint, there are only two types of municipalities in Arizona, charter or "home rule" cities and general-law cities and towns. There is also a classification based on population. According to law "towns" have less than 3,000 people. When a "town" grows beyond this level, it may, with voter approval, have its status changed to "city." Change from town to city does not involve any fundamental gain or loss of powers.

Basic forms of government used in general-law cities and towns are simple. In towns of less than 1,500 population, five councilmen are authorized, and in large towns and all non-charter cities, seven councilmen are required. All councilmen are elected at large and a mayor is selected by the council from among its membership, except in those cities using a ward system. In the latter, a mayor is elected at large. In all cases, the mayor is the "executive officer." Except for councilmen in cities using overlapping terms, all elections to the council are for two years.

Those cities not operating under the general-law form and having a population of more than 3,500 may adopt "home rule" government. All "home rule" cities must have charters consistent with the constitution and laws of the state. Further, no municipality, regardless of type, may pass an ordinance which is in conflict with the constitution. A city with "home rule" government has essentially these advantages, provided they are incorporated in the city's charter: (1) to select any form of governmental organization preferred which permits tailoring of the municipal organization to fit the desires and needs of individual cities; (2) to compensate mayor and councilmen, and other municipal officials and employees, as much as the city deems necessary; (3) to control the method and manner of conducting municipal elections; (4) to maintain its own assessor and make its own assessment on its own valuations; and (5) to raise and use funds for advertising purposes without the usual legislative limitations.

The most popular form of government in "home rule" cities is council-manager. In general, under this system the mayor and council select a manager who is vested with authority to administer policies adopted by the governing body. In addition, the manager, subject to some limitations, may select the major city department heads. Although this system has worked well in Arizona's smaller cities, there have been problems in both Phoenix and Tucson with council-manager government. Basically, the troubles have stemmed from attempting to determine what is policy and what is administration. Most observers agree that there is no absolute distinction between the two. The upshot is that elected officials frequently complain that managers are involving themselves in policy. On the other hand, managers are disturbed when mayors and councilmen appear to meddle with administration.

Tucson has had more difficulties of this kind than Phoenix. In fact, since 1965 there have been suggestions that Tucson's charter be altered to establish a strong mayor-council form of government. Since 1967, Tucson's city government has been the scene of a continuous battle between the governing body and the manager. Conflicts, although evident in Phoenix, have not been nearly as serious as those in Tucson, a fact sometimes attributed to Tucson's partisan government while Phoenix operates under a non-partisan system. There are those in Tucson also who would support charter changes to establish a non-partisan type of government for that community. The consequence could become a serious battle over the form of government to be followed in Tucson.

Despite struggles over the form of government in the state's two largest municipalities, the problems actually go much deeper. Disagreements over governmental forms may be construed as manifestations of the strains accompanying growth. As municipal populations become larger and more heterogeneous, problems become more acute and visible. Both elected officials and managers are subject to more varied pressures from citizens to provide services. It is perhaps only natural that mayors and councilmen, regarding themselves as directly responsible to the people, apparently feel they should have greater authority to solve problems. In this context managers may be viewed as obstacles to meeting the demands of citizens. Rightly or wrongly interpreted, this situation is not unique to Arizona. More and more large cities are shifting to some form of stronger mayor-council government. As the 1970s progress, the demand for changes in the form of governments, particularly in Phoenix and Tucson, can be expected to come into sharper focus. Ultimately citizens of the larger municipalities may be called upon to decide what type of government they desire.

It should be noted also that in both Pima and Maricopa counties, associations of governments have been formed — MAG and PAG. These associations involve the cities and towns together with the county governments. Their formation was stimulated by the national government's requirement that for certain federal funding, there must be metropolitan-wide planning and agreement. In no sense are either MAG or PAG "metro" type governments, since each governmental unit retains its autonomy and has an equal vote. For all practical purposes, MAG and PAG operate as coordinating councils where problems common to the metropolitan area can be discussed, and requests for certain types of federal monies affecting several jurisdictions or the entire area can be acted upon. Both organizations have small staffs with virtually all of the planning activities carried on by the member governments in consultation with each other. MAG does have a more elaborate structure than PAG. The former group has sub-committees comprised of non-member governments, such as school boards, which discuss metropolitan-wide problems, e.g., the environment. By contrast, any involvement of non-members in PAG is on an *ad hoc* basis.

There are indications that in the foreseeable future, neither PAG nor MAG will develop into anything more elaborate than it is at present. Three reasons can be advanced for this speculation. First, the governmental units tend to be jealous of their authority and prerogatives and suspicious of any super-agency which would diminish their powers. Second, planning in both counties is at a fairly advanced stage and relatively good cooperation exists among governments. Third, there is strong sentiment against an agency which might duplicate already existing activities. In other words, there are serious reservations in certain quarters against spending money and hiring more people to do jobs which are presently regarded as being performed in an acceptable manner. Yet the problems of metropolitan areas know no geographical boundaries. There are serious issues which arise from overlapping of governmental jurisdictions. In order to solve adequately the needs for water, police and fire protection, sewerage disposal, ambulance service, transportation, and a multitude of other services, there must be planning that is either metropolitan or state-wide. At the beginning of the 1970s in Arizona there were no clear-cut answers to how these issues would be resolved. But there was every indication that as people in metropolitan centers develop an "urban consciousness," the demand for more services and more effective delivery of them will increase. In order to achieve these goals it will be necessary to develop even greater cooperation among governments. This will not be easy in view of the long-standing jealousies which exist, particularly between cities and counties, regarding their legitimate spheres of operation.

There is state legislation authorizing intergovernmental arrangements to provide services. Only limited use of this authority has occurred among local governments in Arizona. However, intergovernmental arrangements could be vehicles to facilitate meeting metropolitan-wide problems, regardless of the particular governmental jurisdiction in which people live. For example, in the Tucson area by 1970, there was an agreement among the city, county, and town of South Tucson to utilize law enforcement officers from all three jurisdictions in a metro-narcotics squad.

Aside from the local governments already discussed, there are quasi-autonomous school districts and certain other special districts. For obvious reasons, school districts are of great importance both from the standpoint of their educational activities and the taxes they levy. School districts are well established and their patrons are reluctant to give up "local" control of the educational process. However, it is possible that in order to provide for more equitable taxation, a statewide school taxation district will be established. This would mean that school property taxes would be uniform throughout the state. In general, a statewide tax base is favored by citizens in metropolitan areas, because some of the more lucrative sources of tax monies, e.g., the mines, are generally located in small rural districts. Currently, the tax rate in most of these districts is lower than those in the larger cities.

Other single-purpose districts exist in Arizona, including electrical, hospital, irrigation, fire prevention, and flood control. Perhaps the most important of all such agencies is the Salt River Project Agricultural Improvement and Power District, which supplies water and electricity for both residential and agricultural uses. Like other local governments, special districts are subject to state regulation and control.

In addition to special-district governments, independent of county and municipal control, there are various types of county and municipal agencies existing to serve specific areas or purposes, i.e., zoning and improvement districts. These agencies can be distinguished from special districts in that the latter are controlled by locally elected boards and are authorized to incur debt and levy taxes, and, where appropriate, to finance by special-benefit assessments or service charges.

On the other hand, agencies such as street-improvement districts are subject to municipal control and are created with the consent of local governments.

The preceding comments on the forms and problems of local governments in Arizona have merely skimmed the surface of a highly complex field. One most distressing aspect of the local political scene is that despite its closeness to the people, the average citizen probably knows few of his local officials, let alone the great variety of tasks they perform. It has been pointed out repeatedly that there is almost always a lower voter turnout in local than in either state or national elections. One reason advanced for this is that so much of what local governments do is taken for granted by citizens. Another explanation is that unlike the national government, local jurisdictions are not as heavily involved in the great issues of our time — war and peace and the economic well-being of citizens.

There perhaps is an additional reason for the failure of citizens to become familiar with and involved in local political affairs. Americans have become increasingly mobile. Arizona, as a focal point for substantial immigration, offers a test for the notion that physical mobility makes it difficult for people to comprehend the importance of local governments in their lives. Without some sense of the significance of government, it is difficult for people to develop lasting loyalties to cities or counties. In effect, people on the move have no feeling of local political identification. As a result, there is no deep-rooted idea of community. In particular, this attitude has been pointed out in the metropolitan areas of Phoenix and Tucson. Many citizens view cities as little more than places to work and live. This may result in taking what the cities have to offer without any commitment of time and energy to improve the general quality of life.

The conditions briefly sketched point up the fact that most citizens know little about the affairs of their communities and sometimes seem to care less. On the other hand there are citizens who care sufficiently that local governments can operate at a fairly high level of responsiveness to needs. Nevertheless apathy is still recognized in Arizona and elsewhere as one of the most serious diseases that can occur in a democracy. Regardless of how mobile citizens may become, it seems desirable that they spend the time and energy necessary to sustain local governments. In the final analysis, local governments, such as those in Arizona's cities and counties, are the cornerstone of the entire American political structure.

Faculties of the
Colleges of Medicine and Nursing,
University of Arizona

18

HEALTH

BLUE SKIES, CLEAR DRY AIR, and mild temperatures have made Arizona a leading health center for the people of the United States, and other countries as well. With adequate shelter, clothing, and conditioning of his environment, modern man has buffered himself against many of the more primeval effects of nature, but his response to the Arizona environment indicates that weather is still a dynamic force in daily life.

With the recognition of this force has come the development of the state's own health services, basically equivalent to those in other places, but frequently intensified to solve the special problems of health-seekers from all over the world.

Department of Health

The nucleus of this department was the Arizona Board of Health, created by the Twenty-Second Territorial Assembly in 1903, with Dr. R. M. Dodsworth as the first superintendent. The department functioning as of 1970 was created by legislation in 1941 and has been supervised by a director, appointed by a state commissioner of health. Directly or indirectly, with financial assistance and consultative services to local departments, the Department of Health serves Arizona through a large number of operating divisions under the guidance of five assistant commissioners. Administrative Services includes the Survey and Construction Division and Personnel; Environmental Health Services includes Sanitation, Air and Water Pollution; Mental Health Services combines Mental Health, Mental Retardation and Alcohol and Drug Abuse Divisions; Epidemiology and Program Design includes Health Records and Statistics, Education and Training, and the Laboratory; and Health Programs includes Nursing and Health Care, Maternal and Child Health and the Preventive Health

Services Division. The latter incorporates, into a single division, such programs as Dental Health, Chronic Disease, Migrant Health, Venereal Disease, and Tuberculosis. The organization is illustrated in the accompanying chart, Figure 18.1.

Arizona has been obliged to record one of the highest death rates in the nation due to tuberculosis because of the attraction that Arizona's climate holds for persons with this disease. The Tuberculosis Control Section of the State Health Department has been especially active in combating the impact of tuberculosis and has operated a mobile chest X-ray unit, provided tuberculin testing for school children, and otherwise participated with other state and private agencies in making available welfare assistance to indigent persons with tuberculosis, foster home protection for children of tuberculars, and transportation for needy, nonresident patients to their homes after treatment in Arizona.

Published under the auspices of the Department of Health are *Arizona's Health, Vital Statistics Annual Report, Weekly and Monthly Morbidity Report,* and *Arizona Health.*

The Health Department also provides state nutritionists who function as health educators and participate in well-baby and prenatal clinics with the Division of Maternal and Child Health, and a Public Health veterinarian, chiefly concerned with diseases such as rabies, which are transmittable from animal to man.

Like all other health departments, Arizona's has administrative and public health problems, related in many instances to funds insufficient for a rapidly growing population. Problems of air pollution and waste disposal are consequent upon the growth of the state and can be expected to increase with the influx of health-seekers, retired people, and more recently, of industry, into the state.

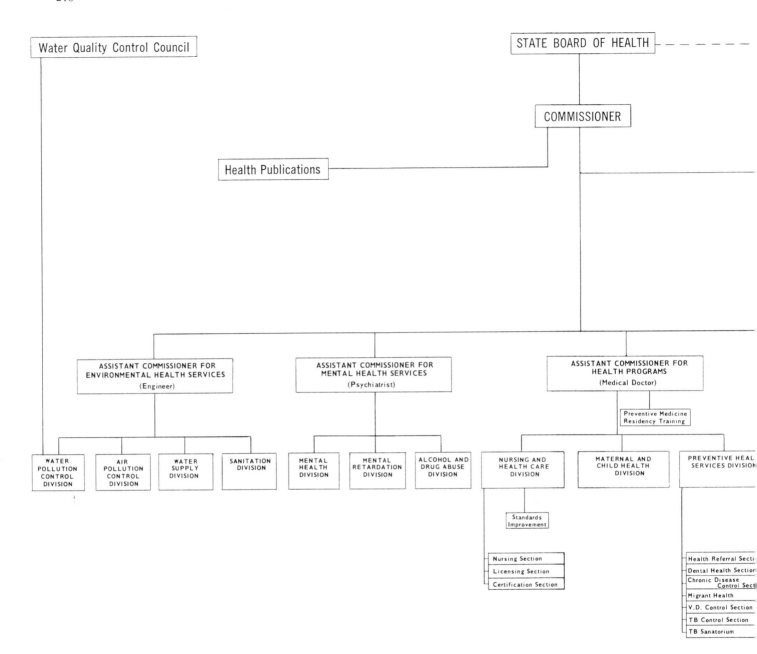

Fig. 18.1   The Arizona State Department of Health is headed by a commissioner.
The organization serves the state under several operating divisions which are headed by five assistant commissioners.

Of special significance in Arizona are the problems of tuberculosis and of the migrant worker population, putting a burden on sanitation, venereal disease control, and health education.

In common with other state health services, Arizona's is a complex structure of coordinated efforts, centered around the practicing physician, supported by nurses, pharmacists, technologists — the efforts of all conveyed to the community through the public and private clinics, laboratories, and hospitals of the state.

Hospitals

Early Arizona needed hospitals for the same reasons as other areas — westward migration was increasing the population, and frontier life was marked by violence, by the everpresent possibility of accidents, and by communicable disease.

Arizona needed hospitals more than any other areas, however, because of the influx of people with tuberculosis, who, even in those days, had begun to seek recovery in a mild, dry climate.

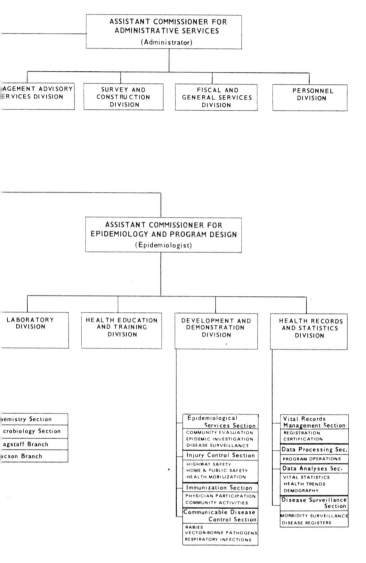

Air Pollution Control Advisory Council

Air Pollution Control Hearing Board

ASSISTANT COMMISSIONER FOR
ADMINISTRATIVE SERVICES
(Administrator)

AGEMENT ADVISORY
ERVICES DIVISION

SURVEY AND
CONSTRUCTION
DIVISION

FISCAL AND
GENERAL SERVICES
DIVISION

PERSONNEL
DIVISION

ASSISTANT COMMISSIONER FOR
EPIDEMIOLOGY AND PROGRAM DESIGN
(Epidemiologist)

LABORATORY
DIVISION

HEALTH EDUCATION
AND TRAINING
DIVISION

DEVELOPMENT AND
DEMONSTRATION
DIVISION

HEALTH RECORDS
AND STATISTICS
DIVISION

emistry Section

crobiology Section

agstaff Branch

icson Branch

Epidemiological
Services Section
COMMUNITY EVALUATION
EPIDEMIC INVESTIGATION
DISEASE SURVEILLANCE

Injury Control Section
HIGHWAY SAFETY
HOME & PUBLIC SAFETY
HEALTH MOBILIZATION

Immunization Section
PHYSICIAN PARTICIPATION
COMMUNITY ACTIVITIES

Communicable Disease
Control Section
RABIES
VECTOR-BORNE PATHOGENS
RESPIRATORY INFECTIONS

Vital Records
Management Section
REGISTRATION
CERTIFICATION

Data Processing Sec.
PROGRAM OPERATIONS

Data Analyses Sec.
VITAL STATISTICS
HEALTH TRENDS
DEMOGRAPHY

Disease Surveillance
Section
MORBIDITY SURVEILLANCE
DISEASE REGISTERS

Military life was another factor. Wherever army personnel were concentrated on the frontier, hospital facilities had necessarily to follow. Modern Arizona has a number of these installations still thriving, filling the need for a special segment of the population.

In many different ways the government of the United States has helped to supply needed hospitals for Arizona residents. In 1969 there were Veterans' Administration Hospitals at Prescott, Phoenix, and Tucson, and the Public Health Service was taking care of members of various Indian tribes on reservations across the state.

In urban centers — primarily Phoenix and Tucson — community support and fund drives and contributions by private citizens have frequently energized and expanded hospital building. Cases in point are Tucson's Joint Hospital Drive in 1957 with $1.6 million divided between Tucson Medical Center and St. Mary's for expansion, and the original gift of the Desert Sanitorium by Mrs. A. W. Erickson to Tucson for a community hospital — the Tucson Medical Center of the 1960s.

Federal grants have probably been the most significant financial factor in making it possible for the urban hospitals of the state to keep pace with the rapidly increasing population. In 1948, the Eighteenth State Legislature passed an act which allowed the participation of the state in the benefits of Public Law 725. Known as the Hill-Burton Act, this law provides federal assistance to states for hospital construction. Under the provisions of this act, a federal grant to a hospital can equal up to 50 percent of the total cost of construction and equipment, with the remainder of the cost being contributed by the sponsors in the community. The Arizona State Department of Health through its Division of Hospital Survey, Planning, and Construction, became the state agency to administer the Hill-Burton Act. This division is responsible for conducting an annual survey of hospitals in Arizona to determine needs, for preparing an annual revision of the state plan for hospitals, for investigating requests for federal funds for construction, and for supervising construction projects. The first hospital plan for construction in Arizona was approved in May, 1948.

In 1954 the Wolverton Amendment to the Hill-Burton Act extended federal aid to states for surveying needs and developing plans with respect to five new classes of projects: hospitals for chronically ill and impaired; nursing homes, public health centers, diagnostic and treatment centers, and rehabilitation facilities. The construction of a fifty-three-bed nursing home addition to the Pinal General Hospital in Florence was the first project to be approved by the U.S. Public Health Service under this category.

Although many new hospital beds have been added under the Hill-Burton program and substandard beds have been replaced in many areas, a shortage of beds in the state continued to exist in the 1970s. This can be ascribed to the remarkable growth that has taken place throughout the state since the passage of the Hill-Burton

Many factors have contributed to filling the need. Church and mission groups pioneered the field for hospitals in Arizona. St. Mary's in Tucson was the first. Numerous other church-sponsored institutions followed. Even as late as 1930, Sage Memorial Hospital was founded by a Presbyterian mission on the Navajo Indian Reservation at Ganado in the northernmost part of Arizona. The tradition of founding and maintaining hospitals by religious groups continues in modern times. A number of such hospitals date back to pioneer days.

Fig. 18.2 The Arizona Medical Center at the University of Arizona
includes the College of Medicine and the University Hospital.

Tucson Daily Citizen

Act. Not only was there a deficiency in general hospital beds, but there was a shortage in categorical resources such as long-term care beds, diagnostic and treatment centers, rehabilitation facilities, and Public Health Centers in 1971. The Planning and Construction Section of the Arizona State Department of Health was publishing annually a state plan which provided information, by regions of the state, about the current availability of health-related facilities. This information has proved to be of great value to community planners.

In the spring of 1966, the Arizona State Board of Health requested the governor to designate the state of Arizona as a "Region" for the purpose of implementing Public Law 89-239, the Regional Medical Programs for Cancer, Heart Disease and Stroke. The governor responded by suggesting that the newly developing College of Medicine at the University of Arizona in Tucson become the applicant organization on behalf of the state. Subsequently, the college received a planning grant and started the development of a regional medical program.

In the spring of 1968, the Arizona State Legislature created a state health planning authority in compliance with Public Law 89-749, the Comprehensive Health Planning Act. The eleven-member authority held its first meetings in the summer of 1968 with the objective of encouraging the establishment of areawide health plans as a part of a state plan for comprehensive health planning. One of the most unique contributions of this program in Arizona may prove to be the interrelationship that has been established between the Advisory Council for State Health Planning and that of the Regional Advisory Group for the Regional Medical Programs for Cancer, Heart Disease and Stroke, through the use of the same personnel.

Medical Practice

The practice of medicine in early Arizona forms a chapter which is as full of adventure as any in the history of the state. Medical reports, diaries, addresses, newspaper clippings, and personal correspondence of early physicians, as of 1970 in the possession of the Arizona Historical Society at Tucson, are readily available to provide endless material for presentation by historians and storytellers.

Among the first medical men to enter Arizona were those who came with federal exploration parties. These men not only treated the ills and bandaged the wounds of the explorers, but also served as naturalists, collecting plant and animal specimens wherever they went. Several species of plants and animals are named for some of the first physicians to enter this area. The pink-flowered *Phylox woodhousei,* for example, and the common toad, *Bufo woodhousei,* were discovered by and named after Dr. S. W. Woodhouse, physician and naturalist who accompanied Captain Lorenzo Sitgreaves and twenty

men in 1851 on the first official survey across northern Arizona.

In those early years, and into the middle of the nineteenth century, numerous army, mining, and religious camps were established in the Arizona Territory. Many had medical centers of sorts, usually pitifully equipped and understaffed.

In 1886 Arizona's commissioner of immigration, Patrick Hamilton, started propagandizing the Arizona climate in an effort to bring more people to the territory. His book, *Arizona for Homes, for Health, for Investments,* contained a section by Dr. M. H. Matas of Tucson and Dr. D. J. Brannen of Flagstaff entitled "Arizona as a Sanitarium." E. H. Peplow, Jr., in his *History of Arizona,* states that Hamilton's promotional material had a great deal to do with the fact that early in its history the state "achieved the reputation of being a panacea for all ills which were aggravated by dampness; asthma, respiratory ills of all sorts, arthritis, rheumatism . . ."

With this aspect of Arizona emphasized more every year, a number of rest homes and health clinics, especially those designed for tuberculars, were established through the cooperative efforts of physicians. The more rugged type of physician might be attracted to one of the several army installations such as Fort Whipple. That almost all early physicians needed to be rugged is revealed by the surgeons' reports from such installations, describing the hardships besetting personnel who tried to work with the pathetically inadequate facilities.

Good climate and promotion notwithstanding, malaria epidemics developed in a number of Arizona valleys — for example, the San Pedro. A settlement without a medical center presented difficult problems. Dr. W. F. Whitmore tells of Dr. H. A. Hughes who performed the first major surgery in the Salt River Valley in 1888, stating that Dr. Hughes ". . . after a critical survey of the interior of the house, elected to take his chances with Mother Nature and operate beneath a cottonwood tree in the yard." He goes on to say, "Surgery was usually of the emergency class and demanded much resourcefulness and good judgment."

Another famous physician was Dr. George E. Goodfellow of Tombstone, whose adventures from 1880 to 1891 make an exciting narrative. Known as "El Santo Doctor" to the Mexican people, and respected by some of Tombstone's most hardened characters, he distinguished himself in the field of surgery by performing the first appendectomy in Arizona Territory and by perfecting other surgical techniques under very primitive conditions.

In 1892 a group of sixteen physicians (one each from Gila Bend, Mesa, Tombstone, and Tucson, two from Tempe, and ten from Phoenix) founded the Arizona Medical Association, now the official medical body of the state. In 1912 the Association first published the *Arizona Medical Journal* which has since become

Arizona Medicine. The original group of sixteen members expanded to almost two thousand in 1969, according to the *Arizona State Medical Directory.*

As of 1970, the physicians in Arizona represented all recognized specialties and had been highly trained. Arizona has also matured to the point at which its first college of medicine has been developed. The college was constructed on the campus of the University of Arizona in Tucson with funds that were raised by means of an extensive, private gifts campaign. The campaign generated almost $3 million which were then matched with funds from the U.S. Public Health Service and the National Institutes of Health. The college admitted its first class of students in 1967 and by 1971 owned and operated a three-hundred-bed teaching hospital. The hospital was financed by the sale of $8 million in bonds and matched funds from the Bureau of Health Manpower of the U.S. Public Health Service.

Medical Technology

Medical technologists are professional workers who contribute invaluable service to mankind as strong right hands of the physicians and surgeons. They are a vital part of the team constantly crusading for better health and welfare for mankind. The first organized meeting of clinical laboratory workers in Arizona occurred on May 17, 1939. The meeting was held in Tucson at the State Public Health Laboratory. The purpose of the meeting was to discuss the division of work of the private and public health laboratories and to promote the interest, welfare, and efficiency of the laboratory workers. This first organization, which was comprised primarily of laboratory workers from the Tucson area, remained in existence until October 17, 1953, when the first annual convention and organization meeting of the Arizona Medical Laboratory Association was held in Phoenix. This provided an official organization on a statewide basis which has been actively engaged in an effort to provide better medical services for the people of Arizona.

A third organization, the Arizona Society of Medical Technologists, initiated corporation proceedings and the drafting of a constitution and by-laws in November, 1953. The objectives of this organization were "to promote higher standards in clinical laboratory methods for research; to elevate the status of those specializing in medical laboratory techniques; to create mutual understanding and cooperation between the medical technologists and the physician . . . and to promote the mutual aid and understanding between its members." The first organizational meeting was held in Phoenix on September 20, 1954 with twenty-four individuals in attendance. The organization was not officially recognized until it received its charter at the national convention of this society in June, 1954. By 1970 the Arizona Society of Medical Technologists had established two local chapters within the state. The Tucson chapter received its

charter in April, 1959, and the Phoenix chapter in January, 1960. The local chapters were formed in an effort to provide association and fellowship for more medical technologists through bi-monthly meetings of an educational nature.

The rapid growth and increase in population in the state of Arizona has brought about a need for more medical services of all kinds. In addition to the increased need for physicians, nurses, dentists, and physiotherapists, there was in the late 1960s also a need for a substantial increase in the number of medical technologists in the state. In 1970 Arizona State University at Tempe and the University of Arizona at Tucson were both offering a four-year curriculum in medical technology leading toward the Bachelor of Science degree. The students in medical technology completed three years of undergraduate study in the basic sciences, social sciences, and humanities on campuses of these universities and the fourth year in schools of medical technology approved by the Council on Medical Education of the American Medical Association. This cooperative arrangement has been highly desirable in that the hospital schools are better prepared to supply the necessary clinical material and experiences to the student. In the Phoenix area, courses in medical technology in 1970 were offered in the laboratories at St. Joseph's, Good Samaritan, and Memorial Hospitals and, in the Tucson area, by Tucson Medical Center and St. Mary's Hospital. The training and academic requirements for medical technologists in the universities of Arizona have been considerably higher than those required at the national level. The universities have required the completion of courses in basic sciences, social sciences, and humanities in order to satisfy the degree requirements of the College of Liberal Arts and with this background, it has been possible for the student to continue graduate study in some area of the basic sciences upon completion of the requirements for the Bachelor of Science degree.

Nursing in Arizona

Nursing developed in Arizona Territory, as in other parts of the world, in response to human need. Consequently the first persons giving nursing care in Arizona were essentially untrained. They worked in a matrix of pioneer, Indian, and Mexican cultures. They were limited by the existence of folklore, the level of medical practice at the time, and the health problems peculiar to the area. Folk and household remedies played their roles of comfort and questionable therapy. And the "nurses" who gave unstintingly of time and energy were expected to combine with their nursing skill the arts of cook, seamstress, teacher, social worker, and midwife.

Miss Lunette Ready, who arrived in Phoenix from Chicago in 1894, is credited with being the first trained nurse in Arizona. Fifty nurses were reported in 1900, and their growing group-consciousness was reflected in

1918 when two associations were founded, one for Phoenix and one for Tucson nurses. They combined in a state association one year later, developing standards for nursing, and worked for the passage of the nurse registration bill which became law in 1921.

Education for nurses in Arizona began at St. Joseph's Hospital in Phoenix in 1910, at St. Mary's in Tucson in 1914, and at Good Samaritan in Phoenix in 1924. St. Mary's Hospital closed its school in 1966, and St. Joseph's Hospital graduated its last class in 1970. Arizona in 1970 had two baccalaureate programs in nursing, one at the University of Arizona, the other at Arizona State University, both established in 1956 by authorization of the Board of Regents. This expansion of the state facilities came forty years after the first degree program in nursing was organized in the United States. Phoenix Junior College established the first associate degree program in 1959, followed by associate degree programs at Northern Arizona University, Flagstaff; Arizona Western College, Yuma; Glendale Community College; and Mesa Community College. In addition to the schools which prepare registered nurses there were in the late 1960s eight schools of practical nursing at various locations throughout the state.

In 1970, Arizona's institutions were expected to produce approximately 300 graduate nurses and 150 practical nurses. Not all of these graduate nurses will remain in Arizona, but some will be added to the 6,555 active in the state in 1969. This still does not come close to meeting the 7,700 predicted as the need for 1970. If the 1,580 inactive nurses in the state in 1969 could be induced to return to practice the need could be met. The Arizona State Nurses' Association has been conducting a refresher course in an attempt to attract the inactive nurse back into nursing.

Arizona's greatest need is for nurses with master's or higher degrees to function as teachers, supervisors, administrators, and researchers. This was met in part by the initiation of a master's program at the University of Arizona in 1967 and at Arizona State University in 1969. The University of Arizona also has a federally supported program to prepare nurses with Ph.D.'s in anthropology, sociology, and physiology. There were in 1970 several nurses enrolled in the program. In addition, there were a number of other nurses at the University of Arizona working toward doctoral degrees.

Even though progress has been made in education and in the quality of nursing personnel produced, the urgent need remains for Arizona as a state, assisted by national and regional resources, to determine and fulfill its responsibility with respect to the needs for nursing in the state.

Pharmaceutical Services

The rapid strides of pharmaceutical services from pioneer to modern standards are nowhere more observable than in Arizona, where the distance has been traversed almost entirely within the life span of a single, aggressive generation.

The pioneer druggist in Arizona as elsewhere was a compounder of medicines from crude and refined herbs, chemicals and oils, laboriously prepared by mixing, scraping, and pounding in a mortar, emerging finally as handmade pills, suppositories, ointments, and plasters. Most Arizona drug sales were in local coin such as the Spanish do reales coin — or standard "two bit" piece. Higher-priced items were the green paper boxes of opium and morphine sold across the counter in pre-Harrison Act days at one dollar per box. The pharmacist in Arizona Territory might also have been called upon to double as physician and nurse, when quick-trigger sheriffs ordered survivors to the drug shop for patching up.

The modern era in Arizona pharmacy started in 1904, with the first territorial pharmacy law establishing the Board of Pharmacy, later affiliated with the national association. Previously druggists had qualified by "inclination" only. The new law required candidates to pass a state board licensure examination. Such legislation had begun in South Carolina in 1817, formal pharmaeutical education in 1821 in Philadelphia. By 1900 there were sixty colleges of pharmacy in the nation. Although urgently sought by people still active in the profession in the 1960s, Arizona's College of Pharmacy at the University of Arizona was not established until 1947.

In spite of its newness, Arizona's College of Pharmacy in 1951 was among the first four in the nation to advance its program beyond the four-year level. Further distinction came when Phoenician Newell W. Stewart in 1953 became president of the American Pharmaceutical Association.

The state in 1970 had 468 registered pharmacies, operated by state licensees who had college degrees. The average of one pharmacy to 3,000 population compares favorably to the national average of one per 3,300, a fact which can probably be explained by Arizona's prominence as a health center.

The strong current of modern technology since 1900 has carried Arizona's pharmacists with those all over the nation into a different phase of the profession. The majority of pharmaceuticals are of course no longer compounded by hand. Manual compounding had declined from nearly 100 percent of all prescriptions dispensed in 1900, to about 5.5 percent in 1959. With nearly all medicinals sold in final dosage form by pharmaceutical manufacturers, the retail pharmacist has become a supplier of such products, with the information about them, to physician and patient. He must also serve often as a source of general health education to the community.

In 1970, there were 1,013 pharmacists licensed to fill these roles in Arizona. Seventy of them, or 7.0 percent, were women, compared to the national average of 6.7 percent. Arizona's averages differed from the national also in 1969 with respect to the percentage of pharmacists retired or engaged in other business — 8.4 percent in Arizona and 6.8 percent nationally; the percentage involved in retail ownership — 35 percent in Arizona and 50.2 percent in the rest of the nation; in wholesaling and manufacturing, less than one percent in Arizona and 2.47 percent nationally; and in age — a smaller percentage of Arizona pharmacists were under forty years of age than in the rest of the United States.

Arizona joins with other states in licensing pharmacists from out-of-state by reciprocity. Because of the late development of educational standards for pharmacists in this state, Arizona in 1969 led the six states in which reciprocity results in more registrations of pharmacists than does regular registration.

In general, Arizona pharmacists are vigorous participants in professional matters within the state and beyond, and national leaders have expressed interest in the accomplishments of the profession and of its practitioners during the short years of its history.

Raymond A. Mulligan
Public Administration

19

SOCIAL AND CORRECTIONAL SERVICES

SOCIAL SERVICES WERE CARRIED ON in Arizona through the 1960s by the state department of public welfare, and, in certain kinds of cases, through local sectarian and non-sectarian social welfare agencies, the Arizona Employment Commission, the federal Social Security Administration, county probation departments, private and public social and correctional institutions, and state parole systems. Also in the social service category are the various plans for unemployment, old age and survivors, and disability insurance.

Probably the earliest welfare work in Arizona was concerned with the protection of children. As far back as 1691, Father Kino was providing Indian youths in the missions at Guebavi and Tumacacori with protection, and with training in religion, agriculture, and habits of industry.

In 1864 the First Territorial Legislature adopted the Howell Code containing several provisions for the protection of children. One of these concerned Indian children, who under the law might be indentured to an individual until age eighteen (for girls) or twenty-one (for boys). The law specified that the individual seeking to have a child indentured had to apply to a judge of the probate court, promising to provide humane treatment, proper food, and clothing, and not to transfer the indenture to another party.

The Howell Code further charged the several counties with providing for the "blind, lame, sick, aged, decrepit, or other disabled or enfeebled, so as to be unable to maintain themselves." Such persons could apply to a justice of the peace who might pay up to twenty dollars per month from a county poor fund to any eligible person.

Consolidation of Agencies

Until the State Board of Social Security and Welfare was created, public aid to the needy in Arizona was administered by a variety of state and county agencies. As facilities were limited, the indigent sick often were privately attended at the expense of the county.

In 1909 the legislature created a state board of control with a measure of centralized authority over various public welfare agencies. The law provided for three board members — the governor, the auditor, and one citizen appointed by the governor — who were given full charge over charitable, penal, and reformatory institutions then existing or later to be established. The functions of this board were not confined to overseeing these institutions but included other powers and responsibilities as well.

During the depression of the thirties, Congress established the Federal Emergency Relief Administration. The Arizona State Board of Public Welfare was accordingly created to enable the state to receive federal funds from this program. The board administered federal, state, and county funds and supervised services for the indigent ill, dependent children, and paupers.

In 1935 the Social Security Act was passed by Congress, and federal funds were made available to Arizona on this basis in 1936. In 1937 the Thirteenth Legislature abolished the State Welfare Board and by an emergency act created the State Board of Social Security and Welfare. The name was changed in 1948 to the Department of Public Welfare.

This department in 1970 was the largest social welfare agency in the state and has been responsible for interpreting social service to the public. Although Arizona lacks many facilities enjoyed by older states, the social legislation has been broad in scope and frequently needs only more complete financial implementation.

The statute setting up this department provided also for county boards of public welfare consisting of three members appointed by the county board of supervisors and under direct supervision of the state department to perform such duties as the state might prescribe.

The county departments of public welfare, under supervision of the state department in 1970, were administering all state and federal social security programs for the needy at county levels. These programs affect the aged, the dependent child, the needy blind, the permanently and totally disabled, and child welfare recipients. County departments also administered state aid through funds for general assistance, for emergency relief, and for foster homes. The case load was the basis of fund allocation to these projects.

Offices of the Department of Public Welfare in each county include the divisions of Child Welfare, and Public Assistance. These divisions have a structure and *modus operandi* generally comparable to other such agencies throughout the United States. The Child Welfare Division in 1970 was providing services to children in their own homes, foster care, adoption services, and day care.

Care for the Aged

Among its welfare agencies and apart from its general public assistance program in 1970, Arizona also had the Veterans Services Commission which serviced disability and pension claims for war veterans, and the Arizona Pioneers' Home and Hospital for Disabled Miners. As of that year the only other institution similar to the latter in the entire United States was Alaska's home for the aged survivors of gold rush days.

The Pioneers' Home at Prescott was established by the Twenty-Fifth Territorial Legislature in 1909, and the building was completed in 1911. Original accommodations provided for forty residents.

The will of W. C. Parsons, a Yavapai County mining man who died in 1914, established a trust fund for an addition to the home for women pioneers. This section was completed in 1916 and provided for twenty residents. In 1925 the legislature appropriated $17,000 to be added to the revenue from the Parsons fund for a Pioneers' Home trust fund, to carry out additions and improvements to the home.

The Disabled Miner's Hospital was established by legislation in 1929, intended for those who had been active in mining in Arizona. It later became an integral part of the Pioneers' Home with both institutions under one superintendent and one legislative appropriation. In recent years, anyone qualifying for admission to the home could be admitted also to the hospital.

Private welfare services in Arizona have been carried on by religious organizations, sectarian and non-sectarian, and by private and community chest funds and specialized institutions financed by fees and endowments. Among such agencies have been the Catholic Social Service, the Jewish Welfare, the Salvation Army, The American Red Cross, and Family Welfare, a private non-sectarian family service agency.

As the 1970s began, organizations in Arizona supporting and carrying on private welfare work for many special groups included Friendly House in Phoenix, which offered guidance to aliens and an Americanization program for non-native residents; the Boy Scouts and Girl Scouts throughout the state; the Young Men's Christian Association and Young Women's Christian Association in several communities; the Arizona Children's Home Association, a private child-care institution; the Florence Crittenton Home in Phoenix for unwed mothers; and the Marshall Home for Men near Tucson, for aged men who were recipients of public assistance.

In the field of social insurance, Arizona has acquired all the services and agencies common to the various states since the inception of the federal Social Security Act. The State Employment Service and Unemployment Compensation Division are administered by the Employment Commission of Arizona. Old Age and Survivors' Insurance, and disability insurance are provided by the federal government and administered on a district basis throughout the state.

Correctional Services

Closely related and often running parallel to social services in Arizona are the correctional services which include probation, institutional care, and parole. Probation for adults and juveniles is administered on a county basis. Three of the four correctional institutions existing in Arizona — the Arizona State Industrial School, the Arizona Youth Center, and the Arizona State Prison — by 1970 were publicly administered under the Department of Corrections. The fourth, the Convent of the Good Shepherd, was privately administered. Adult and juvenile parole was a state function, administered as of July, 1969, by a single board.

Juvenile courts and Superior courts in all counties of Arizona have made provision for some form of probation service. Most counties have only one man assigned to the supervision of both adults and juveniles, however, and while more populated counties do have larger staffs, in 1969 only three counties had separate systems for adults and juveniles. Probation officials in the state were expressing the need for expansion and professionalization of this service and for the development of treatment services to buttress the probation system.

In Arizona as in most other states, juvenile detention has been a continuing problem. Detention is best defined as the temporary care of children in physically restricting facilities, pending court disposition or transfer to another jurisdiction or agency. Five counties in Arizona in 1970 had detention homes in separate buildings with regular staffs under juvenile court jurisdiction. Three other counties provided detention quarters under the control of the jail staff, although not directly connected with the county jail and having separate entrances. In the remaining counties juveniles were placed in the county jail. Officials in this field were looking forward to an implementation of existing state statutes requiring all counties to provide separate facilities.

Adult probation services were operative in Arizona throughout the sixties but regarded as inadequate. Presentence investigations which are essential to ensure the success of probation, for example, were carried on in only a few counties. For individuals working with adult probationers case loads were excessively high and salaries at that time were considered inadequate for professionals.

Among Arizona's correctional institutions, the state prison has a colorful history. Before the territorial prison was established at Yuma in 1876, convicted offenders were held in various jails throughout the Territory. Considering that Arizona in those days was a congregating point for some of the boldest desperadoes in the nation, the facilities for imprisoning offenders were notably inadequate.

In 1867 an Act of Congress provided for a penitentiary to be constructed in the Territory, leaving the choice of location up to the legislature. Phoenix was selected in 1868, but nothing more was done until 1876 when the location was shifted to Yuma, and construction of the prison was started.

On a granite bluff overlooking the Colorado River, with desert for hundreds of miles in all directions, the site seemed ideal for imprisoning maximum security offenders. The prison started with seven inmates and at a later date had 376, many from distant parts of the country.

From the standpoint of the prisoner, Yuma was not popular. They dreaded the heat of the summers and bleakness of the terrain. Prison escapes were frequent in spite of isolation and the cooperation of local Indians who were paid fifty dollars for each escaped convict they apprehended.

The prison proper was little more than an open corral surrounded by a thick adobe wall with watchtowers on each corner. The prisoners were locked in long tiers of rock-built cells at night, but there was little to hinder their escape by day except the rifles of the guards and the pepper-box Gatling gun mounted in one of the corner towers.

In 1907, the legislature decided to move the prison to Florence and appropriated $120,000 to construct several modern buildings on a site near the city. The title to the old prison lands returned to Yuma and the offices of the city government were placed within the old adobe walls. The former prison hospital was used to house the first high school in Yuma and from this the present Yuma High School football team derived its latter-day name, "The Criminals."

In 1909, the new territorial prison was constructed and soon after acquired its present status as the Arizona State Prison. The original cellblock, Number 1, was built with a capacity of 275 inmates, but by June 30, 1957, the total number of inmates in custody at the prison numbered 1,249 occupying two cellblocks and eight dormitories. In 1961 and 1964 two additional cellblocks were constructed and the original cellblock was closed. In 1967 a diagnostic center was opened in the main

prison and is equipped with quarters for 120 inmates. The inmate housing facilities at the prison may be classified into four categories: the main prison, the Institute of Educational Rehabilitation, the trusty unit, and the women's section.

The main prison unit houses the majority of the inmates and handles those individuals considered maximum security prisoners, as well as a small percentage of inmates who could be considered minimum security. The Institute of Educational Rehabilitation is reserved for first offenders who are twenty-five years and younger. The trusty unit is a complete honor-system unit and is limited to inmates who have showed exemplary behavior. The women's ward is situated across the road from the main prison and is an independent and self-sufficient unit. In 1969 the total prison population was 1,700, seventy of whom were women.

The prison population, as is the case of the state, was increasing each year as the seventies approached. Officials and citizens were realizing the need for physical expansion of the prison, along with an increased industrial or working program for the inmates.

Fort Grant Industrial School

The history of the Arizona Industrial School goes back to 1891. Governor Murphy urged the legislature to provide a reform school for "vicious youth of both sexes." At that time in Arizona, youthful offenders could be placed nowhere except in jails or the penitentiary, and the citizenry felt an urgent need for a juvenile industrial school.

In 1893 the legislature empowered the governor to appoint a board of trustees to select a site and plan suitable buildings. Flagstaff was chosen, and construction started. By 1897, after more than $33,000 had been spent on construction, the authorities decided against Arizona's having such an institution, and the new building was made into a normal school in 1910.

Various proposals followed for solving the problem of youthful delinquents, and in 1903 the Territorial Industrial School was opened at Benson, housing both boys and girls, although on a segregated basis. By 1912 the school population was overtaxing the buildings' capacity, and a commission was appointed by the legislature to select a suitable new site. Fort Grant was chosen and a federal enabling act secured. The building at Benson was leased to the town for use as a high school.

The State Industrial School at Fort Grant was situated by the 1960s on 3,900 acres with fifty-five acres under cultivation and three acres in orchards. Most of the physical plant was constructed in the 1950s, many of the fort's original buildings having been replaced. Major structures included the administration building, school and gymnasium, four dormitories, repair shops and garage, infirmary, industrial arts building, dairy, laundry, kitchen-dining unit, warehouse, maintenance shops and twenty staff homes and bachelor quarters. Completed during the sixties were two dormitories, a recreation building, and a combination garage and maintenance shop. The school received boys aged twelve to eighteen when committed by juvenile court.

Provisions for girls at Fort Grant proved unsatisfactory and various proposals for change were considered, but no action was taken until 1927. A separate school for delinquent girls was completed in 1929, but because of the high cost of operation it was abandoned in 1933. Girls were then sent to the Florence Crittenton Home and similar institutions. These girls in 1970 were, for the most part, received by the Convent of the Good Shepherd in Phoenix, with their care paid for from state funds.

The original Convent of the Good Shepherd was founded in France over 300 years ago by members of a Catholic sisterhood. Today it operates homes for delinquent girls and prisons for women in all principal countries of the world. All convents are governed by the original "mother house" in France, and those in the United States are grouped under six provinces, the one at Phoenix being in the St. Louis province.

The curriculum of the school at the convent in 1970 was the same as that of the Arizona public schools. Industrial training was given in steam press operation, laundry and office work, and domestic science. The school had a department of social living, a department of social science, and one of education, staffed with professionals in social work, education, psychology, and psychiatry.

Daily enrollments at the institute in 1969 averaged over 200. Residents were girls between the ages of twelve and eighteen, committed to the State Department of Corrections by the county juvenile courts.

In 1967 the Arizona Youth Center, just to the north of Tucson, was established by the state. It was considered in 1969 to be an intermediate institution for male juvenile delinquents in contrast to the Arizona Boys School which was housing more seriously delinquent youth.

The Youth Center has functioned as a diagnostic center and as a treatment center. Milder delinquent youth are committed directly to the Center by the county juvenile courts throughout the state. Its capacity in 1969 was 120.

As of July 1, 1968, the Board of Directors of State Institutions was dissolved through legislative action. The board's administrative duties were assumed by a new state Department of Corrections. In addition, the Arizona State Prison which formerly functioned independently as an administrative entity, has been included in the administrative responsibilities of the new department.

David J. Hall
Civil Engineer

20

HIGHWAYS

SPEEDING ALONG A PAVED HIGHWAY across the Arizona desert, one wonders how the pioneers could have made their way through such forbidding country, barren of sustaining vegetation and with no visible source of water. However, in the pioneer period many of the streams which are now wide, sandy channels, dry most of the year and carrying only flood water, were smaller and ran continuously. Fish swam in the streams, lush native grasses grew along the flood plains, and even some of the uplands provided good grazing. A natural erosion cycle which began in the 1890s, together with overgrazing by cattle and sheep, killed much of this grass, destroying the roots which held the soil in place, thus allowing the summer rains to wash the soil away. But even under the somewhat better physical conditions of those early days, travel into and across the area now designated as Arizona was most difficult. By the late 1960s, conditions of travel were far different. Not only were excellent transcontinental routes being developed under the Interstate system but also roads within the state which interconnect the major cities and vacation spots. As in the experience of older states in the Union, so in Arizona the network of highways represents a joint activity of the federal and state governments.

In 1866 the Territorial Assembly authorized the county boards of supervisors to divide the counties into road districts and to appoint overseers to levy a road tax not to exceed five cents per $100 valuation, and a poll tax not to exceed $6 per ablebodied man. Two days' labor on the roads could be substituted for the poll tax payment. Later legislative acts authorized the counties to issue bonds for road construction. Territorial bonds for road work were issued for $70,000 in 1877, for $15,000 in 1885, and for $19,000 for a bridge across the Gila at Florence in 1905. A territorial engineer was appointed in 1909. But the construction and maintenance of roads was primarily the responsibility of the counties during territorial days and for a considerable period thereafter.

Beginning in 1871, toll road companies were permitted to incorporate under county authority. Requirements were in general the same as for incorporation under territorial authority, except that the county could, after five years, purchase the toll road at its appraised valuation. Two percent of the gross proceeds from all toll roads went into the territorial school fund. There was also a regulation to the effect that if, after three years of operation, the net annual proceeds from any toll road exceeded 50 percent of the cost of the construction of the road, the excess above 3 percent would go into the territorial school fund. All toll roads were under the supervision of a commissioner who reported to both the governor and the Assembly.

When Arizona became a state in 1912, the title of territorial engineer was changed to state engineer. The state engineer was under the Board of Control until 1917, under the Commission of State Institutions until 1919, then under the Board of Directors of State Institutions until 1927, at which time the Arizona State Highway Commission was established. Prior to 1922, the state engineer operated more or less as a stepchild, improving and maintaining such roads as seemed most needful, to the limit of the funds which might be furnished him. If he spent any money in improving a road, it was considered a state highway. If he ceased to maintain it, then it ceased to be a state highway. Counties were authorized in 1909 to levy from five to twenty-five cents per $100 assessed valuation for road purposes, the rate to be decided by the counties on basis of need. This act was superseded in 1912 when the legislature voted a property tax levy sufficient to raise an annual road fund of $250,000, of which 25 percent was to be expended on state roads and 75 percent returned to the counties in proportion to collections. This tax remained in effect until 1917, at which time the law was modified by a general tax levy of ten cents per $100, of which 25 percent was for state roads and 75 percent for county roads. Though the revenue laws were revised by the legislature from time to time, this 10 percent per hundred property tax continued to be collected until 1933, at which time the raising of funds by property tax for highway purposes was discontinued.

Soon after Arizona became a state in 1912, a number of significant things occurred which presaged the end of the period of toll roads, poll and property taxes for the support of road programs, and the responsibility of the counties to bear the major burden of providing roads for the rapidly increasing traffic demands. These were the passage of the Federal-Aid Act of 1916 and the gasoline tax of 1921, the establishment of the State Highway System of 1922, and of the State Highway Department under a State Highway Commission in 1927.

Federal Aid

World War I brought to the attention of Congress the woeful inadequacy of the roads in the United States as a means of transport during emergency. There were few good roads and no system at all. To correct this, the Federal-Aid Act was passed in 1916. An initial appropriation of $75 million was made to be allocated to the states on a basis of population, area, and mileage of post roads, provided the states would match the allocation on a fifty-fifty basis. Then there were other requirements. To participate in this program, a state had to set up a comprehensive and adequate system of highways equal to 7 percent of its total road mileage. To prevent the far-reaching effects of unwise decisions, which sometimes occur because of local political pressures, and to insure that the systems of the several states would connect in such a way as to form a satisfactory national system of highways, approval by the U.S. Bureau of Public Roads was made necessary before any funds would be allocated. Other requirements were the formation of an adequate state highway department, headed by an experienced and competent civil engineer, the approval by the Bureau of Public Roads of all construction plans on projects upon which federal funds were to be spent, and a guarantee by the state that such projects would be adequately maintained.

A division office of the U.S. Bureau of Public Roads was established in Arizona in 1919. This office does not initiate road projects, nor does it do the engineering work in connection with road projects, except on occasional jobs such as the Hitchcock Highway into the Catalina Mountains, which was built by federal prison labor. Its responsibility has been to examine and approve or reject plans and specifications of all road projects for which federal funds are requested by the state, counties, cities, the Bureau of Reclamation, or the Indian, Forest, and Park services. All projects upon which federal funds are to be expended must be submitted to this office, whether they are highway systems, road locations, research work, bridge work, or road construction.

The Federal-Aid Act was modified and clarified by the Federal Highway Act of 1921. Without the passage of these acts, and subsequent revisions and additions, highways as an adequate facility for transportation simply would not exist. The states and counties could not have done the job. Over the years many appropriations have been made by Congress in support of the federal aid program. But except for some special appropriations during the Depression, the federal government has collected from the highway users, in one tax form or another, funds equal to or greater than the total of federal aid appropriation.

The initial 7 percent Federal-Aid Primary System (FAP) proposed by the Arizona Highway Department was approved in 1922. Subsequent actions raised this to 8 percent. The interconnections of the primary systems of the several states enabled the federal government in 1925 to create a federal system of highways. These are the highways marked with the United States shield. They are not really federal roads, but are connected state primary roads designated as U.S. Highways.

The Hayden-Cartwright Act of 1934 stipulated that 1.5 percent of the federal funds allocated to any state should be used for engineering, economic, and planning studies; in the early seventies this was known as the Highway Planning and Research Program. In conformance with this act, the Arizona Highway Department in 1936 established a Planning Survey Division where William E. Willey, state engineer from 1955 to 1962, devised a method known as "Sufficiency Rating," by means of which it can be determined scientifically how and where to apply most advantageously the currently available funds. Inasmuch as there are never enough funds currently available to make all the needed highway improvements, a choice must be made. Application of the "Sufficiency Rating" enables the state engineer and the state highway director to present the facts to the Highway Commission. Many other states were also using this formula in the late sixties.

Subsequent congressional acts provided for the states to set up a Federal-Aid Secondary System (FAS) on which federal funds could be spent. Many important county roads could be included. An urban system (FAU) was also approved. The ratio of matching funds was changed from fifty-fifty to sixty-forty, with the federal government contributing the larger amount, and with a provision that in those states containing a large amount of public land, the federal participation would be raised. In Arizona the federal government in 1969 was contributing 72 percent and the state 28 percent.

The 1956 Federal-Aid Highway Act not only continued the FAS, FAP, and FAU support at an increased rate, but also made provisions for a national system of superhighways to cross all states. These strategic high-

Fred Wehrman

Fig. 20.1 Freeways and first-class highways link modern Arizona's major cities to vacation spots that were formerly remote.

ways were to reach all major cities and defense plants, generally forming a system of importance in the defense of the country, as well as carrying the heavy load of transcontinental motor transport. The matching funds on this system were to be on a 90–10 percent basis, but in Arizona, because of its large area of public land, the basis was 94.6 percent federal, and 5.4 percent state. Motorists, not the real property owners, were to pay for these highways.

The most significant act of the Arizona Legislature relating to highways was the passage in 1927 of an act

which set up the Arizona State Highway Commission of five members, with broad powers to establish a highway system and a highway department, to employ a state highway engineer, and, in fact, to determine all matters concerning highways. The whole burden of the actual operation of the department was on the shoulders of the state highway engineer under the original arrangement, but by a later legislative act, the executive secretary of the commission was vested with authority, under the commission, on all except technical matters. These remained under the state engineer. The first commissioners were appointed without consideration of residence, but later the state was divided into five districts, with one commissioner from each district. These districts are marked on Figure 20.1. Figure 20.2 shows the State Highway System as it was officially approved by the Highway Commission in 1927. At that time, the system contained a total of 1,988 miles of roads, of which 219 were paved, 869 gravelled, 758 graded, and 142 unimproved. In 1968, the system included a total of 5,410 miles, of which 2,978 were Federal-Aid Primary, 1,783 Federal-Aid Secondary, and 647 nonfederal-aid. These are shown on Figure 20.3, which also shows that most of these roads in the state system are paved. Although the state system includes most of the important highways, its mileage in 1967 amounted to only 13 percent of all the roads in the state; however, this 13 percent was carrying over 50 percent of the state's traffic in the late 1960s. Arizona roads in other jurisdictions were classified as follows:

Classification	Mileage
Counties	17,616
Incorporated places	5,087
Indian Service	4,627
Forest Service	7,005
Parks and Monuments	1,098

These roads, when added to the other mileage, totaled 40,843 miles in 1967.

As of January 1, 1968, road conditions in Arizona, including all classifications, were approximately as follows:

Condition	Mileage
Paved	5,698
Surface treated	2,638
Select soil or gravel	5,478
Graded and drained	4,490
Unimproved	13,105

THE U.S. INTERSTATE HIGHWAY SYSTEM. The U.S. Interstate System of highways, authorized by Congress in 1956, was planned to total about 41,000 miles of which 1,168 miles were scheduled to be built in Arizona. Two of the five major east-west arteries of this system cross Arizona. One north-south artery was planned to extend from Nogales to Flagstaff. The approximate location of these superhighways in Arizona is shown on Figure 20.3. The general design plan of these limited-access superhighways is four-lane, divided cross-section with numerous grade separation structures. Some sections were already under construction in the late 1960s. As of June, 1968, Interstate expenditures were $421,-990,299. These expenditures had built 626.7 miles of Interstate or 53 percent of Arizona's allocation.

Revenue and Federal Aid

FEDERAL AID. In compliance with legislative action, the state pledged itself in 1917 to match such federal funds as might be allocated in the following years. The first project agreement signed in that year was for additional spans to the bridge over the Gila River at Florence. Bonds were authorized for the construction of this bridge by the Territory in 1905. It was actually built in 1910 by prison labor but suffered flood damage in 1914 and was left high and dry in 1916 when flood water cut a new channel. The state has continuously availed itself of such federal-aid funds as have been allocated from year to year. Up to and including 1967, the state had received $535,878,161 in federal-aid funds. Appropriations for Arizona for 1967 were:

Interstate System	$45,743,400
Primary System (FAP)	6,354,111
Secondary System (FAS)	4,117,139
Urban (FAU)	1,868,888

GASOLINE TAX. In 1921 the state levied its first gasoline tax of one cent per gallon, the money going into the state road fund. This tax was superseded in 1923 by a three cent per gallon levy, one-fourth of the funds accruing to go to state roads, one-fourth to the county road fund, and one-half back to the county in which collected. This was again superseded in 1927 by a four cent per gallon tax of which five-eighths was to go to the state road fund and three-eighths to be returned to the counties in proportion to sales made within the county.

The gasoline tax was raised to five cents per gallon in 1931. This tax was to be reduced to four cents in 1933, but this cut was not made. Again it was fixed at five cents, of which the state was to get seven-tenths and the counties the remainder. In 1932, gasoline distributors were required to obtain a license from the state at a cost of $25 which went into the road fund. In April, 1963, the motor fuel tax was increased from 5 cents to 6 cents per gallon. This 6-cent rate was raised to 7 cents in July, 1965. For 1967 the motor fuel tax amounted to $50,389,826, of which 1.2 cents were returned to the counties where collected, 1.3 cents to the incorporated places within said counties, and 4.5 cents to the state highway fund. In the late 1960s the federal tax was four cents per gallon, and the average state tax in other states was six cents per gallon. In 1967, Arizona collected tax on 656,343,439 gallons. The Hayden-Cartwright Act of 1934 stopped a practice which had become prevalent in many states of diverting gasoline tax to uses other than highways by the simple expedient of withholding federal aid if this practice was followed.

MOTOR VEHICLE FEES. In 1913 motor vehicle operators were required to pay a license fee varying from $5.00 to $15.00, motorcyclists $2.00, and chauffeurs, $5.00. In 1921 a surtax was levied upon trucks up to a maximum of $25.00. All of these collections went into the state road fund. In 1923 a tax of one-half mill per mile, per passenger capacity, was levied against all highway common carriers, and a two mill tax per mile,

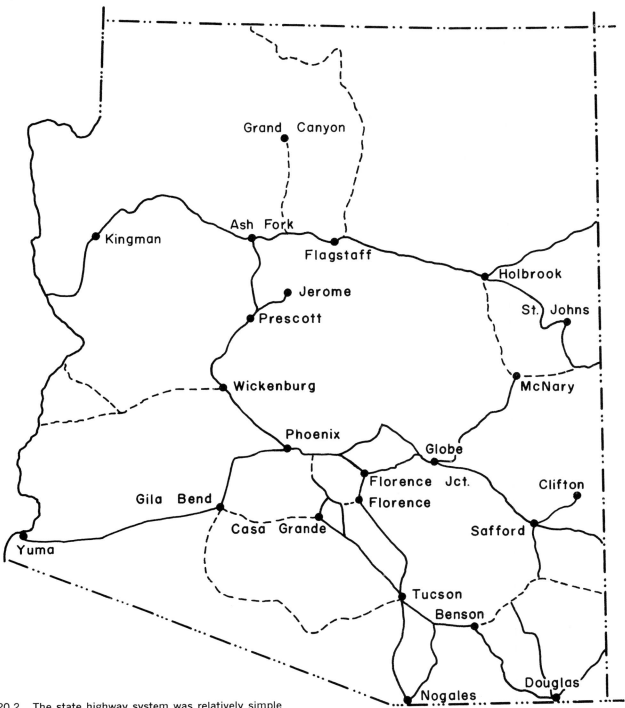

Fig. 20.2 The state highway system was relatively simple in 1927 when definite rules were set forth concerning motor vehicles.

per truck ton, on scheduled highway carriers. In 1925, motor vehicle registration with the secretary of state for title was required at a cost of $1.00. Duplicate plates to dealers were required at a cost of $3.00 per pair, and used-car dealers were required to obtain annual licenses at a cost of $5.00. In 1927 the rules concerning motor vehicles were definitely outlined, the major changes being the raising of the car license fee to $3.50, and truck fees at varying rates from $5.00 to $40.00. These fees were to be collected by county assessors, the counties to retain fifty cents per car for this service. Common carriers of passengers were required to pay a license tax of 2 percent of gross receipts from operations within the state and other common carriers 2.5 percent. In 1931, the rates on commercial vehicle registrations were raised substantially in accordance with gross weight, tires, and number of axles.

It should be understood that whereas federal funds are used only for construction and planning research,

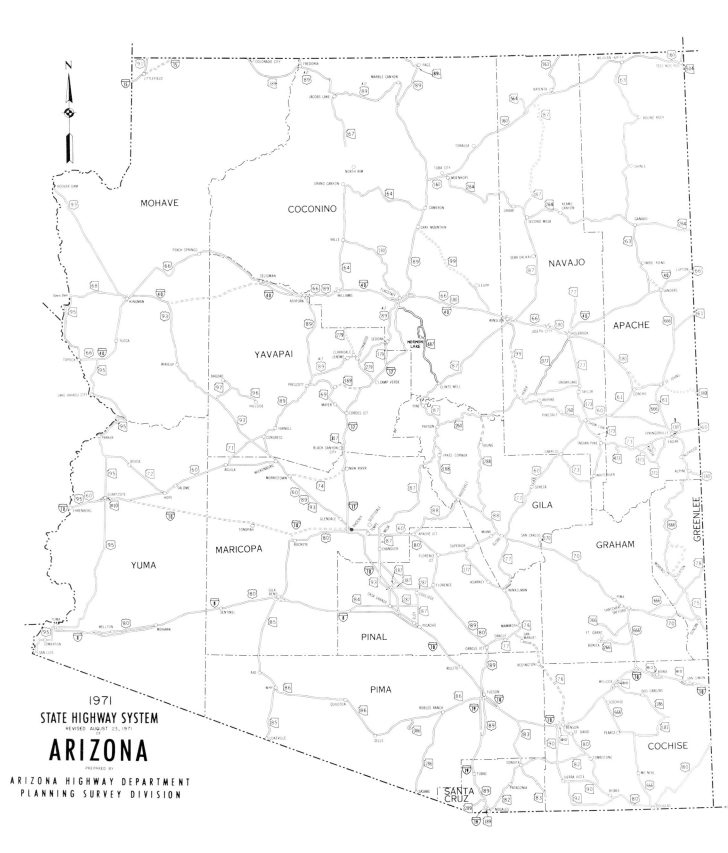

1971
STATE HIGHWAY SYSTEM
REVISED AUGUST 23, 1971
OF
ARIZONA
PREPARED BY
ARIZONA HIGHWAY DEPARTMENT
PLANNING SURVEY DIVISION

Fig. 20.3 By 1971, two major east-west arteries of the U.S. Interstate System crossed Arizona.

the state's own funds must take care of the expense of maintenance, administration, policing, and other miscellaneous costs. It is estimated that the actual investment in the State Highway System, including both state and federal monies, was $887,157,876 as of 1967.

Design

The path of least resistance was followed by the pioneers in crossing the Territory of Arizona. But when it became necessary to set up an adequate highway system to include all population centers, county seats, major industries, and scenic attractions to connect with major traffic arteries in contiguous states, and, in fact, to accommodate all of the state's population, the path of least resistance had to be forgotten and the roads located where the system required, regardless of difficulties. In one instance, where a temporary road had been constructed in territorial days, a better location was later found and a new road built, but the search for the best ultimate location was continued over a period of thirty years. It was finally found after the science of photogrammetry was developed sufficiently to transfer the search to aerial photographs. Difficult mountain terrain adds enormously to the expense of construction of high-standard roads. The great distances across the barren stretches of desert add to the cost which must be met by a relatively small population. The only plan which could be followed in developing a good road system was that known as stage construction. First the road was located, then graded, then graveled, and finally paved, each step being taken when funds became available.

By 1927 most of the main arteries were graveled. Beginning in 1928 Arizona utilized, as did other states, an inexpensive pavement type known as mixed-in-place oiled gravel. As most roads were already graveled, it was only necessary to add some more gravel, spray it with 60–70 road oil, mix it with a road grader, and let the traffic compact it. This was a notable development, one which enabled the state to cover most of its main traffic arteries with pavement at a cost equal to that of a few years' maintenance of a dusty, dangerous, corrugated, gravel road. Those oiled gravel pavements which were laid in areas where the subgrades were solid and unaffected by water carried the traffic for many years without much maintenance. In areas where the subgrade was of the type that softened when wet, the pavements soon went to pieces. This type of pavement continued to be used for many years, a gravel base being placed under it in areas where the subgrade was poor. As traffic increased and funds became available, better types of plant-mixed asphalt pavements were used. Early pavements were mostly two-lane and were eighteen feet wide. These widths were increased to twenty, then to twenty-two feet, and finally to a cross-section road twenty-four feet wide, with an eight-foot paved shoulder on each side. In the 1960s, broad four-lane divided arterial highways were being built across the state.

One of the expensive items of pavement construction on desert roads is the large number of culverts needed to bridge washes. In country which appears to be perfectly flat and level, washes which are normally dry but carry considerable water after rains, are often encountered at intervals of half a mile or less. In the early days of highway improvement, the pavement merely followed the contour of the land. As a result, dips in the road were an ever-present danger to the motorist. Most of them have now been bridged. The Interstate System of national highways has been planned to high standards with broad, four-lane divided roadways, bridged washes, grade separation structures, and limited-access approaches.

Two county paving projects are noteworthy. In 1921 Maricopa County voted $4 million in bonds for funds with which to lay a gridiron of concrete pavements in the flat, irrigated lands of the Salt River Valley. This was the largest county paving project attempted in any county in the United States at that time, and it was widely reported in national engineering magazines. Many of these pavements were still in use in 1969. In 1932, Pima County constructed two miles of mixed-in-place oiled aggregate pavement on East Broadway; aggregate crushed stone was used on one mile, and river-run gravel on the other. The latter material proved to be quite superior, and it was used on all subsequent projects.

Mileage tabulation checks on the several classifications of roads in Arizona proved that county roads have the greatest mileage. The construction and maintenance of these roads make it necessary for the boards of supervisors to employ county engineers and set up departments for this purpose. Some of the departments in the more populous counties are quite large. To finance the operations of these departments, the counties in 1969 were receiving 17 percent of the gas tax collected within their boundaries, plus 19 percent which went to incorporated communities in the county. In addition, the counties received one-half of the federal-aid funds allocated to the state for the Secondary Highway System. The state was using the other half for its Secondary System, which included many roads of importance to the counties.

Bridges

In earlier days, good bridge sites were selected and the traffic detoured to the bridge. Now, except under unusual circumstances such as are presented by the Grand Canyon, the highway is located for the convenience of traffic, and the bridge erected where the highway meets the stream, regardless of the difficulties encountered. A case in point is the bridge built across the Salt River at Tempe. Former short span bridges used pony trusses, and large spans were of the through

Arizona Highway Department

Fig. 20.4   Burro Creek Bridge, constructed in 1966 on State Highway 93 between Wickenburg and Kingman, was named one of 10 outstanding bridges in the United States.

truss type. Now the short spans are of the girder type, and the long spans are girders supported by steel arches or piers. The old bridges were one or two lanes wide, whereas the new ones are as wide as the pavement, regardless of whether it is two-lane or four-lane. This type of construction is safer and more convenient for traffic but adds enormously to the cost. The best estimate available in the late sixties indicated that about 800 new bridges were required on the new Interstate System of highways in Arizona, with approximately 150 grade separations required for the freeways in Tucson and Phoenix.

Progress in bridge design includes the use of electronic computers in lieu of the old desk calculators. Welding and high-tensioned bolts have practically replaced rivets in steel structures. Much use has been made of shear connectors to produce composite action of wide-flange steel beams with concrete deck slabs. The long used cast-in-place concrete structure has lost favor to the newer precast-prestressed type. The three types of short-span bridges which have been designed for use in Arizona include the two types mentioned above and the steel girder.

There were five interstate bridges in the Arizona Highway System in the late 1960s, not counting the crossing at Hoover Dam. These were at Yuma, Ehrenberg, Parker, Davis Dam, and Topock. The bridges at Yuma, Topock, and Parker were built by the Department of the Interior which paid half the cost, the other half being shared equally by Arizona and California. The bridge at Ehrenberg was built by private capital as a toll bridge and later purchased by the two states. All of these bridges have been jointly maintained by Arizona and California.

The Pinto Creek Bridge on Highway 70 near Superior, built in 1948, received the Institute of Steel Construction award for the most beautiful steel bridge built in that year. This is a 516-foot, deck-girder bridge supported by a steel girder arch 350 feet long.

The Navajo Bridge, which carries the traffic of Highway 89 across the Colorado River at a point about six miles below Lees Ferry, was built in 1929 at a cost of $260,000, of which the Indian Service of the Department of the Interior paid half. At this bridge site the solid rock walls of the canyon are vertical, about 600 feet apart and 600 feet high. A deck girder bridge, supported by a steel arched truss, was designed for this site. It was erected by anchoring the ends of the steel arch into the solid rock walls on each side and cantilevering the ends of the arched truss out until they met at the center of the span. This was a difficult and dangerous procedure, but it was about the only method which could be used at a site so high above stream.

The Colorado Bridge at Glen Canyon is an unusual structure built in 1957–59 at a cost of $4,139,277. The erection presented more difficulties than the design, though that was not simple. It is a deck-girder bridge forty feet wide and 1,271 feet long, supported by steel columns. These, in turn, are supported by a steel arch truss anchored against the solid rock walls of Glen Canyon, which at this point are 1,028 feet apart. The deck of the bridge is 680 feet above the stream. The only possible way to erect the bridge was to cantilever each half from its skewback canyon wall support until the two halves met at the center. The steel truss members which formed the cantilevers were lowered into place from cableways anchored to towers on each side of the stream. The cantilever sections were so long that it was necessary to support them by ties from towers until connection was made at the center of the arch. In order to make sure of exact fit at the center of the steel truss, members were milled to one ten-thousandth of an inch, an unprecedented precision for bridge members, and a trial fitting made at the fabrication yard. A precise preliminary survey was also necessary under dangerous and difficult circumstances. The precision of this survey, made by men dangling on ropes against the steep rock walls of the canyon, was equal to that expected of surveys made under normal conditions.

The hazards of highway construction in Arizona have not deterred the development of an excellent system of roads. Financed by federal and state money, these highways have come to be known by the tourists in Arizona. As an economic activity within the Arizona economy, highways have contributed much to the wealth and mobility of both citizen and visitor within the state.

Another major bridge constructed in the sixties, and a winner of an award for one of the 10 outstanding bridges in the United States (1966) is the Burro Creek Bridge.

Located on State Highway 93, approximately midway between Wickenburg and Kingman, the bridge links a new alignment, saving more than one and one-half miles and eliminates steep grades in and out of the canyon.

The bridge is approximately 400 feet above the stream-bed and has a roadway 30 feet wide with a one-foot six-inch safety curb on each side. It is 965 feet long.

Designed by the bridge department of the Arizona Highway Department, the main span is a steel trussed arch with east and west approaches of steel plate girders. There are 1667 tons of structural steel and 172 tons of re-enforcing steel in the unit and 2200 cubic yards of concrete.

U.S. Steel Corporation built the bridge at a cost of $1,500,000. It was opened to traffic May 1966.

Fuel Tax
(Gasoline Tax)

March 17, 1921
First gasoline tax 1¢ per gallon on sales. Credited to State Road Tax Fund.

March 20, 1923
Gas Tax increased to 3¢ per gallon.
Credited —
    25% to State Road Tax Fund
    25% to County Road Tax Fund
    50% returned to Counties — Pro-rata on sales.

August 11, 1927
Established *Division of Motor Vehicles*.

August 11, 1927
Gas Tax increased to 4¢ per gallon on imports and acquisitions.
    3/8 to Counties — Pro-rata on sales.
    5/8 to State Highway Fund
Motor Vehicle Division Gasoline Tax Distribution Reports began this date.

January 30, 1931
Gas Tax increased to 5¢ per gallon — Temporary until January 31, 1933.
    3/10 to Counties
    7/10 to State Highway Fund

January 18, 1932
Gas Tax 5¢ extended to June 30, 1933.

March 2, 1933
Gas Tax fixed at 5¢ per gallon.
    3/10 to Counties
    6/10 to State Highway Fund
    1/10 to Reconstruction Finance Corporation for
        ensuing two years.
After 2 years, the State Highway Fund's portion was to be 7/10.

Beginning Fiscal Year 1935–1936
    3/10 Counties
    7/10 State Highway Fund

July 1, 1941
"Use" Fuel Tax Law effective. In addition to 5¢ gasoline tax, 5¢ tax on all fuel other than gasoline. Same 3/10-7/10 distribution as gasoline.

June 26, 1952
H.B. 294, 20th Legislature requires payment to Aviation Authority of unclaimed refunds of 5¢ tax on Aviation fuel as shown by duplicate invoices in MVD files over 6 months old.

April 4, 1963

H.B. 238, Chap. 84 — 5¢ Gas Tax and 5¢ Use Fuel Tax increased to 6¢. The 3/10-7/10 distribution of initial 5¢ Use Fuel Tax not disturbed. The additional 1¢ Gas Tax — Chapter 84 — H.B. 234.

100% to Counties — Pro-rata on sales.

20% of this 1¢ gas tax distributed to the counties retained by the counties. The 80% balance distributed by each county to the several incorporated cities and towns on a population basis.

The additional 1¢ Use Fuel Tax distributed as before:

3/10 to State Highway

7/10 to Counties

July 20, 1965

Chap. 99 — Increased the Gas & Use Fuel from 6¢ to 7¢. The distribution 3/10-7/10 remained the same on the 5¢ Gas Tax Portion and 7¢ Use Fuel Tax. Changed the distribution of the 2¢ Gas Tax as follows:

20% to the Counties

40% to the incorporated cities and towns in each county on population basis

40% to the State Highway Fund

Registration Fees

In 1927, the original $3.50 fee was imposed for the registration of all motor vehicles, trailers, or semi-trailers. County Assessors were appointed as agents of the Motor Vehicle Division. A half-dollar of each registration fee was retained by the assessor.

In 1931, in addition to the $3.50 registration fee imposed on all motor vehicles and trailers, an unladen weight fee was imposed on all commercial vehicles based on unladen weight and number of axles in accordance with the following schedule:

Under 2600 lbs. — $2.00	2-axle	3-axle
2600 lbs. to 4000 lbs. per cwt.	.35	.50
4000 lbs. to 6000 lbs. per cwt.	.50	.65
6000 lbs. to 8000 lbs. per cwt.	.65	.80
8000 lbs. to 10000 lbs. per cwt.	.75	1.00
10000 lbs. to 12000 lbs. per cwt.	1.00	1.35
12000 lbs. and over	1.00	1.60
Maximum Fees	120.00	185.00

In 1937, the 2600 lb. base was changed to 2900 lbs. for the minimum $2.00 commercial weight fee. The weight fee schedule was not changed in any manner and has not been changed up to 1969.

In 1941, the Arizona Constitution was amended to provide for a Standard Vehicle License Tax (Auto Lieu tax) to be assessed in lieu of personal property tax, the tax base being on valuation of the vehicle, with an annual 25% decrease on the assessed valuation, the tax rate not to exceed $4.00 per $100.00.

In 1955, the $3.50 Registration fee was increased to $4.00. The 50¢ portion of each registration fee retained by the county assessor was increased at this time to $1.00 of each registration.

In 1964, the $4.00 Registration fee was increased to $6.25. Of this $2.25 increase, $2.00 was specifically "earmarked" by legislative enactment to be credited to a special fund designated as "primary and secondary state road fund" and this amount to be expended by the highway department for the construction and maintenance of primary and secondary state roads only. The $1.00 portion retained by the assessors was not changed.

Title Fees

The $1.00 Certificate of Title fee enacted in 1927 remained in effect until July 1966, at which time it was increased to $2.00. The following fees were also increased at this time:

Duplicate Title — from	.50 to $2.00
Transfer Reg. Card	.50 to $2.00
Duplicate Reg. Card	.50 to $2.00
Lien Filing Fee	.75 to $2.00
Lien Clearance Fee	.25 to $1.00

Motor Carrier Tax

The license tax of 2% of gross receipts from operations within the state imposed in 1927 on common carriers of passengers was increased on March 18, 1933 to 2¼%. The 2½% tax rate on common carriers of property, also enacted in 1927, was not increased. The same tax rate of 2¼% and 2½% on these two categories of "for-hire" carriers prevails today.

ARIZONA'S ECONOMY

George F. Leaming
Economist

21

DEVELOPMENTS ON MANY FRONTS

THE DECADE OF THE 1960s saw many changes in the Arizona economy. Most of these could be summarized in a single word — growth. The population of the state had grown from almost one million in the mid-1950s to nearly two million by the end of the 1960s. New businesses, expansions of existing activities, and increases in employment in both business and government accompanied this population growth. In the mid-1950s total employment in the state was slightly less than 300,000. By the mid-1960s, this had risen to almost 500,000, and by the end of the 1960s the state's total employment was over 600,000.

The growth in Arizona employment since the mid-1950s has not been uniform throughout the various sectors of the state's economy, but neither has it been confined to a few industries. Between the mid-1950s and late 1960s all of Arizona's major economic activities except agriculture increased the number of persons employed. Service industries, manufacturing, and government all more than doubled employment during the 1960s. The number of retail and wholesale trade workers in the state also rose at a faster pace than the population. Employment in other sectors likewise increased by significant amounts. The number of workers in Arizona's contract construction industry swelled by more than half and in the state's transportation and public utilities by more than a quarter. The number of self-employed persons in Arizona grew by a third, and mining (although employment in the mineral industry was declining in many parts of the nation) increased its Arizona employment by more than ten percent. The number of persons working on farms and ranches, however, declined.

Arizona's growth in employment since the late 1950s has been qualitative as well as quantitative. Along with changes in the size and industrial composition of the employed labor force, have come changes in individual earnings. In the mid-1950s the per capita annual personal income of Arizonans was estimated by the Department of Commerce at approximately sixteen hundred dollars. By the late 1960s this had increased to twenty-eight hundred dollars. Average hourly earnings in Arizona industries had also increased since the 1950s. One of the sharpest rises occurred in contract construction. The average hourly rate of about three dollars, earned by construction workers in the mid-1950s, rose by more than two-thirds. Average hourly earnings in public utilities have risen by almost as much, while increases in other industries also have been substantial, ranging from one-third to one-half in the decade between mid-1950s and the mid-1960s. Even in the state's relatively low-paying agricultural sector, average wage rates for hourly employees rose by almost a fourth.

Economic Emphasis Shifts

Arizona on the eve of the 1970s no longer had an economy based principally on the production of raw materials. A strong emphasis in the state was on wholesale and retail trade, services, and government activity. In addition, the importance of manufacturing (particularly in electronics) had grown substantially within a decade. Although the rush for industrial development had been accompanied by a tendency to neglect or relegate to secondary importance the state's mineral industries, mining was still a significant factor in the economy. Copper mining alone was almost completely responsible for the existence of such communities as Ajo, Bagdad, Bisbee, Douglas, Miami, San Manuel, Superior, Kearny, and others that in the late 1960s accounted for approximately ten percent of the state's population outside Maricopa County. Even the largest metropolitan area, however, had also been affected by the minerals industry that produced many of the basic materials necessary for urban housing and other construction. In the late 1960s mining payrolls in Arizona had climbed to almost eighty percent above the level of the previous decade. The value of the state's mineral output climbed even more as the 1970s approached, rising to more than double the 1960 average.

Construction has been an important part of Arizona's economic progress since World War II. Although there was a decline in the late 1950s and early 1960s in construction activity, the mid-1960s marked a resurgence. By early 1969, construction payrolls in Arizona were more than a third higher than the 1960 average, while total construction sales had risen by a like amount. Although in the latter part of the 1960s, rising prices played an important part in the growing value of construction in Arizona, there was also definite increase in the physical volume of residential, commercial, and industrial structures completed.

Manufacturing was the glamour industry of Arizona in the 1960s. By late 1969, manufacturing payrolls in the state had risen to almost three times the 1960 average. Except for a small decline in early 1967, the growth was steady throughout the decade. As the state's manufacturing industry developed, it became more varied in nature. As of 1970, the output of Arizona factories ranged from low-priced food products to expensive and highly complex electronic equipment. Electronic products themselves ranged from tiny transistors to large data processing systems. Metal fabrication, printing and publishing, and the aerospace industries are also important in Arizona's manufacturing sector. While most of the growth in Arizona manufacturing in the 1960s took place in the Phoenix and Tucson metropolitan areas, near the end of the decade significant expansion also began on the state's Indian reservations, particularly in Northern Arizona.

One of the major sectors of the Arizona economy since World War II has been government — federal, state, and local. Of greatest economic influence has been the federal government, with such major Department of Defense installations as Davis-Monthan, Luke, and Williams air force bases, as well as numerous other activities involving particularly the departments of Agriculture and Interior. Arizona state government has been a significant economic factor in many areas of the state, primarily through the Arizona Highway Department and the three state universities. Local government, including school districts, has also been of substantial economic consequence in virtually all parts of the state.

Increase in Retail Sales

As population and personal income levels have increased, so have retail sales. The climb in retail sales and trade payrolls was particularly persistent throughout the 1960s. By the end of the decade, retail sales in the state were double the 1960 figure, and retail industry payrolls were close behind. As elsewhere in the nation, retail sales activity in Arizona has reflected seasonal characteristics, with normal highs occurring in December of each year and rather persistent seasonal slumps occurring during June, July, and August. Payrolls in the industry, however, have not followed the same pattern. While retail trade payrolls in Arizona tend to peak sharply in December, over the past decade there has been no noticeable difference between summer and winter retail payrolls.

Transportation has produced a wide variety of relationships within the Arizona economy. Because of the state's distance from major population centers, interstate air travel — particularly from and to the Phoenix and Tucson metropolitan areas — has become increasingly significant as a reflection of overall economic growth and development. The great distances also between population centers within Arizona has made local air traffic important in the state's economic progress. By the late 1960s, the total number of passengers arriving and departing by air through Arizona's two major metropolitan areas had reached approximately four times the level of activity existing in 1960. Throughout the late 1960s, air travel in Phoenix and Tucson was increasing at a rate between 15 and 20 percent per year.

Automobile and truck traffic has also been important in the economic picture. Completion of large segments of the interstate highway system within the state continued throughout the 1960s. This factor, combined with the increasing use of automobile air-conditioning was undoubtedly a major cause of the increase in summer tourism in the southern part of the state. Commercial truck traffic in Southern Arizona has also increased, with the essential completion of the interstate highway system through that portion of the state. By 1970, interstate truck traffic through southern Arizona had increased by approximately fifty percent over 1960 levels. In the northern part of the state, however, truck traffic had declined, reflecting not only the failure to complete the interstate system through northern Arizona but also the increased use of piggyback transportation by railroads through that part of the state. Although declining sharply in importance as passenger haulers, Arizona's railroads, the Santa Fe and the Southern Pacific, continued to increase substantially their importance as cargo movers during the 1960s. In addition, the number of minor railroads hauling mining specialty cargoes also increased in importance.

North Is Tourist Haven

Arizona tourism has been closely linked to transportation throughout the past two decades, and tourists have contributed a consistently larger share to economic activity. Despite the common conception of Arizona as a winter visitor haven, throughout the 1960s summer tourism in northern Arizona was far more important than winter tourism in the south. This was true both in terms of numbers of visitors and in the size of the contribution they made to business activity. In fact, based on the number of visitors to national parks and monuments, winter tourism in southern Arizona is about equivalent to winter tourism in the north where winter is the slack season. During June, July, and August, however, tourist activity skyrockets in northern Arizona, primarily because of the fame of the Grand Canyon. After a moderate slump in Arizona tourist activity during the mid-1960s, such activity increased significantly.

Trade and Travel in Mexico

Tourist travel to Mexico through Arizona also climbed during the late 1960s despite the apparent failure of the 1968 Olympics to draw many additional tourists to Mexico City through Arizona border points, and despite also the travel-inhibiting regulations and procedures adopted by the United States. Traffic to Mexico's West Coast increased from 10 to 15 percent during most of the late 1960s. Immediate border traffic, however, did not increase during the late 1960s, after the U.S. imposition in 1965 of import restrictions on liquor and other tourist purchases abroad. Commercial trade across the international border, however, did increase substantially throughout the 1960s. A large part of the trade from Mexico consisted of tomatoes (even during 1969, when imports of smaller sizes of tomatoes were prohibited) and other fresh fruits and vegetables as well as shrimp and cattle. In the late 1960s, a growing factor in trade back and forth across the Arizona-Sonora border was the twin cities program of industrial development aimed at increasing manufacturing activity along the Mexico-United States border and concentrating on electronic components and sub-assemblies. In 1968, the value of such trade exceeded $10 million in semi-conductor components alone.

Arizona's agricultural sector changed more than it grew during the 1960s, with decreased emphasis on cotton and greater emphasis on more speculative crops, such as fresh fruits and vegetables. Cattle and other livestock, however, have continued to form a significant part of Arizona's agricultural picture. Throughout the late 1960s the value of the state's agricultural output was highly erratic, reflecting the seasonal nature of the industry, although there was sharp recovery in the late part of the decade from a moderate slump that occurred during the middle-1960s. Despite diversification, the seasonal pattern of Arizona's agricultural activity still closely follows the pattern of the cotton industry, with greatest activity during the autumn and early winter. In recent years, however, a secondary peak has occurred in the early spring when winter vegetables for northern and eastern markets are harvested and shipped. Nevertheless, at the start of 1970, cotton, cattle, and citrus remained a significant part of Arizona's economy.

County an Economic Unit

In many respects what is often called "the Arizona economy" does not really exist. The state actually embraces many separate and distinct economies. In some areas agriculture forms the principle base, while in others manufacturing, mining, lumbering, tourism, or trade predominate. Business activity in the state's northern counties reaches a peak normally in the summer months and drops off sharply during the rest of the year. In some of the southern counties activity is generally higher during the winter and early spring. In areas where cotton is king or where melons, lettuce, or cattle prevail, activity tends to coincide with the seasonal characteristics of the prevalent crop. Still other parts of the state show a marked stability in economic activity throughout the year. This lack of uniformity makes it extremely difficult if not impossible to develop any valid economic generalizations for the whole state. The county thus is a more realistic economic unit.

APACHE The economy of Apache County, in northern Arizona, is based heavily on its forest industries and the vacation travel of both in-state and out-of-state tourists. In the 1960s more than a third of total employment in the county and nearly half of all business payrolls were provided by firms producing forest products. Government has also been a major factor in the county's economy. Although Apache County experienced a severe economic slump during the early 1960s, a strong resurgence developed during the latter part of the decade.

COCHISE Cochise County, which once had its seat of government at Tombstone — the legendary silver camp "too tough to die" — is still basically a mining county. Mining and smelting continue to form the primary economic base despite the growth in the western part, since the mid-1950s, of Fort Huachuca and Sierra Vista. In the mid-1960s, more than a quarter of the county's civilian employment and nearly half of its business payrolls were directly attributable to the mineral industries. A substantial part of the remainder was directly attributable to activity at Fort Huachuca where combined military and civilian payrolls in the late 1960s approached fifty million dollars annually.

COCONINO In Coconino County in the middle of Arizona's northland, the traveler and the tree are the mainstays of economic activity. In the late 1960s more than half of the county's employment was found in the retail trade and service industries, reflecting a strong dependency upon tourism, while another fifth was in the production of lumber and wood products. The dependency of retail trade and service firms in Coconino County on tourism is evident from the strong relationship that exists among retail sales in the county, national park visitations, and highway traffic.

GILA Gila County is another of Arizona's mining counties, with the operations of five major copper producers located within its borders. In the late 1960s, mining and smelting accounted for more than two-thirds of Gila County's employment and more than three-fourths of the business payrolls. The only other substantial source of employment and personal income in the county has been retail trade, most of which has been centered in the Globe-Miami area, a major mining center.

GRAHAM Agriculture, the processing of agricultural products, and the provision of supplies and services to the agricultural sector are the principal economic activities of Graham County in the east-central portion of the state. In the late 1960s more than sixty percent of the nonagricultural employment in the county was accounted for by retail trade and services, and more than ten percent of this employment was in food-processing. In the late 1960s, however, tentative mining development began in the county and the character of the economy began to show signs of change from agriculture to greater diversification.

GREENLEE Minerals are the mainstay of Graham County's eastern neighbor, Greenlee County. Greenlee is undoubtedly the least diversified of Arizona's fourteen county economies. Aside from the provision of service to a short segment of U.S. Highway 70 that travels through the southern part of the county, the only basic economic activity of any consequence is a large open pit copper mine and its associated reduction works at Morenci. Mining and smelting operations in Greenlee County account for almost ninety percent of total business payrolls, and more than eighty percent of those employed are in these activities. Retail trade operations provide the bulk of the remaining employment and payrolls. With announced expansions planned for the copper industry in the county, the importance of the mineral industries in Greenlee was expected to increase even more during the 1970s.

MARICOPA The state's most populous county, Maricopa, (identical with the Phoenix Metropolitan Area) is also one of the most economically diversified. In the late 1960s, manufacturing provided more than one-fourth of all Maricopa County nonagricultural employment, and almost a third of its business payrolls. As in other counties, retail trade was also an important source of jobs and personal income. Contract construction and the service industries have likewise been significant in the Phoenix Metropolitan Area, each consistently contributing more than ten percent of total business payrolls. Growth in the Maricopa County economy during the 1960s closely paralleled the growth of manufacturing activity in the center of the state. This, in turn was allied with developments by a relatively small number of companies principally in the electronics industry. Although the county experienced a slump in construction during

the late 1950s and early 1960s, there was a sharp rebound as the 1970s approached.

MOHAVE Mohave County, in Arizona's northwestern corner, has been a county once again in transition. Long dependent on tourist and other travel on U.S. Route 66 and on its advantageous location between Phoenix and Las Vegas, Nevada, Mohave County in the 1960s returned to its former status as one of Arizona's principal mining counties. Originally a gold mining center, with the opening of the Duval Corporation's multi-million dollar Ithaca Peak Mine near Kingman, Mohave County became another Arizona copper county. Subsequent growth in other copper-mining activity has added to this position. Tourism has not been neglected in Mohave County, however, with increased activity along the Colorado River in both the Lake Mead National Recreation Area and further south at Lake Havasu.

NAVAJO As in adjoining Apache and Coconino counties, timber and tourists form the base of the Navajo County economy. While retail trade and service establishments accounted for approximately half of the county's employment in the late 1960s, the manufacture of lumber and other forest products accounted for more than a fifth of nonagricultural employment and a fourth of the county's business payrolls. As in Coconino County to the west, there appeared to be a strong relationship between the activity of retail trade and service establishments and the use of national parks and highways in Navajo and nearby counties.

PIMA Pima, the second largest of Arizona's metropolitan counties, is probably the most economically diversified. Throughout the 1960s, no single major industrial category provided more than one-fourth of the county's business payrolls. As in Maricopa County, manufacturing was responsible for the biggest share of business payrolls during most of the decade. In the latter part of the 1960s, however, manufacturing was joined by mining as an important employer. Retail trade, contract construction, and service industries also accounted for significant portions of the county's employment and payrolls. The most important and fastest growing sector of the Pima County economy throughout the 1960s, however, was government. This included government at all levels, national, state, and local, and significant influence was exercised by each of these three levels. A major part of both local and state government activity in the county has been in education, with local school districts and the University of Arizona numbered among the area's largest employers. The Department of Defense has accounted for the greatest share of federal government activity.

PINAL Pinal County, in southern Arizona, is actually two distinct economies. The eastern part of the county is a mining district, while the western portion is a farming and trading area. For the county as a whole, however, mining is undoubtedly the dominant sector. In the late 1960s, there were also developments in western Pinal County to indicate that minerals would become important in that area as well.

YUMA The economy of Arizona's lowest and warmest county, Yuma, is based primarily on agriculture and trade. Agriculture has consistently provided more jobs than any other major industry in Yuma County, while retail trade has provided the major share of nonagricultural employment. Packaging and processing of farm products also has accounted for a notable portion of employment and payrolls in Yuma County. In addition, national defense activity at Yuma and tourist activity along Interstate 8, as well as along the Colorado River, have significantly augmented economic growth.

SANTA CRUZ Commerce is by far the most important element in the economy of Santa Cruz County. Throughout the 1960s, retail wholesale trade and transportation accounted for approximately three-quarters of the county's business payrolls and more than half of its total nonagricultural employment. Tourist services have also contributed significantly to the Santa Cruz County economy.

YAVAPAI The site of Arizona's earliest persistent mining activity, Yavapai County, still ranks as one of the state's mining regions. Throughout the 1960s, mining provided approximately one-fourth of Yavapai County's business payrolls but less than a fifth of its nonagricultural employment. Retail trade, service industries, and manufacturing have been of moderate importance, but of far greater impact has been federal government activity. In several respects, the economy of Yavapai County has reflected many of the characteristics of the state as a whole. Despite this, Arizona has no really typical county economy.

During the 1960s, firm bases for future economic growth and development were firmly established in many parts of Arizona. In the major metropolitan areas, manufacturing of a wider variety of commodities promised increased diversity and stability in both Tucson and Phoenix. New manufacturing installations in northern Arizona, particularly on the Indian Reservations, also portended strong economic growth and rising personal incomes for a long-neglected part of the state. New mineral resource development in the southern and eastern regions likewise forecast a justified economic gain during the 1970s for many of Arizona's non-metropolitan communities. Other developments — in technology, education, trade, and tourism — imminent at the start of the 1970s, foretold a prosperous future for virtually all of the state.

Editor: George F. Leaming
Economist

22

MANUFACTURING AND COMMERCE

LONG IMPORTANT in more industrialized sections of the country, manufacturing became in the sixties one of the most important types of economic activity in Arizona, providing employment to more than 80,000 persons and payrolls of over a half billion dollars annually. Over the decade of the 1960s the number of manufacturing jobs in the state doubled, making it the leading category of industrial employment as well as the state's largest source of outside income.

The total value added annually to manufacturing output in Arizona had risen nearly three times since the start of the post-Korean war boom in 1954. From that time, the total values added by manufacturing activity in Arizona climbed almost without interruption. Employment and payrolls in the industry increased in similar fashion.

Character and Location of Industry

CHANGE IN THE INDUSTRY. As Arizona's manufacturing industry grew, its character changed. Over a decade and a half, generally better paying electronics and metal-working industries have noticeably diminished the earlier dominance of the lower-wage food processing industries. At the beginning of the seventies the state's manufacturing industry was moderately diversified, with the production of electrical and electronics equipment accounting for more than one-fourth of all manufacturing employment. This type of manufacturing, which produces items ranging from transistors to complex computers, was the largest single type of manufacturing in Arizona. In 1967, the production of electrical and electronic equipment accounted for more than twenty thousand jobs. Motorola, Inc., long a leader in the electronics field, became the largest single employer in the state.

Other machinery and aerospace products including missiles and aircraft parts, were second in importance only to electronics equipment. AiResearch, Hughes Aircraft, Goodyear, and Sperry are some of the more prominent firms producing machinery and aerospace products in Arizona. Numerous other smaller firms also have contributed to the state's output of such goods.

Food processing was still a significant factor in Arizona's industrial activity by 1970, occupying eight percent of all manufacturing workers. The industry includes a wide range of activities, ranging from small chili and tortilla factories to large meat-processing plants, bakeries, and dairies. In recent years, a number of major meat packing firms expanded or began operations in the state, supplying meat and meat products to other areas of the country. Much of Arizona's food processing industry, however, has been involved with meeting local consumer demand, primarily in the Phoenix and Tucson metropolitan areas.

Printing and publishing and the manufacture of apparel also have provided substantial numbers of manufacturing jobs in Arizona in modern times. Printing and publishing, including the production of daily newspapers in the state's two major metropolitan areas, employed more than 5,000 persons in the late 1960s. Apparel production employed more than four thousand.

Plants producing manufactured items from the raw materials output of the state's mines and forests have added further strength and diversification to the Arizona industrial sector. These plants range from sawmills and paper mills, utilizing raw materials from the state's northern forests, to cement plants, copper wire mills, and brick factories using the state's mineral resources. In 1967, plants manufacturing products from the state's forest resources employed more than 2,000 persons. In the same year, manufacturing industries using products from the state's mines and quarries employed more than 7,000.

METROPOLITAN CONCENTRATION. Despite scattered activity throughout the state, most of Arizona's manufacturing has concentrated in the Phoenix and Tucson metropolitan areas. These two areas together contained more than three-fourths of the manufacturing firms in the state by 1970, and an even larger share of total manufacturing employment. Furthermore, most of this was in the Phoenix metropolitan area, with Tucson and Pima County accounting for only about 10 percent of the statewide total. Only five counties, outside of Maricopa and Pima Counties, contained more than two dozen manufacturing firms, and most of these were very small. Nearly half of the state's fourteen counties possessed less than twenty manufacturing firms.

In addition to its relative concentration in one area (Maricopa County), Arizona's manufacturing employment was also concentrated in the hands of about a dozen large firms, each employing more than 500 workers. The state's largest manufacturer was Motorola, Inc., with plants of several divisions located at various sites within the Phoenix metropolitan area. Motorola provided approximately three times as many jobs as the state's second largest manufacturer.

Patterns of Growth

COMPONENTS OF EXPANSION. Through the 1960s most of the growth in Arizona manufacturing was the result of expansion by firms that were already established in the state by the end of the 1950s. Some additional growth was also achieved, however, by the entrance of new firms, both large and small, into the growing industrial sector. Although there was relatively little increase in total industrial employment brought about by the entrance of new firms to the Arizona economy in these years, there were significant additions to manufacturing employment in some of the state's smaller areas. At Kingman in Mohave County, at Safford in Graham County, at Casa Grande in western Pinal County, and

TABLE 22.1
Employees and Payrolls In Manufacturing

Year	Average Annual Employment	Annual Payrolls
1960	48,400	$246,918,000
1961	49,700	258,087,000
1962	53,900	285,687,000
1963	57,000	317,168,000
1964	58,500	330,034,000
1965	64,300	378,522,000
1966	76,100	466,570,000
1967	77,700	478,555,000
1968	83,800	534,642,000
1969	93,400	613,256,000
1970	91,200	627,437,000

Source: Unemployment Compensation Division, Employment Security Commission of Arizona, *Arizona's Current Employment Developments.*

TABLE 22.2
Types of Manufacturing With More Than 1,000 Employees

Industrial Class	Number of Employees
Ordnance and Accessories	3,071
Food and Kindred Products	6,259
Apparel and Related Products	4,938
Lumber and Wood Products	2,980
Printing and Publishing	5,591
Chemicals and Allied Products	1,224
Stone, Clay and Glass Products	3,246
Primary Metal Industries	5,514
Fabricated Metal Products	4,205
Machinery, Except Electrical	16,112
Electrical Equip. and Supplies	26,334
Transportation Equipment	2,373
Administrative and Auxiliary	2,790

Source: U. S. Department of Commerce, Bureau of the Census, *Arizona County Business Patterns 1967.*

at Nogales in Santa Cruz County, new manufacturing plants have made a strong impact on the local economy. In several locations, the development of industrial parks and the installation of new manufacturing plants on Indian reservations also contributed substantially to the increasing employment of Arizona's Indian population in manufacturing. Much of the manufacturing in outlying counties, however, has remained closely related to the production of farm, forest and mineral products.

Growth of Trade

Retail and wholesale trade in Arizona in the late 1960s employed more than one hundred thousand persons. In 1958, such commercial activity in the state employed only about two-thirds of that number. In 1968 there were more than 63,000 Arizona workers engaged in retail trade activities alone, and annual payrolls in retail trade reached a total of nearly $300 million. In 1960, there were fewer than fifty thousand persons employed in retail trade, and the industry's annual payrolls were well under $200 million.

The total dollar volume of retail sales in the state also grew considerably over that decade. In the early 70s, the total volume of retail sales was exceeding two billion dollars. Ten years before, it had totalled only about one billion dollars. The increase resulted from the combination of a more prosperous Arizona economy, higher personal incomes, increasing population, and higher price levels.

Concentration and Types of Trade

PHOENIX AND TUCSON CONCENTRATION. As would be expected, most of the state's retail trade activity was carried on in its major metropolitan areas. In the late sixties, the Phoenix Metropolitan Area accounted for far more than half of the state's total retail sales volume, while the Tucson area accounted for about one-fourth. The retail sales totals of other counties showed relation-

Fig. 22.1   By the 1970s, manufacturing was a main source of Arizona's industrial employment and income from out of state.

ship directly to their population and inversely to their proximity to the major metropolitan areas.

Employment in retail and wholesale trade throughout the state has occurred in even more concentrated form than total retail sales volume. In the sixties Maricopa County provided more than sixty percent of the state's employment in wholesale and retail trade, while Pima County provided less than twenty percent. Apache, Graham, and Greenlee Counties each provided less than one percent. With the continuing modernization of the state's highway system and the ready availability of rapid motor transportation facilities, the importance of the Phoenix Metropolitan Area in the state's retail and wholesale picture has increased and can be expected to increase even more.

HIGH VOLUME ITEMS. Automobiles and food have accounted for the greatest volume of retail sales in Arizona. According to the latest census of business, food stores have provided about twenty percent of total retail sales in the state, and automotive dealers have contributed only a slightly smaller amount. Gasoline service stations have contributed another ten percent to the state's total retail sales volume. Exceeding that figure, however, have been the purchases made at general merchandise stores. The only other types of retail sales activity contributing more than five percent of the total have been eating and drinking places and the single

category which includes lumber, building materials, hardware, and farm equipment dealers.

Increased Demand for Wholesaling

WHOLESALING SIGNIFICANT FACTOR. Wholesale trade has also been important in Arizona's economic picture. As would be expected from the pattern of retail sales, the most important type of wholesale trade conducted in the state has involved groceries and related products. Such items in the late 1960s accounted for approximately twenty-five percent of the state's total wholesale sales, according to the most recent Census of Business. Also a reflection of the state's buying habits and the emphasis on motor transportation in the retail sales pattern, petroleum bulk stations and terminals accounted for approximately ten percent of Arizona's total wholesale sales, while wholesalers of motor vehicles and automotive equipment accounted for a similar amount.

Reflecting activity in the state's manufacturing and basic industry sectors have been substantial volumes of wholesale trade in farm products and agricultural raw materials, in electrical goods and in machinery, equipment and supplies, each of which has accounted for slightly less than ten percent of the state's total wholesale trade volume.

Because of the increasing demand for wholesale activity from a growing retail trade sector, combined with the increasing availability of wholesale items from an expanding manufacturing and industrial sector, the rate of growth in Arizona wholesaling has outpaced the national average through the fifties and sixties. The total sales of Arizona wholesalers have risen four times faster than the national average, and the number of wholesale establishments has increased six times faster than the national rate. In terms of dollar volume, wholesale trade in groceries and related products increased the fastest within Arizona, followed by the wholesale trade in motor vehicles, petroleum bulk stations, and machinery wholesalers. This again reflected both the pull of consumer demand and the push of industrial diversification.

A significant part of Arizona's wholesale trade picture has been its international commerce, primarily with Mexico. In 1968 total imports from Mexico to Arizona amounted to more than $115 million, while exports through the state totalled nearly $47 million. Fresh fruits and vegetables, shrimp, and cattle have in recent years formed the bulk of the import trade from Mexico. Arizona has been one of the primary channels for the wholesale importation of tomatoes into the United States during the winter season, notwithstanding controversy over new border regulations in 1969-70. Other fresh produce items have also been important, pouring through Arizona's ports every year before similar items in the United States are able to ripen and supply the nation's retail markets. Many of the feeder cattle for Arizona's feed lots (and eventually for its meat packing operations) also come in from Mexico and have formed a significant part of the state's international trade. Wholesale exports through the state largely have been composed of motor vehicles and industrial and agricultural machinery. While not affecting all parts of the state, this particular category of wholesale trade has been of extreme significance in the counties lying along the Mexican border, and has contributed substantially to their economic growth over the past ten years.

TABLE 22.3

Employment in Wholesale and Retail Trade by County

County	1969	Percent of Total	1959	Percent of Total
Apache	550	.5%	300	.4%
Cochise	2,400	2.0	2,300	3.1
Coconino	3,450	2.9	2,000	2.7
Gila	12,200	1.0	1,100	1.5
Graham	700	.6	800	1.1
Greenlee	300	.2	200	.3
Maricopa	74,700	63.9	42,800	58.5
Mohave	1,200	1.0	500	.7
Navajo	1,800	1.5	900	1.2
Pima	21,300	18.2	14,700	20.1
Pinal	2,100	1.8	2,000	2.7
Santa Cruz ...	2,050	1.8	1,200	1.6
Yavapai	1,400	1.2	1,300	1.8
Yuma	3,800	3.2	3,100	4.2
TOTAL	116,950	100.0%	73,200	100.0%

Source: Employment Security Commission of Arizona, *Basic Economic Data.*

TABLE 22.4

Employees and Payrolls in Retail Trade[a]

Year	Annual Average Employment	Annual Payrolls
1960	49,200	176,833,000
1961	51,700	186,395,000
1962	52,800	195,281,000
1963	55,300	213,982,000
1964	58,200	228,995,000
1965	59,000	232,413,000
1966	59,300	248,043,000
1967	61,400	263,608,000
1968	63,000	287,057,000
1969	93,767	456,724,054
1970	101,950	516,197,318

[a]except eating and drinking places.
Source: Unemployment Compensation Division, Employment Security Commission of Arizona, *Arizona's Current Employment Developments.*

TABLE 22.5

Taxable Retail Sales by County

County	1969-70	Percent of Total	1959-60	Percent of Total
Apache	$ 8,765,065.50	.3%	$ 7,136,815.50	.5%
Cochise	76,871,894.00	2.5	45,975,315.00	3.0
Coconino	75,530,335.50	2.5	42,078,270.00	2.8
Gila	37,382,856.50	1.2	22,149,634.50	1.4
Graham	22,862,265.00	.7	14,233,732.00	.9
Greenlee	13,520,497.00	.4	7,897,793.50	.5
Maricopa	1,894,180,338.50	61.2	897,907,913.00	58.9
Mohave	43,313,020.00	1.4	9,077,894.00	.6
Navajo	39,414,195.50	1.3	22,082,719.50	1.4
Pima	581,168,875.50	18.8	306,527,464.00	20.1
Pinal	69,191,447.50	2.2	47,927,165.50	3.2
Santa Cruz	20,763,988.50	.7	19,276,224.00	1.3
Yavapai	46,443,607.50	1.5	28,264,757.00	1.9
Yuma	164,232,545.00	5.3	53,760,479.00	3.5
TOTAL	$3,093,640,931.50	100.0%	$1,524,296,176.50	100.0%

Source: Arizona State Tax Commission.

TABLE 22.6
Types of Retail Trade, 1967

	Type of Business	Number of Firms	Total Sales
1.	Lumber, Building Materials, Hardware, Farm Equipment Dealers	533	$ 111,797,000
2.	General Merchandise Group Stores	520	343,365,000
3.	Food Stores	1,762	577,673,000
4.	Automotive Dealers	888	485,683,000
5.	Gasoline Service Stations	2,175	232,550,000
6.	Apparel, Accessory Stores	752	106,621,000
7.	Furniture, Home Furnishings, Equipment Stores	790	107,606,000
8.	Eating, Drinking Places	3,088	204,378,000
9.	Drug Stores, Proprietary Stores	404	111,641,000
10.	Liquor Stores	357	29,486,000
11.	Antique Stores, Secondhand Stores	286	9,764,000
12.	Book, Stationery Stores	NA	NA
13.	Sporting Goods Stores, Bicycle Shops	189	12,937,000
14.	Farm, Garden Supply Stores, Including Feed Stores	NA	NA
15.	Jewelry Stores	251	17,442,000
16.	Fuel, Ice Dealers	59	6,717,000
17.	Other Stores	NA	NA
18.	Nonstore Retailers	745	34,208,000
	TOTALS	12,908	$2,391,868,000

NA = Not Available
Source: U.S. Department of Commerce, Bureau of the Census, *1967 Census of Business.*

TABLE 22.7
Types of Wholesale Trade, 1967

	Type of Business	Number of Firms	Total Sales
1.	Motor Vehicles, Automotive Equipment	302	$ 261,562,000
2.	Drugs, Chemicals, Allied Products	71	58,749,000
3.	Dry Goods, Apparel	24	17,007,000
4.	Groceries and Related Products	355	573,275,000
5.	Farm Products — Raw Materials	50	135,789,000
6.	Electrical Goods	160	170,974,000
7.	Hardware, Plumbing, Heating Equipment, Supplies	101	69,022,000
8.	Machinery, Equipment, Supplies	405	227,443,000
9.	Metals, Minerals (Except Petroleum Products, Scrap)	43	35,218,000
10.	Petroleum Bulk Stations, Terminals	234	201,090,000
11.	Scrap, Waste Materials	41	16,127,000
12.	Tobacco, Tobacco Products	11	19,998,000
13.	Beer, Wine, Distilled Alcoholic Beverages	52	97,723,000
14.	Paper, Paper Products (Except Wallpaper)	62	35,107,000
15.	Furniture, Home Furnishings	54	27,837,000
16.	Lumber, Construction Materials	108	70,599,000
17.	Amusement, Sporting Goods	36	16,959,000
18.	Books, Periodicals, Newspapers	18	8,052,000
19.	Farm Supplies	38	30,929,000
20.	Jewelry	11	2,199,000
21.	Gifts, Art Goods, Advertising Novelties, Specialties	13	849,000
22.	Other Products	54	30,933,000
	TOTALS	2,243	$2,107,441,000

Source: U.S. Department of Commerce, Bureau of the Census, *1967 Census of Business.*

James D. Forrester and
Fred L. Stubbs
Mining Engineers

23

MINING

THE ECONOMIC PROGRESS and development of Arizona have been phenomenal since the 1950s. Many of these advances can be attributed directly to the wealth of mineral resources that abound in the state and to the great mining enterprises which have been established to make the mineral deposits effective in the economy of Arizona and the United States.

In 1969 Arizona ranked eighth in the value of production of all minerals and rock materials. This was, in itself, an excellent position, but a fact of greater significance is that Arizona led all other states in the value of metals produced. That is, those states that outranked Arizona in the total value of their mineral production achieved their positions largely because of the production of mineral fuels such as coal, petroleum, and natural gas.

Arizona produces appreciable quantities of over thirty types of minerals and is especially famous for its tremendous tonnages of copper and other nonferrous metals. Among the states of the Union, including Alaska and Hawaii, Arizona ranked first during 1968 and 1969 in copper production, yielding over twice as much copper as its nearest competitor state, Utah. In 1969 it ranked third in production of molybdenum, second in silver, fourth in gold, seventh in lead, and fourteenth in zinc; in 1970 it continued second in production of silver. Arizona supplied over 51 percent of the total copper output of the United States in 1969, thus leading all other states, something it has done consistently since 1910.

In the period from 1860 through 1969, Arizona's mines produced about $14 billion of mineral wealth. Since 1874, when the first specific records were kept, the state has yielded more than 50 billion pounds of copper. This is a truly remarkable total which in the late 1960's was being added to at the rate of approximately one and one-half billion pounds a year. In Arizona mining, copper is king.

The copper production is supplemented by the values of many other mineral commodities. To secure these, the removal of tremendous quantities of mineral-bearing rocks is required. A mineral deposit in the ground has, as such, no value to man. It is only when a deposit is brought into production that real benefit is derived. This benefit is achieved by the building of a mining enterprise which, in every modern case requires the diligent application of economic analysis, capital investment, and labor. These activities have broadened the tangible value of the state's resources, and the mining industries of Arizona are magnificent developments, lending much to economic and cultural advancement.

Modern man has always been prone to explore first for the glittering metals of comparatively high unit value. Thus, the history of the exploitation of mineral resources of any region is that metallic mineral deposits are sought and worked before those of the nonmetallic (industrial mineral) type. The development of industrial or nonmetallic mineral bodies ordinarily awaits the settlement of a region and the growth of local industries. Since the coming of the white man to what is now Arizona, the situation has paralleled this common pattern. However, the mining pursued by the prehistoric inhabitants was mainly for nonmetallic commodities.

Aboriginal Period

The original Indians were agrarian peoples who engaged primarily in agriculture with little or no knowledge of, or apparent interest in, the use of metals, either for commercial purposes or for ornamentation. However, these early inhabitants learned, in the course of time, of the benefits of such resources as salt, coal, building stone and pottery clay, and, also, of the applicability of particular nonmetallic substances for making mauls, knives, spear points, pigments, and ornamental beads. There is clearcut archaeological evidence that mining enterprises, crude as judged by present standards but nonetheless effective and important to such prehistoric peoples, existed by A.D. 1000. The aboriginal mining period, therefore, is considered to extend from A.D. 1000 to about the middle of the sixteenth century.

John T. Hack has written of a coal mining industry which was well developed by the prehistoric Hopi Indians in the Jeddito Valley along the southern edge of Black Mesa, north of the present town of Holbrook, Arizona. He has noted that the early Hopi people apparently had discovered the use of coal as a means of securing heat at about the same time a similar discovery was made

by the early inhabitants of England. By the beginning of the thirteenth century, the Hopi were exploiting the Jeddito Valley deposits to a marked degree.

The main coal seam, which is comprised of rather "bony" (impure) coal ranging from lignite to sub-bituminous, is a flat-lying bed in rocks of Cretaceous age. It is covered by varying amounts of younger rocks. The ancient mining method which was used is very similar to that of modern strip-mining. It was a procedure of removing the overburden and excavating the exposed coal. The waste (overburden and "bone") was piled to the rear of the working area. The result was to leave a tract stripped of coal and overlying rock and stacked high with heaps of waste material. When the overburden was

Fig. 23.1   The open pit copper mine at Morenci exemplifies the use of large-scale production methods to work relatively low-grade ores.

Ray Manley

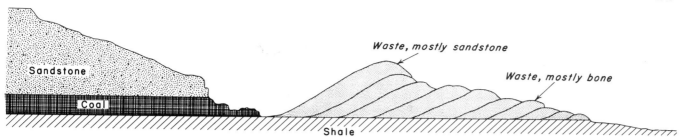

Fig. 23.2   Ideal section of a typical Hopi strip mine — after John T. Hack.

too thick to remove by the crude excavating and hauling devices, the mine area was usually abandoned. In at least one locality, however, there is evidence that underground mining by a primitive "longwall" method was pursued successfully.

The coal mines were operated through a period of about three hundred years, and the total amount of coal extracted probably exceeded one hundred thousand tons. This is an amazing amount considering the primitive tools and equipment then available. Coal was used for domestic heating and cooking and for the firing of pottery vessels, which was a companion industry.

The well-known archaeologist, Earl Morris, in his monograph "An Aboriginal Salt Mine at Camp Verde, Arizona" (Anthropological Papers of the American Museum of Natural History, Vol. XXX, Part III, New York, 1928) has described an aboriginal salt mine near Camp Verde in central Arizona. Here, in comparatively unconsolidated manner there are intercalated, essentially flat-lying layers of sands, gravels, clays, and various salt compounds. The early peoples worked these deposits, seeking supplies of sodium chloride, or common table salt.

In his study cited above, Morris described the methods of salt mining of the aborigines. When the natives found a promising salt stream they followed where it led, often unsystematically. They used no timbers or pillars in such salt mining. These early miners, working between A.D. 1200 and 1400, apparently developed several mine levels and at least one subsurface shaft, and they removed several thousand cubic yards of rock material. There can be no question that the ancient inhabitants of the region were engaged in a salt mining enterprise of important industrial nature. Indeed, it was probably the first of Arizona's mining industries.

The aborigines also mined turquoise for making jewelry and similar artifacts. Prehistoric turquoise mines have been reported on the east side of Canyon Creek just above its confluence with the Salt River, on Turquoise Mountain in Cochise County, in the Mineral Park area of Mohave County, and in other locations throughout the state.

It is evident that the early aboriginal people of Arizona, though following primarily an agricultural way of life, also carried on noteworthy mining industries as a part of their total existence. These prehistoric activities may be considered as harbingers of the great modern mining enterprises of Arizona.

Spanish Period

The Spanish period extends essentially from the middle of the sixteenth century to the time of the Gadsden Purchase in 1853, when the region of Arizona was opened to occupancy by citizens of the United States. It is distinct from the earlier period for several reasons, but chiefly because it marked the beginning of the white man's exploitation of Arizona's mineral resources.

Soon after the conquest of Mexico by Cortés, the Spanish explorers entered Arizona in quest of the gold, silver, and other mineral riches that were reputed to be fabulous in quantity and richness. Fray Marcos de Niza in 1539 led the first expedition. His glowing though false reports resulted in the expedition led by Francisco Vásquez de Coronado in 1540 in search of the legendary Seven Cities of Cibola. These expeditions were doomed to failure because the Indians had not developed metal commodities, and, as these substances were not important in their cultures, they had never accumulated them. Thus, there was no wealth of the precious metals which the Spanish conquistadors could plunder.

It was not until 1582, when Antonio de Espejo prospected near the headwaters of the Verde River, that actual mining of silver ore occurred. Although historical records do not indicate what quantities of ore were produced by Espejo's venture, it was an important occasion, if for no other reason than that it marked the beginning of metal mining in Arizona.

Juan de Oñate is reported to have found rich silver ore during an expedition in 1604 along the Santa Maria and Bill Williams rivers. However, it was not until 1705, when Father Eusebio Kino did some prospecting for silver near the present Mexican border, that further active mining took place. Frank P. Knight, in his *Mining in Arizona* (Department of Mineral Resources, State of Arizona, January, 1958) argues that the Planchas de Plata silver deposits near Nogales stimulated mining beginning about 1736. When the Spanish settled Tucson, they mined gold and silver, and it is reported that gold placer operations existed in 1774 at Quijotoa, which is located on the present Papago Indian Reservation, about sixty miles south of Casa Grande, Arizona.

According to G. M. Butler ("Arizona and Its Heritage," University of Arizona *Bulletin,* Vol. VII No. 3 [April 1, 1936]), it is impossible to estimate closely how much mineral wealth was removed while the Spaniards and Mexicans controlled the region of Arizona, but it is certain that there was appreciable mining before the Declaration of Independence by the United States. Butler writes: "There is a tradition that $60,000 worth of silver utensils once decorated the altar of San Xavier Mission and that this metal was mined in the Santa Rita Mountains. The padres at Tumacácori Mission certainly directed silver mining operations in those mountains, and the Spaniards are known also to have operated in the Arivaca district and in the Baboquívari, Patagonia, Tucson, and Catalina mountains. There is some evidence that they or the Mexicans mined as far north as the Sierrita Mountains north (sic) of Tucson."

After the Mexican Revolution of 1822, the Mexican military garrisons which protected the Spanish-Mexican prospectors in the Arizona region were withdrawn, and the area was subjected to increased depredations by Apaches and outlaws. Mining waned thereafter until about 1849, when other military forces concerned with the United States-Mexican Boundary Commission were established in the Territory.

American Prospector Period

Several essentially contemporaneous events occurred in the mid-1800s to contribute to the renewal of vigorous prospecting and to the development of mining activities. For example, the protection afforded by the establishment of new military posts in the area, the Gadsden Purchase of 1853, which opened the Territory to citizens of the United States, and the great gold rush to California that led many people into the region of Arizona all served to spur the development of mining and prospecting.

Frank P. Knight
Fig. 23.3 An early-day prospector pans gold in Arizona.

This period, which was characterized by the work of intrepid pioneers, extended from the mid-1800s to the turn of the twentieth century. These people were developers of the country, bent on wresting their fortunes from the ground by the vigor of their own labors. They were fortune seekers, it is true, but they were willing to devote much individual effort and to endure many hardships in their quest for mineral wealth. Except for the Civil War years, prospecting and mining activities continued unabated throughout the period. In fact, the influence of these enterprises showed in a really phenomenal growth.

Soon after the Gadsden Purchase, United States citizens came in increasing numbers to prospect for ore in Arizona. The large copper deposit at Ajo, known in 1969 as the New Cornelia Mine, was located, and the Arizona Mining Company — the first incorporated mining company in Arizona — was organized to work it.

The placer gold deposits along the lower Colorado River were important sources of the metal in the early period. The Gila City placers — some twenty miles east of Yuma — were discovered in 1858, and a series of rich placers was located along the Colorado north of Yuma between 1861 and 1864. At about the same time, gold placers were discovered on Lynx Creek and at Weaver and Rich Hill in Yavapai County. The rich Vulture Mine, which began gold mining operations in 1863, caused the settlement of nearby Wickenburg. In the Patagonia Mountains a large lead-silver deposit, which in later years was operated as the Mowry Mine, had been worked by Spaniards but was relocated by a group of American soldiers in 1858. It is claimed that this mine produced a considerable portion of the lead for bullets used by Confederate soldiers. Forty miles southwest of Tucson, the great Cerro Colorado Mine was begun in about 1855, and it had yielded $100,000 worth of silver by 1860.

With the outbreak of the Civil War and the withdrawal of federal troops from the Territory, the Apaches once more took over, and most of the mines were closed. During this period the few active mining camps were around Prescott, Wickenburg, and Mineral Park, and near Oatman in the Black Mountains, and north of Yuma. All were gold and silver mines except the Planet Copper Mine near the Bill Williams River.

The end of the Civil War and the re-establishment of military posts caused the renewal of prospecting activity with increased vigor, although the menace of Apache attacks continued until 1882. In the decade of the seventies, many of Arizona's famous copper deposits were located, including those at Globe, Bisbee, Morenci, and Jerome, as well as the Silver Bell and Twin Buttes ore bodies near Tucson.

Silver discoveries continued to be made, and in 1876 the silver deposits north of Globe, including those of the McMillan Mine, and the profitable Silver King north of Superior were found. In 1878 Ed Schieffelin discovered ore at Tombstone, and one year later the

Fig. 23.4 Arizona was the leading copper state shortly after 1900, when ore was extracted and processed in places like this.

bonanza silver deposit there was located. For several years silver production at Tombstone spread that city's fame around the world until the flooding of the mines made the extraction of ore prohibitively expensive.

With the completion of the transcontinental railroads, the exhaustion of the richer silver deposits, and the lowered price of silver, copper began to come into its own. By 1888 copper production in Arizona was worth over $5 million a year, or more than the value of all the other metals produced. Copper production gradually increased until, by 1910, it was worth $37.8 million. In that year, Arizona became the leading copper-producing state in the union, a position which it was still holding at the opening of the 70s.

Modern-Day Mining Period

The advent of the twentieth century marked another turn in the history of the mining industry of Arizona. By 1900 the importance of copper as a source of mineral wealth had become pronounced, and it was further advanced soon thereafter by at least two extremely salient factors. These were (1) the development of large-scale mining procedures which were adaptable to the exploita-tion of comparatively low-grade mineral deposits, and (2) the discovery and perfection of "flotation" as a process for the profitable beneficiation of sulphide-bearing ores. These factors, together with the growth which continued to prevail in the production of gold, silver, lead, zinc, and other metals in Arizona, and with the vigorous economic and scientific developments since 1900, have all contributed to Arizona's outstanding stature as a mineral-producing state.

As shown in Figure 23.5, much of the total value of mineral wealth supplied by Arizona since the turn of the century has been derived from copper. Although it has not been defined specifically in Figure 23.5, the production of molybdenum and uranium ores and petroleum and natural gas also has become particularly noteworthy in recent years.

It should be realized that the economic importance of nonmetallic minerals, as a whole, continues to increase each year as the population of Arizona expands — with the resultant local development of new industries. For example, the production of "common" sand and gravel in the late 1960s ranked high in value of all minerals annually secured in Arizona, averaging nearly 16 million tons valued at more than $17 million.

TABLE 23.1

Varieties and Values of Mineral Production in Arizona in 1969

Commodity	Quantity	Value	Percent of Total Value
Clays	120,000 tons	$ 394,000	0.05
Copper (metallic)	801,363 tons	761,840,000	88.66
Diatomite	725 tons	(Not available)	Less than 0.01
Gem stones	(Not available)	153,000	0.02
Gold	110,878 ounces	4,603,000	0.54
Gypsum	83,000 tons	424,000	0.05
Helium, grade A	56,300,000 cubic ft.	1,126,000	0.13
Iron Ore	18,000 long tons	136,000	0.02
Lead	217 tons	65,000	0.01
Lime	283,000 tons	5,074,000	0.59
Molybdenum	12,699,000 pounds	20,947,000	2.44
Natural gas	1,136,000,000 cubic ft.	199,000	0.02
Petroleum	2,433,000 barrels	7,056,000	0.82
Pumice	910,000 tons	814,000	0.09
Sand and gravel	16,481,000 tons	18,066,000	2.10
Silver	6,141,000 ounces	10,997,000	1.28
Stone	2,827,000 tons	5,812,000	0.68
Tungsten (concentrate)	1 ton	2,000	Less than 0.01
Zinc	9,039 tons	2,639,000	0.31
Undistributed [a]		18,956,000	2.21
Total		$859,303,000	

[a]In addition to the above specific items there are several mineral commodities which were produced in 1969 but for which quantities and/or values have not been cited. This has been done to avoid the disclosure of confidential data held by individual companies. Mineral substances of this type include: Asbestos, cement, coal, feldspar, mercury, mica, perlite, pyrites, uranium, vanadium, vermiculite, and zeolite.

TABLE 23.2

Major Copper Mines in Arizona in 1969 Ranked in Order of Copper Produced

Mine	Operated by	County	Type of Operation	Ore Mined (tons)	Copper Produced (tons)
Morenci	Phelps Dodge Corp.	Greenlee	Open Pit	19,271,000	136,773
San Manuel	Magma Copper Co.	Pinal	Underground	15,203,000	100,100
Ray	Kennecott Copper Corp.	Pinal	Open Pit	12,209,000	96,190
New Cornelia	Phelps Dodge Corp.	Pima	Open Pit	10,736,000	67,792
Pima	Pima Mining Co.	Pima	Open Pit	14,235,000	67,000
Inspiration	Inspiration Consol. Copper Corp.	Gila	Open Pit	8,855,000	51,757
Mission	American Smelting and Refining Co.	Pima	Open Pit	7,940,000	50,034
Lavender Pit	Phelps Dodge Corp.	Cochise	Open Pit	5,550,000	35,528
Copper Queen	Phelps Dodge Corp.	Cochise	Underground	783,000	29,555
Mineral Park	Duval Corp.	Mohave	Open Pit	6,034,000	28,721
Copper Cities	Miami Copper Co.	Gila	Open Pit	4,645,000	22,446
Esperanza	Duval Corp.	Pima	Open Pit	5,488,000	22,288
Silver Bell	American Smelting and Refining Co.	Pima	Open Pit	5,376,000	20,599
Bagdad	Bagdad Copper Corp.	Yavapai	Open Pit	2,030,000	17,624
Magma (Superior)	Magma Copper Co.	Pinal	Underground	422,000	18,217
Miami	Miami Copper Co.	Gila	Leaching	—	8,736

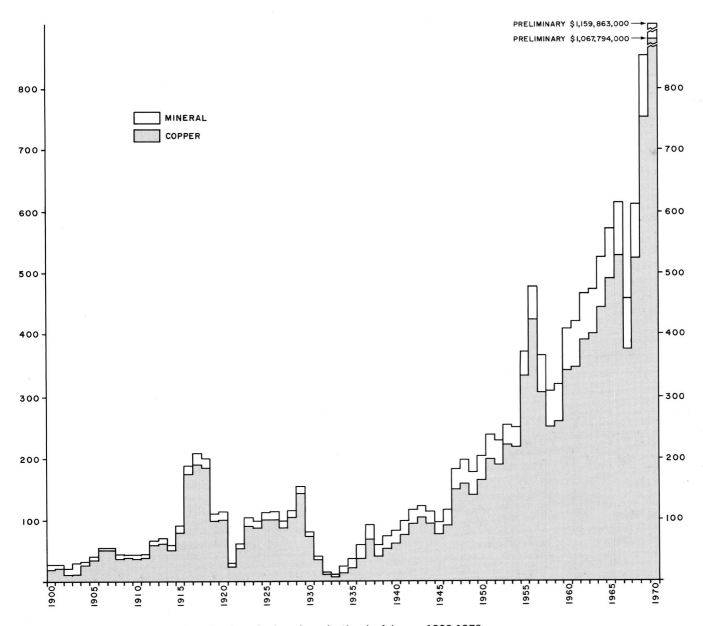

Fig. 23.5 Value of copper and total value of mineral production in Arizona, 1900-1970.

Table 23.1 presents the varieties and values of mineral production in Arizona for 1969. It demonstrates that of the total value of minerals produced, over 93 percent was furnished by metallic mineral substances, of which copper alone accounted for 88 percent. The nonmetallic mineral commodities, including asbestos, cement, clays, coal, gem stones, mica, feldspar, fluorspar, gypsum, lime, pumice, sand and gravel, and stone supplied approximately 5 percent of the total.

COPPER. Seven counties — Pima, Pinal, Cochise, Greenlee, Gila, Mohave, and Yavapai — annually have yielded about 99 percent of Arizona's copper output. Of these, the first three account for approximately 62 percent of the total, although the largest single copper mine in the state in the 1960s was situated in Greenlee County.

Table 23.2 shows the major copper mines operating in Arizona during 1969. It is evident that the majority of these modern mines are operated by open-pit mining procedures where comparatively low-grade ores are worked by large-scale production methods. These activities require much ingenuity and engineering skill and would not have been economically possible prior to the invention of large-scale excavating and hauling machinery, improved drilling and blasting techniques, and the development of flotation and other modern recovery methods. It is not to be inferred, of course, that all Arizona mineral occurrences are of low-grade character, but it is a fact that many of the great mining enterprises of the state have been established and maintained only by the application of outstanding engineering skills. This is true of the major underground mines as

Fig. 23.6   This Arizona mine, mill, and smelter encompass the outstanding techniques that have increased modern copper reserves.

well as of those mines being worked by open-cut methods, where in order to secure each ton of the ore-bearing material it is quite commonly necessary to remove also about two tons of nonproductive material and waste rock.

Because of discoveries of new deposits by scientific prospecting practices and the extension of other earlier-known ore bodies, together with the perfecting of improved mining and metallurgical methods, which tend to make low-grade mineral occurrences exploitable at a profit, the known copper reserves of Arizona in the late 1960s were at least twice as great as they were at the beginning of the twentieth century. This is remarkable considering the large amounts of copper that have been mined in the state since 1900.

It is noteworthy that in addition to the very important copper mining operations in the state, as cited in Table 23.2, several of the existing mines in 1969 were

TABLE 23.3
Production of Gold and Silver in Arizona During 1969

County	Mines Producing		Material Sold or Treated (Short Tons)	Gold (Lode and Placer)		Silver (Lode and Placer)	
	Lode	Placer		Troy Ounces	Value	Troy Ounces	Value
Cochise	5	—	6,372,138	31,948	$1,326,000	861,006	$1,542,000
Coconino	1	—	163	16	1,000	225	400
Gila	15	—	21,726,457	5,250	218,000	298,218	534,000
Graham	4	—	41,867	2	100	1,767	3,000
Greenlee	3	—	19,315,709	13,455	559,000	727,230	1,302,000
Maricopa	3	—	300	487	20,000	1,182	2,000
Mohave	9	1	6,288,024	251	10,000	535,015	958,000
Pima	11	—	43,697,924	29,835	1,238,000	2,451,502	4,390,000
Pinal	9	—	27,550,832	29,037	1,205,000	1,139,788	2,041,000
Santa Cruz	5	—	144	2	100	470	1,000
Yavapai	18	—	3,031,703	587	24,000	111,517	200,000
Yuma	7	—	324,644	8,000	300	13,072	23,000

being expanded and, also, new properties were in the process of development. Such activities will have a significant effect on the production of copper, and accessory metals, in future years. Examples of the expansion projects and the new developments include those being undertaken by Anaconda and Banner (Twin Buttes); Duval Sierrita (Sierrita); Magma (Superior and San Manuel Divisions); Kennecott (Ray Mines Division); Phelps Dodge (Morenci Branch).

GOLD AND SILVER. The position of Arizona as an important supplier of gold and silver has been maintained for many years. Since 1860, more than thirteen million ounces of gold valued at more than $360 million, and 390 million ounces of silver, valued at $316 million have been produced. The value of these commodities in 1969 was, respectively, $4,602,000 and $10,997,000. Value by counties is shown in Table 23.3.

In the early days a large proportion of these metals was obtained from mining operations developed primarily for the production of precious metals. This led to the establishment of several famous mines such as the Vulture near Wickenburg, the Tom Reed and United Eastern near Oatman, the Silver King near Superior, and the various mines established to work the bonanza silver deposits at Tombstone. In the late 1960s, however, about 88 percent of the gold and silver from Arizona was secured as a by-product of copper mining enterprises, about 10 percent was recovered in smelting lead-zinc ores and the balance was obtained from gold, gold-silver, silver and miscellaneous lode material. In 1969 the Morenci, New Cornelia, and Copper Queen branches of the Phelps Dodge Corporation and the Magma and San Manuel operations of the Magma Copper Company produced more than 86 percent of the gold. In the same year, 80 percent of the silver was produced by Phelps Dodge Corporation, American Smelting and Refining Company, Magma Copper Company, Duval Corporation and Shattuck-Denn Mining Corporation.

LEAD AND ZINC. Lead and zinc have played major roles over the years in the development of the mining industry of Arizona, but, of the various mineral commodities produced in the state, they seem to have been subject to more economic fluctuations than any other materials. This was especially true in the 1960s when cheap foreign production led to the dumping of these substances on the domestic market, to the detriment of local operations. From a peak of 104,226 tons of lead-zinc in 1949, the output declined to only 217 tons in 1969, and most of this came from less than six of the larger lead-zinc properties which were able to operate, it seems, only because of their income from copper, gold, and silver by-products. Lead output reached a thirty-five year low in 1969, and zinc declined 51 percent below the production level for 1965. The Iron King mine of the Shattuck-Denn Mining Corporation in Yavapai County was the principal producer. Other producers included the Glove mine in Santa Cruz County and the Old Dick and Copper Queen mines in Yavapai County.

Ray Manley

Fig. 23.7   Modern flotation is an aid to recovery of ore.

URANIUM AND VANADIUM. Although there was no uranium mining of consequence in Arizona prior to the demand for sources of material to yield atomic energy, the uranium industry was to become of such importance as to rank comparatively high in the state's mining economy. Production of uranium-bearing ores has been obtained primarily from sedimentary rock occurrences in Apache, Coconino, and Navajo counties. Thirty uranium mines in Apache, Coconino, Navajo and Yavapai counties were active during 1966. The largest of these, the Orphan Lode mine of Westec Corporation, which is located within the boundaries of Grand Canyon National Park, was closed at midyear when production exceeded the allocation established by the U. S. Atomic Energy Commission. Special legislation will allow Westec Corporation to continue operation of the twenty-acre claim until 1986, at which time title to the claim will pass to the National Park Service.

Uranium ores containing significant quantities of vanadium, principally from Apache County, were processed for recovery of vanadium. The quality recovered in 1969 was notably lower than in 1965.

MISCELLANEOUS METALS

Manganese. The United States Geological Survey estimates that about 200 million tons of low-grade manganese ore occur in Arizona. Utilization of this ore in the future is predicted since the United States is now largely dependent upon foreign sources. However, there was no reported production of manganese in Arizona for 1969. This seems to be because the production of manganese ore and concentrate, under a marketing program administered by the General Services Administration of the federal government, ended in 1959.

Mercury. Mercury production in Arizona has never been of major consequence and has shown a pronounced tendency to fluctuate in response to prices fixed by world marketing conditions. Several years of sustained high prices led to a 1966 production of 363 flasks produced by seven mines in the Mazatzal Mountains in Gila and Maricopa counties.

Molybdenum. The molybdenum produced in Arizona is secured as an important by-product material of several of the major copper mining enterprises. In 1969 the value of molybdenum was in third place among the various metalliferous commodities produced. Eight mines yielded concentrates containing 12.7 million pounds of molybdenum, valued at $20.9 million. This has accounted for about 10 percent of the total domestic production of the United States.

Iron. The possible potential of iron in Arizona has continued to attract interest. In 1969 a small amount of magnetite ore was produced and shipped from operations in Navajo and Yavapai counties.

The CF&I Steel Corporation signed a ten-year lease with the White Mountain Apache Tribal Council in 1964 and is mining a 36,000-acre iron deposit on the Fort Apache Indian Reservation.

Pyrite. Pyrite (FeS_2) which is used chiefly in the manufacture of sulphuric acid, was being obtained in the late 1960s as a by-product material in the concentrating of copper ores by the Magma Copper Company and the Kennecott Copper Corporation.

Tungsten. Tungsten has been obtained sporadically in Arizona, and in 1969 one ton of concentrate was produced.

SAND AND GRAVEL. The major rank of sand and gravel as mineral commodities often is not fully appreciated by people who are not broadly versed in mineral affairs. This is probably because of the comparatively low unit value of these substances and also because of the "common" character and wide distribution. As previously noted, these materials ranked third in value to copper as a source of mineral wealth in Arizona during 1969. County values are shown in Table 23.4. They are used chiefly in all types of building and highway construction, and their importance undoubtedly will continue to grow as Arizona becomes more densely populated.

TABLE 23.4

Production of Sand and Gravel in Arizona in 1969

County	Quantity (tons)	Value
Apache	(W)	(W)
Cochise	(W)	(W)
Coconino	1,904,000	1,735,000
Gila	112,000	257,000
Graham	76,000	90,000
Greenlee	117,000	142,000
Maricopa	6,785,000	7,858,000
Mohave	180,000	235,000
Navajo	503,000	602,000
Pima	2,570,000	3,014,000
Pinal	1,487,000	1,421,000
Santa Cruz	141,000	282,000
Yavapai	715,000	701,000
Yuma	1,650,000	1,457,000
Undistributed	130,000	272,000

(W) Withheld to avoid disclosing individual company confidential data; included with "Undistributed."

ASBESTOS. Asbestos as an industrial mineral commodity is of some consequence in Arizona. Eighteen properties, practically all in Gila County, were listed in 1969 as potential producers of chrysolite, which is a cross-fiber and slip-fiber type of asbestos. It is believed that this substance will continue to grow in economic importance in the state.

CEMENT. Cement is manufactured primarily from suitable limestone and shale rocks, and its production records show a continuing tendency to increase in Arizona as more and more construction projects are instituted in the state.

Arizona had two dry-process cement plants in 1969, namely the Arizona Portland Cement Company

Fig. 23.8   The Arizona Portland Cement plant at Rillito draws on the state's considerable resource of limestone.   *Ray Manley*

plant in Pima County, near Tucson, and the American Cement Corporation plant at Clarkdale, in Yavapai County.

Cement production for 1969 shows a general increase during the late 1960s. Most of this production is marketed within the state.

MISCELLANEOUS INDUSTRIAL MINERALS. The demand for various other industrial minerals has shown a continuing upward trend in Arizona since the 1930s. This trend is attributed primarily to the growth of population in the state and, as a result, many small operations have sprung up to satisfy the needs of local markets. In some cases, of course, the output of certain commodities has gone to satisfy out-of-state consumers.

Clays. Common clays used in pressed-brick and adobe-brick manufacture are produced in a number of plants. The total value and quantity of all clay in 1969, was, respectively, $121,394 and 89,000 tons. Bentonite, which is a special, very fine-grained variety of clay material, was obtained in considerable quantity at an open-pit operation of the Cheto Mine near Sanders, Arizona. Its chief use has been in foundries as a conditioner of molding sand and as an agent in oil refining and in oil-well drilling fluids.

Feldspar. Up to 1971 feldspar was mined by the International Minerals and Chemical Corporation in Mohave County. The crude material was ground at a mill in Kingman. It is used in glass, pottery, and enamelware manufacturing, and as a fluxing agent in metallurgical processes. A considerable part of the feldspar was shipped to consumers in Arkansas, California, Colorado, Louisiana, Ohio, Texas, Canada, and Mexico.

Gemstones. Gemstones have been secured in Arizona for many years and, though the production has never been great, it has been persistent. Most of these substances are obtained by surface gleaning rather than actual mining operations. During 1969 the collecting activities were centered in Yavapai, Gila, and Navajo counties, yielding a total of over $153,000 worth of materials. Copper specimens, including gem-quality chrysocolla, which is a copper silicate mineral, were the most important in terms of value although appreciable quantities of turquoise, agate, and petrified wood were obtained also.

Gypsum. Gypsum, a calcium sulphate mineral, is used chiefly in the manufacture of plaster wallboard and lath, as a retarder in cement, and for agricultural purposes. Its production in Arizona has continually increased as industrial activities have grown in the state. There are three mines in Pinal County and one in Yavapai County.

Lime and Stone. Several limestone quarries which are operated to secure lime used in treatment of copper ores and other industrial processes have become established in Arizona. During 1966 quarries and limekilns were worked by the Paul Lime Plant, Hoopes and Company, Phelps Dodge Corporation, Magma Copper Corporation, and United States Lime Products Division. These operations were chiefly in Cochise, Gila, Greenlee, Pinal, and Yavapai counties.

In addition to limestone deposits exploited as a source of cement and lime, there have been a number of quarries operated in Arizona to supply industrial rocks used in construction projects of various kinds. These include operations yielding granite, basalt and related volcanic rocks, marble, sandstone, and other stone substances. For example, a considerable amount of flagstone has been and will be used for residential construction and related enterprises. In 1969 production was chiefly from Pima, Cochise, and Yavapai counties.

Mica. Scrap variety mica used chiefly for roofing and paint manufacture has been obtained in Cochise and Maricopa counties. Deposits at Buckeye were mined in 1969.

Perlite. Perlite, a rock substance used chiefly as a lightweight aggregate and insulating medium, has been produced mainly from Pinal County. Production in 1969 was somewhat more than that for previous years.

Pumice. The securing of material classified as pumice is of considerable importance in the current mineral-industry economy of Arizona. It is of volcanic origin and consists primarily of cinder rock, although some tufa is used also. The output in tons of cinder rock (scoria) and its value have decreased gradually in the last few years due to a reduction in the quantity of low-value material (used for railroad ballast) produced, and a growing demand for higher quality rock used in manufacturing light-weight building blocks. The Winona scoria deposit near Flagstaff was worked as surface quarries by the Atchison, Topeka and Santa Fe Railway Company, Harenberg Block Company, Inc., and Superlite Builders Supply Company. This made Coconino County the principal producing area in the state. San Xavier Rock Company obtained its scoria for building block from a deposit east of Douglas; the Gila Valley Cinder Company from claims near Safford; and Arizona Precast Concrete Company from properties near Mesa.

Mineral Fuels. Although some of the first mining for coal in Arizona was that done by the prehistoric Hopi Indians, the production of the mineral fuels, such as coal, petroleum, and natural gas has only recently become of major importance in the state.

In 1966 the Peabody Coal Company contracted with the Navajo Tribal Council to strip-mine 150 million tons of coal from the Black Mesa area of the Hopi and Navajo Indian reservations. The contract requires the Peabody Company to supply a minimum of 17 million tons of coal over a thirty-five-year period to the 1.5-megawatt powerplant being built on the Colorado River by Southern California Edison Company.

Five petroleum fields in Apache County yielded 2,433,000 barrels of crude petroleum in 1969. This was a 2 million plus increase over 1965.

Apache County also produced 1.6 billion cubic feet of natural gas in 1966. New pipeline and compressor facilities were being constructed in 1969 to expand the markets for this fuel.

TABLE 23.5

Mineral Production in Arizona, by Counties, in 1969

County	Value	Chief Mineral Commodities in Order of Value
Apache	$ 12,190,000	Petroleum, helium, clays, natural gas, sand and gravel, pumice, stone, vanadium, uranium.
Cochise	65,157,000	Copper, lime, silver, stone, gold, sand and gravel, lead, zinc.
Coconino	3,452,000	Sand and gravel, pumice, uranium, stone, copper, gold, silver.
Gila	99,637,000	Copper, lime, molybdenum, asbestos, stone, silver, sand and gravel, gold, clays.
Graham	(Not available)	Sand and gravel, lead, zinc, copper, zeolite, pumice, silver, gold.
Greenlee	134,492,000	Copper, lime, silver, stone, gold, sand and gravel.
Maricopa	8,403,000	Sand and gravel, lime, stone, mercury, clays, gold, mica, silver, copper, lead, vermiculite.
Mohave	35,326,000	Copper, molybdenum, silver, sand and gravel, stone, zinc, feldspar, gold, lead, tungsten concentrates.
Navajo	(Not available)	Sand and gravel, iron ore, stone, pumice.
Pima	251,563,000	Copper, cement, molybdenum, silver, sand and gravel, gold, stone, zinc, clays, lead, mica.
Pinal	212,540,000	Copper, molybdenum, silver, sand and gravel, gold, perlite, lime, gypsum, stone, diatomite, pyrites, pumice.
Santa Cruz	(Not available)	Sand and gravel, copper, lead, tungsten concentrates, silver, stone, gold, zinc.
Yavapai	35,503,000	Copper, cement, zinc, stone, sand and gravel, molybdenum, lime, silver, gypsum, clays, gold, lead, iron ore, pumice, tungsten concentrates.
Yuma	(Not available)	Sand and gravel, copper, stone, silver, lead, gold, zinc, gypsum.
Undistributed	4,230,000	
TOTAL	$859,303,000	

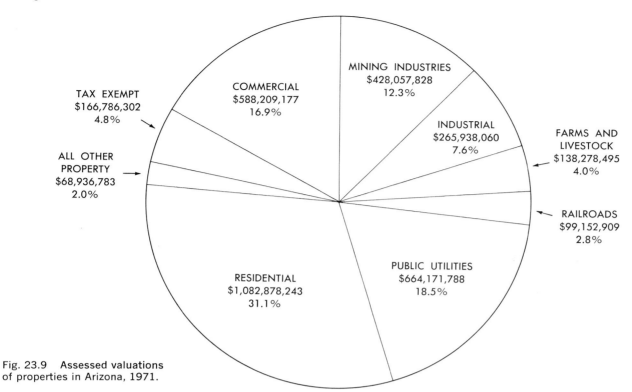

Fig. 23.9   Assessed valuations
of properties in Arizona, 1971.

Helium. The largest known reserve of helium in the free world in 1969 was in Arizona. Ownership of helium properties and production of this gas have been limited to the federal government until recently. However, a bill passed by Congress in the summer of 1960 authorizes private ownership of helium properties and the purchase of this noncombustible gas from private firms by the government.

Grade A Helium (99.995 percent purity) was produced in 1969, from the Navajo plant of Arizona Helium Co. Approximately 56.3 million cubic feet of helium valued at about $1.1 million was recovered from three wells in the East Navajo Springs field, Apache County.

Summary

The values of minerals produced in the respective counties of Arizona during 1966, as compiled by the United States Bureau of Mines, are given in Table 23.5.

The diversity and quantity of mineral materials which have been and are being produced and treated in Arizona contribute to the employment of many people. As indicated in Table 23.5, every county benefits from the exploitation of these commodities, and conservative estimates indicate that at the beginning of 1969 over 18,800 Arizonans worked in the mining and processing of mineral-bearing deposits. The total annual payroll during 1966 was almost $147.5 million and so-called "fringe" benefits added another $15.5 million to the overall compensations paid to employees. In addition, the mining companies experienced a net cost of

$4,352,250 in operating hospital and recreation facilities for the benefit of employees and other residents of the mining communities. If a favorable economic climate can be maintained, it is entirely probable that these figures of wages and other forms of compensation may be markedly expanded in the future. This is because several existing major mining enterprises have plans for expansion of current operations and, also, new metal and industrial mineral deposits will be discovered, developed, and brought into production. In addition to the direct employment of many people, the mining industries contribute to the support of allied service and manufacturing industries. For example, the annual expenditures of Arizona mining companies for supplies and power presently are estimated to be approximately $100 million. The assessed net valuation of all mining properties in Arizona amounted to $343,554,901 in 1967. This is essentially 14.6 percent of the total assessed valuation of property in Arizona. Its relation to the whole and also to the assessments of certain other classes of property is shown above in Figure 23.9.

According to information furnished by C. J. Hansen of the Arizona Mining Association, the taxes paid by the mining industries of Arizona in 1966 were essentially as follows:

Property taxes	$16,360,800
Tax on metal value (severance tax) . . .	8,107,800
Sales and use taxes on purchases	2,275,700
Vehicle taxes	78,500
State income taxes	4,500,000
Total	$31,322,800

TABLE 23.6

Major Sources of Arizona Income

Year		Tourism	Agriculture	Mining	Manufacturing
1960	. . . . . .	290,000,000	439,570,000	$415,512,000	$ 810,000,000
1961	. . . . . .	320,000,000	463,641,000	425,995,000	870,000,000
1962	. . . . . .	350,000,000	508,317,000	474,131,000	980,000,000
1963	. . . . . .	375,000,000	537,919,000	481,115,000	1,070,000,000
1964	. . . . . .	400,000,000	460,979,000	534,364,000	1,130,000,000
1965	. . . . . .	420,000,000	505,709,000	580,092,000	1,255,000,000
1966	. . . . . .	450,000,000	500,949,000	622,079,000	1,500,000,000
1967	. . . . . .	480,000,000	533,030,000	465,255,000	1,610,000,000
1968	. . . . . .	500,000,000	570,386,000	617,549,000	1,820,000,000
1969	. . . . . .	530,000,000	662,004,000	859,475,000	2,010,000,000

The Arizona Department of Mineral Resources estimates that 50 percent of the total value of the six principal metals (copper, gold, silver, lead, zinc, and molybdenum), which have been produced in the state up to the end of 1966, has been expended in Arizona for wages, supplies, and state, county, city, and school taxes. The balance has gone for out-of-state purchases, federal taxes, refining, marketing, and as dividends to investors, many of whom are citizens of Arizona.

It is evident that much revenue accrues annually to Arizona and to many of its individual residents through the operations of mining enterprises and, therefore, these activities have significant and profound effects on the state's economic development. The data of Table 23.6 have been adapted from information issued by the Valley National Bank of Arizona (1970); they depict the comparative relations of major sources of income in Arizona during the period of 1960 through 1969. They do not directly reflect, of course, such supplementary items as taxes and wages.

Large permanent investments of plants and equipment have been, and are being, made by the mineral industries to insure economical and efficient production of the state's inorganic resources. Mining operations create new wealth, and collectively it is certain that they constitute a very important segment indeed of Arizona's growing economy.

Jimmye S. Hillman
Agricultural Economist

24

FARMING AND RANCHING

THE COMBINED VALUE of output from crops and livestock was second only to manufacturing in the economy of Arizona as the 1970s began. In 1967, including payments from the federal government, the gross value totaled $600 million. In general, the number of Arizonans engaged in agricultural pursuits has declined since World War II because of urbanization, increased agricultural efficiency, and the rise of nonagricultural employment opportunities. Although the size of the farm as an economic unit has increased greatly, the expansion of the agricultural population is limited by the fact that only about 15 percent of the land of Arizona is privately owned.

Field Crops

Cotton and other field crops were the main source of Arizona's agricultural income in the beginning of the seventies, even though they were produced on less than two percent of the total area. Over 90 percent of Arizona's 1,222,000 acres of field crops in 1967 were grown in the southern counties of Maricopa, Pinal, Yuma, Cochise, Pima, and Graham. The remaining field-crop acreage were in the mountain valleys and floodplains of the northern counties. With the exception of a small acreage where dry farming was practiced in northern Arizona, field crops were being grown only in those areas where irrigation water was available.

Field-crop production in Arizona has been characterized by large, highly mechanized, irrigated farms which are operated by progressive farmers. High yields from soils rich in native fertility and a climate with long growing seasons compensate for the high production costs associated with irrigation and high-value land. Although irrigation water is costly, its use provides optimum moisture for crops throughout the growing season, eliminating the drouth hazard so common in areas where crop production is directly dependent upon rainfall. The wide variety of crops grown, and the practice of double cropping in the lower valleys where winter and summer crops are grown on the same land, are also characteristic of the desert agriculture of Arizona.

In addition to keeping abreast of the most recent improvements in the traditional cultural practices of planting, cultivating, and harvesting his crops, the Arizona farmer has found it necessary to develop new skills and methods of crop production unknown two or three decades earlier. He now must know when and how to control harmful insects with an ever-increasing array of newly developed insecticides. He has long known that the fertility of his soil is not an unlimited resource and that he must replenish the supply of certain nutrients, especially nitrogen and phosphorus, through the application of fertilizers. He has found that certain weeds can more effectively be controlled through the use of herbicides than by machine cultivation and hand-hoeing. He has lined his canals and ditches with cement and re-leveled his land to help prevent loss of costly water and to irrigate his crops more effectively. The increase in labor costs has been met by using machines to perform many of these tasks.

COTTON. Cotton by the late sixties was the major crop produced in Arizona. The lower elevations of the southern part of the state are ideally suited to this crop. Some cotton was grown by the American Indians long before the white settlers arrived. Since 1900, the crop has changed from a curiosity to the most important source of Arizona's agricultural income. From a few thousand acres in 1910, the harvested acreage increased to nearly 300,000 acres in 1969; however, this was more than 350,000 acres below the peak production in 1953 before the federal acreage control program went into effect. Lint yields of Upland cotton were averaging 1,000 pounds per acre and yields of 1,500 were common. In

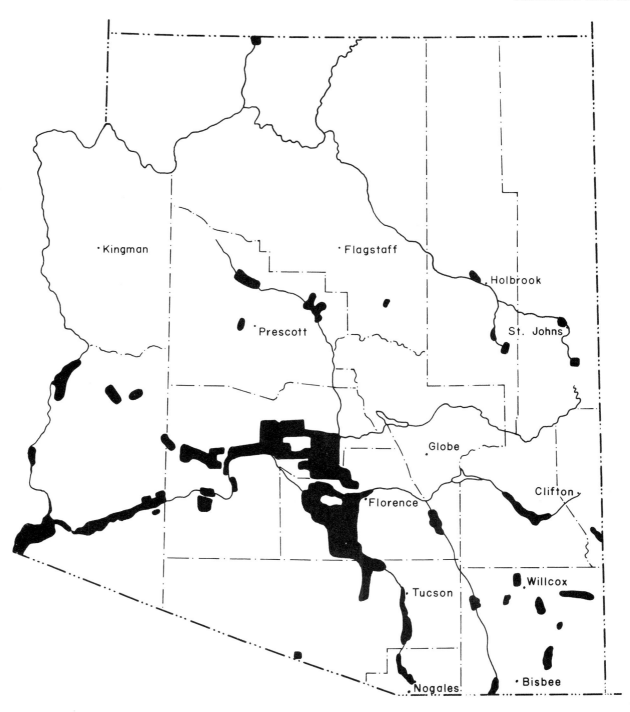

Fig. 24.1   The irrigated croplands of Arizona.

most years Arizona has led the nation in cotton-lint yields per acre. In addition to its reputation for high yields, Arizona has become well known for high quality cotton. Release of improved varieties by University of Arizona plant breeders, together with proper fertilization, pest control, irrigation, other cultural practices, and almost complete mechanization has contributed to these achievements.

Although the total acreage of American-Egyptian long-staple cotton grown in Arizona is not large — about 30,000 acres annually — the state in 1969 was producing half of the long-staple cotton grown in the United States. With better production practices and a new superior variety, long-staple lint yields have climbed from a little over half a bale per acre in the 1940s to over a bale per acre in 1969. New varieties of Pima cotton, Pima S-3 and Pima S-4, developed by cooperative work of the University of Arizona and the U.S. Department of Agriculture, are replacing the earlier released Pima S-1 and Pima S-2 long-staple varieties. It was the variety Pima

Salt River Project

Fig. 24.2   Irrigation is the key to successful farming of field crops in central Arizona and most other parts of the state.

S-1 that paved the way for a revival of long-staple cotton production in Arizona and the Southwest. The Supima Corporation, an organization of growers and processors of Pima varieties, has promoted the use of long-staple lint for the production of fine fabrics. It has also encouraged consumer buying.

Cotton has become the financial yardstick by which other field crops are judged, for there has been a greater potential for higher profits from this crop than from other major field crops. Since federal programs reduced cotton acreages, farmers have searched for a crop as profitable to grow on the acres formerly planted to cot-

Fig. 24.3   Harvesting cotton is a mechanized operation on high cost, high yield farms in central and southern Arizona.

ton. When cotton cannot be grown, field crops are produced primarily for livestock feed. Alfalfa, barley, and sorghum are the main field crops used for animal feeds. The annual planting of each crop in the late sixties was about 200,000 acres.

ALFALFA AND GRAINS. Alfalfa has been the most important forage since territorial days. Alfalfa is grazed and cut for hay or wafers. Some is used for winter sheep pasture and a small acreage for the production of green-chopped feed. Most hay has been fed locally, although some has been shipped to adjacent states. A portion of the crop has been dehydrated. In Yuma and Maricopa counties, six to eight cuttings have been common and yields have exceeded ten tons of hay per acre annually. The invasion of Arizona by a new insect, the spotted alfalfa aphid, eliminated the old standard varieties such as Hairy Peruvian and Chilean. The principal varieties grown in 1970 in lower elevation counties were the aphid-tolerant Mesa-Sirsa and Moapa and several commercial varieties. In the northern counties or at higher elevations, winter-hardy varieties such as Lahonton, Washoe and Ranger were being grown.

Barley was the principal small grain planted in Arizona during the 1960s. Spring varieties such as Arivat, Arimar, and California Mariout have been grown as a winter crop in the southern counties. The newly released hybrid barley, Hembar, was expected to be widely used in central Arizona. Early fall plantings are frequently used as winter pasture for sheep and cattle. Barley may be grazed once or twice and then allowed to mature grain. Barley grain yields usually averaged over a ton and a half per acre for the whole state, with good fields producing over two tons. Arizona's barley yields per acre thus ranked first or second in the nation during the sixties.

Tom Parks

Fig. 24.4   Land is prepared for crops by large-scale modern equipment, as in this disking near Sulphur Springs Valley.

Sorghum, when planted in June, often has been alternated with winter plantings of barley in a double-cropping program. Ratooning of sorghum, or growing two crops from one seeding, has become popular. Sorghum can be harvested for grain or silage, or green-chopped. Yields of over 8,000 pounds of grain, or 60,000 pounds of silage per acre have been common. The highest yields of grain sorghum usually have been obtained in Cochise County, where the record yield has exceeded six tons per acre. Sorghum production in the 1960s was greatest in Maricopa, Pinal, and Cochise counties. The open-pollinated varieties have been generally replaced by hybrid sorghums which produce higher yields. Arizona's sorghum yields were the highest in the nation in 1969, which is evidence that this crop is well adapted to the warm climate.

Irrigated perennial pastures are also important, especially when used in connection with a ranching operation, or for small paddocks.

Limited acreages of other crops also have been grown for livestock food. A small acreage of oats, grown as a winter crop, have been used for pasturing. Gaines wheat fits the higher and the Rockefeller wheats fit the lower elevations especially well. These high-yielding wheats have been used for livestock feed in Arizona. Corn is planted in the spring for silage or grain. Sudan grass is grown for summer pasture. Bermuda grass pastures, which have become popular, are grazed during most of the year at lower elevations where growth continues because of warm temperatures.

For many years the production of planting seed for such crops as alfalfa, Bermuda grass, and sorghum has been an important agricultural industry in Arizona. Favorable growing conditions, including a minimum of damaging rains as the seed crop is matured and harvested, facilitate production of high-quality seed. Alfalfa seed production decreased during the 1960s due to lack of pollinating insects and increases in harmful insects caused by changing land use. Common Bermuda grass seed is important in Yuma County where more than 90 percent of the nation's crop was grown in the 1960s. Limited amounts of seed of several other perennial grasses are produced for range reseeding. Until the development of hybrid sorghums, large quantities of seed of open-pollinated sorghum were produced in Arizona. Production of hybrid sorghum seed is possible from summer plantings at higher elevations and at lower elevations if seed is matured in the spring or fall. Most of the pearl millet seed used in the Southeast is grown in Arizona. About one-half of the nation's sugar beet seed in 1969 was being produced in the Salt River Valley. All seed was of the monogerm type and used for establishing stands in the cooler parts of the sugar beet growing areas of the United States. Seed wheat for the plant breeders in many states has been grown in winter plantings in Yuma County.

Production of oilseed crops, other than cotton, has varied with their price fluctuations. Flax increased after

World War II, but decreased to a few hundred acres when the price dropped. Castor beans are adapted to Arizona but the acreage remained low in the sixties because of low prices, disease problems, and lack of high-yielding varieties suitable for mechanical harvest. Soybeans enjoyed brief popularity until it was discovered that early frosts caused severe shattering losses; they have continued to be grown on a limited acreage. The production of safflower in southern Arizona has increased since the release of Gila, a variety resistant to phytophthora root rot, a common disease in the irrigated soils of the state.

Most growers practice some type of crop rotation. Alfalfa, cotton, sorghum, small grains, and other crops may be included. Prices, irrigation costs, soil conditions, federal controls, and other interests of the grower determine which crops are used in a rotation. Fallow periods are included to control weeds and other pests. Green manure crops, such as sesbania, papago peas, and guar are plowed under to improve the soil.

Field crop production in northern Arizona has been primarily for livestock feed, and restricted to a few small irrigated areas. Dryland farming had decreased to a few thousand acres by 1969, with corn and wheat being the principal crops.

By 1970, predictions were that yields of all field crops in Arizona would increase as growers turned to new varieties and utilized more effective cultural practices. However, crop production acreage was expected to be limited by water supplies. As cities expand into rural areas, farming operations will have to move. Unless new sources of water are found, the acreage of field crops cannot be expected to expand economically. Production of the less profitable crops will decrease. Cotton production may have to be concentrated on the remaining areas. Urban expansion and water costs will force farmers to be highly selective of the crops which they grow, although the climate is adapted for growing many types of field crops.

A new sugar factory was built by Spreckels Sugar Company near Chandler, Arizona and began processing sugar beets in 1967. Arizona farmers harvested 11,400 acres of beets for sugar in 1967. Of this acreage, 9,100 acres were grown in Maricopa and Pinal counties and approximately 2,300 acres in Graham, Greenlee, and Cochise counties. Some sugar beets that were grown in an adjoining county in New Mexico were also shipped to the new factory for processing.

In central Arizona, sugar beets are planted in the fall and harvested in May, June, and July. An average acre in 1967 produced 16.6 tons of sugar beets with 14.9 percent sugar. Based on an estimated net selling price of $8.50 per hundredweight for sugar, central Arizona farmers received an average gross income of $235 per acre from their beets, including government payments and returns from beet tops.

In the higher elevation areas of southeastern Arizona, beets are planted in the spring and harvested in November and December. Those areas produced an average of 14.0 tons per acre of beets containing 13.9 percent sugar, returning a gross income of $185 per acre in 1967.

Higher yields and income per acre from sugar beets probably can be expected over the long run as farmers gain more experience in growing this new crop.

Horticulture

Horticulture includes breeding, selection, growing, protection, harvesting, processing, distribution, and selling of fruits, vegetables, flowers, and landscape materials. Arizona has a wealth of horticultural crops which includes lettuce, melons, carrots, potatoes, pecans, peaches, dates, and roses. Associated with the rapid urbanization developments of the Southwest, there are expanded landscaping needs for turf, trees, shrubs, and flowers. The importance of landscaping for better Arizona living is being increasingly recognized.

The diversified nature of the state's horticulture is associated with the different climatic conditions of the geographic areas. The subtropical climate of southern Arizona has been attracting a very important tourist business, resulting in rapidly increasing numbers of year-round residents.

Fruit-Growing Industry

The value of products from the Arizona citrus industry has amounted to more than $20 million annually. Citrus grown in Arizona includes Washington Navel oranges, Valencia oranges, Marsh grapefruit, and Eureka and Lisbon lemons.

Navel oranges are grown chiefly in the Salt River Valley, where appropriate climatic conditions favor this high-quality citrus fruit for fresh market purposes. The successful fruit production of the variety has been related to applied research findings of adequate nitrogen fertilizers and appropriate irrigation. Navel oranges are harvested and marketed during November and December for shipment throughout the United States.

The increased planting of Valencia oranges is the result of favorable markets for the fresh fruit during the spring season. Recent developments in orchard protection of Valencia oranges from low temperatures have encouraged expanded plantings. The appropriate areas for Valencia oranges are in the warmer localities in the Salt River Valley, Wellton area, and on the Yuma Mesa. Wind machines have been used very effectively, when coupled with good orchard management, in winter cold protection of the young plantings and the bearing orchards. The Arizona Valencia oranges are harvested and marketed during March, April, and May before the California Valencias are available on the markets.

The lemon-growing industry of Arizona has expanded in the Yuma area, especially in the warmer areas of the Yuma Mesa. Earlier-bearing acreages of

Fig. 24.5   Yuma citrus orchard with propeller device for the prevention of damage from frost.

lemons in the Salt River Valley consist largely of the Eureka variety. During the late sixties, the Lisbon lemon was very popular for plantings in the Yuma area. This variety seems to have foliage and tree characteristics well adapted to the area, with high fruit yields. In 1969 it was anticipated that development of frozen concentrated lemon juice might have an application in the Yuma area as the acreage would come into heavy fruit bearing. The advantages of lemons grown in the Yuma area have included high production with harvesting at one time, resulting in lower harvest costs.

The Marsh grapefruit grown in Arizona has proved popular in various markets of the United States. The existing acreages of grapefruit have been supplying good quality fruit for the fresh markets from October to June. A major portion of the grapefruit have been harvested in the spring months when the quality of the fruit is best.

Other citrus varieties showing promise in Arizona in the 1960s were the Hamlin orange, Algerian tangerine, Minneola and Orlando tangelos, and Kinnow mandarin. The commercial plantings of citrus in Arizona during 1969 were made by the use of virus-indexed budwood on appropriate rootstocks.

During the late sixties, there was increasing interest in fresh table grape plantings, especially in the Salt River Valley and the Dateland area of Yuma County. The increased grape plantings in the Salt River Valley were made up largely of the Thompson Seedless and Cardinal varieties. Newest commercial table grape variety being planted in Arizona in 1969 was the Exotic, a dark blue grape which ripens soon after the Thompson Seedless. Extending the table grape harvesting season by appropriate new varieties has been important in this expanding horticultural industry.

Since the turn of the century, 150 date varieties have been tested in Arizona, both for fruit quality and local adaptability. Due to lower atmospheric moisture conditions and more heat for fruit development, the Yuma area has proven better adapted to commercial date growing than the Salt River Valley. Dates, however, became of decreasing economic importance in the sixties.

The most promising variety proved in Arizona as of the late sixties was the Medjool. Its fruit size is large, with excellent flavor and flesh consistency. The bright amber color, coupled with the attractive shape of the fruit, appeals to consumers. The variety was introduced into the United States from Morocco. Other leading commercial date varieties grown in Arizona have been Khadrawy, Zahidi, and Halawi.

Commercially, peaches have been grown successfully in southeastern Arizona at elevations of 3,500 feet and above. By using early and late maturing varieties, the harvest period was extended from late June until early September at these higher elevations. The peach industry is based upon the Elberta and other Elberta strains to extend the harvesting seasons. In the Salt River Valley, recent commercial ventures included establishment of peach orchards of newly developed varieties having low winter chilling requirements.

Apples in Arizona are successfully grown in mountains and mountain canyons in rather restricted areas above 4,500 feet. In these areas, red strains of Delicious, Rome Beauty, and Winesap, together with Golden Delicious, comprised the leading varieties in 1969.

Vegetable Growing

The vegetable industry of Arizona is important, the value of vegetable production varying between $75 and $90 million annually. Total vegetable acreage in 1969 was approximately 100,000 acres.

Lettuce has accounted for more than half the Arizona vegetable industry in the late 1960s. The specialized areas of Arizona for lettuce growing have been the Salt River Valley, where the major portion of the crop was grown, Yuma, Aguila, and Willcox. The Salt River Valley, approximately 1,100 feet elevation, has two principal harvesting seasons, fall and spring. The Yuma lettuce, grown at an elevation of 100 feet, is harvested during the winter. Aguila, at an elevation of 2,300 feet, has two harvesting seasons, early spring and fall. In the Willcox area, at approximately 4,000 feet, fall lettuce is harvested in September and October, and the spring crop in June.

There was a revolution in the lettuce industry during the 1950s and early sixties when Great Lakes varieties replaced the Imperial types. With this change in varieties came the vacuum-cooling development and the use of fiberboard cartons to replace wooden crates. These technological changes — especially the mobility resulting from the cooling equipment — made it possible to grow lettuce in various localized areas of Arizona.

Through horticultural research, Arizona lettuce yields had increased 150 percent since the mid-twenties when the lettuce industry was threatened by blight. During the late 1960s a low-mosaic lettuce seed was developed, resulting in a better quality of lettuce.

Annual value of Arizona melons in the late 1960s was approximately $15 million. Cantaloupe production was increasing, especially in the Yuma area, due to decreasing production in the Imperial Valley of California. The Yuma area in 1969 was the leading cantaloupe-producing area for the Southwest. The popular variety was the Powdery Mildew Resistant strain, No. 45, developed by the United States Department of Agriculture. The superior cantaloupe-growing conditions in the Yuma area are related to the high light and heat intensity and availability of water from the Colorado River for irrigation.

Arizona Photographic Associates

Fig. 24.6   Lettuce, Arizona's most important horticultural commodity, accounts for over half of the state's vegetable industry.

Potatoes have been grown chiefly in the lower elevations of Maricopa County and harvested and shipped as early potatoes during June and July. The annual value of Arizona's potato crop in the 1960s was nearly $8 million.

Carrot acreage has been localized in two principal districts, the Salt River Valley and the Yuma area. An important potential carrot-producing area was recognized as the lower Gila Valley, northeast of Yuma. Carrot harvesting begins in November. Most of the Yuma area shipments have been made from January through April. The Phoenix area has followed with heavy shipments in May and early June.

The commercial carrot variety is the large-type Imperator. The deep orange color of Arizona carrots is indicative of high vitamin A content. The handling of carrots during the late sixties has changed markedly due to prepackaging. Topped carrots were frequently shipped in mesh bags and then packed in film packages at terminal markets.

Thirty different kinds of fresh vegetables were being commercially grown and shipped from Arizona in 1969. Arizona's vegetable industry has shown the further diversification potential of processing through freezing and canning. Through appropriate research and its application, the development of a vegetable-processing industry can be expected to contribute to Arizona's expanding economy. The rapidly increasing population of the West has obviously been an important factor in Arizona's increasing vegetable industry.

Fig. 24.7 Onions are one of Arizona's 30 commercial vegetable crops.

Landscaping

Home beautification and park developments emphasize the increasing importance of horticulture all over the country. More than 80 percent of Arizona's population lived in urban areas in 1969, and the percentage was increasing. This has meant increasing interest in home landscaping, recreational parks, improved schoolground landscaping, and other turf landscape areas for urban use.

Groups of plant materials important in the Arizona landscape picture include lawns, basic for home landscaping; palms for bold tropical effects; citrus trees as evergreens with fruit, for the patio; shade trees, both evergreen and deciduous, for fruit and shade; shrubs for flowering, fruit, color, and tropical effects; roses for all home gardens; vines and ground covers for texture and color; flowering bedding plants, bulbs and herbaceous perennials for all seasons; and cacti and succulents for desert effects.

The $100 million annual urban horticultural industry in Arizona has been expanding rapidly with increased urbanization. The landscape attractiveness of the state has been recognized as important, with increased attention to landscaping of homes, parks and parkways, school grounds, college and university campuses, athletic fields, golf courses, business and industrial sites, highways, and government grounds. The nursery industry of Arizona has been represented by the Arizona Nurserymen's Association. The Southwestern Boyce Thompson Arboretum, located near Superior, Arizona, has tested many trees and shrubs, bringing forth several new and unusual landscape materials. The Experimental Garden at the Arizona-Sonora Desert Museum at Tucson is co-sponsored by various organizations to test native desert plants showing promise for landscaping southern Arizona homes. The relatively new organization of Arizona Landscape Architects was expected to help nurserymen and attract more landscape architects to the state.

Another important phase of Arizona's urban horticulture includes the activities of many garden clubs. The state's representative group is the Arizona Federation of Garden Clubs. The Arizona Gardeners' Association was organized late in the 1960s to promote better gardening practices. The Arizona Shade Tree Conference has sponsored a greater appreciation and appropriate maintenance of community tree plantings. The combined interests in home landscaping, park and public grounds plantings, and the nurserymen's role in serving these interests led to the first landscape design conference in the state in 1969 at the University of Arizona.

Lawns and turfs are basic to urban horticulture. An annual turf conference held each year resulted in the formation of the Arizona Turf Association. In southern Arizona, the practical lawn grass, Bermuda, is especially well adapted and by good management is green most of the year. Hybrid Bermudas have proved to be well

John Burnham

Fig. 24.8 Both rural and urban efforts at landscaping flourish in Arizona's mild and sunny climate and fertile soil.

adapted to southern Arizona. Specialized uses of turf in Arizona are effectively served by other kinds of grasses and ground covers and include bent grasses, Dichondra, Kentucky Bluegrass, Australian Rye, Lippia, White Dutch Clover, and Zoysias.

Insects of Economic Importance

Of the more than 20,000 species of insects estimated to occur in Arizona, not more than one percent may be regarded as significantly injurious or beneficial to man and his interests. The injurious species, although relatively few in number, are prolific and well adapted to the climate, agriculture, and general economy and are responsible for direct and indirect losses extending into the tens of millions of dollars annually.

To protect the Arizona cotton crop from damage by insects in an average year requires the equivalent of more than eight million pounds of technical insecticidal material and expenditures of upwards of $14 million, including application costs. A moderate to heavy infestation of grasshoppers on ten acres of range land will consume as much vegetation as a cow. The commercial timber crop of northern Arizona has been subject to destruction by insects to an equivalent of hundreds of thousands of board feet annually.

The control of termites and other pests in homes and other structures has required the services of a large and growing pest control industry, now involving at least ninety-four firms in Arizona. Large expenditures by growers are needed to control pests and produce fruit and vegetable crops free from insect injury and yet without harmful pesticide residues. To meet these and other insect problems requires continuing, large-scale efforts by individuals, commercial organizations, and governmental agencies.

Early evidences of Arizona insects of economic importance include tunnels of wood-boring insects preserved in petrified wood from northern Arizona and representations of grasshoppers, ants, and other insects on Indian pottery. Relatively little is recorded concerning insects of economic importance until the closing years of the last century. Historical notes provided by Senator Carl Hayden, however, indicate that honey bees were first brought to Arizona from California in 1872.

In 1893 the University of Arizona Agricultural Experiment Station issued its first entomological publication devoted largely to insects discussed in correspondence and including such latter-day pests as the green June beetle, the bagworm, and the grapeleaf skeletonizer. A second bulletin, issued in 1895, discussed scale insects, including the San Jose scale, date palm scale, and the California red scale, all of which in modern times have been introduced into Arizona on nursery stock.

In 1899, Professor T. D. A. Cockerell reported, in a third University of Arizona bulletin, that the Salt River

Valley was "remarkably free from insect pests and especially from injurious scale insects. It would be difficult to find another locality so favored, and at the same time producing such an abundance of different crops." He attributed this freedom from insect pests to a hot, dry climate which discouraged most pests introduced from moister regions, and to the extreme isolation of the Valley from other agricultural areas. He correctly surmised that "while the present condition of affairs in the Salt River Valley is highly satisfactory, the cheerful optimism which assumes that pests cannot live there is hardly justifiable."

Indeed, the relative freedom from insect pests did not continue. Within the first dozen years of this century Arizona's large-scale, irrigated agricultural industry was launched with the completion of Roosevelt Dam and the Yuma Project, to be followed in later years by other projects. This new and intensively cultivated acreage served to attract local insects that had previously fed on native plants, as well as insects from other areas that entered the state through natural dispersal or through human activities. With irrigation added to temperatures generally favorable for insect development, the southern Arizona deserts were transformed into what were aptly described by an eminent British visitor as "insect incubators." Over the years, these insects have tended to follow usually predictable patterns of activity and injury, subject to variations in weather and crop conditions, natural enemies, and control practices.

Some of the insects of particular importance during the decade of the 1960s are mentioned below. Continuing quarantine and eradication efforts are needed to prevent or retard the introduction and establishment of additional potentially serious pests.

The leaves of cotton seedlings are weakened and distorted by the feeding of thrips. Foliage of older cotton plants is attacked by beet armyworms, cabbage loopers, cotton leaf perforators, salt marsh caterpillars, spider mites, and aphids. Squares and developing bolls are injured or destroyed by lygus bugs, bollworms, and stink bugs. To control these pests required in the sixties an average of three insecticide applications annually for the 297,000 acres of cotton grown in the state. The pink bollworm, a serious pest of bolls and developing seeds, has been introduced and apparently eradicated several times since the 1930s. The largest new outbreak observed was in 1966 and 1967. Hopes were that the eradication program of the 70s would be successful. The boll weevil, the most important cotton pest of the southeastern United States, had been found in the state by the sixties but was not an economic problem yet.

Alfalfa is attacked by a variety of insects. Hay and seed crops are injured by various species of leaf-feeding caterpillars, the spotted alfalfa aphid, and the three-cornered alfalfa hopper. Early season hay crops may also be attacked by the pea aphid, the Egyptian alfalfa weevil, and clover mites. Seed crops are also injured by lygus bugs and the clover seed chalcid. Alfalfa seed production requires pollination by adequate numbers of honeybees, which must be protected from exposure to harmful insecticides. The spotted alfalfa aphid, a native of the Old World, was first found in the United States and in Arizona in 1954 and continued through the sixties to be a pest. Increased activity of native and introduced

Fig. 24.9   Aerial application of insecticide has been of vital importance in control of the cotton bollworm.   *Ray Manley*

natural enemies and the introduction of resistant varieties of alfalfa have brought this aphid within controllable limits. Among the numerous pests of other field crops are aphids, which attack small grains, and the lesser cornstalk borer, corn earworm, and southwestern corn borer on sorghum and field corn.

Prominent among important general feeders on a number of crops are the seed-corn maggot, spider mites, aphids, thrips, flea beetles, a number of species of cutworms and armyworms, and the salt marsh caterpillar, locally known as the "woolly worm." The commercial lettuce crop is attacked by aphids and by several species of caterpillars, including the corn earworm, cabbage looper, salt marsh caterpillar, yellow-striped armyworm, beet armyworm, and diamond-back moth larvae. The commercial cantaloupe crop has been attacked particularly by the beet leafhopper (a transmitter of the virus causing curly top disease), serpentine leaf miner, spider mites, and cucumber beetles. Onions are injured by the onion thrips and potatoes are attacked by a number of pests including aphids, leafhoppers, and the potato psyllid. Sweet corn is attacked by various pests, including the corn earworm, lesser cornstalk borer, and southwestern corn borer.

The principal citrus pest in Arizona is the citrus thrip, which injures developing leaf growth and the rinds of fruits. Occasionally injury is caused by the cottony cushion scale, citricola scale, and spider mites. The citrus red mite was a serious pest in the Yuma area in 1967. The California red scale, a major pest of citrus in that state, has been brought to Arizona many times on nursery stock but has so far been successfully intercepted or later eradicated. Grapes are attacked by leafhoppers and other pests, usually controlled readily with available insecticides.

Arizona has been reported to have more species of grasshoppers than are present in any other state, although only a few species are regarded as pests. The most important injury by grasshoppers has been reported from range lands, and to an extent that fluctuates with yearly changes in weather, food plants, and the prevalence of natural enemies.

Insects in growing timber crops in northern Arizona are estimated to destroy the equivalent of hundreds of thousands of board feet of lumber annually. The principal pests of timber crops are several species of bark and engraver beetles which, together with the spruce budworm, the fall webworm, and the great basin tent caterpillars, have also injured the trees in adjacent watershed and recreational areas. These infestations have, in the sixties, required substantial expenditures for control.

Beef and dairy cattle in Arizona are attacked by cattle grubs, screwworms, horn flies, and several species of lice and ticks. Recently developed insecticides of greater safety and effectiveness have led to improved control of these pests and other benefits resulting from healthier animals. A most significant breakthrough came with the introduction of safe and effective systematic insecticides capable of destroying developing cattle grubs within the body of the animal. Fly control has been a continuing problem in dairies, corrals, feedlots, poultry houses, and in adjacent residential areas. Insecticides have become available which, when properly and regularly used, are capable of minimizing the fly problem to an extent never before possible.

A specialized and increasingly competent pest control industry has developed in Arizona to deal with the control of termites and other insects of homes and commercial buildings. Arizona shares with most other states an assortment of common household insects such as houseflies, roaches, silverfish, clothes moths, carpet beetles, and various pests of stored food products.

Among the Arizona insects of economic importance are those beneficial to man, including the honeybee and insect predators and parasites on injurious insects. The honeybee is doubly valuable since it serves as a commercial source of honey and as an essential pollinator of agricultural crops. Approximately 85,000 colonies of honeybees were being maintained in Arizona in 1969. It has been estimated that flowers of desert plants, such as mesquite and catsclaw, furnish two-fifths, alfalfa one-third, and cotton one-fifth of the nectar for the annual Arizona honey crop. Honeybees are more important as pollinators than as honey producers. Production of alfalfa seed, cantaloupes, watermelons, vegetable seeds, and tangerines is largely dependent on honeybees for pollination. Predatory and parasitic insects may contribute materially to the control of certain insect pests and, under favorable conditions, may delay or reduce the need for insecticide treatments.

A most important breakthrough in the history of insect control came with the wholesale introduction of new synthetic organic insecticides, starting with DDT in 1942 and continuing as of 1970. This worldwide development has had an enormous impact in Arizona, where it has contributed to the present high production levels of high-quality crops and to the positive and improved control of most of the pests discussed above. More than 98 percent of the insecticides now used in Arizona have become generally available only since the end of World War II, including such common synthetic compounds as carbaryl, azinphosmethyl, toxaphene, parathion, malathion, demeton, and many others.

Although the net effect of these new insecticides has been overwhelmingly on the positive side, they have created new problems, some of which were still being resolved by 1970. These problems have included possible hazards to beneficial insects, including honeybees, predators, and parasites; hazards to improperly protected or uninformed applicators; a trend toward resistance of insects to the action of certain insecticides; the prevention of environmental pollution and residue deposits on edible crops and animal products; and the increasing number of restrictions on the sale, use, and application of insecticides and on the harvesting, sale, and use of treated crops. Most of these problems are regarded by agriculturists as capable of being solved or minimized through education and research without sacrifice of the benefits received from the improved control.

Problems created by insects of economic importance in Arizona now require the attention of numerous public and private agencies. The Arizona Commission of Agriculture and Horticulture is responsible for preventing the introduction and spread of dangerous plant pests. The United States Department of Agriculture has participated in this cooperative work and is particularly concerned with the eradication and control of local outbreaks of insects of national importance and the control of important pests on publicly owned range and forested areas. The U.S.D.A. also enforces quarantine regulations pertaining to entry of plants and plant products from Mexico.

The University of Arizona as of 1970 was actively engaged in teaching, research, extension, and regulatory work relating to insects of economic importance. A full undergraduate and graduate teaching program has been offered. Through the Agricultural Experiment Station, various University of Arizona entomologists are engaged in research projects dealing with the identification, biology, and control of the insects of greatest economic importance and with insecticides and related problems. Research is conducted on a statewide basis with the aid of three field laboratories. Through the state chemist, the University of Arizona administers laws relating to the composition, registration, and the use of insecticides in the state. Instruction in entomology was also being offered at Arizona State University and Northern Arizona University in 1970. The Arizona Board of Pesticide Control regulates the use and commercial application of insecticides.

The United States Department of Agriculture has contributed much to the knowledge and control of Arizona insects of economic importance through its research laboratories maintained in cooperation with the University of Arizona at Tucson, Mesa, and Phoenix.

Beef Cattle

Beef cattle and calves were first in importance as a source of cash income from Arizona farms, feedlots, and ranches in the mid-sixties. Lands used for grazing make up about 85 percent of the total land area of about 72 million acres and have characterized Arizona chiefly as a range state. In the 1940s, when Arizona had some 64,000 cattle on feed, cattle feeding began to be more than a casual sideline in the agricultural picture. In 1967 cattle finished in Arizona feedlots totaled 680,000 head. In 1968 the number rose to more

Fig. 24.10   Cows and calves graze on summer range in Coconino — one of the state's northern counties.   *Chuck Abbott*

than 700,000 head, and Arizona was in the top ten of the cattlefeeding states, producing more and more feed crops on irrigated lands. Arizona is a surplus cattle-producing state but a slightly deficit area in meat processing. Population growth has exceeded the expansion in packinghouse facilities and capacity, although there were approximately fifty establishments in 1969 in Arizona licensed to slaughter livestock, including one new one with a capacity of 5,000 head per week.

CATTLE NUMBERS AND INCOME. Income from cattle and calves was $206.2 million in 1967. Of this, $64.3 million was estimated to be the value of weight gained on cattle in Arizona feedlots. Total shipments of cattle and calves out of the state during 1967 were 791,659 head. Inshipments were 630,552 head. The growth of feedlots has prompted the increase in inshipments from an average of 59,000 head in the 1930-34 five-year period. Inshipments come from many sources including Mexico and as far away as Florida.

As of January 1, 1968, Arizona was credited with 1,023,000 beef cattle of which 376,000 were cows and yearling heifers. Although the state's cattle population has not changed materially since the turn of the century, the number of range cattle has decreased and the number of other cattle, such as feeders in commercial feedlots, has increased.

Numbers of purebred registered cattle have increased gradually. Herds of Hereford, Angus, Brangus, Santa Gertrudis, Charolais, and Shorthorn are found in the state. Herefords predominate in numbers of both herds and cattle.

FEEDLOT OPERATIONS. Arizona in 1969 had feedlot capacity for approximately 385,000 head, with individual feedlots ranging in capacity from a few hundred to 35,000 head. Some lots own all the cattle fed in that lot, others are custom feeders, feeding for other owners, and a third type of operation is a combination of the above two methods. The bulk of fed cattle shipped out of Arizona in the late 1960s went to California. The most common marketing practice for fed cattle is direct sale from the feedlot.

The increasing productivity of tillable irrigated acres, the growing human population, and the necessity for further diversification of big farming companies have made cattle feeding a natural part of Arizona's modern growth. The feeds commonly used have been alfalfa hay, milo, barley, cottonseed products, and silage. Alfalfa green-chop programs, once popular, have been followed in certain areas but the practice was declining by 1969. Large trench silos, mechanical equipment, and the practice of double cropping the forage sorghums for silage have made silage an economical feed for some operators. Approximately 30 to 45 tons of silage per acre are produced by double cropping. At certain times many by-product feeds — vegetable waste, cantaloupe meal, cantaloupe silage, or citrus pulp — are used, especially in the Yuma area.

A majority of the feedlots have their own feed-processing equipment concentrated in a feed mill installation. These plants usually include, besides grain storage, a large-capacity hay grinder, grain-rolling mills equipped with steam plants, elevators, molasses blending equipment, and provisions for the addition of fat or grease to the ration. Until the 1960s practically all hay was baled and stacked in neat bale piles in the vicinity of the feedlot and was fed as ground or chopped hay. By 1969 alfalfa cubes were being used by several of the larger feedlots. The feeding of total mixed rations was the rule rather than the exception, with starting rations formulated for 45 percent concentrates and finishing rations running 75 percent or more in concentrates. Both percentage and batch-type mills have been in operation in Arizona. Self-unloading trucks, fence-line troughs, and well-arranged yards allow a few men to feed several thousand head of cattle. Most lots feed anywhere from two to five times daily and the troughs are never without feed. The feedlots are designed without the usual shelter or windbreaks, but with some provision for shade. Experimental work at the Yuma Experiment Station has shown that forty square feet of shade per steer will save several dollars per hundredweight in producing gains on cattle of the English breeds during the warmer months of the year. There is a preference among feeders

John Burnham

Fig. 24.11 Cattle feeding is one of the more important industries in Arizona's agricultural economy.

Helga Teiwes Photo, Arizona State Museum, University of Arizona

Fig. 24.12   Sheep in Arizona are predominantly owned by Indian stockmen on the reservation — especially the Navajo.

for cattle showing some Brahman blood for summer feeding in Arizona.

The Arizona Cattle Feeders' Association by 1970 was an active and growing organization of cattle feeders with headquarters in Phoenix. Similarly, the Yuma cattle feeders' together with other individuals from southern California, represent feeders in the Yuma and Imperial valleys. The Arizona Cattle Feeders' Association has maintained an active research committee working closely with animal scientists in state institutions, to carry out needed and appropriate research on feedlot problems and cattle.

RANCH ORGANIZATION. Yearlong grazing on definite ranch units is a nearly universal practice in the state. Carrying capacity of ranches varies from 100 to 2,500 or more breeding cows. In general, ranch units are under fence and comprise privately owned, state owned, and federally controlled lands under lease. The bulk of the range area in the 1960s was under public control, falling within grazing districts, Indian reservations, national forests, and state lands. The more desirable portion of this area lies within elevations of 3,000 to 6,000 feet. Rangelands also include many desert areas which are used by livestock in winter and spring and in other seasons with good rainfall. In addition, there are mountain areas which, because of altitude and climate, are

suited only for summer grazing, often with steers.

Calving seasons vary with the area, but the big movement of feeder cattle from the ranges is in the fall months. A second seasonal movement is in the spring and includes feeder cattle from those ranches selling spring yearlings. The demand for feeder cattle by the feedlots of the state is yearlong, with many operators buying and selling cattle every week, or at least every month of the year.

The Arizona Cattle Growers' Association is an organization of the state cattle producers and has for years been one of the prominent and influential state organizations of the nation.

RANCHING AREAS. While cattle ranching is a statewide activity, it can be divided into five areas differentiated principally by vegetation types, ranching methods, and location. Their designation and descriptions follow:

Mohave Strip. The entire northwestern portion of the state lying beyond the Colorado River is designated as the Mohave Strip. The deep-cut canyon of the Colorado River forms a natural barrier isolating this area from the rest of the state. The Kaibab Plateau which borders the Grand Canyon and extends northward toward Fredonia by 1969 had been closed for a number of years to all but a limited number of livestock. In House Rock Valley to the east of the plateau there is open grassland used by cattle. North and west of the plateau is a large area of the northern desert-type range being used by a few flocks of sheep from the bordering state of Utah.

Navajo Indian Reservation. The Navajo Indian Reservation in northeastern Arizona constitutes an area of 12,000,000 acres or one-sixth of the state's total area. As of 1970, it is used almost exclusively by the Indians for grazing livestock—more sheep and goats than cattle.

Southwest Desert. This area stands apart from the rest of the state because of its limited use as grazing land. It consists almost exclusively of the desert-type vegetation. It embraces all of Yuma County, western Pima and Maricopa counties, and southern Mohave County. Only in certain areas are cattle raised on a permanent basis. Some areas contiguous to the Salt River and Yuma valleys are used by cattle and sheep for late winter grazing. With the development of irrigation farming, the feeding of cattle and production of purebred cattle have increased rapidly.

Southeastern Area. This southeastern area includes all of Cochise and Santa Cruz counties and more than half of the adjoining counties of Graham, Pinal, Pima, and southern Greenlee, all lying south of the Gila River. Approximately one-third of the range cattle were to be found in this area in the late 1960s. It is particularly well adapted as a cattle breeding country and for the production of early spring calves. For the most part it affords yearlong grazing on ranges that are largely grassland bordering on scattered mountain ranges and some desert strips at the lower elevations.

Central Mountain and Foothill Area. The central mountain and foothill area circumscribed by the four districts just described is the principal range livestock section of the state. In 1970 most of the sheep owned by Anglos and more than half of the cattle were in this territory. It lies in a diagonal direction northwest and southeast, centering on high mountain ranges. Pronounced topographic features and wide differences in climate account for the presence of the several vegetation types and as many systems of range livestock raising. The various forms of land ownership are also represented. In 1970 the national forests and Indian reservations were administering practically all of the grazing in the mountain ranges. Separate allotments for cattle and sheep have been provided wherever possible on the forest.

Research and Education. By the late sixties the Animal Science Department of the University of Arizona was working closely with both the cattle feeders and cattle growers in matters of research and education.

Research projects dealing with problems of cattle production or feeding were being conducted by the Arizona Agricultural Experiment Stations at both Yuma and Tucson. In addition, some problems were being studied cooperatively with producers and feeders. By 1970 several animal breeding projects were being carried on cooperatively with individual ranchers and with the San Carlos Apache Tribal Enterprises. A total of eight faculty and three staff members made up the teaching, research, and extension group in Animal Science as of the beginning of the seventies. The University of Arizona Animal Science Farm at Tucson was maintaining herds of registered Hereford and Angus cattle.

THE SHEEP INDUSTRY. Arizona's sheep population, following a steady decline since the 1940s had become stabilized at a level of approximately 300,000 breeding ewes by 1969. Over 200,000 of these were Indian-owned on reservations, with Navajo flocks predominating. The remaining ewes were grazed on the north central mountain range area of the state, and wintered on irrigated pastures in the lower valleys. These sheep, bred for early lamb production, rely chiefly on alfalfa together with some barley and oat crops as winter pasture feed.

Outfits start lambing in early November and continue for a period of about forty days. Both ewes and lambs are kept on pasture until the lambs reach market finish in April. Under this practice the ewes are shorn in February and March and are returned to their summer ranges soon after the lambs are marketed.

Confronted with high pasture costs, sheepmen in the late sixties were seeking an alternative method to the long-established pasture system. It was felt that a continuing high level of green-feed prices, death losses from bloat, and declining sources of available pasture could eventually lead to pen-feeding or some modification of the usual practice.

Considerable interest in ewe flocks has developed in the Yuma area, with alfalfa pasture and bermuda straw as the principal feed crops.

A total of about 3,000,000 pounds of wool was produced in Arizona in 1967. It sold for approximately 37 cents per pound, exclusive of the federal support payment. The major portion of the state's wool clip, exclusive of the Indian-owned-sheep wool, has been marketed through the Arizona Wool Growers Association, a subsidiary of the National Wool Marketing Association.

Breeds. Arizona range sheep owned by whites have been almost exclusively Rambouillet. The Indian-owned sheep have been of less well-defined breeding. Rams of the Hampshire and Suffolk breeds have been used exclusively by the white operators for producing market lambs.

Lamb Feeding. Commercial lamb feeding has been of little importance in the state. Only one major feed yard was in operation as of 1969. The bulk of the fat lambs marketed have been sold direct from the irrigated pastures of the Salt River, Casa Grande, and Yuma valleys.

Hog-growing. By the early 1970s, commercial hog growing was of increasing interest in Southern Arizona, still a small agricultural industry but showing signs of growing in importance.

The Dairy Industry

Dairy farming in Arizona in the sixties was a highly competitive and specialized industry, characterized by large-sized herds which were becoming larger. At the same time, small herds were being consolidated or sold. The average number of milking cows per herd (on Dairy Herd Improvement Association test) doubled. At the beginning of 1968, this stood at an average of more than 200 cows per dairy farm with a total of approximately 192 dairy farms in the state. The total dairy cattle population in 1969 was between 100,000 and 105,000, of which 49,000 were milking cows. Although the state of Arizona ranked only forty-third in total number of dairy cattle, it ranked second in average yearly production per cow of 10,370 pounds of milk and 350 pounds of fat. Arizona also enjoyed the enviable reputation of having a greater percentage of cows on test — 46 percent — than any other state.

Dairy farming is limited to the irrigated sections of the state. About 75 percent of the dairy cattle in 1969 were in the Salt River Valley of Maricopa County. The other 25 percent were in the irrigable valleys of the upper Gila, Casa Grande, Santa Cruz, Chino, Verde, San Pedro, Sulphur Spring, and Yuma. There was some dairying in the Joseph City and Snowflake areas of Navajo County, and there was a tendency for dairy production to decrease in areas other than Maricopa and Pinal counties.

Prolonged high summer temperatures, particularly in Yuma, Maricopa, and Pinal counties, have a depressing effect on milk production and breeding efficiency. Fall, winter, and spring temperatures in central and southern counties are more favorable for maximum production. Because of favorable climatic conditions in all of Arizona, the requirements for housing are minimum. The dairy cows are maintained in open corrals and are milked in milking parlors. Shades are essential for maximum production in the central and southern counties.

With the smaller herds of former years, most of the feed was home-grown. With the large modern herds, however, a large portion of the feed is purchased. Alfalfa hay is the basis for most dairy cattle rations. There is an abundance of alfalfa grown in all irrigated sections of the state because alfalfa is popular in crop rotation. The quality of alfalfa hay produced in the state has been excellent because of the favorable weather conditions for curing. In some of the southern counties, five to eight cuttings of alfalfa are made per year. Other roughages that are used quite extensively are grain sorghum or corn for silage, grasses of cereal grains, sudan grass, and alfalfa for green chop. For all practical purposes,

Harold Wylie

Fig. 24.13   As southwestern dairy herds increase in size, the industry grows more competitive and more specialized.

pastures are not used for milking cows. Pasture is used primarily for young stock and dry cows.

Barley and hegari are the principal grains used in dairy concentrate mixtures, and provide a relatively cheap source of energy. Because cottonseed meal is locally available and competitive in price, it is used extensively in concentrate mixtures. It is needed as a source of protein when the bulk of the roughage is other than alfalfa hay, but when alfalfa hay is fed liberally, the protein of cottonseed meal is competitive with that of barley and hegari on a total-digestible-nutrient basis. Some whole cottonseed is used either as a part of the concentrate mixture or, by a few dairymen, fed alone.

Five major dairy breeds — Ayrshires, Brown Swiss, Guernseys, Holsteins, and Jerseys — were represented in the state as of 1969. Approximately 90 percent were Holstein, and 5 percent Guernsey, with Jerseys, Brown Swiss, and Ayrshires making up the other 5 percent. A few dual-purpose cattle were maintained.

The local cost of milk production does not encourage the production of milk for manufacturing purposes. A federal milk market order is administered by the United States Department of Agriculture.

The processing plants for milk in the 1960s were confined largely to the population centers of Phoenix and Tucson. A high percentage of the milk produced in the state was used for fluid consumption. The excess over fluid needs was used mostly for the manufacture of ice cream and cottage cheese. Practically all of the cured cheeses, butter, evaporated and condensed milk, and powdered whole milk were shipped into Arizona. There was a limited amount of powdered skim milk and butter produced in the state.

Poultry

The gross income from poultry products on Arizona farms has increased from $2 million in 1935 to almost $7 million in 1968. Most of the poultry income came from the sale of eggs and chickens. Turkey and broiler sales contributed small amounts to the gross receipts. Additional minor income was derived from ducks, geese, and rabbits.

Major poultry enterprise in Arizona in the late 1960s was production of eggs for market. A few poultry operations were associated with other agricultural activities, but most poultry plants were specialized farms where a large number of laying hens were kept in special buildings on small acreages.

Greater specialization in poultry production has brought larger units. A compilation of location and size of commercial poultry ranches (defined as having 300 layers or more) in Arizona in the late 1960s illustrates the structural changes in the industry which have occurred since the early years of the decade. In 1963, 26.8 percent of the total birds were in flocks of over 50,000, compared to 49.6 percent in 1967. Flocks of 10,000 or more birds accounted for 84.4 percent of

total birds in 1967, whereas in 1963 flocks of this size accounted for only 68.4 percent of total birds.

Although commercial poultry ranches in the state have increased in size in terms of number of birds, the number of poultry ranches showed decline from 167 in 1963 to 84 in 1967. There were 1,129,025 birds located on these 84 commercial poultry ranches. Of the total birds, almost 49 percent were in Pima County, 32 percent in Maricopa County, 9 percent in Pinal County, and 6 percent in Yavapai County.

California has been the principal point of origin for eggs shipped into Arizona, followed by the midwestern states of Nebraska, Kansas, Colorado, Minnesota, Iowa, and South Dakota, ranked respectively.

The general tendency of the poultry industry to locate itself near densely populated centers for easy marketing has been noted in Arizona. Maricopa and Pima Counties, with the two largest metropolitan areas, in 1969 were also the largest egg-producing areas.

Arizona markets have for some time maintained higher wholesale and retail prices for poultry products than those in neighboring states. A favorable price differential, coupled with a deficiency of local products, places the industry in an enviable position in Arizona. However, improved packing and transportation facilities in California and in the midwestern states have made it possible for poultry products from these areas to be shipped into Arizona at competitive prices.

An Arizona egg law sets standards of quality grades and sizes. The law requires that the temperature of eggs must be held below sixty degrees Fahrenheit by the dealers and retailers. This prescribed temperature feature for egg handling as of 1969 was found in the egg laws of only five other states. All handlers of eggs sold in Arizona have been subject to the egg law, whether the product was produced in the state or shipped in. The law has been administered by a state egg inspector appointed by the Egg Inspection Board, which in turn is appointed by the Governor.

Poultry producers are serviced by franchised hatcheries which obtain foundation stock yearly from the major breeders, and proceed to "multiply" them for the local producer. The hatcheries cooperate with the National Poultry Improvement Association, which assures that the chickens are from pullorum-inspected and tested flocks.

Generally, in Arizona, the egg producer sells his product to the processor, either ungraded, graded for size, or graded for size and candled. Producers in all major egg producing areas of the state may call on several processors for service. A significant portion of the eggs are marketed by the producer directly to the retailer, and a few marketed to the consumer.

Some diseases are prevalent in the poultry flocks of the state, but not to the extent found in areas where rainfall is heavy or where the poultry population is greater. Educational activities and cooperative inspections have aided in the control of poultry diseases and have been major factors in preventing epidemics. The University of Arizona in 1969 was operating two diagnostic laboratories, staffed by veterinarians and technical personnel, where free diagnostic services were available to poultry producers.

Turkeys were the second most important poultry product of the state as of 1970. Most of the turkeys were produced in large flocks on a year-round basis. Some of the producers dressed and marketed their turkeys through their own facilities, but most of the live turkeys were handled by commercial processors.

In 1970, the bulk of cull hens were being sold out of state. Local processing plants distributed close to five million broilers a year for local consumption. On January 1, 1959, the new federal Poultry Inspection Law went into effect, applying to inspection of poultry and poultry products in interstate or foreign commerce and in designated consuming areas.

The Department of Poultry Science at the University of Arizona, established in 1919, has remained actively engaged in research embracing all fields of poultry production. A new poultry research center established by the University of Arizona was completed in 1955, providing poultry housing, hatching, brooding, feed-mixing, and laboratory facilities for instruction and research.

Development of inexpensive raised-platform poultry housing was pioneered by the workers at the Southwest Experiment Station at Glendale. Subsequently, University of Arizona extension engineers redesigned and modified these structures for use in more efficient commercial operations. Mechanical cooling by means of mist, sprays, water coolers, natural shade, and ground cover have been studied by Arizona poultry researchers. State and federal personnel have been engaged in the development of a heat-resistant strain of single-combed White Leghorn. Several projects on specialized feed additives during hot weather, and the effect of such supplements on the quality of the egg, were in progress by 1970.

Income From Agriculture Compared With Income From Other Industries in the State

In 1970, the gross income generated by agriculture in Arizona was $714 million. This consisted mainly of the value of the crops and livestock produced in that year, but it also included $52 million received as payments from the federal government.

The $714 million from agriculture accounted for 15 percent of Arizona's primary income. Primary income is defined as that derived from developing the natural resources and processing the raw materials, or that which supports the economy of the area. The other major basic industries that generate primary income are mining, manufacturing, and the travel business. (The latter is a primary industry in the sense that it causes people to come to Arizona where they spend money earned elsewhere, and thus provides the basic support for a portion

of Arizona's population.) Agriculture's relation to the other basic industries of Arizona is shown in Table 24.1.

TABLE 24.1

Sources of Primary Income in Arizona, 1950 and 1970

Basic Industries	Gross Income Produced (In Millions)	
	1950	1970
	(Dollars)	
Agriculture[a]	271	714[b]
Mining[c]	207	1,167
Manufacturing[c]	145	2,300
Tourists[c]	100	565
Total	723	4,746

Sources: a. College of Agriculture, the University of Arizona
b. Includes $52 million in government payments
c. Valley National Bank estimates

Since 1950, the income from agriculture has more than doubled. Income from other sources, however, has increased even faster.

As of 1969 only 7 percent of the Arizona labor force was engaged in agriculture. This contrasted with 25 percent at the time of statehood — 1912 — and 14 percent in 1950. A declining proportion of the labor force in agriculture is a well recognized sign of economic progress. Mechanization, improved seed, improved fertilizers, and other technological advances have made it possible to produce an output of greater value with a relatively (or even absolutely) smaller labor force.

Comparison Among Agricultural Commodities of the Effect on Income Generated by Their Production

Arizona's economy is an interrelated structure. Each economic sector not only produces goods or services but is also a consumer itself, purchasing other goods and services for use in the production process.

Such interdependence may be analyzed into two separate components. First, there is direct dependence — the direct purchases by one industry from another, of things necessary to produce the first industry's product.

The second component is less obvious and more difficult to measure. This is the indirect effect generated by the original direct purchases. This occurs because any sector supplying inputs to another must, in turn, have its own inputs and so on, ad infinitum.

Both of these components of interdependence can be measured by a research method called "input-output" or "inter-industry" analysis. An input-output "model" has been developed for Arizona. (An economic "model" is economic theory put into mathematical terms so that empirical estimates can be made.) The following material summarizes a few of the relevant relationships brought to light by this model.

Direct Dependence Between Economic Activities

Table 24.2 shows where Arizona agriculture buys the inputs for each dollar of production.

For example, the livestock industry in 1969 purchased about 32 cents' worth of inputs from other Arizona industries, plus 41 cents' worth of goods from outside of Arizona and had 27 cents left over to pay for labor, interest, profits, and taxes. Of the purchases of Arizona products, .92 cents were from other livestock producers themselves, 20.69 cents were crops for feed, 2.38 cents were from processors of agricultural products, only .97 cents were from manufacturing and mining and 4.15 cents were of services and utilities.

Trade and transportation took but 1.78 cents of the livestock dollar. These 1.78 cents were the wholesale and retail margins.

Purchases from the construction industry were worth .35 cents per dollar of output, while purchases of "scrap and by-products" were 1.06 cents. "Scrap and by-products" is not a particular Arizona industry. Purchases of "scrap and by-products" actually have come from other industries listed. However, these purchases have been separated out in order to show only purchases of those other industries' primary product. For example, hides are a by-product of the livestock industry. Major purchases from this industry are milk, meat, and eggs and the industry would exist whether or not it produced the by-product hides.

Imports of inputs from outside of the state netted 40.98 cents for the livestock industry. The largest portion of this figure was the purchase of out-of-state cattle to feed in the feedlot industry.

The other two columns in the preceding table for crops and for agricultural processing industries may be read in the same way.

Some comparisons between sectors in 1969 are indicated. Agricultural processing industries have been quite dependent on other Arizona industries for their inputs.

Out of every dollar of production, agricultural processing industries have spent 66.67 cents on other Arizona products. Almost one-half of these purchases (31.96 cents) have been for livestock and livestock products. Only 4.53 cents have been spent for crops since most Arizona crops have been either sold fresh in Arizona or exported out of the state for further processing.

Agricultural processors in 1969 purchased relatively large amounts of inputs from manufacturing and mining (6.88 cents), services and utilities (5.99 cents), and trade and transportation (7.67 cents). Labor costs, interest, profits and taxes totaled only 25.30 cents, the smallest total of the three agricultural sectors.

The crop sector in 1969 was the largest purchaser of manufacturing and mining products per dollar of output (9.09 cents) and a relatively large purchaser of services and utilities (5.25 cents). Since purchases of other produced inputs were quite small and imports were only 3.45 cents, 74.96 cents were left over for wages, interest, profits and taxes. Obviously, a high percentage of this 74.96 cents goes to labor.

The livestock sector had large purchases of crops (20.69 cents) but relatively small purchases from other Arizona industries. It was more closely related to other Arizona industries than crops (36.32 cents versus 21.59 cents), but less related through its input structure than agricultural processing (32.32 cents versus 66.67 cents). However, because it needed such a large quantity of imports (40.98 cents), only 26.70 cents were lefe over for wages, interest, profits and taxes.

These direct relationships are the ones usually thought of with regard to the dependence of one economic sector upon another. There are, in addition, indirect effects which sometimes outweigh them. These and other phenomena can be studied in "Importance of Agriculture to Arizona's Economy," Chapter III of the Tenth Arizona Town Hall.

In summary, agricultural processors are very much related through their inputs to most other industries in the state, but use a relatively small amount of labor.

TABLE 24.2

Direct Purchases by Arizona Agriculture per Dollar of Production

Producing Industry	Dollars of Direct Purchases by:		
	Livestock	Crops	Agricultural Processing
Livestock	.0092	—	.3196
Crops	.2069	.0633	.0453
Agricultural Processing	.0238	—	.0683
Manufacturing and Mining	.0097	.0909	.0688
Service and Utilities	.0415	.0525	.0599
Trade and Transportation	.0178	.0019	.0767
Construction	.0035	.0047	.0040
Scrap and By-products	.0106	.0024	.0242
Total Purchases from Arizona Industries	.3232	.2159	.6667
New Imports	.4098	.0345	.0803
Total Purchases All Industries	.7330	.2504	.7470
Labor, Interest, Profits, Taxes	.2670	.7496	.2530
Total	1.0000	1.0000	1.0000

Crops are closely related only to manufacturing and services and utilities, but use large quantities of labor. The livestock industry is closely related only to crops per dollar of input.

Agricultural Education and Research

The Land Grant Colleges and Universities were started as teaching institutions to give instruction in agriculture and mechanic arts, but not to the exclusion of other cultural subjects. From this beginning there evolved for agriculture the Agricultural Experiment Station and the Cooperative Extension Service, giving these institutions the entire function normally associated with universities and colleges; i.e., resident teaching, research and extension. Each segment supplements the other.

The teaching activity of the College of Agriculture at the University of Arizona has contributed greatly to the scientific, social and economic development of the state and nation. Out of it have come men and women to attain heights in their careers, whether in business, science, government, professions or as farm and ranch operators. Graduates have led great industries and occupied leadership roles of many types.

The field of agriculture, broadly defined, has sometimes been less glamorous than some other areas. The salary of graduates has tended to be lower than in certain other fields. In spite of this, the future for agricultural graduates still looks bright and is getting brighter. The population explosion and resulting world food problems have caused many leaders to predict a greater need for these graduates in the years ahead.

Arizona farmers are very knowledgeable about technology. Further advances in cropland agriculture in the state by 1970 were predicted as being in areas of complex relationships between soil, water, plant nutrients, and insects and diseases, coupled with a sophisticated economic analysis previously attempted by only a few operators. Thus, future research will call for a team approach in which varied specialists cooperate to solve production problems of a specific crop. Advances in animal agriculture may be expected to follow this same general pattern. The research program in Arizona will continue to require services of the most highly skilled and imaginative research scientists available. Future national agricultural policy should take into account the need for adequate funds to support the competent agricultural scientists in all the state colleges of agriculture, the U. S. Department of Agriculture, and industry.

In Cooperative Extension, the county agent has evolved from the generalist toward the specialist. Today, with increased specialization at the farm, ranch, and home level, the trend toward highly trained specialists among the county extension personnel has been accelerated. In Arizona, these highly trained specialists have been available in the larger agricultural counties for many years. Area specialists, and in some commodity areas the utilization of state specialists in a traditional county agent role with producers, plus the use of specialized county personnel in adjoining counties, have added strength to the Cooperative Extension program.

The team approach is part of the extension program plan in Arizona. It involves county agents, specialists, and appropriate research and teaching personnel.

Fig. 24.14   Cattle grazing in a pasture of wildflowers form a pastoral scene that is still a part of Arizona life.   *Chuck Abbott*

George F. Leaming
Economist

25

TOURISM AND RECREATION

Tourism, travel, and recreation have long been an important part of the Arizona economy, involving residents of the state, the rest of the nation, and many parts of the world. In the mid-1960s, the various tourist-serving industries in Arizona employed approximately 40,000 people — about eight percent of the state's total employment. These workers were employed in gasoline service stations; eating and drinking places; hotels, motels, and other lodging places; automobile rental agencies; and various types of transportation. The full economic impact of recreational tourists on the entire state has never really been accurately determined, but undoubtedly the financial evaluation exceeds $100 million per year.

TABLE 25.1

Employment in Tourist Service Industries in Arizona, 1970

1) Gasoline Service Stations	7,226
2) Eating and Drinking Places	27,582
3) Hotels and other Lodging Places . . .	12,946
4) Automobile Rentals — without Drivers	697
5) Air Transportation Services	431
Total	48,882

Source: U.S. Department of Commerce, Bureau of the Census, *Arizona County Business Patterns 1970.*

Visitors come to Arizona and travel within the state by diverse means. In the mid-1960s a total of more than 4,000,000 automobiles entered the state through the various state border inspection stations. More than 2,000,000 of these contained out-of-state visitors. The total economic significance of these visitors to Arizona has been substantial. In the mid-1960s, recreational tourists alone directly contributed a sum of more than $40 million per year to the economies of Arizona's five northern counties. More than a third of this contribution was made through the purchase of gasoline and petroleum products. Throughout the sixties, the economic impact of recreational tourism in the northern part of the state increased approximately five percent per year.

TABLE 25.2

Arizona Interstate Highway Traffic Inbound Autos and Busses

	Northern	Southern	Total
1960	1,634,570	1,624,017	3,258,587
1961*	1,688,972	1,615,620	3,304,592
1962	1,867,005	2,051,356	3,918,361
1963	2,028,694	2,073,472	4,102,166
1964	1,995,509	2,208,669	4,204,178
1965	2,062,206	2,459,568	4,521,774
1966	2,097,902	2,454,638	4,552,540
1967	2,050,897	2,490,733	4,541,630
1968	2,184,491	2,739,898	4,924,389
1969	2,448,301	3,191,501	5,639,802
1970	2,534,649	3,938,225	6,472,874

*Data for 11 months only.

Source: Arizona State Department of Agriculture and Horticulture, Office of the State Entomologist.

The direct contribution of the recreational tourist to the local economies of the northern part of Arizona has been greatest in Coconino County, the locale of the Grand Canyon and the city of Flagstaff. Late in the sixties, the annual effect of the recreational tourist on the economy of Coconino County amounted to something close to $20 million. In adjoining Navajo County, the site of Petrified Forest National Park and extensive pine forests, the economic impact of recreational tourism was only about a third as important as in the Flagstaff-Grand Canyon area. In Navajo County, total business income directly attributable to recreational tourism amounted to a figure approximating $7 million per year. In Arizona's

Ray Manley

Fig. 25.1   Mount Lemmon in the Santa Catalina Mountains is just 45 minutes away from the desert floor of Tucson.

other northern plateau county — Apache — tourism has been persistently less important than in either Coconino or Navajo counties. The direct contribution of recreational tourists to Apache County's economy amounted to less than $2 million per year, despite the presence of extensive pine forests, mountains, lakes, and other tourist and recreational attractions. In the northwestern part of the state, recreational tourists have made contributions to the economies of Yavapai and Mohave counties that are comparable to those made in Navajo County. In Yavapai County recreational tourists directly accounted for about $6 million worth of business activity each year. In Mohave County direct tourist business varied between $6 and $8 million per year.

Seasonal Variations

Tourist activity in Northern Arizona has had a strong seasonal characteristic with substantial numbers of visitors during June, July, and August dropping off sharply in September and relatively few throughout the rest of the year. This is true of all of the state's northern counties except Mohave, along the Colorado River. There, although there is a summer tourist peak, it differs less drastically from the level of winter tourist activity. In Mohave County, the principal tourist season extends from April through September but summer tourist activity normally amounts to no more than 50 percent above the overall monthly average nor does winter tourist activity fall to less than 50 percent of that average. In the other northern counties, however, summer tourist activity may go as much as 300 percent above the monthly average, while dropping to only 25 percent during the winter months.

In southern Arizona, winter tourism has had its most significant development. In the economies of the Tucson and Nogales area alone, recreational tourists in the mid-1960s directly accounted for approximately $20 million worth of business activity per year. In Southern Arizona, the seasonal pattern of tourist activity has been distinctly different from that in the northern part of the state. In Southern Arizona tourist activity is generally highest in the period from January through April with a decline during May and then a moderate increase during the summer months of June, July, and August. This is usually followed by a severe drop during September and October followed by another moderate rise during late November and December. This has resulted in a primary peak season during the winter and early spring with a somewhat lesser secondary summer peak, flanked by lows in the late spring and autumn.

The winter tourist has been a significant element in the growth of both central and southern Arizona. A study of tourism in Maricopa County (including the Phoenix Metropolitan Area), in the mid-1960s showed that the typical out-of-state group visiting the area during the winter consisted of a couple of middle age or older, travelling without children or other family members. They arrived in Arizona from almost every part of the United States, but particularly from the north central states, including both the Midwest and northern plains. Most of them had visited Arizona before or had heard about the state from friends or relatives. Most travelled by car with an additional significant portion coming by air. Very few arrived in the state by bus or train. Many were vacationing or visiting. Friends or relatives living in Arizona have become an important element in the state's winter tourist activity, since winter visitors are more apt to stay with friends or relatives in southern and central Arizona than they are to use motels or hotels. Despite this (or perhaps because of it) the average winter tourist in central and southern Arizona stays approximately a month (sometimes longer), and spends an average of $15 a day per person.

Natural Attractions

Arizona's natural resources — climate, scenic settings, deserts, forests, and mountains, and lakes — have been its principle tourist attractions. The dry, warm climate has been one of the major attractions for winter visitors, while the scenic grandeur, forests, and cool climate of the northern part of the state have been important in luring vacationers during the summer months. Travelers are drawn to and through Arizona during the summer months also by the interstate highway system connecting California with Texas. The state also has many national parks, monuments, and recreation areas, in both the southern and northern parts, that draw many visitors each year. The largest such single attraction in the state of this nature is the Grand Canyon. In the late 1960s, the total number of visitors to Grand Canyon

National Park approached 2,000,000 per year. Yearly visitors at Petrified Forest National Park, also in northern Arizona, averaged slightly less than 1,000,000 in the late 1960s.

Flagstaff, flanked by the Grand Canyon to the northwest and the Petrified Forest to the east, has been made the virtual center of tourist activity in the northern part of the state. Attractions other than Grand Canyon and Petrified Forest have also helped to make tourism important in northern Arizona, perhaps more so than in any other part of the state save Maricopa County. Coconino County contains, in addition to the Grand Canyon, the Glen Canyon Dam and Lake Powell (both of which are now in the Glen Canyon National Recreation Area), parts of the large Navajo and Hopi Indian reservations, as well as the lesser known Hualapai and Havasupai reservations, the Wupatki, Sunset Crater, Navajo and Walnut Canyon national monuments, the San Francisco Peaks (almost thirteen thousand feet, the highest moun-

TABLE 25.3
Recreation Visitor Days in National Forests in Arizona in 1970

National Forest	Total Visits
Apache	920,700
Coconino	1,167,300
Coronado	1,397,000
Kaibab	1,123,700
Prescott	715,200
Sitgreaves	699,600
Tonto	1,914,200
Total	7,937,700

Source: U.S. Department of Agriculture, Forest Service, Southwest Region.

Fred Wehrman

Fig. 25.2 San Francisco Peaks, highest in the state, the Snow Bowl, and the Grand Canyon are very close to Flagstaff.

Fig. 25.3   Havasu Falls in the Grand Canyon can be enjoyed along with other spectacular scenery by tourists of the hardier sort.

tains in the state) skiing facilities, museums, astronomical observatories, Oak Creek Canyon, and vast expanses of the Coconino, Kaibab and Sitgreaves national forests.

The largest recreation development in the state in the decade of the sixties was the Glen Canyon National Recreation Area, containing both the Glen Canyon Dam and the 186-mile-long Lake Powell behind it.

The lake, which began to fill in 1963, has on its 1,920 mile shoreline some of the most spectacular scenery of the West. Famed for its fishing, boating and scenic beauty, it attracts visitors from all over the nation. More than 750,000 registered in the area in the late sixties.

The Petrified Forest National Park, in the northeastern part of the state, straddling the border between Navajo and Apache counties, has been a major tourist attraction, accommodating nearly a million people annually in the late 1960s. These persons, together with the many who visited the White Mountains in the southern part of Navajo and Apache counties (as well as those who visited Canyon de Chelly National Monument in northern Apache County and those portions of the Navajo Indian Reservation lying within this area) made tourism important in northeastern Arizona as well. The eastern portion of the state also contains the high mountains of the Apache National Forest with its numerous small lakes, Lyman Lake State Park, and the Fort Apache and San Carlos Indian reservations.

Yavapai County, in northwestern Arizona, has relatively little (compared to the rest of northern Arizona), in the way of natural tourist attractions. However, advantageously situated with respect to the Phoenix Metropolitan Area, in the past decade Yavapai has gained business from tourism comparable with both Navajo and Mohave counties where natural attractions predominate. The county, however, does have Tuzigoot and Montezuma's Castle national monuments, both ruins

of ancient Indian civilization, and a number of museums and other attractions of historical interest, including the former mining town of Jerome, a portion of which has now become a state park. Yavapai County also contains the Prescott National Forest, but the county's area of tall pine forests is relatively small compared to the vast expanse of Ponderosa Pine forest found in the northeastern counties of the state.

The major tourist attraction in Mohave County, northwestern Arizona, is the Colorado River and the several lakes that have been created along its length, from Lake Mead on the north (formed by the construction of Hoover Dam) to Lake Havasu on the south. Mohave County also has other attractions, including Pipe Springs National Monument, the Kaibab, Hualapai and Fort Mohave Indian reservations, and a number of ghost towns dating from the gold mining activity of the 1860s. Nevertheless, the water of the Colorado River is still the prime drawing card for the county's recreational tourists. The nature of Mohave County's major attractions as well as its more arid and warmer climate, compared to the rest of northern Arizona, have given the county's tourist industry a less severe seasonal characteristic than those of the other northern counties. While more of Mohave County's recreational tourists visit the county in the summer, substantial numbers seek the county and its environs during the winter months. In the 1960s, approximately 3.5 million people visited the Lake Mead National Recreation Area between Mohave County and Southern Nevada each year. This was an average of approximately three hundred thousand persons per month. Many of the tourists who visit Mohave County enter from either California or Nevada and throughout their stay remain relatively close to the river.

California and other West Coast visitors are also important to winter tourism in the southern part of Arizona. Throughout the southern part of the state, a

TABLE 25.4

Number of Visitors at Selected National Parks and Monuments in Arizona

Year	Grand Canyon National Park	Petrified Forest National Park	Saguaro National Monument	Organ Pipe Cactus National Monument	Glen Canyon National Recreation Area	Casa Grande National Monument
1958	1,063,529	713,080	122,709	358,620	—	70,677
1959	1,168,807	878,423	133,938	374,082	—	68,103
1960	1,186,916	911,531	141,012	262,062	—	76,924
1961	1,252,183	671,014	145,139	246,420	—	87,516
1962	1,446,453	705,013	146,258	290,051	9,828*	83,860
1963	1,538,666	786,025	177,049	329,844	44,285	105,738
1964	1,575,737	884,049	215,893	324,700	196,422	132,416
1965	1,689,230	867,782	229,708	362,837	303,548	88,129
1966	1,806,033	849,819	228,374	293,402	359,659	110,485
1967	1,804,874	797,411	267,787	340,693	390,037	82,882
1968	1,986,270	869,431	307,147	374,844	654,505	80,075
1969	2,192,574	1,005,500	409,026	332,975	781,250	89,827
1970	2,258,195	1,151,448	351,844	415,380	788,482	116,559

*March through December only.

Source: National Park Service, U.S. Department of the Interior.

number of major and numerous minor attractions serve the recreational tourist. Important among these are the several national monuments found in the area. In the 1960s, more than 200,000 persons each year visited Saguaro National Monument in the Tucson Metropolitan Area, while more than fifty thousand annually visited Tumacacori Mission National Monument, located between Tucson and Nogales. Each year something more than 300,000 persons visited Organ Pipe Cactus National Monument situated in southwestern Pima County, while approximately 100,000 visited Casa Grande National Monument, the ruins of an ancient Indian civilization. Several other national monuments are also scattered throughout southern Arizona.

Unique Features

Non-federal areas are also important as tourist attractions. In the Tucson area, the Arizona-Sonora Desert Museum annually draws more than two hundred thousand visitors, while other privately owned attractions such as Old Tucson, a reconstructed western frontier village, and the San Xavier Mission, dating from the early Spanish missionaries, are visited also by large numbers of tourists. Public (but non-federal) facilities such as Kitt Peak National Observatory, operated by the Associated Universities for Research in Astronomy, and Colossal Cave County Park similarly serve as important tourist attractions. Kitt Peak alone drew approximately fifty thousand visitors per year in the mid-1960s. The sprawling Papago Indian Reservation as well as various scattered areas of the Coronado National Forest and several state parks are also important as tourist attractions in southern Arizona.

There are numerous sites throughout the state related to the days of the early west. These have been widely publicized and have helped to make Arizona famous. Indian reservations form a significant portion of

Fig. 25.4   Panoramic beauty and a full display of Arizona-Sonora animals and plants keep tourists coming to the Desert Museum.
Ted Offret

Fig. 25.5 Old Tucson, created in 1940 for the movie "Arizona," became a county park, later a home for the movie industry.

the state's entire area and range in size from the large Navajo, Hopi, Apache, and Papago reservations, covering thousands of square miles, to the small Colorado River and Camp Verde reservations. The state's Indian reservations also range from those of such ready accessibility as the Salt River Indian Reservation, located between Scottsdale and Phoenix in the heart of the Phoenix Metropolitan Area to the tiny Havasupai Reservation deep in the western portion of the Grand Canyon.

Cowboys are also an important tourist attraction in Arizona, and rodeos are a significant element in both the summer and winter tourist seasons. Rodeos in the winter in the Phoenix and Tucson areas are widely attended by both residents and tourists alike. Summer rodeos as well as colorful Indian ceremonies form a major part of the visitor-attended activity in the northern part of the state during the summer.

Old mines, existing mines, and ghost towns comprise another important share of Arizona's tourist attractions. These range from Tombstone, "the town too tough to die," in Cochise County, southeastern Arizona, to Jerome, now a state historical park, in the northern part of the state. They include many other long-abandoned ghost towns scattered throughout the desert and mountain areas of central, southern and northern Arizona. Also of historical interest to visitors are several missions

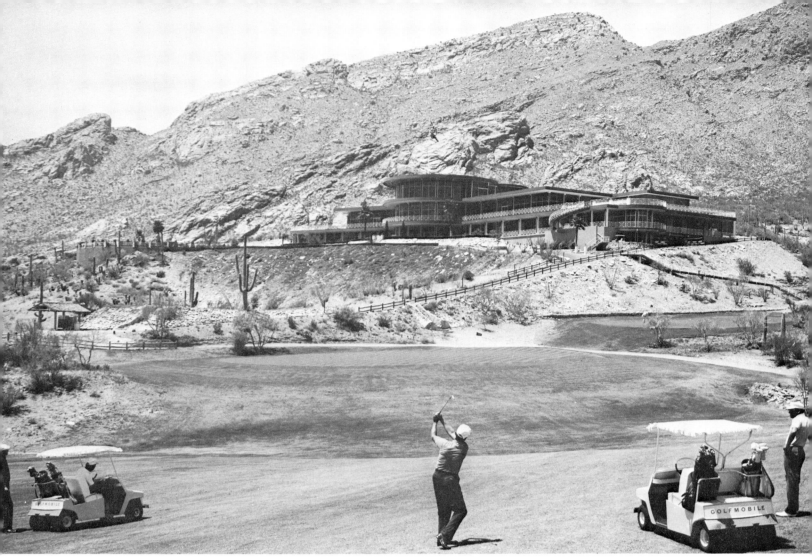

Fig. 25.6   Golfing is a year-round activity on many fine Arizona courses.

Fig. 25.7   Pena Blanca Lake, an hour south of Tucson — built by Arizona Game & Fish Department as a year-round fishery.

located in the south, which include the Tumacacori Mission National Monument as well as the still-in-use San Xavier del Bac, just south of Tucson.

Mexico serves as a major tourist attraction for Arizona, bringing visitors into the state from other parts of North America as well as providing a tourist attraction for Arizonans themselves. For Santa Cruz County, Mexico is undoubtedly the chief tourist attraction, resulting in considerable traffic each day back and forth across the border between the twin cities of Nogales, Arizona, and Nogales, Sonora. The Mexican west coast along the Gulf of California and points further south also serves as a tourist attraction for Arizonans and visitors to Arizona.

Sports and Other Activities

Aside from things to see and places to visit, things to do are likewise an important part of the tourist picture. Because of the climate and varied geography of the state, outdoor sports play a large role in the leisure time activities of tourists and residents alike. The year-round warmth of the desert regions of southern and central Arizona gives the state a strong advantage in outdoor sports, and spring sports have had an opportunity to develop as in few other states. In the late winter and early spring, one of the state's biggest attractions is the spring training activity of both major and minor league professional baseball teams. Late winter and early spring golf tournaments in the Phoenix and Tucson areas are also significant tourist attractions.

Water sports, both on the lakes along the Colorado River and on the lakes formed by the various dams of the Salt River Project in central Arizona are also significant in winter tourist and recreational activity in Arizona. At the same time, the more traditional winter sports in the mountainous areas of the southern part of the state as well as in northern Arizona have grown in their significance as tourist attractions. Collegiate sports, interscholastic sports, and individual recreational activities of all types are also extremely important to Arizonans as well as to those visiting the state. Fishing is a favorite pastime of many and the state offers fresh-water fishing in the streams and lakes of the northern and central part of the state, along the Colorado River, and in salt water of nearby Mexican ports on the Gulf of California. Hunting for a variety of game birds and animals that range from the white wing dove to elk, bear, and mountain lion is also significant in the recreational picture.

Since the end of World War II, tourism and recreational activity in Arizona have grown by leaps and bounds, both in volume and variety. Today it ranges from winter activity on the snow-covered slopes of the San Francisco Peaks to basking in the sun on the warm deserts of the southern part of the state, from sightseeing and spectator sports to participation in athletic activity by many tourists of all ages. Arizona's tourism and recreation are strongly seasonal, but with high levels of activity in some parts of the state offset by declines in seasonal activity in other areas. Better transportation, improved lodging and other tourist-serving facilities have helped the growth of the state's tourism, travel, and recreational industry throughout the 1960s. With the current trends in the economy of the nation and the continent, further increases during the 1970s can be fully expected.

Fig. 26.1   The railroad's "piggyback" trailer-on-flatcar service has speeded and simplified freight-moving.
Southern Pacific

G. L. Gifford
Economist

26

TRANSPORTATION AND UTILITIES

IN THE 1936 ISSUE of *Arizona and its Heritage*, the late eminent historian, Howard A. Hubbard, closed his article "Transportation" with the following statement:

The depression, the opening of airways, the development of good roads together with motor-bus and automobile travel, the competition of motor trucks have forced the railroad companies in Arizona, as in other states, to tear up the tracks of the weaker branch lines in order to reduce tax costs. It is not a wild flight of the imagination, however, to conclude that the untold narrative of Arizona's future, like the rich history of its past will be intimately and inseparably connected with the story of transportation.

Since any modern economy is highly dependent upon transportation for its very existence and development, and since growth is retarded in the absence of good transportation, the prophecy quoted above carried very little risk. The state of Arizona, located as it is on the main southern east-west routes connecting California to the rest of the nation, has always been a "bridge" state with a great deal of through traffic of all kinds. As more and more people have moved into the "sunshine" areas, more and more passenger movements have originated or terminated in Arizona. As more industries have located within the borders of the state, an increased amount of freight has terminated and originated within Arizona boundaries. The phenomenal growth of population and industry in Arizona could hardly have been forecast, even as late as 1936.

Since Arizona was the forty-eighth state to come into the Union, the framers of the constitution had a sturdy base of precedent upon which to base the laws fostering the growth and development of the new political entity.

Recognizing the importance of proper control over the utility industries, Arizona's founding fathers made provision for a Corporation Commission which, among other duties, was given the power to regulate "public service corporations." These are defined in the constitution as corporations "other than municipal engaged in carrying persons or property for hire; or in furnishing gas, oil, or electricity for light, fuel, or power."

Since the railways were already operating over considerable mileage in the Territory before statehood, the constitution also declared that all railways "heretofore constructed or that may hereafter be constructed, in this State" be common carriers subject to control by law. Also included in this provision were "car, express, electric, transmission, telegraph, telephone, or pipeline corporations."

It was on this firm foundation that the new state, with a population of slightly more than 200,000 persons, took its place with the other forty-seven states in the Union. In the years since statehood, the population growth has been great. By 1959 greater Tucson had an estimated population larger than that of the entire state at the time of admission to the Union in 1912, and greater Phoenix in 1959 had an estimated population equal to that of the entire state in 1930.

The prophecy of Hubbard regarding trends in rail mileage has been fulfilled. The peak of mileage was reached in 1930 with 2,494 miles of line owned and operated by the two railroads serving Arizona. By 1958 that figure had fallen to 2,177 miles of line, a drop of 12.7 percent which was 0.5 percent greater than the national reduction of 12.2 percent for the same period.

Served by Strong Railroads

Arizona has been fortunate to have two of the nation's strongest railroad companies serving it, furnishing transportation service east and west, and also within the state itself. The Atchison, Topeka, and Santa Fe Railway has served the northern part of the state with the main line passing through Winslow, Flagstaff, Ash

Fig. 26.2   Petroleum-distribution costs are cut by the use of railroad right-of-way for the pipeline.   *Southern Pacific*

Fork, Williams, and Kingman. Branch lines have served Phoenix and the Grand Canyon.)

In 1970 the Santa Fe ranked twelfth in operating revenues among the transportation companies of the United States. It has been a consistently strong rail carrier.

(The Southern Pacific Company tracks pass through the southern part of the state) serving such cities as Douglas, Tucson, Phoenix, Gila Bend, and Yuma) Nationally, the Southern Pacific ranked third in operating revenues in 1970 and, like the Santa Fe, has always been a strong rail carrier. The Southern Pacific in 1970 wholly owned and operated two subsidiary transportation companies in the state of Arizona; the Southern Pacific Pipe Lines, and the Pacific Motor Transport, a truck line. In addition to this, the company has pushed ahead with another type of service known as "piggyback," where the company hauls truck trailers on flat cars. The advantages of this trailer-on-flatcar service include greater speed (freight moving at passenger train speeds), rates competitive with highway carriers, pick up and delivery at each end, no weather delays, and virtually no loss and damage. It also eliminates the cost and construction of side tracks or loading trucks for individual industries.

The Southern Pacific was the first rail company in the United States to use its right-of-way for a petroleum pipeline, thus furnishing Arizona with a different type of service, which has lowered the cost of distribution of refined petroleum products to the consumers in the state. Gasoline, jet fuel, and other products from refineries around Los Angeles and El Paso are moved into the Phoenix and Tucson consuming areas by this pipeline.

Both railroads serving Arizona have specialized in providing rapid movement of perishables from the producing areas of the Southwest to the consuming centers of the middle and eastern markets — lettuce, cantaloupes, carrots, watermelons, potatoes, onions, cabbage, and other products. In 1970, trucks moved 1,019,518,507 pounds of perishables and rail moved 34,955,174 pounds from Mexico's west coast through the Nogales gateway to consuming points in the United States.

As it did throughout the nation, rail passenger service declined to a marked degree in Arizona in the 1950s and 1960s. Various factors causing the decline included (improved highways, buses, air carrier service, and most of all, the modern automobile.)

(Arizona in the early seventies was being served by many local bus lines and two large interstate carriers, Southwest Greyhound Lines and Continental Trailways) Because Arizona is a "bridge" state, these two lines have provided excellent service to all points east and west from the major cities in the state, with rapid, limited-stop schedules as well as local service. The national program of modernizing the highways has been materially improving operating conditions for bus operators as well as truck operators in Arizona, as in other states, but it has also increased the competition of the private automobile, which was estimated to be moving 90 percent of the intercity passenger traffic in United States in 1970.

Indicative of growth, truck registrations in Arizona increased from 78,657 in 1953 to 239,820 in 1969, which is a 33 percent increase, compared to the national increase during the same period of 54 percent. In 1968 there were sixty major truck firms providing truck service to and from all parts of the United States.

The state of Arizona maintains checking stations on all highways entering the state, and the records from these stations show that as many as 13,000 commercial vehicles entered the state during certain months in 1958 and 1959. The same records indicate that a total of 400,235 motor vehicles of all kinds entered the state in July 1960, while 726,588 entered in July 1970, which was an increase of 55 percent over the same period in 1960.

It has been estimated that tourists spent a total of $480 million in Arizona during 1967. Of this amount, it is estimated that $114 million was spent directly and indirectly on transportation, analyzed as follows: gas and oil and repairs, $80 million, and other transportation $34 million.

Nogales, Arizona, has become an important gateway for tourists and for trade with its neighbor to the south, Mexico. In 1970, 64,475 vehicles and 142,862 persons entered Mexico through this port, while 20,339 entered through the port of San Luis.

In 1970 the Arizona Customs District reported the value of exports to Mexico as $107,667,547 versus a total of $19,594,000 in 1944, and of imports as $208,559,821, as compared with $21,007,000 in 1944. These totals are indicative of the tremendous growth in trade with Mexico through the state of Arizona. Much of this trade has consisted of fresh fruits and vegetables from Mexico, and of machinery and other manufactured items moving into Mexico. No estimates are available of the amount of money spent by tourists and others in the border towns adjacent to Arizona.

Along with other forms of transportation, air service has increased tremendously in a relatively short time. In an area where the terrain is difficult to traverse and the distances great, the airplane is a special boon to rapid travel. In 1970 Arizona was being served by two transcontinental lines — American Airlines and Trans World Airlines — both of which were providing non-stop service from Phoenix and Tucson to Chicago and New York City, and regular flights to all points east and California. Elapsed time to Chicago was three hours and to New York, four and one-half. From Phoenix it was possible in the early seventies to fly directly to 110 cities in the United States — 38 non-stop — and to get connections to any city in the world having commercial air service.

In addition to the transcontinental lines, Arizona was being served by Western Airlines, which provided service to such cities as Denver, Minneapolis, and Seattle, as well as to the main cities of California. Continental Airlines has connected Arizona with California, Texas points, and Hawaii.

Local service in the West was being provided by two scheduled regional lines, Air West and Frontier Airlines. The one intra-state carrier, Apache Airlines, in 1971 was replaced by a new one, Cochise Airlines.

Air West in 1970 was providing daily flights between Phoenix, Yuma, Prescott, Kingman, Flagstaff, Grand Canyon, and Page, as well as giving service from these Arizona points to southern California, Las Vegas, Reno, and Salt Lake City. Air West also connected Arizona with Mazatlán, La Paz, and Puerto Vallarta. Frontier Airlines connected Clifton, Safford, Tucson, Phoenix, Prescott, Flagstaff, and Winslow, Arizona, with cities in New Mexico, Colorado, Utah, North and South Dakota, and Nebraska.

Southern Arizona, blessed with good flying weather virtually all year round and with excellent airports at Phoenix and Tucson, has continued to increase as an air transport center. The Phoenix airport ranked twentieth in the nation in volume of air traffic in 1970, with nearby Litchfield and Deer Valley airports as satellites to help carry the rapidly growing general aviation load at Sky Harbor. Tucson had taken on Ryan Field as a satellite. Air freight terminals were completed in 1970 at both Phoenix and Tucson. In the fall of 1960 Tucson became an international port with Aeronaves de Mexico providing flights to Mexico City and points on the Pacific. Full international status was acquired in 1963. In August, 1967, Tucson International Airport was designated a port of origin, making it possible to ship anywhere in the world from this port, and in 1970 Phoenix also gained international status for commercial aircraft and gained direct flights to Mexico.

Telephone Expansion

Telephone communication has been provided by the Mountain States Telephone and Telegraph Company (changed to Mountain Bell) for the majority of the state, while the General Telephone Company and a few small independent firms were serving some of the communities in northern Arizona in 1970. In all cases, the lines of these other firms were tied in with those of Mountain Bell company for national and international service.

Like other industries, the telephone companies have spent millions of dollars to expand facilities to keep up with the growing population. The majority of Arizona towns in 1970 had a dial system, and many cities were enjoying dial-direct service across the state and nation.

A few statistics serve to illustrate the growth of the telephone industry. Between 1940 and 1950, greater Phoenix showed an increase of 192 percent in the number of telephones in service, while the increase in greater Tucson for the same time was 202 percent. In the ten years between 1950 and 1960 telephones in service in the greater Phoenix area rose from 72,749 to 216,780 for an increase of 198 percent, while in greater Tucson during the same period the number of instruments increased from 35,967 to 91,850, for a gain of 155 percent. Growth throughout the state has been comparable. In 1970 Phoenix had 555,212 telephones in service; Tucson had 191,741, and the entire state, 918,471.

While good transportation and communication facilities are vital to a growing economy, a modern community is also dependent upon an ample supply of electric energy, especially for industry and, in Arizona, for pumping underground water for irrigation.

In 1944 the Arizona legislature passed the Power Authority Act which provided the legal basis for the state to secure and utilize its share of the power from Hoover Dam. The Authority was required to be self-sustaining and was given no funds for operation or for construction of the necessary transmission lines. However, the Federal Bureau of Reclamation proved willing to build into Arizona high-tension transmission lines within reach of customer taps, and to accept as payment an annual wheeling charge. These lines in 1969 had a total mileage of about 1,723. They reached, either directly or by connection with company or project lines, all of the major population centers in the state. This same act required the Authority to prepare a preference list of public bodies such as irrigation districts, electrical districts, cooperatives, and municipalities. Any excess of electricity over and above the needs of customers on the preference list could be sold to corporate electrical producers and distributors. The Authority was not confined to sales of hydroelectric power; it could also purchase and sell steam-generated power. During the year from July 1, 1958, to June 30, 1959, the Authority sold 865,816,690 kilowatt-hours of Colorado River power and 197,065,492 kilowatt-hours of steam-generated power. The Authority does not sell directly to the consumer, but to organizations which distribute it to users.

During the hearings on the Authority bill, responsible and respected individuals in the state testified that, in their considered judgment, the state would not need all the power and energy from Hoover Dam until possibly 1970. These individuals could not be blamed for not foreseeing the tremendous growth that was to take place in the Southwest. By 1959, Hoover power had long since been fully utilized and so had Arizona's share of power produced by Davis Dam, which was completed in 1951.

The rapidly increasing population, and especially the growing industrialization of Arizona, have increased the demand for electrical energy far above the hydroelectric capacity and the generating plants of yesteryear.

In 1941 the Salt River Power District constructed a steam generating plant to augment the power supplied by the dams on the Salt and Verde rivers. But this did not prove adequate. Between 1941 and 1958 power customers increased from 8,000 to 59,455. To keep abreast of the increasing demand, the first unit of the Kyrene steam generating plant, located about four miles southwest of Tempe, was put into service in 1952, and the second unit in 1954. This plant, which cost $12,383,845, added 90,000 kilowatts to the project generating capacity. In 1957–58 two units of the Agua Fria Steam Generating Plant were constructed by the District on the outskirts of northwest Phoenix at a cost of $25,000,000. These units generate 227,272 kilowatts, bringing the total generating capacity of the Salt River Project to 428,162 kilowatts. By 1970 generating capacity had been increased to 993,000 kilowatts, 14,000 of which were produced in Arizona by use of natural gas, oil and hydro, and 379,000 kilowatts were produced by a coal plant near Farmington, New Mexico.

The Arizona Public Service Company has also

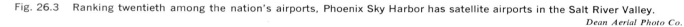

Fig. 26.3   Ranking twentieth among the nation's airports, Phoenix Sky Harbor has satellite airports in the Salt River Valley.

Dean Aerial Photo Co.

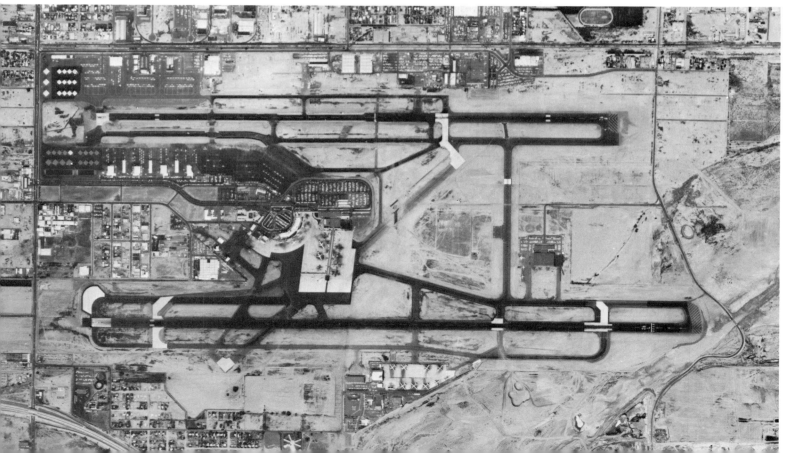

Fig. 26.4   Tucson International Airport has full international status, plus being a port of origin for global shipment.

found it necessary to expand its facilities several times. In 1950, at a cost of $15 million, it increased the capacity of its Phoenix plant to 145,000 kilowatts. In 1954–55 it constructed the Saguaro plant at Red Rock to develop 200,000 kilowatts, built the Yucca plant at Yuma in 1957–59 to provide 80,000 kilowatts, and the Ocotillo plant at Tempe to provide 110,000 kilowatts. These plants, together with the other seven smaller plants operated by this company, provide a total generating capacity in Arizona of 728,000 kilowatts in 1970. In addition to this, the Arizona Public Service Company imported 812 kilowatts of coal-produced electricity.

The Tucson Gas, Electric Light, and Power Company was able to meet the needs of Tucson and environs for many years with the power generated by its combined diesel and steam plants at Sixth Street and Cortaro. In 1948 it was necessary for this company to erect its DeMoss-Petrie plant with a capacity of 105,000 kilowatts, and in 1958 it completed its Plant Number Four on Irvington Road with a capacity of 160,000 kilowatts, which by 1968 had been increased to 429,000 kilowatts.

Besides these large plants, there are numerous smaller power plants around the state bringing the total to more than seventy in 1970. In 1970 the total sales of electric power in Arizona was 15,070.6 million kilowatts compared to 8,515.8 million kilowatts in 1963.

In 1968 no further plans were being made for construction of any more dams in Arizona on the Colorado River. However, construction of additional steam-generated capacity was being rapidly pushed. Salt River Power District, Arizona Public Service Company, and Tucson Gas and Electric Company, along with Southern Cali-

fornia Edison, Public Service of New Mexico, and El Paso Electric Company have a joint interest in a 755,000-kilowatt steam generating plant at Four Corners near Farmington, New Mexico. One-half began operating in 1969 and the other half in 1970. These same utilities have joined in an organization known as Western Energy Supply and Transmission Associated (WEST) comprising twenty-three member utilities in six states.

The first project under the WEST concept was an addition to the Four Corners plant consisting of two 750,000-kilowatt generators. The second project in which Arizona had an interest was in Nevada, known as the Mojave Plant which was fueled by coal from the Black Mesa coal fields in northwest Arizona via a new 270-mile pipeline built and operated by the Southern Pacific Company.

Another steam generating project was being constructed at Page, Arizona to meet the anticipated demand of the 1970s. In addition to the above, Arizona as of 1970 was interconnected to other utilities so that it could draw on power available in other western states to take care of peak loads.

A new source of power has been growing in importance in the state since 1960. Natural gas consumption in 1970 was 181,437,676,000 cubic feet, compared to 97,624,569,000 cubic feet in 1957, an increase of about 50 percent.

With an assured supply of power for the future and a dynamic, modern transportation system, the state of Arizona at the beginning of the seventies seemed to be well prepared for continuation of its amazing growth in population and industry.

Robert H. Marshall
Economist

27

BANKING AND FINANCE

ONE OF THE BASIC REQUIREMENTS of a developing complex economy is an adequately established and functioning financial system. The satisfactory provision of the essential commodities of money and credit is vital for economic growth and development. Arizona, indeed, affords an excellent example of the significance of financial factors in the state's growing economy.

Arizona's expanding population increases the need for financial services. During the period from 1956 to 1966, Arizona exhibited the second highest rate of population growth of any state in the nation. In the Rocky Mountain states, Arizona's population has been exceeded only by that of Colorado. Between 1956 and 1966, nonagricultural employment in Arizona increased by almost 180,000 persons, reflecting a relative growth of about 35 percent. In this same period, Arizona's employment in the finance, insurance, and real estate industry rose from 9,500 to 22,500, a percentage increase of over 135 percent.

Out of total employment in the finance, insurance, and real estate grouping, some 45 percent in the sixties were employed by commercial banks, credit agencies, and security dealers. Insurance companies accounted for 30 percent of the total, with real estate firms providing one-fourth of total employment.

Financial developments in Arizona in the late 1960s reflected the operations of several different groups. It is worthwhile to examine briefly the standing of the major types of financial institutions operating within the state.

Commercial Banks

The banking industry comprises the most important single group within the state's financial structure. Between 1956 and 1966, total bank deposits reached a new high level approaching $2.25 billion, a percentage increase over that period of 161 percent, the highest relative growth for any state in the nation. Arizona in the mid-1960s ranked second among the eight Rocky Mountain states in banks' holdings of deposits, capital accounts, and total assets, exceeded only by Colorado.

In addition, on the basis of deposits, the largest and second largest banks in the Rocky Mountain region in 1969 were the Valley National Bank of Arizona and the First National Bank of Arizona, respectively. According to deposits-size, these two banks stood in the top 100 commercial banks in the United States.

The existence of a statewide branch banking law contributes to the active role of Arizona banks in financing economic development. In 1969 seventeen states and the District of Columbia were permitting statewide branch banking. These seventeen included the Rocky Mountain states of Arizona, Idaho, Nevada, and Utah.

A majority of Arizona's commercial banks in 1969 did not hold membership in the Federal Reserve System, although all banks had their deposits insured by the Federal Deposit Insurance Corporation. However, member banks in the state operated a preponderant number of banking offices, located principally in the head office county and in counties contiguous to the head office county.

At year-end 1967, Arizona had a total of seventeen commercial banks which operated as a group 265 branch offices. Although the total number of commercial banks in Arizona had increased by a net of twelve between 1946 and 1967, the relative increase in the number of banking offices has been appreciably above that for various state groupings, classified according to branch banking law. In the early 1960s the state had a smaller percentage of its total population residing in "bankless towns" compared with an estimated percentage of United States population living in "bankless towns." Arizona compared even more favorably with national results on the basis of population living in towns immediately serviced by only one bank.

Generally speaking, banks with statewide branches can participate in greater and more diverse lending activities than can unit banks. Statewide branch banking facilitates the flow of savings funds from urban to rural areas and from relatively more developed areas. In effect, statewide branch banking provides the basis for a more economic allocation of banking resources within a state. Indeed, the Arizona branch banking law establishes a legal framework for the development of a viable banking system, well adapted to financing the needs of a rapidly growing state.

Although commercial banking in Arizona in the 1960s was characterized primarily by statewide branch banking, some relatively small unit banks operated in the metropolitan areas of Tucson and Phoenix. The demonstrated ability of these smaller unit banks to compete successfully with the larger branch systems (both in price and nonprice ways) has enhanced the viable performance of commercial banking in the state.

Commercial banks in Arizona have been active participants in the state's growth, especially as reflected in the high rate of lending to private borrowers in the form of loans and discounts. Loans and discounts constitute the primary type of output of commercial banks. In recent years insured commercial banks in Arizona, as a

Ray Manley

Fig. 27.1   Modern banking is tangibly expressed in Arizona bank branches by the use of highly contemporary structures.

Bob Osbahr

group, held a higher proportion of their total assets in the form of loans and discounts than did all insured commercial banks in the United States, as a group. Among the Rocky Mountain states, Arizona-insured commercial banks, taken together as a group, exhibited the highest ratio of loans and discounts to total assets during the 1960s. Since June of 1957, insured commercial banks in Arizona have held more than half of their total assets in the form of loans and discounts, attaining a loan ratio of well over 60 percent in mid-1968. As of 1967, only three states had 60 percent or more of their insured commercial banks' assets in the form of loans and discounts. These three states and their respective loan ratios included Vermont with 63.4 percent, New Hampshire with 61.3 percent, and Arizona with 60.3 percent.

Another aspect of the changing structure of banking in Arizona has been the increase in the number of bank mergers. Bank-merger activity in Arizona constitutes a part of the overall bank-merger movement in the United States. This general merger movement is the principal factor accounting for the gradual reduction in the number of commercial banks in the nation and in Arizona during the post-World War II period. In the five-year period between 1953 and year-end 1958, the total number of commercial banks in Arizona declined from fourteen to eight, while in this same period a total of seven banks with combined banking resources of over $86 million were absorbed by three banks having head offices in Phoenix. It should be noted, however, that in this same five-year period, the total number of banking offices (exclusive of banking facilities at government establishments) increased from 71 to 137.

Although it is difficult to weigh precisely specific factors operative in a particular bank merger, some of the significant general economic factors contributing to bank mergers include the following: (1) moves by banks to strengthen market positions through diversified operations, particularly in the growing area of "retail banking"; (2) adaptation to appreciable population shifts into outlying suburban areas through the acquisition of "ready-made" banking facilities, which are often more legally accessible than *de novo* offices; (3) adjustment to the enhanced role of commercial lending which has prompted banks to merge to counteract lagging growth in deposits and business, to expand legally stipulated loan limits, to meet rising competitive pressure of non-bank lenders, and to forestall officer shortages; and (4) attempts to offset the undervaluation of bank shares and to augment financial prestige.

An additional distinguishing characteristic of the banking structure in Arizona in the late 1960s was the relative importance of group banking. In simple terms, group banking exists where two or more banks are controlled by a holding company which itself may or may not be a bank. The intrinsic nature of the group banking relationship derives from use of the corporate device to obtain control of banks, whether by direct purchase of

stock or by the exchange of holding company stock for the stock of individual banks. Group banking is found in varying degrees in every state in the Rocky Mountain region. At year-end 1968, the latest date for which data were available, one banking holding company owned or controlled 25 percent or more of the outstanding stock of two banks in Arizona. These two banks had ninety-nine branches and total deposits of $977 million, or in percentage terms, 34 percent of all commercial bank deposits in the state. As compared with Arizona, banks in holding company groups accounted for a higher proportion of all commercial bank deposits within the following Rocky Mountain states: Nevada, Montana, Utah, and Idaho.

Life Insurance Companies

Life insurance companies are important institutional investors, and individuals have increasingly resorted to life insurance purchases as a form of saving. The Institute of Life Insurance states that life insurance is the principal type of long-term saving for the majority of families in the United States. In return for premium payments by the policyholders, life insurance companies contractually agree to make installment or lump-sum payments to the policyholders when they reach a certain age or upon their disablement, or to their beneficiaries in the event of death of the policyholders. Life insurance companies use premium funds to purchase such obligations as mortgages and corporate and governmental securities.

Life insurance in force in Arizona exhibited a large relative growth during the 1960s. Between year-end 1957 and year-end 1967, life insurance in force with legal reserve life insurance companies in Arizona increased from $2,139 million to $7,512 million, for a percentage gain of over 250 percent. Balanced off against the great growth in life insurance in force in the state is the significant increase in the number of Arizona life insurance companies from 63 companies at year-end 1957 to 221 companies in mid-1967. As of June, 1967, Arizona had the second largest number of life insurance companies in the United States, exceeded only by 231 companies in Texas. At mid-1967 the home offices of 123 life insurance companies were located in the city of Phoenix alone. In addition to domestic companies, 389 life insurance companies of other states were licensed to do business in the state of Arizona in December, 1966. Within Arizona during the calendar year 1966, the latest year for which data were available in 1969, Arizona legal reserve life insurance companies wrote direct premiums including disability in the amount of $19 million, whereas out-of-state life insurance companies wrote direct premiums totaling nearly $193 million.

At the end of 1966, mortgage holdings by life insurance companies in Arizona were distributed as follows: $103 million in farm mortgages, $192 million in nonfarm FHA and VA insured and guaranteed mortgages, and $501 million in nonfarm conventional mortgages.

Savings and Loan Associations

Another important group within the financial structure of Arizona is that of savings and loan associations. These associations are cooperative thrift groups that are chartered by either federal or state government. Holders of share accounts in savings and loan associations are actually stockholders rather than depositors, and they receive dividends rather than interest on their shares. Savings and loan associations have become increasingly more competitive with commercial banks in recent years, especially with regard to attracting savings funds from commercial banks. The associations are generally able to pay a higher rate of return on savings than can commercial banks because the associations hold a high proportion of their assets in long-term, relatively high interest-bearing, first mortgages of the conventional type.

Arizona ranked second in 1969 among the eight Rocky Mountain states in holdings of total assets by savings and loan associations, being exceeded only by the holdings in Colorado.

At year-end 1966, savings and loan associations in Arizona held total assets of some $807 million, whereas eight years earlier at year-end 1958, total asset holdings were $227 million. In the mid-1960s, savings associations accounted for about one-third of the total combined liquid savings held by savings and loan associations, commercial banks, and credit unions in the state.

In mid-1958, nine out of a total of ten savings and loan associations in Arizona were insured by the Federal Savings and Loan Insurance Corporation. All federally chartered associations are required by law to belong to the corporation, while state-chartered institutions may join if they elect to do so. As of June, 1958, these nine federally insured institutions held over 85 percent of the aggregate assets of all savings and loan associations in Arizona. In June, 1959, the sole non-federally insured savings and loan association was placed in receivership by the state. As a result, the Arizona legislature at its 1960 session enacted legislation prohibiting the establishment of any savings and loan association until federal insurance was obtained.

In the mid-1960s a total of fourteen savings and loan associations operated in the state. Twelve of these associations had state charters, while the two federally-chartered institutions — First Federal (Phoenix), and Tucson Federal — were the first and second largest, respectively, in total asset holdings.

James E. Wert
Finance

Maurice M. Briggs
Real Estate

28

REAL ESTATE

IN A TECHNICAL SENSE, real estate and real property are synonymous terms meaning land and all that is attached to it. But in a practical sense, real estate means improvement, development, investment, speculation, brokerage, management, financing, marketing, and other activities which occur with increasing frequency in connection with real property as population rises. A population of 1.67 million will support a substantial volume of these activities, but in Arizona where the population in 1969 was more than a quarter greater than in 1960, and was expected to increase early in the seventies to 140 percent of the 1960 figure, real estate activities were on their way to boom proportions.

Much of this growth has been concentrated in the Phoenix and Tucson areas, in Maricopa and Pima counties, although several other areas — Yuma, Flagstaff, Casa Grande, and Lake Havasu — have had substantial population increases.

Cities and towns are the places in which real estate development has been most pronounced, but speculative interest in Arizona real estate covers the whole of the state, from the deserts of the south to the mountains of the north. People from all over the United States have purchased a stake in the glamorous future they foresee for Arizona.

An important stimulus to Arizona real estate has been the establishment of retirement communities. In 1970 there were at least a half-dozen well-established ones in existence, and more were being launched. The attraction of the state for retirement is more closely associated with lack of humidity than with year-round mild temperatures, which are a main attraction in Florida and California. For this reason northern Arizona (average elevation over one mile) with low winter temperatures and southern Arizona with high summer temperatures are both able to attract retired people who

find high humidity rather than variable temperature the greatest threat to comfortable living.

From 1960 to 1969, contract construction activity in Arizona averaged about $67 million per year. Much of this construction took place outside of incorporated cities, though in their environs; thus the figures on building permits do not reveal the extent of the boom in Arizona, since permit procedures are limited largely to incorporated cities.

In both Tucson and Phoenix, the value of building permits issued has been constantly increasing. Around the state, substantial increases during the sixties occurred in Casa Grande, Mesa, Scottsdale, Tempe, and Yuma.

The Economy of Real Estate

That phenomenon of intensive urbanization, the regional shopping center, made its entrance into the state during the sixties. A shopping center study of the Phoenix Metropolitan Area listed approximately 110 separate centers, of which at least 8 were of a regional type. In Tucson there were about 40 centers, including one regional center which was being extensively enlarged.

Although both of Arizona's principal cities were still small, quiet communities in 1912 when the Territory was admitted to the Union as the forty-eighth state, they were both, by the late sixties, sufficiently large and developed to be in need of urban renewal. Each of them in 1969 had applied for federal assistance in this respect and in 1970 had embarked upon a program of slum clearance and rehabilitation. The average value of authorized housing units in the late 1960s in the Phoenix Metropolitan Area ran in the $11,800 range for single family units, $6,900 for multiple units, with an overall average of $10,300 per unit. In the Tucson Metropolitan Area, comparable figures were $18,800 for single family units, $9,200 for multiple units, with an overall average of $16,600.

Although the majority of Arizonans live in moderately priced homes, since World War II there have been built many exclusive subdivisions and magnificent estates for those who can afford them.

The spectacular views that Arizona topography creates have offered a considerable stimulus to architectural imagination. The many unusual custom-built homes in modern Arizona attest to the challenge of desert and mountain scenery.

Most Arizonans in 1970 owned their own homes. This was made possible by the FHA and VA financing provided by many life insurance companies and mutual savings banks located in the northeastern part of the United States. These institutions have shown their confidence in Arizona's future by the amount of money they have made available for home mortgages. Mortgages owned by life insurance companies in Arizona in 1969 totaled over $750 million, of which FHA and VA comprised about $200 million.

For years Arizona had relatively few savings and loan associations upon which to depend for home mortgage financing, and the bulk of local funds made available for this purpose had to be provided by commercial banks. In the late 1960s, the state could boast of many well-established savings and loan associations with sizeable assets and, as elsewhere in the United States, these were Arizona's fastest growing financial institutions.

Styles and Materials

Arizona homes are usually of the ranch style with enclosed patios. This patio is an important part of Arizona life, providing an extra living room during most of the year. Often the patio has a swimming pool, barbecue facilities, and paved areas for parties and dancing. Within the house, design and arrangement of the rooms are very similar to those found in ranch houses throughout the United States, but one modification in southern Arizona is the cooling system that is found in almost every house. Until recently this cooling was by the evaporative method, which was inexpensive and, because of the lack of humidity, quite effective. Since the 1950s more and more homes have been cooled with refrigeration, and the use of typical desert cooling has been on the wane.

Mud blocks baked in the sun — adobes — have been the traditional Arizona building material. These blocks, twelve to eighteen inches wide, are grouted with cement or mud into a tapering wall which is covered with chicken wire and plastered. Adobe walls are probably the best insulation known to man, but with the cost of labor ever on the rise there are few who can afford to construct such an adobe house. In the late sixties, pumice block, brick, and burnt adobe were the principal Arizona building materials.

Instant Real Estate

Real estate transactions in Arizona are handled with a speed and a dispatch that will amaze most easterners. When a purchase contract is signed, the earnest money is placed in escrow, and a title policy is ordered immediately. As soon as the title policy is ready, the escrow agent — who may be the title company, a broker, or a lawyer — will make the closing adjustments, draw the papers and have the parties come in at their convenience to sign and to make the remaining payments. The escrow agent then completes the transaction by recording the instruments and paying the sellers the balance due. All this may take place without buyer and seller ever meeting and can be completed in three days if necessary. Many title companies are to be found in both the large cities, and most of them operate on an almost statewide basis.

Ownership of Land

Of a total land area of 72,688,000 acres, in 1969 the United States owned 32,475,263 acres, or 44.68 percent of the area of the entire state. An additional 19,650,323 acres, or about 27 percent, was Indian land held in federal trust. The state owned 9,203,669 acres, or 12.66 percent, of which about 8,000,000 acres was a state trust for the benefit of the public school system. Private interests owned 11,358,745 acres, or 15.63 percent. While this last figure seems small, the actual area is greater than the entire land area of Massachusetts, Connecticut, Rhode Island, and Delaware combined. Also, the federal and state lands are not unproductive, and may be put into private use by way of mineral and grazing leases, for some commercial purposes, and, in the case of Indian lands, by tribal development.

Most Indian lands in federal trust in Arizona are owned by the tribes as cooperative units, rather than by individual members. Many non-Indians have difficulty in understanding how this form of land-ownership works, but within the Indian groups there is every evidence that it is a satisfying arrangement. Because Indian cooperative ownership makes possible long-range comprehensive planning for enormous reaches of land, it is anticipated that the Indian reservations will play a very significant role in the future of Arizona real estate.

Arizona's Spanish heritage is revealed in the frequently found separation of mineral rights from surface rights in real estate. The Spanish crown reserved to itself all the minerals in the lands in its colonies, and this pattern of reserving mineral rights has persisted in modern times in the practice of the federal and state governments and of private owners. Since minerals abound in Arizona, it is easy to envision the owner of a home in a swank subdivision keeping a pack of mastiffs to drive off the hordes of prospectors seeking to find a rich strike on his lot. But this would be a fantasy since prospecting is not permitted in developed areas. Moreover, most of the minerals in Arizona are not of the "get-rich-quick" variety that the prospector can find with an ordinary pick, and haul off on a burro's back; they are, rather, predominantly of the type that requires large-scale equipment and, to an ever-increasing degree, the latest in modern technological skills and knowledge.

Another inheritance from Spain of importance in real estate is the community property law which is the basic property system for husbands and wives in Arizona. The essence of the law is that real estate bought out of the earnings of either spouse belongs in equal undivided shares to both. The community property system is one of almost complete equality; the only element of inequality to be found is the right of the husband to manage personal property. In real estate the husband enjoys no preference, and each of the spouses must join in any sale. Community property rights do not extend to property owned by either party before marriage or to property received by inheritance or gift.

Planning the Future

Out in the wide stretches of desert a man may do what he will with his land if he has the money to pamper his fancies, and many wealthy cattlemen have indulged themselves in lavish homes or outbuildings. But when individuals live in close proximity, no man may do with his land that which will destroy the value of another's, and the enforcement of this principle requires the establishment of planning and zoning legislation and subdivision controls. In the two most populous counties, Maricopa and Pima, there were, in 1970, both municipal and county planning and zoning commissions, and these bodies have made strenuous efforts to cooperate as closely as possible. This fosters the development of consistent goals and facilitates the expansion of the corporate limits of the city.

Many of the other cities in Arizona had established zoning by the late 1960s and were actively engaged in full-scale planning to enable them to handle their land-use programs.

The Division of Economic and Business Research of the College of Business and Public Administration at the University of Arizona was functioning in 1970 as the state agency for Urban Planning Assistance grants for municipality, county, and Indian reservations. This program was funded under Section 701 of the Housing Act of 1954, as amended.

Real estate brokers and salesmen in Arizona are licensed, and in 1970 their activities were being supervised by the state Real Estate Department. The Real Estate Act first passed in 1937 has been periodically strengthened, most recently in 1968. As of January 1, 1969, all applicants for an original salesman's license were required to show that they had completed at least thirty classroom hours of instruction in a real estate course prescribed and approved by the state real estate board. All applicants for an original broker's license were to have completed at least ninety classroom hours.

Several private schools organized to fulfill the above requirements were in existence, both in Phoenix and in Tucson, as of 1970.

There are very few states in which the term "real estate" covers such a wide variety of climates, soil types, agricultural lands, extractive processes, and urban and rural uses as it does in Arizona. Though much of the state is desert and much of it is mountainous, there is very little land that Arizonans will admit cannot be used. Many new developments, therefore, were on the board for the decade of the seventies.

Philip N. Knorr
Forestry

29

FOREST INDUSTRIES

FOREST AND RANGE LANDS give Arizona much of its distinctive charm. The forests, 28 percent of the state's area in the 1960s, were the major watersheds which provided water for the state; the forests also furnished wood for industry, forage for livestock, habitat for wildlife, and recreational areas for Arizona residents and visitors.

Much of the forested land is in piñon pines, junipers, and oaks, but because these species are usually short and scrubby they are seldom cut for industrial use. The commercial forest land in 1969 occupied about 4 million acres or 5.5 percent of Arizona, with ponderosa pine the principal species.

Location of Forests

Much of Arizona's commercial forest land is found in a band along the Mogollon Rim, the great escarpment which runs from the southeast to the northwest across the middle of the state. However, scattered high mountain ranges, particularly in southeastern Arizona, have beautiful timber stands at high elevations. In most of the western United States the occurrence of tree species is determined chiefly by availability of moisture and by temperature. Precipitation and temperature vary with elevation; thus there is a close relationship between elevation and the kind of forest in any area. Arizona's noncommercial forests of piñon, juniper, and oak are found mostly between 4,500 and 7,500 feet where precipitation ranges from ten to twenty inches a year. The commercial forests generally occur above 5,500 feet in northern Arizona, above 6,500 feet in southern Arizona, and where the precipitation exceeds nineteen inches. Ponderosa pine in the 1960s made up about 90 percent of the commercial forest, reaching its best development between 7,000 and 8,500 feet. Douglas fir begins to

displace ponderosa pine at 8,000 feet and is found up to 9,500 feet. Above 8,500 feet and up to timberline (about 12,000 feet) the fir-spruce type occurs, in which Engelmann spruce, corkbark fir and subalpine fir predominate. Limber pine and white fir are found in the upper elevations of the ponderosa-pine type and in the Douglas-fir type. In the southern mountains in the state, Arizona pine, Apache pine and Chihuahua pine mix with or, in some cases, replace ponderosa pine. They represent such a small portion of the commercial stand that they are lumped with ponderosa in reports. Aspen occurs above 8,000 feet in large or small patches in the forest.

Only 4 percent of the commercial timberland in the state in the 1960s was in private hands. The seven national forests in Arizona had 66 percent, and the Indian reservations — principally the Fort Apache and Navajo — had 29 percent of the commercial forest lands. The forest industries in Arizona, therefore, were almost entirely dependent upon U.S. Forest Service and Indian timber harvesting.

In 1962, the annual harvest cut was 66 million cubic feet from a total forest inventory of 6,091 million cubic feet (see Table 29.1). This 1.1 percent cut is conservative (in that the older, larger trees contain most of the volume), and purposely so, in order that the growing stock of the forest can be increased to provide greater harvests for the future. The lumber production in Arizona, in lumber tally, was 326 million board feet in 1962; the Forest Service projects an annual cut 78 percent greater by 1992. A problem exists for this projection in that intermediate tree size classes are in short supply, but professional forest managers have plans to bridge the critical years.

Of the 66 million cubic feet of timber products harvested in 1962, 75 percent went into sawlogs and

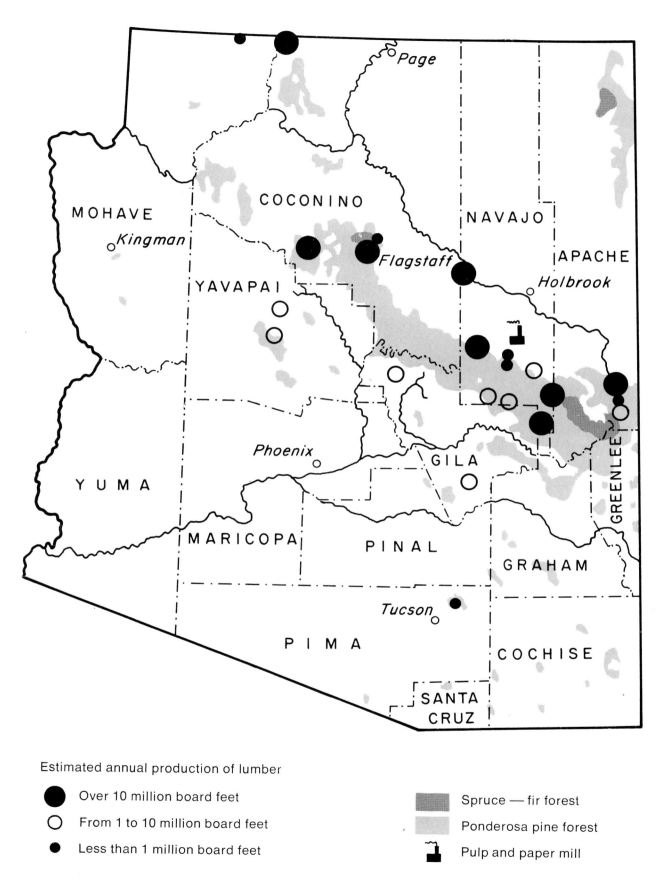

Estimated annual production of lumber

⬤   Over 10 million board feet

◯   From 1 to 10 million board feet

•   Less than 1 million board feet

▨   Spruce — fir forest

░   Ponderosa pine forest

🏭   Pulp and paper mill

Fig. 29.1   Location of the forests and forest-based industries in Arizona.

TABLE 29.1

The Volume of Timber in Arizona Commercial Forests

	Sawtimber		Growing Stock	
	Million Board Feet	Percent of Total	Million Cubic Feet	Percent of Total
Ponderosa pine	17,534	87.7	3,100	83.8
Douglas fir	1,449	7.3	335	9.0
White fir	454	2.3	110	3.0
Engelmann and blue spruces	181	0.9	45	1.2
Other softwoods	199	1.0	34	0.9
Total softwoods	19,817	99.2	3,624	97.9
Hardwoods (broadleaves)	171	0.8	76	2.1
Total all Species	19,988	100.0	3,700	100.0

12 percent into round pulpwood. The remaining wood was used for such things as poles, mine timbers, converter poles, charcoal wood, posts, fuelwood, and farm timbers. Earlier estimates of Arizona's use of its own lumber have been about 10 percent. The studies in the late 1960s showed that 24 percent of Arizona-produced lumber was marketed within the state, and this figure may increase further. Certainly the metropolitan areas of Phoenix and Tucson have provided growing markets. New Mexico and Texas purchased 28 percent, and the five midwestern states of Michigan, Missouri, Illinois, Ohio, and Indiana took over one-fourth of the lumber produced in Arizona in the 1960s. Figures from the Bureau of the Census show that the lumber industry alone generated more than $20 million into the state's economy.

Southwest Forest Industries, Inc. established a pulp and paper mill near Snowflake, Arizona, in 1961. In addition to round pulpwood obtained mostly from thinning operations in ponderosa pine forests, sawmill residues were being used in the late 1960s to manufacture about 150,000 tons of newsprint and kraft linerboard per year, with about half of the tonnage going into each product. Most of the linerboard was further manufactured into cardboard boxes near the state's metropolitan areas, and the newsprint was sold to newspapers in Arizona and Southern California. This pulp and paper mill is unique because its source of water comes from a series of very deep wells and because the effluent from the manufacturing process goes into a dry lake bed for evaporation so that neither surface nor ground waters downstream are polluted.

Fig. 29.2 Twenty-four percent of Arizona lumber has been marketed in the state since the late sixties. *Southwest Forest Industries*

Southwest Forest Industries

Fig. 29.3   During the 1960s, a pulp and paper mill was established near Snowflake, with unique avoidance of pollution.

The Forest's Multiple Values

Arizona's forests, managed on a multiple-use basis, yield products and services of great value other than wood, including water, forage, game, recreation and scenery. It is impossible to estimate even for individual stands all of the values for products and services. Eventually forest economists will probably have a part in deciding how to allocate the benefits from the forest, but, in the meantime, wildland managers are limited to value judgments in their attempts to determine practices which will optimize yields of products and services. As in much of the arid western United States, water is probably the most important single product from Arizona's forests. For its population and land area, Arizona in the 1960s had a greater water deficit than any other western state. Groundwater was declining steadily due to heavy pumping, with the result that some land had gone out of agriculture. Most of the surface runoff of the state was being controlled for city and agricultural use by the Salt River Project which collected the runoff in a series of dams on streams flowing into the greater Phoenix area. Just how important the forested area is to surface water production is shown by Forest Service estimates of the average number of inches of annual runoff from forest types: 4.7 for fir-spruce; 2.8 for pon-

derosa pine; 1.1 for piñon-juniper. The desert areas in the state produce less than 0.1 inch of runoff. A large quantity of the 2.1 million acre-feet of water consumed annually in the 1960s in Arizona came from the runoff from forested lands.

Citizens of the state have been seriously concerned about the water supply. In 1956, an Arizona Water Resources Committee was formed and has been a moving force in the state. Experts were asked by the committee to summarize research results and to give opinions. A Department of Watershed Management was established in the State Land Office. The committee in the 1960s was hosting an annual watershed symposium which brought together most of the professors, researchers, managers, and administrators concerned with water and watershed management in Arizona.

Many research projects and some pilot studies were under way in 1970 to determine the effects of vegetative manipulation upon water yield and quality. The timber and aesthetics-recreation values in the spruce-fir and ponderosa-pine zones probably will limit, but not discourage, practices designed to increase runoff. However, in the much larger acreages of piñon-juniper-oak which covered 16.6 million acres in 1969 there was considerably less recreation value, and since the wood grown was noncommercial there was little opposition to management practices to clear away the scrubby growth. Pilot studies, thousands of acres in size, have been made wherein the piñon-juniper-oak has been cleared and seeded to grass. The process is costly and will require continuing funds for maintenance of the desired forage cover. Concerned Arizona people hope that replacement of the scrub forest with grass will afford more precipitation runoff of equal or better quality and greatly improved forage for livestock. The pilot studies in the 1960s were large enough to give figures through the 1970s as to costs versus benefits received, so that careful economic guidelines could be set and the margins for the feasibility of this vegetative manipulation could then be determined.

Improvement of Forest Lands

Arizona's history of grazing on forested land dates back to Vásquez de Coronado, who in the period from 1538 to 1540 led his forces, complete with bands of horses, cattle, and sheep, from Mexico into Arizona near the modern site of Fort Huachuca, and proceeded over hills, valleys, and mountains past present-day Whiteriver and McNary on northward to the Zuñi River. Much later the lower forested areas in the southern parts of the state were grazed by Spanish mission livestock, and still later most of Arizona was grazed by American cattle and sheep. It is believed that overgrazing before the turn of the century caused much sheet and gully erosion that seriously reduced forage production capacity. Overgraz-

ing before 1900 and fire protection not long after the turn of the century are believed to have favored the spread of the piñon-juniper type. Grazing practices on national forest lands have taken into consideration their multiple uses, with the result that cattle numbers were decreased 63 percent between 1918 and 1963, and in 1963 there were only one-eighth as many sheep as in 1918, grazing in the national forests. The great improvement in forest range lands has been due for the most part to cooperation between government administrators and grazing permit holders.

The forested areas of Arizona provide habitat for wildlife. Projects to improve wildlife habitat are often cooperative enterprises between federal agencies and the Arizona Game and Fish Department. Man-made lakes in the forested areas have increased trout fishing. Over $12 million for coldwater fishing (trout) was spent in 1960, almost all of it in the higher forested lands. Fishing in streams and lakes in Arizona's national forests has increased twenty-one times from 1946 to 1963. Estimates from questionnaire sampling for 1960 indicated that money spent by big-game hunters totaled over $8 million. The increase in hunters in Arizona's national forests in the seventeen-year period ending in 1963 was tenfold. The estimated big-game harvest from these same national forests for 1963 totaled 27,000 (deer, elk, wild turkey, antelope, and javelina). Forested lands under the stewardship of other federal agencies

Southwest Forest Industries

Fig. 29.4 By-products of lumbering at McNary Wood Products include newsprint and kraft linerboard for cardboard boxes.

Southwest Forest Industries

Fig. 29.5 Up-to-date technology accounts for the manufacture of linerboard and other marketable wood products.

and Indians, and in private ownership, yielded additional numbers of big game.

Recreational use of forest lands in Arizona has boomed because of a burgeoning population with more leisure time, improved transportation, and greater affluence. The White Mountain Apaches, the Navajo Tribal Parks Commission, the Fish and Wildlife Service, the Arizona Parks Board, the National Park Service, and the U.S. Forest Service all had recreation programs in the 1960s. The Forest Service estimated that the number of recreation visitors to national forests in Arizona increased sixteen times between 1946 and 1963. Visits to these forests for this period are shown by classes of recreation use in Table 2. Visits to national parks and monuments in the 28 percent of Arizona that is classed as commercial and non-commercial forest land totaled 2,688,000 visits for 1967; this figure excludes desert parks and monuments and the Colorado River boating.

Forest research in Arizona was initiated by the U.S. Forest Service in 1908 with a ponderosa pine study at the Fort Valley Experimental Forest and with range management investigations at the Santa Rita Experimental Range. In 1970 the Rocky Mountain Forest and Range Experiment Station had research centers at Tempe, Flagstaff, and Tucson which carried on a broad-based program dealing with most aspects of forest and range land use. The University of Arizona has always carried on research regarding wildlands; this research was given considerable impetus by the establishment by the Board of Regents in 1958 of a Department of Watershed Management. Much of the department's research is carried out as a part of the program of the University of Arizona Agricultural Experiment Station. Graduate and undergraduate programs deal with aspects of special and multiple use of forest and range lands. Also, in 1958, the Board of Regents authorized a Department of Forestry at Northern Arizona University at Flagstaff. Its emphasis has been on an undergraduate curriculum.

Pressures To Increase

By law most of the publicly owned forests of Arizona have been committed to multiple use. However, all indications are that future demands will intensify and that there will be pressure on wildland managers by single-interest groups. Plans in 1969 for the production of wood fiber for industry called for better than a 75 percent increase in the following thirty years. Some shrinkage in the acreage base would be expected, however, because of the new campgrounds, summer homes, roads, power lines, reservoirs, and urban and suburban developments. Pilot programs in the late 1960s began the conversion of the piñon-juniper-oak to grassland for better forage and water yields. It is also possible that drastic timber-cutting measures in commercial forest lands to increase runoff water yields may alter forest growth schedules. Projected use of the forest and associated range lands by hunters, fishermen, campers, hikers and other recreationists have indicated severe pressures on management to please this important segment of the public. All indications in 1970 were pointing to a much more intensive use of the wildlands in Arizona. Such an increase in use of Arizona forests was expected to mean a further complication of the already complex interrelationships involved in multiple-use management. It was anticipated that the strong support Arizona's citizens have given its educational and research institutions in this critical area must be continued in order that forest and range management personnel may be produced, and research expanded to provide wildland managers with information for making wise decisions regarding one of Arizona's greatest renewable resources — the forest.

ARIZONA'S CULTURAL INSTITUTIONS

Fig. 30.1   Painting and sculpture are important to the lives of modern Arizonans
who have leisure that the pioneers lacked.

Faculties of the
Colleges of Fine Arts and Architecture,
University of Arizona

30

THE ARTS IN ARIZONA

THE ARID LAND of Arizona was a rugged environment in the early days for cultural institutions, as for all growing things. In pioneer soil the seeds of culture in its various forms germinated and struggled, frequently lying dormant from aridity or dying, neglected by men and women wholly absorbed in the quest for survival and the conquest of the frontier.

Ultimately, however, the favorable climate of Arizona and the nurturing of many talents brought the fruits of culture to times of harvest. The fine arts — painting, sculpture, architecture, music, drama, dance, and literature — have developed in Arizona as hybrids of varying ethnic strains, combining native and cosmopolitan influences with Southwestern history. They afford great pleasure and satisfaction to the Arizonans of modern times who have the leisure to enjoy them and to contribute to their continuing growth, as well as to visitors who are constantly enriching the harvest.

Architecture

Architecture, perhaps the most socially sensitive of the arts, reflects the culture and the progress of the people, and this concept is nowhere more clearly illustrated than in Arizona. The state has had phenomenal growth in population — 71 percent since 1950 — with rapid urbanization of its cities, and predictions abounding that Phoenix and Tucson will someday be among the largest cities in the nation. Hand in hand with this progress is the rate of Arizona's building — proportionately greater than in almost any other section of the country, and still accelerating as the seventies opened.

This growth, of course, brings both blessings and disappointment, more noticeable in metropolitan areas than elsewhere. Both Phoenix and Tucson by 1970 had many high-rise buildings, both publicly and privately constructed and all locally designed. These are fresh and

clean in design, sturdy in structure, efficient of operation, and reflective of the steadily advancing position of the architectural profession in the state. Many people feel, however, that the newer buildings have taken a toll of the older architecture, some of which has rich historical, if not strictly stylistic, significance. This is a problem in Tucson, for example, where relatively large sections of the older city have been removed for rehabilitation in an urban renewal program.

Arizona and the Southwest are among the regions of the United States that have a special stylistic architectural heritage. During the period of expansion in population and construction in the late 1960s, Arizona architects were frequently reminded to keep this tradition in sight and not to bury it in a structural style without regional roots. The argument was not that Spanish or territorial architecture only is appropriate for Arizona, but rather that the state does have a virile tradition of distinction which in its own design takes cognizance of temperature, sun, and nature in the arid regions. Among the state's newer architects, Bennie Gonzales is only one of many who have been particularly successful in synthesizing contemporary concepts with Southwest traditions. The maintenance of this tradition is of importance both to the old resident and to the visitor, who comes to Arizona not only for sunshine, but also for a look at its colorful past.

With respect to Arizona history, the frontier architecture of Arizona ghost towns in mining areas, the territorial design, and the Spanish missions such as San Xavier all are important resources for modern designers to develop a valid "technology," that is, a happy marriage of regionalism and technology to suit the area.

Phoenix, a city planned and completely built in modern times, does not have an architectural heritage such as Tucson's, where many of the existing monuments relate to a historic style and background. But there are in Phoenix excellent tributes to this heritage, such as the Heard Museum, widely recognized as one of the finest modern examples of Spanish architecture in the Southwest. Design devices drawn from the past and useful in the present — for example, walks shaded by the over-arching buildings — are evident in the Chandler area near Phoenix.

On the contemporary scene, examples in both Phoenix and Tucson show that these cities have been keeping pace. The extended highrise section in Phoenix has especially notable office buildings, as has Tucson's downtown district. Other outstanding structures are the Scottsdale Civic Center, and the Grady Gammage Auditorium, designed by Frank Lloyd Wright, at Arizona State University. Reflecting progressive design in Tucson are the Kitt Peak National Observatory by William Varney of Phoenix, the Pima Building, and the Tucson Gas Company's new building. In 1970 urban renewal

was on its way in Tucson and civic centers in both Phoenix and Tucson were under construction.

On the other side of the stylistic picture are many fine structures blending a full measure of contemporary technology and traditional flavor. A few examples include two branches of the Bank of Douglas in Tucson, the new main building for the First National Bank, and the eastside branch of the Great Western Bank, as well as both the Casas Adobes and Broadway Village shopping centers, all by Gordon Luepke. The Southern Arizona Bank in Tucson by Lew Place has been stylistically controversial, but has fitted itself easily and decoratively into the city pattern.

The churches of a city are perhaps among the most conspicuous of its architectural adornments. Phoenix and Tucson abound in churches, and here again the traditions of Arizona and the contemporary vision are both strongly represented. Among those notable for

Al Ruland Photo, City of Phoenix

Fig. 30.2 Shaded walks, reflecting pools, and playing fountains invite visitors to the Phoenix city building.

Bob Broder, University of Arizona

Fig. 30.3 The College of
Architecture at the University
of Arizona expresses regional
and contemporary
adaptation of design.

clean-cut functional quality and basic respect for the materials used are All Saints' Episcopal Church in Phoenix, a winner of national awards; First Christian, Trinity Presbyterian, and Faith Lutheran churches in Tucson (the latter perhaps the most radically contemporary of any in that city); and also in Tucson the Lutheran Church of Christ, the Chapel of Christ the King, and the Temple Emanu-El. A striking example of contemporary architecture is the Chapel of the Holy Cross, high in the foothills outside Sedona.

A number of churches in both cities are adaptations of traditional styles, with the Spanish mission influence apparent in many, such as St. Phillip's in the Hills, St. Michael and All Angels, St. Mark's Presbyterian, and the St. Augustine Cathedral in Tucson. There are also highly individualized spots of architec-

tural interest, for example the little chapel (and the unique art gallery), built by Tucson artist Ted de Grazia in the Catalina foothills.

Some of the newer residential subdivisions are thoughtfully designed and are tributes to contemporary architecture. Others have successfully reflected the historic styles while at the same time showing their modernity. The question within the design professions of whether regionalism or technology should dominate is not easily answerable. Architectural trends in the late 1960s favored a combination of what is aesthetically pleasing with what is functionally sound, blending humanism into the organic whole, as evidenced in the newer skyscrapers of Manhattan and in the industrial parks of large metropolitan areas. It is often desirable in regions such as Arizona to soften the rigidity of some of the more modern design concepts with local tradition. This approach tends to foster the growth of the architectural profession in a given area, because local architects are so much more familiar than are their imported colleagues with the details of the regional heritage.

This factor is especially significant in a booming locale such as Arizona, where architectural opportunity is great. In the cities of Arizona, the status of the architectural profession is being raised substantially since more and more of the major work is being done by local architects with fewer and fewer large projects going to out-of-state firms. This gives real indication of the prestige enjoyed by local members of the profession and acts as well to preserve some of the spirit and tradition of the state.

Courses of study in the field of architecture were well established by the seventies in both major Arizona institutions of higher education. The previously existing course at Arizona State University has been reorganized to meet professional standards, but continues also as a training program for entrance into the construction industry. The University of Arizona began its professional course in the fall of 1958 with strong curricular

Bill Sears

Fig. 30.5   St. Andrew's grows from foothills setting.

emphasis on design. Both schools have been flourishing, and their influence on the profession already has been felt in the Southwest and elsewhere in the country. At the University of Arizona, considerable emphasis has been placed on the architectural problems of arid regions and the possibilities of solar energy as it may influence design in the future.

Professional architectural groups have been active in Arizona, not only in experimental architecture concerned with advanced technology, but also in the preservation of historic architecture. Civic design committees have been working prominently with developmental problems for the metropolitan areas and fast-growing smaller communities. Architects in Arizona have been deeply concerned with urban redevelopment programs, and they are assisting in the planning of large projects. Great efforts have been made to assist governmental units and retail merchants in reorganizing the central business districts, to return to them a distinctive quality of merchandising while at the same time creating appropriately progressive shopping centers for the Southwest.

Contemporary developments in architecture in Arizona have received nationwide attention through the existence in Scottsdale of Taliesin West, school and firm established by the late Frank Lloyd Wright, and — also in Scottsdale — the Cosanti Foundation and learning center, where architects, fine arts students, and craftsmen have worked with Paolo Soleri's future-oriented concept of city development.

Fig. 30.4   Natural light is important in design.   *Neil Koppes*

Art

Art is more than a thousand years old in Arizona but renews itself every day with the influx of new people and new ideas into the state. The Southwest sheltered the northernmost of the great Indian cultures, and art of anthropological and ethnological interest was produced here in quantity, occasionally rising to a level of aesthetic excellence.

In modern times, the Indian artist has been placed in a difficult position by the clash of cultures he has endured. Today, however, he is beginning to develop a means of expression that takes cognizance of the facts of modern life. Satisfying blends of Indian tradition and contemporary styling have been achieved. Among outstanding artists of Arizona tribes are the Navajo painters Harrison Begay, Beatien Yazz, and Andy Tsihnahjinnie, and Fred Kabotie, a Hopi. Able artisans and craftsmen are also contributing abundantly to Arizona's treasury of contemporary art. Hopi silversmiths Charles Loloma and Paul Saufkie, and Kenny Begay, Alan Kee, and Tom Bahe from the Navajo tribe are all distinguished. The great tradition of Indian crafts has been carried on by such potters as Fanny and Elva Nampeyo, Charles

Loloma and his wife Otellie, and Faye Avachoya, all Hopis. Other excellent craftsmen are Sam Begay, a Navajo outstanding in sand-casting silver, Otto Penewa, a Hopi maker of kachina dolls, and Tommy Yazzie, a Navajo expert in figure carving. The art of weaving is being continued, although in this field names of individuals are not so familiar.

Spain also contributed to the rich heritage of art in Arizona and the Southwest. The missions established by Spain are interesting not only for their history and architecture but also for their painting and sculpture, which relate them to age-old Iberian traditions. The finest of these missions, San Xavier del Bac, south of Tucson, houses works of art whose sophisticated and folk traditions reveal relationships to Gothic, Baroque, and Churrigueresque styles of Spain and Mexico.

In view of the bond between Arizona and the Latin traditions of the past, it seems fitting that in 1960 the University of Arizona Museum of Art became the home of a great Spanish work of art from the sixteenth century, the Retablo of Ciudad Rodrigo by Fernando Gallego. Presented to the University by the Samuel H. Kress Foundation, this collection of twenty-six paintings

Fig. 30.6   Navajo Andy Tsihnahjinnie's painting of "The Gamblers."   *Ray Manley Photo, Mr. and Mrs. John Tanner Collection*

in 1970 comprised the largest and finest representation of the Hispano-Flemish School of painting outside of Spain.

After the rugged pioneer period of Arizona's settlement, life in the desert became more attractive and artists began to come to Arizona from many other places. Since 1920 Arizona has been the home of many well-known artists, such as the late Hutton Webster, Jay Datus, the late Maynard Dixon, Edith Hamlin, Gerry Peirce, Philip Curtis, and Stanford Stevens. These people have painted in Arizona, and all at one time or another painted *of* Arizona, although their palettes are wider than the state and their talents varied enough for a multitude of subjects. Tucson artist Ted de Grazia's painting "Los Niños" was reproduced as a Christmas card sold by the United Nations Educational, Scientific and Cultural Organization.

Artists formerly lived and worked in Arizona in a spontaneous, individualistic milieu, for before World War II there were almost no shows and until the 1950s no real galleries. There were, however, small informal organizations, such as Tucson's Palette and Brush Club, to which many excellent artists belonged.

In 1970 the state's most important collections were in the possession of two universities. Arizona State University had a collection of 149 paintings, sculptures,

Phoenix Museum

Fig. 30.8   Renaissance art — Palmezzano's "Holy Family."

Fig. 30.7   The "Wolf Kachina" was painted by a Hopi, Peter Shelton (Hoyesva).

Neil Koppes Photo, H. S. Galbraith Collection

and prints, mostly American, given by Oliver B. James in 1950. There were also twelve paintings in the Ruskin Collection of works attributed to Renaissance and Baroque masters. Fine displays of the traditional Indian arts could be found at the Heard Museum in Phoenix, the Arizona State Museum in Tucson, the Museum of Northern Arizona in Flagstaff, and the Amerind Foundation near Dragoon.

In 1945, the University of Arizona at Tucson received the Charles Leonard Pfeiffer Collection of 104 American paintings. In 1950 and 1951, Oliver James added five items of importance. The Samuel H. Kress Foundation in 1951 gave the University twenty-six works of Renaissance art, the most important single collection in the Southwest, and in 1952 the Samuel Lotta Kingan bequest of 100 paintings and *objêts d'art* was added. The gallery in the Fine Arts Center opened in 1956, housing all of these, as well as the Edward Joseph Gallagher III Memorial Collection of 175 works of modern art.

By the late sixties civic art events were growing in number in the two major cities, and activity was spreading to other areas in the state as well. The Phoenix Art Museum in the Civic Center opened in 1959 with a permanent collection valued at three-quarters of a million dollars, and including Renaissance, nineteenth-century, and modern European painting. The Tucson Art Center in 1970 was continuing a full program of

Harry L. Bell Collection, Museum of Art, University of Arizona

Fig. 30.9   Early Americana—Halsey portrait by Gilbert Stuart.

Phoenix Art Museum

Fig. 30.10   The contemporary sculpture — "Walking Man."

Fig. 30.11   The Phoenix Art Museum is part of an attractive complex that also houses the main Public Library.

Neil Koppes

Beimlich Photo, Mr. and Mrs. Norman Herschl Collection

Fig. 30.12 "The Laundress" by American Robert Henri.

local, state, and interstate competitions initiated in 1948, as well as touring shows. The Verde Valley Artists maintained a gallery at Jerome, sponsoring exhibits and festivals, and a growing art colony at Sedona suggested the possibility that the fine arts might flourish in the mountain country of northern Arizona, as they have in the wooded hills of New England and New York, and at Aspen, Colorado.

Prescott and Douglas by 1970 were among smaller Arizona cities having active art collections. Interest in art among residents of Arizona towns was evidenced by the fact, for example, that members of the University of Arizona art faculty were enlisted to teach extension art courses in Ajo, Bisbee, Douglas, Globe, Miami, Pinetop, Safford, and Warren. The state and county fairs of Arizona through the sixties included art sections which were heavily subscribed and well attended, the Arizona State Fair at Phoenix having an especially important show.

A show gaining increasing importance has been the Southwestern Invitational, begun in 1965 and held each May in Yuma. Arizona artists are invited to enter their works, which include ceramics, oil paintings, pottery, photographs, weaving, and stitchery, and in 1969 a purchase award of $1,000 was being given. Sponsored by the Yuma Fine Arts Association, the exhibition has traveled each year to other cities in Arizona.

Harry L. Bell Collection, Museum of Art, University of Arizona

Fig. 30.13   Remington's "Cattlemen Warning Sheepmen Away From Their Water" — artistic expression of the frontier.

Fig. 30.14　The multi-relationships of art to life are experienced by school children visiting the University of Arizona gallery and other museums.

Among craftsmen, the accomplished Indian peoples have continued their work, and other groups have been strengthening. The artisans and craftsmen of Scottsdale near Phoenix have developed a notable center since 1945 and have a loosely knit organization called the Arizona Craft Council. Another group, the Scottsdale National Indian Arts Council, has made many diversified contributions. In Tucson, the Craft Guild is associated with the Tucson Art Center. A later group, the Arizona Designer-Craftsmen, was organized in 1960.

The scenic drama of Arizona has fostered the development of photography as an art. The technical excellence of the modern camera and the science and skill of the modern cameraman could scarcely be more at home than in Arizona, where subject matter ranges from aspen forests and blue lakes to saguaro-studded deserts, all treated each season to a marvelously varied play of light and shadow. Through *Arizona Highways* magazine and national publications featuring Arizona's pictorial beauty, the scenic wealth of the state has become the property of the entire world. Many of the pictures in this volume testify to the skill of Arizona photographers.

Arizona's individual photographers, professional and amateur, rank high in ability and have exhibited nationally, winning prizes and gaining prominence through magazines and newspapers. Many of these photographers have had all their training in the state, often beginning in school photography courses.

The state's contemporary interest in art continues to grow, fostered by the universities and colleges of Arizona. Art has been a part of the curricula since the founding of these institutions. Degrees are offered on graduate and undergraduate levels, and in 1970 enrollment in studio courses, history of art, and art education courses totaled well over 2,700 at the University of Arizona alone.

Because the Arizona environment is multifaceted — plateau, mountain, desert, and in later years teeming city as well — because the state's history is complex and its population woven of various ethnic strands, the art of Arizona cannot be summarized as regional, parochial, or provincial. The inspiration of local qualities is strong and ever present, but the art and artists, like Arizona itself, are many-sided and are bound in many ways to traditions of art all over the world.

Dance

Sister to drama, dance by the sixties had begun to attract strong interest in Arizona where, until a few years before, the religiously oriented dancing of Indian peoples was probably the only well-defined expression of the dance art. Tucson and Phoenix both abounded in dance teachers. Literally thousands of children in these and other Arizona cities were enrolled in classes in ballet, acrobatics, and modern dance. The universities, colleges, and high schools regularly scheduled courses in modern dance, and Tucson hosted an annual symposium giving a panoramic view of work done in modern dance by leading participants in the community. In the late 1960s Arizona State University was planning a bachelor's degree program in dance.

The indigenous Latin influence has naturally been an influential factor in the development of dance in Tucson. Phoenix through the sixties had a school of Flamenco, the Andalusian form of Spanish dance improvisation which has so engaged audience attention in the U.S. The dances of Spain, Latin America, and above all, Mexico, have frequently been performed in Phoenix and Tucson by traveling troupes as well as by resident performers. The dances of the various Indian tribes have attracted increasing attention for their artistic as well as ritual significance.

The state's first civic ballet was incorporated in Tucson in 1965. By 1971 it was a company of about fifty dancers with as many members on production crews, all on a non-profit basis. In the late 1960s the Tucson Civic Ballet's typical year included fall and spring major productions plus a free summer ballet in Randolph Park's outdoor theater, sponsored by the City of Tucson. In December of 1967, the company engaged Richard Holden, from the staff of the Metropolitan Opera Ballet Company of New York City, as artistic director. In Tucson twice yearly, Holden had directed several major productions by 1970, including an original version of "Alice in Wonderland" which later became the first color videotape produced by NET station KUAT at the University of Arizona. In April, 1970, the Civic Ballet joined hands with other civic groups in a gala music festival under Tucson Symphony Orchestra auspices, to present orchestra, ballet and opera to the community. In 1970 also, the new Scottsdale Civic Ballet was planning its first production.

The Kadimah Dance Theater was established in Tucson at the Jewish Community Center in 1955 by Frances Smith Cohen, director. Kadimah's modern dance section, as the seventies opened, was led by Mrs. Cohen. A ballet troupe, started in 1965, was under the direction of Stephanie Stigers. The Kadimahs by 1969 performed about thirty-five times annually, presenting

Neil Koppes Photo, Mr. and Mrs. John Brandon Collection

Fig. 30.15   Navajo Tony Begay's "Ye-Bi-Chi" — the persistence of dance through varying cultures.

Fig. 30.16   The Tucson Symphony rehearses for the International Music Festival opera production of "Il Pagliacci."

their programs in Arizona, California, and Texas. All Kadimah dancers were students of both ballet and modern dance, and its performers have gone on to teach and dance professionally in other parts of the United States.

The regular seasonal fare of the dance devotee in Phoenix and Tucson includes several performances by world-famous dance ensembles, both modern and ballet. These troupes have frequently held workshops and master classes for Arizona dance teachers and students. Notable among such visiting teachers have been Merce Cunningham at Arizona State University, Eric Hawkins, and, in 1969, the Joffrey Ballet at the University of Arizona. The Joffrey company and the San Francisco School of Ballet under Lew Christiansen's direction auditioned in Tucson in 1969-70, picking up for scholarship several promising young dancers from the Civic Ballet and from local dancing classes.

Music

Since 1900 Arizona has developed a notable musical life. During this time the history of music in the state has been one of creative change, reflecting the work of dedicated citizens, community groups, schools, colleges and universities of the state.

The greatest concentration of musical activities has naturally been in the metropolitan centers of Phoenix and Tucson. Both communities as well as Flagstaff have long had symphony orchestras, civic choral groups, and concert series which are sponsored by music clubs and by the three state universities.

Musical activities at the University of Arizona began as early as 1903. Since that time, growth in the curricula and number of performing organizations has been continuous. In 1969 the School of Music was sponsoring 15 student musical organizations including a University Symphony Orchestra, Symphonic and Marching Band, Symphonic Choir, Choral Society, Opera Workshop and a Collegium Musicum in addition to a Faculty Woodwind Quintet, and Faculty String Ensembles. Many of these organizations have brought excellent guest performers to Tucson, and members of these groups have appeared in various communities throughout the state and the nation.

The University Artist Series Concerts, established in 1927-28, annually draw not only members of the faculty and student body but townspeople as well to the auditorium on campus to hear concerts by world-renowned instrumentalists and singers. The series has expanded from six events in 1927 to twelve events in 1971. In 1968 two new concert series were inaugurated: the Celebrity Concerts and Connoisseur Concerts.

Students from the School of Music join with the Department of Drama annually to present full-scale musical productions such as "My Fair Lady," "Oklahoma!" and "Showboat."

Fig. 30.17 Performing arts on ASU campus at Tempe are at home in the Frank Lloyd Wright-designed auditorium.

Beyond the campus, Tucson is a musically busy community. The Tucson Symphony Orchestra, whose eighty members are drawn from the University community as well as from the city of Tucson, was giving in 1970 an annual series of six subscription concerts. Distinguished soloists appearing with the Tucson Symphony for its fortieth season in 1968-69 included Ozan Marsh, pianist, and Gordon Epperson, cellist, both artists-in-residence at the University of Arizona. Igor Gorin, a third artist-in-residence, also presented a recital in 1969 at the University. The Symphony through the sixties was presenting a series of children's concerts annually for boys and girls of the Tucson Public Schools. The orchestra was founded in 1928 largely through the efforts of the late Harry Juliani, Tucson attorney; the late John Mez, professor of history at the University of Arizona; and Camil Van Hulse, composer, organist, and first conductor of the Symphony. These men played chamber music together in their homes and engaged in a number of other musical activities leading to the eventual establishment of the Symphony as a performing group. Since 1967, with Gregory Millar as conductor, the Tucson Symphony has been greatly expanded, and in 1969 inaugurated an annual International Music Festival.

The Tucson Youth Symphony was begun in 1956 under the auspices of the Tucson Symphony Society. James Stevenson became conductor in 1966. The Youth Symphony is composed of junior and senior high school students and gives two public performances each year. Scholarships to summer music camps are awarded to some of the orchestra members, and many go on to play in the Tucson Symphony and in university orchestras.

In 1967 a new professional orchestra was formed in Tucson called the Arizona Chamber Orchestra. This group of thirty musicians from the University and from Tucson gave nine concerts during its first three years.

The Saturday Morning Musical Club, organized in 1907, under the leadership of the late Madeleine Heinemann (Mrs. Harry Berger) built the Temple of Music and Art (now the Tucson Music Center) and within its walls annually presented concerts by the world's great performers, by local artists, and by civic organizations. The Club has also provided scholarships to finance advanced musical studies for many promising young Tucsonans.

Civic groups, including the Tucson Civic Chorus, Tucson Boys' Chorus, and other vocal groups have enriched the community with numerous choral activities. The Boys' Chorus in particular has toured the nation, sung on the steps of the Capitol, presented concerts in Europe, and during 1960 appeared at various points in the South Pacific area, climaxing its tour in Australia.

The Tucson Festival Society sponsors appearances by nationally known artists and musical groups and presents activities emphasizing Arizona's heritage of Indian and Spanish-American cultures. Among these are the San Xavier Fiesta and the Fiesta of La Placita. At each of these springtime events, the songs, dances, and customs of the Indian and Mexican people highlight a colorful revival of Arizona's cultural past.

An outstanding annual series of chamber music recitals was established in Tucson in 1948 by the Friends of Music, a town/gown organization under the leadership of Arthur Lanyon Blair and other interested Tucsonans. By 1970, from four to six such programs were heard each year in Crowder Hall at the Fine Arts Center on the campus given by such ensembles as the Budapest Quartet, the New York Woodwind Quintet, and the Pro Musica.

Metropolitan Phoenix has been the other main center of musical activity in Arizona, with a number of active, organized groups. It has indeed come a long way since the 1920s, when Mrs. Archer Linde's Phoenix Light Opera Association was the only musical group in the city. The Phoenix Symphony Orchestra has been in existence for over thirty years, having been established by leading citizens, including Albert R. Etzweiller, Carl Hoyer, and Mrs. Norma Townsend. It is considered to be a major orchestra, with a budget exceeding a half-million dollars. It had Guy Taylor as its musical director and conductor during the 1960s. The Phoenix Orpheus Club, a non-professional male chorus, has given outstanding performances in the state and was highly praised on a European tour. The Phoenix Musical Theatre has given annual performances of works in light opera.

For many years the city of Phoenix has sponsored a concert series by top-ranking soloists and musical groups. On the campus of Arizona State University at Tempe there is an Artist-Concert series, as well as a schedule of performances by soloists and ensembles from the university student body and faculty.

Musical activities in northern Arizona have centered on the campus of Northern Arizona University at Flagstaff. The Shrine of the Ages Choir has achieved a national reputation for singing at the Easter Sunrise Service at Grand Canyon. The Flagstaff Symphony Orchestra draws personnel from the college, the community, and from neighboring towns. An annual music and art festival in Flagstaff draws peformers and audience from across the country. It follows a summer camp for students in the various arts.

A state unit of the Music Educator's Association with five hundred members has been an influential force in developing the music program in the elementary and secondary schools of the state. State conferences held each year by this organization have offered an excellent opportunity for continuing education, since the various sessions feature outstanding music educators and new teaching aids. The Arizona Music Teachers Association, an affiliate of the Music Teachers National Association, is an organization of private teachers working

to maintain and improve standards, ethics, and rapport among its members.

The Society of Arizona Composers, founded in 1931, has been active in developing interest in the works of Arizona composers. It has fostered performances of their works in the various communities of the state. Among its members are a number of composers who have received statewide and national recognition. These include Camil Van Hulse, Robert McBride, Henry Johnson, Richard Faith, Wendell Rider, Warren Wirtz, Grant Fletcher, Andrew Buchhauser, Robert Muczynski, Louise Kerr, David Cohen and Ronald Lo Presti.

The American Guild of Organists has two chapters in the state: the Southern Arizona chapter in Tucson and the Central Arizona chapter in Phoenix. These chapters annually have presented organ recitals and sponsored competitions for the creation of new anthems and organ compositions. The Guild has been influential in standardizing organ consoles and cooperates with

Tucson Daily Citizen

Fig. 30.18   The Arizona Civic Theater, spring, 1971.

church architects and builders in making practical suggestions regarding organ placement and desirable acoustics.

Until the end of World War II, Arizona had only two or three organs suitable for recital use. Since that time, however, with the construction of new church buildings and the remodeling of older facilities, a large number of fine instruments have been installed all over Arizona.

Musical activities in the many smaller communities within the state are centered in the local units of the National Federation of Music Clubs. These civic groups have contributed immeasurably to the growth of interest in music and to its performance. The Federation has sponsored contests and auditions to find and foster outstanding young singers and instrumentalists who compete with other Arizona winners for national recognition. Community orchestras in the late 1960s had been established in Yuma, Navajo County, Safford, and Mesa, in addition to the Phoenix College Community Orchestra. The many new junior colleges in Arizona have also begun to play an important role in the state's musical growth.

The only really indigenous music of Arizona is that of the various Indian tribes. In a limited sense this music has influenced modern American composition, as in the case of the late Frederick Jacobi, whose *String Quartet on Indian Themes* and *Indian Dances* shows the influence of Pueblo music from New Mexico and Arizona. Many of the works of Louise Kerr incorporate American Indian materials.

To a much greater extent, folk music from across the border has influenced Arizona's musical life, and many excellent works have been based on Mexican themes. Notable among them is Robert McBride's *Mexican Rhapsody*. His second composition in this genre, *Panorama Mexicana*, was premiered as a feature of the University of Arizona's seventy-fifth anniversary celebration, and he wrote the music for a ballet premiered in 1970, "The Brooms of Mexico."

Apart from its influence on American music, Mexican music itself is widely heard in Arizona on radio, phonograph records, and from the *mariachis,* the strolling instrumentalists and singers who play and sing *ranchero* music at many of Arizona's gayest fiestas. The rhythms and melodies of Mexico are an everpresent part of Arizona's cultural heritage, dear to residents of the state and transported over this and other continents in the pleasant recollection of visitors to borderlands of the Southwest.

Fig. 30.19   Forms, textures, and feeling of the Arizona landscape in the gallery designed by Artist Ted De Grazia.   *Ray Manley*

Theater

Like many other western states, Arizona owes its theater heritage to the mining camps. Students of the theater are always surprised to discover the rich bill of theatrical fare that was offered to miners of the Arizona Territory. Long before substantial theater buildings were erected in Tombstone, Tucson, and Prescott, the drama had been brought to the desert and wooded areas of Arizona. From across the eastern plains and from the California Gold Coast, the most enterprising thespians and musicians of the day came to offer their art. They brought not only "entertainment and the sensational" but also the finest dramatic performances of the era.

The theatrical entertainment usually reflected the spirit of the mining camps and of the times. The strands of Arizona theater were bound together by common needs in the rough and ready environment of the frontier. Transportation and housing were major problems, the latter solved by the use of saloons, town halls, barns, mining shacks, lecture halls, and outdoor theaters.

First established in the Territory was the Theater Comique, opened in Tombstone in 1879 and owned by Joe Bignon. In 1881, Schieffelin Hall, also in Tombstone, was established and became one of the most popular Arizona playhouses, a home for more or less legitimate drama, and the center of the cultural activity of the mining town. The same year, William J. Hutchinson purchased a property site in Tombstone designated as Lot 9, Block 5, on Allen Street near Sixth, where he built a variety theater which gained great renown as the Bird Cage. Here, unlike in Schieffelin Hall, the variety-revue type of entertainment was presented.

In Tucson, La Concordia on South Meyer Street — long the only established theater — staged performances by Mexican traveling troupes. Later came the Elysian Grove, the Park Theater, and the Opera House to house many Tucson stock and professional companies.

The earliest settlers brought various kinds of entertainment to the Territory. In Patagonia and south, the medicine man and his wagon moved from township to township. Usually a Mexican troubador accompanied the glib talker, whose main interest was selling ointments, salves, tonics, and lightning rods. The Mormons brought with them the songs and poems of the plains. Religious pageants of many faiths were held in every major hamlet of the Territory, and added to these were the ritual dances and festivals of the native Indian tribes.

For two decades, the traveling performers presented their dramas, dances, and music to inhabitants of the mining camps and nearby towns. In 1903, a literary society at the University of Arizona began dramatic activities for the amateur. The following year the Drama Club was organized on the campus. Interest in theatricals flourished in communities and on campuses,

and between 1910 and 1924 many drama groups were organized in the state.

In 1910, the University of Arizona granted credit in drama for the first time. The curriculum soon expanded, and with this growth came the vital promotion of the "Little Theater Movement" in Tucson and in other cities of the state. The necessity for a laboratory theater became apparent, and the Player's Theater, with quarters under the University stadium, was inaugurated. In 1937 the University Players were given a more suitable theater in the converted campus gymnasium, Herring Hall, and in the 1950s a new theater in the Fine Arts Center of the University.

The Phoenix Little Theatre was organized in 1921. In 1923 the group received as a gift from the Dwight B. Heard family the old family carriage house which was opened as a theater in 1924. The drama group has been continuously active; in 1951 the Phoenix Little Theatre moved into a new building, which was expanded and renamed the Phoenix Theatre Center in 1966. Also housed in the Phoenix Theatre Center are productions of the Phoenix Musical Theatre Guild and the Actors Inner Circle, a promising semiprofessional resident company organized in 1966. Other groups in the city include the Phoenix Star Theater and Palace West Theatre.

Drama clubs, little-theater groups, college theaters, and high-school drama departments were organized about the state, in such towns as Benson, Bisbee, Clarkdale, Coolidge, Flagstaff, Gila Bend, Kingman, Nogales, Phoenix, Prescott, Tempe, Tucson, Safford, and Yuma. Many contributions in theater have been made also by the state's junior colleges.

Tucson's Arizona Civic Theatre started in June, 1967, with Sandy Rosenthal as director. Twelve productions were given that year, followed by ten in 1968, including four off-Broadway plays. Sometimes engaging guest directors and actors for specific plays, the Civic Theatre in 1968 had moved toward its goal of becoming a resident professional company, with the hiring of a full-time paid technical director, Bonnie Scott; an assistant director, Roger Miller; and a secretary. The Civic Theatre formerly leased a theater in the Santa Rita Hotel, but by 1971, performances were housed in the new 550-seat theater in the Tucson Community Center.

The Playbox Community Theatre in Tucson was begun in 1958. In 1969 it was producing six shows a year, including one musical and one children's show, and its headquarters were at Traildust Town, east of Tucson.

With expanded state interest in the drama came the need for special training, in turn calling for more comprehensive education in the theater arts. The University of Arizona by 1970 was offering four degrees in the field of drama: Bachelor of Fine Arts, Bachelor of Arts in Drama, Bachelor of Arts in Drama Education, and Master of Arts. Arizona State University was offering a major in speech, as well as drama courses leading to a Bachelor of Arts degree through the College of Liberal Arts. Phoenix Junior College was giving extensive collegiate drama offerings in Maricopa County. Northern Arizona University at Flagstaff also listed its drama courses through the College of Liberal Arts and offered a combined major in drama, speech, and English. Grand Canyon College in Phoenix and Eastern Arizona Junior College at Thatcher offered a combined major in speech and drama and an active program of dramatic presentations.

In Phoenix and Tucson high schools, drama had moved by the 1960s from the extracurricular program to more specialized offerings for credit in the dramatic arts departments. Many other Arizona high schools offer drama in individual courses or through drama clubs. Creative dramatics is also being made a regular part of elementary and junior high school curricula throughout the state.

Standards for the drama in Arizona are said to be high, and recognition of merit has been received in every field of the arts and crafts of the theater.

The Scottsdale Community Players, after performing for fifteen years in a coachhouse converted into a theater, succeeded in 1968 in building their own new 200-seat theater. Built on land donated by the city of Scottsdale, the new theater was financed through con-tributions and through the treasury of the Community Players. In 1969, the group was presenting five productions for thirty-five performances each season.

Drama has also played an important part in the international exchange of cultural programs with the neighboring state of Sonora, Mexico. The Department of Drama at the University of Arizona has been a vital force in the cultural work of the Arizona-Sonora Project for Intellectual Cooperation sponsored by the Rockefeller Foundation. The University of Arizona also houses a regional office for the American National Theatre and Academy.

The Arizona institutions of higher learning, and many of the major little theaters, have felt a responsibility to encourage new playwrights and, therefore, to emphasize the production of their plays.

As an outgrowth of this attitude and activity, the Playwright Directors Laboratory Theater to foster original plays was begun in 1965 by the University of Arizona. The premiere performance of William Gibson's *Dinny and the Witches* was presented by the University and ran concurrently with Gibson's *Miracle Worker*. Charles Finney's *The Circus of Dr. Lao* was also premiered on the campus and was later presented professionally by Burgess Meredith.

Jack W. Huggins
Regional Literature

31

LITERATURE

THE FIRST INHABITANTS of Arizona were the Indians, whose literature was oral. Among any people whose traditions and stories must be passed down by word-of-mouth, particular prestige attaches to those who tell stories. This is especially true of the keepers of religious myths and rituals. The singer, the shaman or medicine man, was a person of great influence. He carried in his memory the rituals necessary for curing the sick, the religious myths which told of the origins of the world and of his own people, and tales of his tribe's wanderings before they came to the land of their residence. These stories were the ethical documents of his people, explicit in their precepts of right and wrong. These rituals appear in the works of Washington Matthews and Father Berard Haile, who have made translations of Navajo myths. A reader brought up in a different tradition finds here a completely new world.

But not all Indian oral literature is religious. There are folk tales of great variety: amusing and frequently ribald stories involving the sneaky trickster, Coyote; moving tales of love; and exciting ones of adventure in strange places. Though the folk tales are not primarily religious, the supernatural figures even more prominently in these Indian stories than it does in the European variety, for to the Indian there is spirit, life in everything. Though Indian folk tales have all the fascination of the unfamiliar to one brought up in another culture, one often recognizes elements and themes similar to those found in Indo-European folk stories. Incidents in some of the stories, for example, explain an everyday phenomenon: why the mosquito has bent legs, why the coyote has pale eyes, or why the gnat darts here and there before he settles down to bite. There is a beautiful Zuñi folk tale whose theme is exactly that of the Orpheus legend: a youth goes to the Other World to bring back his dead beloved and is allowed to do so if he observes certain conditions. Of course the conditions are not observed, and the maiden returns to the world of the dead forever. To those interested in this kind of Indian literature, Frank Cushing's *Zuñi Folk Tales* is recommended.

In addition to the public arts of rituals, myths, and folk tales, the Indian composed in more personal forms. Margot Astrov's *The Winged Serpent* and Frank Cronyn's *The Path on the Rainbow* contain many moving poems or songs, for the Indian, like Homer, and the bard in the time of *Beowulf,* always chants or sings his verses. Indian poetry is always concrete and is most frequently incantatory.

An Image Influx

Indians, then, produced a vital literature of their own. They also occupy a prominent position in works written by the Europeans who displaced them. The image of the Indian as it appears in such works has not remained static. In the earliest accounts, the Indian is often presented as a person who, though strange and unfamiliar in his habits and customs, is a friendly and helpful being. In the descriptions given by the early padres and conquistadors, it is impossible to recognize the savage, cruel, villainous Apaches depicted by writers of later histories.

But as the pressure of European immigration increased, and as the Indian realized a threat to his existence, he began to fight. He became, in short, the enemy. It is a natural and understandable human characteristic to vilify one's enemies. One is scarcely likely to praise or even seek to understand the motives of those from whom one daily fears attack. Contemporary accounts, therefore, of such events as the Wickenburg massacre or the events leading up to the Camp Grant massacre depict the Indian as low, treacherous, savage, and cunning. John Cremony's classic, *Life Among the*

Apaches, though not as narrow as other early accounts, clearly implies that it is right for the "inferior" Indian to be replaced by the "superior" white man. Leo Crane, dealing with Pueblo groups in *Desert Drums* and *Indians of the Enchanted Desert,* is contemptuous of them for their opposition to the white man's ways, their superstition, and their peacefulness.

Emotions Shift

These feelings of hatred and contempt were succeeded by a more tolerant and understanding view of the Indian. Even earlier, of course, there was an occasional writer such as John Gregory Bourke whose work is marked by breadths of understanding. In his *On the Border with Crook,* Bourke shows a degree of human sympathy unusual for his day, although he still displays a certain lack of insight.

More modern attitudes toward the Indian have been marked by an attempt to present him, not as an opponent, or even as a quaint member of a noble, though vanishing race, but as a man with all the hopes, aspirations, victories, and losses everywhere associated with the human condition.

Before the new trend in thought had many followers, Adolph Bandelier in 1890 wrote *The Delight Makers,* a novel of the Pueblo Indians who lived in Frijoles Canyon of northwestern New Mexico (now part of Bandelier National Monument). Lawrence Clark Powell says this book is " . . . first of a long line of southwestern Indian documentary novels . . . never . . . surpassed in its faithfulness to the facts of Pueblo Indian culture."

Three books reflecting the changes in feeling were published in close succession. Oliver La Farge's *Laughing Boy* in 1929 was followed two years later by Frances Gillmor's *Windsinger* and Will Comfort's *Apache.* *Laughing Boy* deals with one of the fundamental problems faced by an Indian educated in the manner favored by the government before 1933. It is the story of a Navajo girl in government schools, away from the reservation. She has been deprived of Indian culture without being provided with anything adequate to take its place. Her attempts, misdirected and futile, to work her way back into Navajo life through marriage to Laughing Boy, a conservative, traditional-minded Indian, make an imaginative and moving tale. Miss Gillmor's *Windsinger* presents with great sensibility the inner life of a Navajo singer or shaman. Comfort's story has more action and suspense than the other two and takes the Indian point of view. *Apache* deals with one of the white man's most stubborn opponents, the great Apache leader, Mangus Colorado. Comfort presents the Americans as cruel, dishonest breakers of treaties; Mangus as a brave, honorable patriot, fighting for his beloved land.

The new attitude was consolidated by and is probably best exemplified by Elliot Arnold's *Blood Brother,* a 1947-48 runaway best seller which was later made into an equally popular motion picture entitled *Broken Arrow.* The story is a complex one dealing with the friendship between the Chiricahua Apache leader Cochise and his American friend, Tom Jeffords, and the relationship during the same period between the Apaches and the white men. The reader's sympathies are enlisted on the side of Cochise, who keeps his part of the peace agreement, until it is irrevocably violated by an ignorant army officer. *Blood Brother* has strongly influenced the spread of the new attitude, not only in books, but also in films and television and has given Cochise a permanent place in our national consciousness.

There was truly not much settlement in Arizona before the American period, and there is a corresponding lack of literary documents dealing with the area as it was then. The first European visitors to the region were Spaniards.

Earliest Arizona Literature

Events depicted in some of the earliest literature about the Arizona area began around June, 1540, when an impressive expedition of Spaniards under the command of Francisco Vásquez de Coronado rode down the San Pedro Valley on the way to conquer the fabled Seven Cities of Cíbola. About twenty years later one of Coronado's soldiers, Pedro Castañeda, wrote an account of this expedition in order, he says, to put a stop to the falsehoods that were being told about it. Castañeda was a cool, hardheaded, and somewhat cynical old soldier whose story is one of the most fascinating tales of exploration that have come down to us.

For those who want a complete and judicious history of Coronado's whole career, the outstanding work is *Coronado, Knight of Pueblos and Plains* by Herbert E. Bolton. Bolton was a historian, the leading authority on Southwestern history, whose books are of such quality that they deserve a prominent place in Arizona literature.

Another highly recommended work by Bolton, *The Rim of Christendom,* deals with the most important European to enter Arizona between the time of Coronado and the coming of the Americans — Padre Eusebio Kino. Padre Kino founded a chain of missions in Sonora, Arizona, and Baja California; he introduced cattle into Arizona and is therefore rightly called the state's first cattleman; he brought European grains here; he was a great explorer and cartographer; but, above all, he was a humane, kindly man whose influence on the Indians he converted is still to be seen in their descendants.

So numerous are the books dealing with the period between the death of Padre Kino in 1711 and the establishment of an American population in Arizona in the 1870s that a real problem of selection arises. The works dealing with Indians during this period have been discussed. The literature concerned with the Anglo-Americans was great in volume and high in quality.

A curious and most readable work is *Personal Narrative,* by James Ohio Pattie. In 1824, after a variety of adventures in New Mexico, Pattie and his father, both Missourians, joined forces with several other American trappers and entered Arizona in search of beaver. They trapped on the Gila, the Salt, and the Colorado, all with considerable success. On the lower Colorado, to their ultimate sorrow, they succumbed to the lure of California. Having buried their furs on the banks of the Colorado, they went on to San Diego, where they were immediately jailed by the Mexican authorities. The father died in jail, but James Ohio won his freedom and also that of a companion by knowing how to perform vaccinations during a smallpox epidemic. He vaccinated the entire population of the California missions, from San Diego to San Francisco. After that, finding his cached furs ruined by spring floods, Pattie returned to New Orleans by boat from Vera Cruz. Though parts of the book are obviously romanticized, it is generally a sound and vivid account of an early journey.

Contact With Mexico

Increasing contact between Anglo-Americans and people of Mexico from the Conquest to modern times has generated a wealth of fiction and nonfiction reflecting the incidents and attitudes characteristic of this relationship. One of the most comprehensive treatments of this contact as it expressed itself in American literature is *With the Ears of Strangers,* by Cecil Robinson. The earliest Americans writing about Mexico, primarily in journals of adventure, exploration, and trade, considered the Mexicans to be a backward, lazy, superstitious, dirty, and ferocious people and disapproved of almost everything they observed in Mexican society. Then, toward the end of the nineteenth century when life began to move at a hectic pace, Americans became nostalgic for the quieter times and the traditions of the past; many popular works about Mexico and the Spanish Southwest, written in a highly sentimental and romantic vein, were produced at this time. Modern American authors, often critical of their own society, have written of Mexican culture with increasing understanding and appreciation, realizing that the involvement between the United States and Mexico is a valuable one and that it must be dealt with constructively in the literature of both countries. *With the Ears of Strangers* traces these changing attitudes in American literature through the years and underscores the importance of the Mexican influence in every phase of life in the Southwest.

A great number of books have been published about the Mexican War of 1846-48. Three works about Arizona written by people who participated in the events they describe are outstanding. G. D. Brewerton was a young army lieutenant who, guided by Kit Carson, carried dispatches from California to the States during the last year of the Mexican War. His *Overland with Kit Carson* is more exciting than most fiction and helped to make the quiet Carson famous. Lieutenant William S.

Emory's *Notes of a Military Reconnaissance* describes the terrible struggle of General Kearny and his army across the desert from Santa Fe to California. Lieutenant Philip St. George Cooke — the army seems to have been full of literary lieutenants — was in command of the famous Mormon Battalion and later told its story in his memoirs. In *Scenes and Adventures in the Army,* he describes vividly and with humor the long trek of his battalion. They took Tucson without firing a shot in anger; indeed their only really rough encounter was with a herd of wild bulls in the vicinity of the present St. David, later established as a community by members of the party. More popularly, Ernest Haycox wrote of frontier military life in *Border Trumpet.*

It is the 1870-85 era, however, which has dominated Western and Arizona literature, stimulating the imaginations of millions of people the world over. It was the time of the cattle empire and the open range, of cattle drives, trail-end towns such as Abilene and Fort Dodge, and wide-open mining camps like Tombstone. According to popular fiction, the lean-flanked, gun-toting, quiet-spoken cowboy, a knight in a roping saddle, saved ranches and maidens, put down outlaws, and occasionally even punched a few cattle, while steely-eyed lawmen, cool, deliberate, and as fast as lightning, demolished the badmen, who died with guns half drawn in the hot dusty streets of Western towns.

Cowboy Literature

In short there has grown up in Western fiction what may be called the Myth of the Cowboy. Stories embodying this myth are widely popular not only in this country, but abroad. They fill many books, many hours of television time, and they have been the movie industry's mainstay since the time of Bronco Billy Anderson. Although Owen Wister's *Virginian,* the archetypal cowboy story, was set in Wyoming, countless numbers of Westerns have had an Arizona background. Zane Grey, for many years the dean of Western writers, lived in Arizona and set a large number of his stories here. Harold Bell Wright, also an Arizona resident, sentimentalized its scenes, as did Clarence Budington Kelland with his romance, *Arizona.* Nelson Nye, a popular writer of Western fiction has written from Tucson stories in which the familiar mountains and deserts are recognizable. Thomas Blackburn, Frank Gruber, and W. R. Burnett, although not Arizona residents, have written suspenseful yarns laid in the state. Further, because so many motion pictures are filmed in Arizona, the state provides many viewers with their image of the entire West.

In addition to the prodigious number of fictional Westerns, there are available a great many works dealing with the same period which are, or at least profess to be, factual. Most of the books concerning the confrontation of badmen by frontier marshals deal, of course, with the Tombstone of the 1880s: with Wyatt, Virgil, and Morgan Earp; with Doc Holliday; with Curly Bill, Johnny Ringo, and the Clantons. Of these works, probably the best known, and certainly the most influential, is *Frontier Marshal,* the biography of Wyatt Earp by Stuart Lake. The Wyatt Earp of Lake's book has fascinated or annoyed people for years. The critical question concerns the accuracy of Lake's portrait. This is no place to settle so involved a question, but a few words about the vividness and force of the book are in order. Lake has embodied here the image of the frontier marshal which has dominated the stereotype in countless novels, screen plays, and television scripts. The discerning reader of a book concerning a frontier peace officer will find lurking under the characterization, Lake's "lion of Tombstone," lean, agile, graceful, savage in his loyalties, deadly accurate in shooting, coldly efficient in pistol-whipping, and somehow mysterious in his aloofness and reserve. Whether or not the picture is an accurate one of Wyatt Earp is something for scholarship to settle, but even if research should show that Earp was something different, one feels that the figure Lake has created here will continue to be seen in books and on screens for some time to come. The reader interested in pursuing the problem suggested here should consult Douglas Martin's *Tombstone Epitaph* and Pat Jahn's *The Frontier World of Doc Holliday* for relevant material.

There are many novels based on Wyatt Earp or the Earp type, most of which unhappily amount only to escape reading. There is, however, a novel, *Warlock,* by Oakley Hall which is a serious and ambitious attempt to deal with the moral issues raised by this epoch in our history. The story is plainly based on Tombstone and Wyatt Earp's career there. But unlike other writers dealing with the same material, Hall portrays his characters not as mere stereotypes, but as real people who reveal what may have motivated men like Earp and Holliday.

The cowboy of fiction was one thing, but what of the real cowboy? Cattlemen were the first solid citizens of Arizona — mining camps rose and died — and their traditions are still important in Arizona culture. The first cattlemen were too busy establishing ranches to have time to write memoirs of their activities, but writers of the next generation tried to fill the gap. Ross Santee in *Cowboy* has given a vivid and true picture of the ordinary cowhand of a generation ago. In *Cow by the Tail,* Jesse Benton, who punched cows over some of Texas and all of Arizona, has given his reminiscences of a life spent in the saddle. Dane Coolidge's *Arizona Cowboys* presents a whole gallery, and Frazier Hunt's *Cap Mossman: Last of the Great Cowmen,* provides the reader with a biography of a great early day rancher. The point of view of the small rancher's wife — and a most important point of view that is — is excellently represented in Mary Rak's *A Cowman's Wife and Mountain Cattle.* Another favorite subject of Western writers is the conflict between sheepmen and cattlemen. Arizona had what was possibly the most serious of those wars,

ably recounted by Earle Forrest in *Arizona's Dark and Bloody Ground.*

A different theme of history appeared in the journals of David K. Udall, whose *Arizona Pioneer Mormon* was edited by the late Levi S. Udall, judge of the Superior Court, and published in 1959 by Arizona Silhouettes. The Udalls were called by their church from their home in Utah to an unwelcoming environment at St. John's in the 1870s. The record of their experiences reflects the difficult Arizona life of that period and testifies to the very significant contribution made by several members of the Udall family to the historical and political structure of the state.

Frank Lockwood arrived in Arizona from the Midwest in 1916, and his fascination with the state lasted from that time until his death in 1948. He was vitally interested in Arizona's history, places, and people, and through his writing he was able to share his knowledge and enthusiasm with others. He wrote about famous early Arizonans at a time when it was still possible to talk with the pioneers themselves or with those who had known them. Among his books are *Arizona Characters, Pioneer Days in Arizona, Story of the Spanish Missions of the Middle Southwest, More Arizona Characters,* and *Life in Old Tucson.* All of Lockwood's books are out of print and are unavailable, for the most part, except in libraries. The fact that his books could no longer be found and purchased was the impetus for the 1968 publication by the University of Arizona Press of a volume entitled *Pioneer Portraits.* This is a collection of fourteen biographical sketches of well-known Arizona pioneers, originally published in several of Lockwood's earlier books.

Finally, what of books about Arizona with a more modern setting? They are generally different in nature from the works discussed so far which are peculiarly Arizonan — that is, it seems unlikely that the events described in these books could have happened anywhere else. Exceptions to this might be *Dark Madonna* by Richard Summers, a novel telling of the life of a Mexican family in Tucson during the depression, and exhibiting a sympathetic insight into the Mexican-Indian behavior and community life; and Jack O'Connor's *Boomtown,* an earthy and accurate story of mining camp days in Globe.

The University Press

Moving into the 1970s, the University of Arizona Press at Tucson has become one of the most active book publishers in the Southwest. Its notable contributions to Southwestern literature included the Southwest Chronicles series, books of a biographical nature about vivid regional personalities and events. The chronicles already well established included *Woman in Levi's,* and *Nine Months is a Year* by Eulalia Bourne; *Boots and Bullets* and *Sheriff Thompson's Day* by Jess G. Hayes; *Pioneer Portraits* by Frank C. Lockwood; *XIT Buck* by

C. E. "Buck" MacConnell; and *Around Western Camp-fires* by Mack Axford.

The Press also had released several definitive accounts of territorial history led by Jay J. Wagoner's *The Arizona Territory 1863-1912: A Political History,* and including *Arizona Rough Riders* by Charles Herner; *John Spring's Arizona,* edited by A. M. Gustafson; and Maurice G. Fulton's *The Lincoln County War* in New Mexico, edited by Robert N. Mullin. Ranchers, cowboys, and others active in roles on the frontier were writing of their experiences in a diversity of volumes also published by the Press, including Dan Moore's *Log of a Twentieth Century Cowboy* and *Enter Without Knocking,* and Slim Ellison's *Cowboys Under the Mogollon Rim.*

Many aspects of Indian culture and history have been authentically portrayed through University of Arizona Press books, including *Southwest Indian Painting* and *Southwest Indian Craft Arts,* by Clara Lee Tanner; Anna Moore Shaw's *Pima Indian Legends;* La Verne H. Clark's *They Sang For Horses: the Impact of the Horse on Navajo and Apache Folklore;* Louise Udall's *Me and Mine: The Life Story of Helen Sekaquaptewa; Blessingway,* a fundamental ritual of the Navajos recorded by Father Berard Haile and translated and edited by Leland C. Wyman; *Speaking of Indians,* Bernice Johnston's compilation of forty-three easily-understood capsules paired with striking photographs; Edward H. Spicer's *Cycles of Conquest;* Ruth Warner Giddings' *Yaqui Myths and Legends;* several ethnographic works on the Western Apache edited by Keith Basso from the classic findings of Grenville Goodwin; and *In the Days of Victorio: Reminiscences of a Warm Springs Apache,* by Eve Ball, as narrated by James Kaywaykla.

A bibliography of Arizona fiction from various publishers since 1940 lists forty-five titles. Fifteen of these works are set in modern times; the rest would fall in one or another of the literary categories already mentioned. Of the fifteen, four have as leading characters members of various Arizona Indian tribes and are certainly, therefore, peculiarly Arizonan. The other eleven are set in cities, which, insofar as the effectiveness of the stories is concerned, might as well be in Kansas as in Arizona. The facility of travel and communications has greatly reduced the differences between parts of our nation, with a consequent reduction of true regionalism.

At an earlier time region did differ, and for that reason two-thirds of Arizona's modern novels deal with a time long dead — a time in Arizona's history that fascinates writers and readers alike.

The Academic Side

The universities of the state have done a great deal to encourage interest in all the fine arts and, through their courses of study, have offered instruction to many talented artists, performers, and writers. A number of professors in Arizona's colleges and universities are authors in their own right. In 1970 Northern Arizona University, Arizona State University, and the University of Arizona were all offering courses in creative writing — fiction, nonfiction, and poetry — as well as courses on the literature of the Southwest. At Northern Arizona University a student may earn a Master of Arts degree with a major in English or in creative writing. Arizona State University and the University of Arizona both offer the Bachelor of Arts, Master of Arts, and Doctor of Philosophy degrees, the University of Arizona giving the M.A. in either English or creative writing. At all three schools student newspapers and annual yearbooks are published; in addition, at the University of Arizona two scholarly journals are published: the *Arizona Quarterly* and *Arizona and the West,* a quarterly journal of history.

In 1969 the annual show of the Scottsdale National Indian Arts Council included both poetry and prose writings by Indian children and young adults. Much of this work is very fine, but in 1968 it was not well known to many people, as it had not yet been collated and disseminated. The State Department of Public Instruction under the guidance of the National Society of Arts and Letters was also sponsoring an annual poetry competition in the late 1960s.

An important addition to Arizona cultural institutions is the Arizona Commission on the Arts and Humanities, established by the Arizona Legislature in 1966. Financed by grants from the National Council on the Arts and by contributions from private sponsors, the Commission works in cooperation with many organizations and individuals throughout the state to encourage interest and participation in literature and the other arts.

Fig. 32.1   The educational enterprise flourishes day and night on such campuses as that of the University of Arizona.

32

EDUCATION

Roy M. Claridge
Educational Administration

THE EFFORTS OF ARIZONA CITIZENS to develop schools cover more than a century of phenomenal growth and development. In 1864, the First Territorial Legislature granted $250 each to the mission schools at San Xavier del Bac, Prescott, Mohave, and La Paz, and $500 to Tucson, provided that the English language would form a part of the instruction in each of these schools. Although the measure required the towns to raise equal amounts either through taxation or private gifts, none raised its share. As for the generosity of this legislature, education received $1500 from a total appropriation of $16,137.

In the same legislative session, The University of Arizona was authorized and its constitution written. A Board of Regents was set up and money provided from the sale of lands granted by the federal government for university purposes. The lawmakers even authorized tax levies for free education and the establishment of a territorial library and historical department, the latter evolving into the Arizona Historical Society.

The 1864 legislation lapsed and it was not until twenty years later that new legislation was enacted. Although the initial effort toward the establishment of a university was significant, the people of Arizona were not ready. There was not a schoolhouse, public school, courthouse, nor railroad in the entire territory. The departure of federal garrisons from Arizona at the outbreak of the Civil War encouraged the Indians' belief that the white man was retreating. There followed another twenty-five years of bitter conflict, with men more interested in self-survival than in education.

Congress' passage of the Morrill Act, July 2, 1862, provided for the establishment of an agricultural college in every state or territory willing to avail itself of the provisions of the act and comply with them. Nevertheless the poverty-ridden people of the Territory still were unable to build and support a university, high schools, and common grammar schools.

The First Census

In 1863, U.S. Marshal Milton B. Duffield was ordered to take a census of Arizona. His count of 4,573 people included 750 soldiers in the Territory, and hundreds of Mexicans whose only legal claim to citizenship was two weeks' residence. Tucson was the largest town, claiming 1,568 people, of which 268 were officers and men of the First California Cavalry. Of the people registered in the official census, only 74 men were worth more than $1000. Another 130 men had more than $500, and 357 others claimed to be worth more than $100. The census takers did not list the number of people with less than four dollars, but there were at least 4000 who had less than $100.

Although there were no public schools in the Arizona Territory in 1864, a private school was established in Prescott by R. F. Piatt. Two years later a parochial school for boys was opened in Tucson.

In 1870, the first federal census in the Territory reported that there were 1,923 children of school age. School age was not specifically defined and no territorial schools were mentioned. In that same year, a parochial school for girls was established in Tucson.

The Sixth Territorial Legislature, in 1871, passed a bill providing for a Board of Education, ex-officio county school superintendents, and district trustees. Shortly afterward, the first public school in the Territory was opened in Tucson, and Prescott and Phoenix opened schools, which were later closed for lack of funds. The people continued to express interest as exemplified by the donation of land, materials, and labor for a small school to serve the Salt River Valley settlements.

Teachers were imported from California and the east coast. Most of them married within a few years and the rapid turnover presented a real problem.

Not until 1879 did the legislature create the office of Territorial Superintendent of Schools, and in 1883

Moses H. Sherman was elected the first territorial superintendent.

Schools were by now important and there was a rapid growth of elementary education throughout the Arizona Territory, leading to the establishment of what were called "college preparatory schools," a measure improvised to provide sufficient enrollment in the new university and the state's two normal schools.

The evolution of the modern high school differed from that of the elementary schools, but was plagued with similar difficulties. Enrollment of students to prepare for college and normal school was not great. The people were scattered, and there were few places with the proper provisions.

One of the very first high schools in the Arizona Territory was established in Tucson in 1881, as a consequence of the principal, George C. Hall, reorganizing the public schools of the town into sections. One through four were the primary grades and five through eight were the grammar grades. Beyond this, Hall added grades nine through eleven, which were designated as high school. This organization was short-lived, even though the following year there were 350 students in the school. It was many years before the Old Pueblo again provided public education at the high-school level.

By 1882 there were ninety-eight school districts in Arizona, with over ten thousand students attending. The early historians did not delineate any difference in grade levels. For several years, the University of Arizona maintained a preparatory school and the normal schools provided a similar service.

In 1888, the Latter-Day Saints' Academy of the St. Joseph Stake was established in the Gila Valley. After years of tribulation and slow growth, and nominal transition from St. Joseph's Academy to the Latter-Day Saints' Academy, and later to Gila Academy, this school became a steady source of students for the University of Arizona and the normal schools.

There were few schools, however, providing education beyond the eighth grade level until 1911. In that year, a total of thirteen such schools were established and there were 38,611 school children between the ages of six and twenty-one, and 876 teachers listed in the Territory.

As the population increased, the purposes, goals, and aims of education developed in different ways. Many districts were formed throughout the state to provide education through the twelfth grade. This raised the demand for teachers, and pointed up the foresight of early citizens who had established two normal schools.

Public School Finance

Throughout the history of public schools in Arizona, legislative and legal provisions have been dependent upon the economy of the state. This economy has been so diverse and unequal across the state that as late as 1968 there was a great disparity of physical wealth among the school districts and the types of educational offerings each district could support. For example, the assessed valuation of elementary school districts was $2,298,429,470, with a range of assessed physical wealth of $365.41 to $359,478.20 for each pupil.

The source of this disparity is Arizona's large size in comparison with its population. Large concentrations of population have tended to center around certain focal points; namely, Maricopa County, Tucson, and Flagstaff. These happened also to be the areas of higher education, although not the areas of the greatest assessed value. The richest areas have tended to be those where mining was the major industry. With continuous expansion of mining and Arizona's efforts to equalize and to educate its people, this disparity is expected to decrease, though it will probably not be entirely erased.

Educational finance in Arizona has also been influenced by the fact that over seventy-five percent of the state is in public lands held by the federal government. Though there have been many federal provisions to help local school districts with payments in lieu of taxes to the various counties in Arizona for distribution, these are not sufficient to help provide adequate schooling in many districts.

Over the years, succeeding legislatures have evidenced interest in education by provisions, appropriations, and guidelines set forth for the State Board of Education. Although some of these are not noteworthy, overall Arizona has been competitive in educational endeavor with leaders among the states.

To bear out that statement, slightly more than 100 years after the territorial legislature made its initial appropriation of fifteen hundred dollars for schools, the legislation apportionment of funds for education was 53.82 percent of all of the money appropriated for the state's operation in 1968-69.

Out of a total budget of $482,748,458, Arizona allotted $259,792,872 to tax supported education. This included $152,820,433 to elementary and secondary schools; $74,412,304 to three state universities and $9,291,438 to junior colleges.

As of 1970, functioning in the public schools of Arizona was a foundation program for school financing, with need, ability to pay, and effort as its basis. State and county aid to local school districts was based on the number of students, as determined by average daily attendance in the district, assessed valuation of property, and a basic aid allocation for each student. Any amount received above the basic aid allocation was provided according to the need of each district after it had levied a minimum tax as provided by law. In addition to this, an equalization formula was being used for disbursing any further funds to local districts.

Programs offering services initially funded and supported by federal funds have decreased or been dropped entirely because of lack of local or state funds. Others have not been supported because of the lack of matching funds from the state.

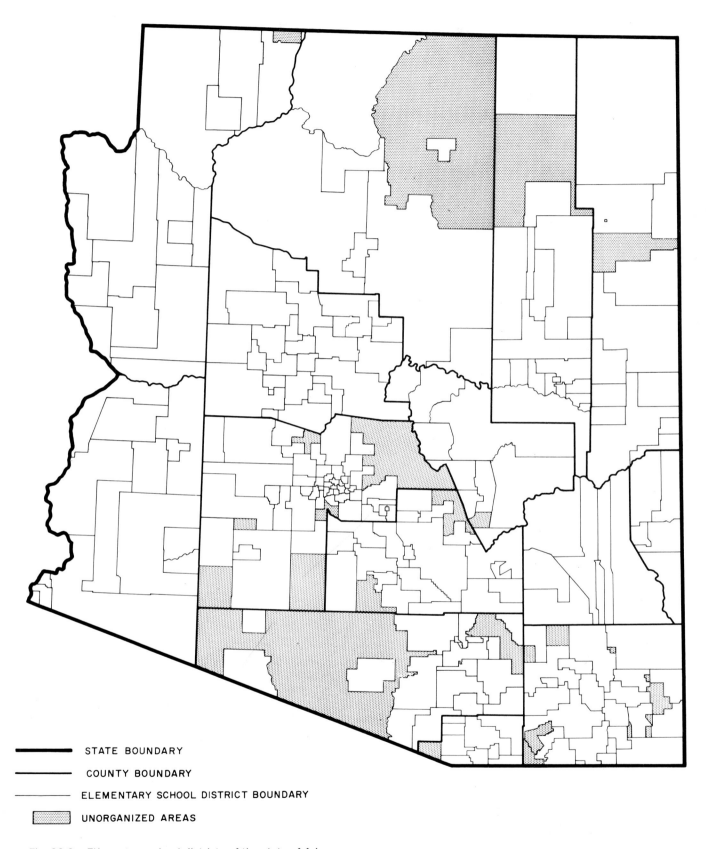

STATE BOUNDARY

COUNTY BOUNDARY

ELEMENTARY SCHOOL DISTRICT BOUNDARY

UNORGANIZED AREAS

Fig. 32.2   Elementary school districts of the state of Arizona.

School Organization and Program

Since earliest territorial days, the local school district has been the basic unit of public school organization and administration below the college level. The people of a given community take the necessary action to establish its schools, and control of the school remains with these people — with an elected governing body determining school policies and the educational and financial programs. Execution and administration of these programs and policies are delegated to trained administrative personnel.

The number of elementary school districts in Arizona decreased greatly in the first half of the twentieth century with the consolidation of some and the lapsing of others. The modern trend toward urban living has resulted in smaller enrollments in outlying areas, with the consequent closing of certain schools having less than the average daily attendance required for continuation. In 1922 there were 255 "one-teacher" schools, which had dropped to twenty-five by 1968. Those remaining were in the most outlying areas of the state, and constituted less than one percent of the school population. This would indicate that practically all of Arizona's elementary school children attend schools where children of only one grade level are to be found in a classroom.

Some of the special provisions for elementary schools have included the selection of textbooks by the State Board of Education, which has purchased and distributed them free through the school districts. These have been paid for by local public school funds. The school lunch program, often financed in part with federal aid, has been another facet of the elementary school complex. Provisions have also been made for the homebound teaching program for handicapped children. During the 1968-69 school year, there were over six thousand handicapped children served throughout the state.

There is considerable freedom of administration within Arizona school districts, although certain legal specifications are made in the elementary school curriculum with respect to providing instruction about the state and federal constitutions, and health education. The State Board of Education prescribes the course of study in all elementary schools and influences the curricula of the high schools by determining the credits necessary for graduation.

As in most other states, Arizona's high schools are classified or accredited according to the size of the staff and the nature of the curriculum. This is done through the State High School Visitor, under the auspices of the North Central Association of Colleges and Secondary Schools.

Course and graduation requirements for Arizona high schools are described in a handbook published by the State Board of Education and under the direction of the State High School Visitor.

As of 1970, general requirements for the high school diploma in Arizona included three units of English, one unit of mathematics, and one unit of science, two units of social studies which must include one unit of American history and one-half unit of civics, divided into one-third of the semester on Arizona history and devoted to the essentials, sources, and history of the Arizona and the United States constitutions, and one-half unit of health education. The remaining units were to be electives, with a unit of physical education highly recommended.

The State Board of Education has established these minimum requirements to help students to become acquainted with and develop interests and abilities in several curricular fields. It is their intent, however, that each school develop an instructional program which will provide for the common as well as the educational needs of its own particular students. The educational program ought to be developed from the school's philosophy and from the knowledge the school has of the needs of its students in the community. The utilization of community resources has enriched the educational programs in many areas of Arizona. Industry in the urban centers of Tucson and Phoenix, the three state universities, agriculture, mining, forestry, and ranching are examples of the many resources now available and made use of by Arizona's public schools.

As elsewhere in the nation, high school curricula in Arizona are being closely scrutinized and considerably modified as experimentation and innovation are evaluated. The effectiveness of such programs and techniques as team-teaching, individual instruction, small and large group instruction, computer-assisted instruction, and many others rely mainly upon the individual district financial resources, organizational, technological, and educational know-how of the administrators, teachers, and their aides. The state's universities have been doing an excellent job in these areas with the preparation and retraining of teachers.

Modern societal problems and current need for trained personnel in technological and professional lines have increased the variety of demands upon the high school. As the demands of curricular offerings increase at the high school level, and where there is little room for enlargement of the curriculum, the preliminary and basic education of certain areas has been dropped into the elementary school. Math and science areas are examples of this. Also, the universities have helped meet this challenge to high schools by permitting high school students to take advanced work not available in their particular high schools.

The solution of various types of educational, vocational, social, civic, and personnel problems has made counseling and guidance an extremely important service to high school students. Naturally, therefore, the educa-

Fig. 32.3   Up-to-date approaches to curriculum have teamed with contemporary structures in some high schools.

Cholla High School Graphic Arts

tional counseling and guidance service alone has great demands for trained personnel. The recommended ratio of one counselor to 450 students has been met in most schools in Arizona, but there are still some schools which have none.

In spite of the increase in the number of high school graduates entering college and the demands for better-prepared freshmen, high school will be the final, organized educational experience for many. In 1967-68, for example, thirty-nine percent of the high school graduates of Arizona did not enter college, not to mention the many who did enter but dropped out. The rather special educational needs of this group must continuously be evaluated if the educational programs of the state are to be adequate.

This foundation program of financial aid to schools has been used primarily for operational expenditures and does not include capital outlay expenses. Land acquisition and building construction comprise the major portion of capital outlay. The Arizona statutes provide two sources from which the local school districts may raise money to finance the acquisition of land and the construction of school buildings.

The first source is with the issuance of school bonds. These bonds are limited to ten percent of the last assessed property valuation for state and county taxing purposes for each district. The second source is the Special District Levy for Building Fund, commonly referred to as the "Ten Cent Levy." This allows each district to levy a supplemental tax of ten cents per $100 of assessed valuation each year upon its taxable property, to be used principally for land acquisition and school building construction. Alterations, additions, equipment, and school furniture may come from this fund also.

School bonds and the interest due thereon are retired by a tax assessment on the real property of the district. This amount is included in the annual budget of each district.

In the school year of 1968-69, with the increase in the national prime interest rate, many Arizona school districts were not able to sell their needed bond issues at the maximum interest rate of six percent as provided by law. With the rapid and ever-increasing school attendance, an effort has been made to place state and county support on a current basis. Arizona has been one of the fastest growing states in population. Thus, the curtailment in the building program will undoubtedly be felt for many years. Already in the 1969-70 school year there were many districts on double session in an effort to overcome the classroom shortage. The public school population in Arizona in 1968-69 was an average daily membership of 289,730 in the elementary schools, and 111,051 in the high schools.

Arizona has endeavored through the years to provide free public education to everyone on an equal basis. Rising school costs, varied tax structures in poor and rich districts, legal restrictions on bond issues, as well as many local divergent circumstances, have in past years thwarted the overall effort of the state. Curtailment of educational services has resulted from the lack of properly motivated political interests. These shortages of services have been in the areas of research and development, proper evaluative measures, auxiliary and student personnel, innovative practices, and the retainment of good professional educators. The drop in the educational advancement has been at all levels of instruction in the state. It should be noted that there has been progress in almost all of these areas, but far below the levels necessary to keep Arizona among the leaders in the nation.

In 1969, Arizona school law provided that all federal monies for public schools and districts must be administered by the districts. Among the sources of federal funds for the schools was an annual interest totaling $1,125,000 on money from the sale of eight million acres of land granted to the state for the schools by the Enabling Act of 1910. Also received on an annual basis were federal monies for school lunches (milk, agriculture commodities, lunch reimbursements), vocational education, Indian education, school construction, Forest Reserve Act, current expenditures for federally-impacted areas, and from year to year, the funding to the state and local districts grants under the National Defense Education Act and the Elementary Secondary Education Act. In any given fiscal year, the public schools of Arizona accept and use in excess of thirty million dollars from the federal government.

Emphasis was increased in the 1960s on educational excellence beyond high school. Arizona, like many other states, has worked through community junior colleges to strengthen this emphasis. By 1970 the state was moving toward having a dozen or so post-high-school public institutions offering two-year college programs in the arts, sciences, and humanities, and including terminal courses of a technical and vocational nature. Such junior colleges also offer education beyond the basic levels for adults, gearing the courses to the civil and/or liberal educational demands of each community.

In 1960, legislation provided for the creation of a state junior college board and the establishment of county junior college districts, to be supported in part by the counties and the state. This board has overall state-wide jurisdiction of the junior colleges, but local jurisdiction is left to an elected board for each junior college district.

State financial support was provided for the operation of these colleges as well as for capital outlay. Operational expenses were covered on a full-time student equivalent basis. Capital outlay appeared in the form of a legislative appropriation amounting to about $500,000 for each new campus and a per annum of one hundred and fifteen dollars for each full-time student equivalent for all campuses. However, a county was required to have a possible minimum enrollment in the number of 320 full-time equivalent students

Fig. 32.4 Starting school helps small children enter a bigger world.

(FTES), and a minimum assessed valuation of sixty million dollars in order to establish a junior college district.

The junior colleges of Arizona are non-selective in their admission policies, and comprehensive in their educational programs. They have a mandate from the State Board of Education to offer full-time students a general education, including courses equivalent to those taken in freshman and sophomore years of college. Vocational-technical and semi-professional programs and a continuing education program, with service and cultural programs for the wider community, plus counseling, guidance, and job placement involve the junior college with a heterogeneous student body and a diversity of community obligations.

The first junior college in Arizona was the Latter-Day Saints' Academy, later Eastern Arizona College, which opened its doors to students in Thatcher in 1891. Since that time, eight other junior college campuses have been established, with three more opening in the early 1970s.

Non-Public Schools

The private and parochial schools of Arizona in 1970 were educating approximately eleven percent of the elementary school children and eight percent of the secondary school pupils. Kindergarten and nursery schools accounted for more than twenty-six percent of the total private and parochial school enrollment. Many educators were strongly advocating the extension of the state's educational system program to include the kindergarten in all public schools. Relatively few districts within the state were providing kindergarten programs at their own expense. /

Parochial schools account for a significant portion of the private school enrollment in Arizona. At the elementary level, all Arizona private schools follow the prescribed state course of study, using state-adopted textbooks. Supplementary work, usually in the form of religious instruction, is given in parochial schools. All of Arizona's private high schools by 1970 had been accredited by the state's three public four-year institutions for higher education.

Increasing school costs as the 1970s began were a cause of great concern to the private and parochial schools. They were endeavoring to garner funds for operational expenses beyond the peripheral funds now received. A financial crisis was considered imminent if not evident. The lack of instructional personnel in the parochial schools was increasing, and as one out of two were certificated personnel, competition with the public schools in salaries and benefits was very difficult. Efforts continued by parochial schools to secure public school funds.

In 1969, there arose the issue of private and parochial schools receiving public school funds for operational expenditures. Arguing the already overcrowded conditions of the public schools and shortage of building and expansion funds, proponents of parochial funding felt that the state's school districts would be hard put to accommodate and educate the influx of students, if the private and parochial schools were to close their doors for lack of operational funds.

Establishing Higher Education

In 1885 action was taken toward the establishment of the university authorized in 1864. The Thirteenth Legislature, sometimes known as the "Thieving Thirteenth" for its reckless, illegal, and many times unnecessary expenditures, were battling over two major political spoils — the state capital and the asylum for the insane. Of secondary importance were a university and a teacher's college which no community really wanted. Maricopa County was considered the winner with an appropriation of $100,000 for the asylum. Tempe, a new ferry landing on the Salt River, received the teachers' college and $5,000, later to become Arizona Territorial Normal School, and in 1958 Arizona State University. Various other towns received appropria-

tions for bridges and levees on the Gila River. Pima County and Tucson were assigned the university, which they did not want, as evidenced by their violent reaction to legislator C. C. Stephens upon his return to Tucson. Matters were worse after the people found out they had received a puny $25,000 for the university. A sum of $4,000 had been sent with Mr. Stephens to buy votes, if necessary, to bring the capital to Tucson.

Legislation providing for the university's establishment required that Pima County, Tucson, or private citizens contribute forty acres of land within a year for the campus, or lose the appropriated $25,000. The people of Tucson preferred largely to ignore the fact they were elected to be the home of a university, and only through the extreme and unwavering efforts of J. S. Mansfeld was the appropriation saved. After appointment to the Board of Regents, and selecting a site on the east mesa of Tucson and practically begging the owners for three months, Mr. Mansfield obtained the forty acres of mesquite-covered land. Neither the townspeople nor the county were interested in providing any land. Nevertheless, the names of E. C. Gifford, W. S. Reid, and B. C. Parker — respectively gamblers and a

Public Information Office, Northern Arizona University

Fig. 32.5   Northern Arizona University at Flagstaff is one of the state's three universities.

saloonkeeper — should be long-remembered as donors.

The filing of the property deed to the Board of Regents on November 27, 1886 did, in fact, establish the University of Arizona. There were at that time no buildings, no teachers, no students.

On October 1, 1891, the doors of the new college opened and thirty-two students enrolled for the first semester. Only six entered as freshmen; the others had to take preparatory courses because there were no high schools in the Territory. This small beginning came after years of struggle. But from it the University had grown, by 1970, to include 254 acres, 96 buildings, over 1,200 faculty members, and more than 24,000 students in twelve undergraduate colleges, one graduate college, and three schools.

From its initial role as a land-grant college, the University of Arizona has come to serve the territorial and state residents through a wide variety of teaching, research, and off-campus extension activities. By 1970, twenty-three county extension offices and seven branch experiment stations and farms extended the university agricultural campus to all parts of Arizona.

Arizona State University, founded in Tempe in 1885 as the Territorial Normal School, first opened its doors to students in 1886.

Northern Arizona Normal School was established at Flagstaff in 1899. It became a four-year degree-granting institution in 1925, under the name of Arizona State Teachers' College, was renamed again in 1945, and finally became Northern Arizona University in 1966. Though not as large as the sister institutions, N.A.U. plays a vital role in the network of higher education in the state.

The American Institute for Foreign Trade, later to be known as the Thunderbird School of International Management, was founded in 1946 to prepare young people for careers in international commerce with global business firms or government or social agencies. Located sixteen miles northwest of Phoenix, in 1969 it claimed annual average enrollment of more than 500 students.

In 1949, Grand Canyon College, with a four-year liberal arts program, was chartered by the Arizona Southern Baptist Convention. Established first in Prescott, it was moved to Phoenix in 1951, and by 1969 had an enrollment of more than 700 students.

In 1966 the Congregational Church established a private educational institution in Prescott called Prescott College. Offering a four-year liberal arts program also, its enrollment in 1969 was about 250.

The three state universities receive financial support from annual legislative appropriations for operations and capital outlay. Student fees, endowments, federal grants, and gifts help to defray the continually increasing costs of college-level education.

Fig. 32.6 Arizona's modern universities offer a broad educational base as well as diverse preparation for careers.

Fig. 32.7   Ethnic variety adds interest to class projects.

The broad picture of higher education in Arizona in 1970 lacked only two elements commonly associated with university programs: dentistry and veterinary medicine.

Arizona has participated actively in the program of the Western Interstate Commission for Higher Education (WICHE), enabling Arizona students to gain admission to a dental or veterinary medicine school in any one of the thirteen western states which has one or more of these schools, and to attend at a cost no greater than that paid by a resident of the state itself. The institution that accepts a student receives compensation also from funds provided by the Arizona legislature, as an additional part of the total annual cost per student.

Under the Arizona statute each participating student in WICHE must either practice in Arizona one year for each year of support received, or refund to the state one-half the money expended for the years in question.

Education of Ethnic Groups

Arizona's population embraces several ethnic minority groups whose educational opportunities, from pre-school through the college-university level, were demonstrably improved during the 1960s. Pre-school training focused on reading readiness, and language

difficulties for Mexican-American, Negro, and Indian children increased yearly throughout the state.

The Mexican-American group is by far the largest, although in general, its numbers decrease with distance from the Arizona-Mexico border. However, many mining towns include great numbers of Mexican-Americans among their residents. In many small towns and in some area schools of the larger cities, the majority of the students have been Mexican-American. Until surprisingly modern times, educators believed that these young children should speak only English in the classroom, and insisted upon it. Many could not do so, and were thus labeled as slow students of low ability. Unable to communicate with the monolingual teacher, they became known as non-achievers and did not learn to read or write. They were placed in "basic" or "slow learner" classes, but still expected to learn strange concepts and attitudes in a tongue that was literally foreign to them. The discipline of the school forced them to adjust not only to a new language but to a new, "strange" culture. The result was often confusion, frustration, and failure, which followed them through the elementary school into the higher grades.

As a natural human reaction, when such children reached the age of sixteen when state law no longer required attendance, they tended to drop out of school. Changing this unfortunate cycle has been a slow process until our times in which great strides have been taken and an increasing number of Mexican-Americans returned to the schools as teachers and administrators. Anglos have joined them also in the realization that bilingual children need a particular kind of education — one that helps them not only to adjust to a new culture, but teaches them to be proud of their own familial heritage of language and culture.

Programs capitalizing on the bicultural and bilingual potential have been initiated in Arizona cities and developed with considerable success. By the 1970s there were many bilingual teachers in the early grades. Special techniques and innovations expanded the program on to secondary school, college, and university levels.

From the beginning of territorial days the federal government has grappled — often inefficiently — with the program of educating the American Indian. Arizona has been the scene of much of this grappling. Inadequacy of schooling has been the story in boarding schools, border-town dorms, or numerous federally financed attempts to get the Indian children into public school. Acting through a myriad of bureaus and agencies, the government seemed for years not to appreciate the abilities and capacities for learning possessed by Indian youth, nor even the wisdom of Indian adults. Educational programs, therefore, have acted more as depressants than stimulants to the development of desired attitudes and concepts. Goals for these children have been set at very low levels. In consideration of the fact that Indian children also aspire to greatness, and that they are capable of becoming doctors, lawyers, and teachers, those who reach their potential usually do so in spite of, rather than because of, the educational support and opportunities afforded by the federal government.

The Bureau of Indian Affairs has seemed too often to lack the foresight and innovative imagination to succeed in educating the Indian children. There are, of course, many competent and dedicated people in the BIA, but the machinery has not been at their disposal to realize their goals.

The Indian boarding schools are an outstanding example of the problem. They have been regarded almost as detention homes. Parents have not been encouraged to visit them, and the facilities have usually been closed to the children after school and on weekends. The curriculum rarely has included anything about Indian culture and heritage. Consequently physical and emotional isolation has resulted in greater separation of the child and parent. The BIA policy of the 1960s was to phase out the boarding schools, moving as many children as possible into public schools. But there will still be many who must be boarded because of school inaccessibility.

With regard to the boarding schools still needed, in 1971 there still was room for improvement. The possibilities have been markedly demonstrated by the Rough Rock Demonstration School on the Navajo Reservation. Success here can probably be attributed in great measure to the inclusion of Indian culture and wisdom as complementary to the required curriculum. The involvement of Navajo parents has been the key. The school board has been composed of Navajos who have had little, if any, formal education, yet they have been making the necessary decisions. Parents on a rotating basis have acted as foster parents and counselors in the dorms. Others have visited the dorms regularly to tell stories and to acquaint the youngsters with Navajo traditions, history, and legends.

The children have been encouraged to go home for weekends and for other vacations, in contrast to other schools where this has not been allowed. Even first graders were not formerly permitted to go home for Christmas. Teachers have visited the homes of the children and acquainted the parents with the program. A cultural identification program exposing the children to the customs and values of their forebearers, as well as those of Anglo society, has eliminated the "either/or" dilemma of the past. Instruction has been carried on in the Navajo language and the children encouraged to use it, while English has been stressed as the second language.

An in-service program for staff members has also been valuable as many of them did not speak English and had little secondary education.

Almost sixty percent of the Indian youth, as of 1970, were attending public schools, the major cost being defrayed by the federal government. Encouraging on the surface, this has created underlying problems.

Fig. 32.8 Language acquired by modern methods is the key to communication in elementary school as in the grownup world.

Federal help has been on the decrease, and this has affected Arizona, which, with its large federal land holdings, has a very inadequate tax base. In the crowded public school, instead of receiving special attention, the Indian child is likely to be thrown in with his Anglo contemporaries with small chance of success.

Religious schools have developed Indian education programs in which the federal government has had no involvement. Mission schools have been supported by several denominations, those of the Catholic Church, of course, extending deep into the past of Arizona as a part of Spanish-America with its teaching and colonizing padres. In more modern times, besides receiving schooling under both Catholic and Protestant auspices, Indian tribes of the western and west central states with "church-member children" have been eligible for a flourishing program sponsored by a prominent Christian denomination. In this program Indian children of the church have been taken from the reservation and placed in the foster homes of church members. These foster parents have been carefully selected to provide an environment in keeping with state standards and including room, board, and all clothing, at no expense to the student or his own family. It is preferred in this program that an agemate of the same sex be already in the foster family to provide companionship and understanding. Students in this program return home for the summer but are encouraged to return to the same foster family until completion of high school. Many foster parents have paid also for college education.

Although Arizona's schools have, in a sense, been integrated racially since the early 1930s, little was done in earlier years to accommodate and take care of disadvantaged children. The problems of the Mexican-American and the Indian children can be retold as far as the Black community is concerned, the major difference being that in Arizona this sector is smaller in number.

Arizona's pre-school training programs, aimed at helping the culturally disadvantaged, have produced results in their short history, although the overall educational value cannot be measured for years to come. The major cost of such programs has been borne by the federal government in the form of research grants and programs, since the state has not been in a financial position to pay for them.

Latter-day grade school programs have been designed to raise the learning potential for culturally

Fig. 32.9   The professions beyond college are served at the state institutions of higher learning.

Ray Manley

disadvantaged people. High school social studies programs have been moulded to develop positive attitudes, individual initiative, and a sense of responsibility in the majority peer group. The state has started to reap the harvest of such programs as more and more bilingual people enter the pedagogic professions to help solve problems for children with backgrounds like their own.

The universities and colleges of the state have cooperated also with local school boards, state, regional, and federal agencies in developing projects to improve the educational experience of the culturally deprived. For the Arizona college curriculum there have been created an increasing number of programs and courses intended to bring students to awareness of urgent social problems. In this context the major problem is finding qualified instructors who are also members of minority groups to teach such courses to members of their own group in a way that will improve the student's self-image.

The history of Arizona's early struggles added to the complexity presented by the modern educational picture point up the fact that Arizona has crossed many frontiers in the effort to establish a good educational system. In addition to the state's economic abundance, the schools, colleges and universities of Arizona have become one of its most prized resources. To keep Arizona abreast of the nation, the administrators, legislators and voters of the state face the multiple challenges of population explosion, the critical problems of school plant construction, the need for provision of equal opportunities, and the growingly acute problems of financing. The response to this challenge will do much to determine the quality of Arizona's education in the future.

Photographs of churches appearing in this chapter represent the old and the new in religious architecture within the state. Architecture was chosen to represent the arts in religion because it is the medium that is most clearly social or communal by its very nature, a building expressing those who use it, even more than those who made it.

Fig. 33.1　A concern for matters beyond the limits of daily experience is shared by all religions active in Arizona. *Jerry Duchscherer*

33

RELIGION

WHEN EUROPEAN MAN first came to the Southwest, it was under a banner of religion. Wherever went the conquistadores, avid for gain or glory, went also the dedicated man, the knight of faith, the Jesuit or Franciscan missionary. Beside the emblem of New Spain was planted the Cross; and both plantings were precarious.

The sea of faith, however, had been at the full in Arizona since the days of prehistory. From the beginning it was a faith combined with works, aimed not only at mystical experience and salvation, but at mastery of external difficulties — poverty, wars, and the weather — and at an adaptation of the individual to living with his fellows on the frontier.

It has been observed that several of the world's major religions took shape in an environment similar to the Arizona desert. Relentless sun, pursuing winds, the monumentality of mountains and sweep of the heavens, told early peoples of the Middle East that man and his lonely efforts were of trifling size. These forces were at work on the pioneers as on the aborigines; and they are with Arizonans today — reminders of the need for humility, broad thoughts, and harmonization with the principles of nature and of human welfare.

The religions that have developed in Arizona all have these concerns in common. Like religions the world over, they are divided into several large groups, these in turn divided according to the needs and inclinations of the believers.

Indian Religions

Religion among the Arizona Indians is basically nature worship. For centuries the chief concern of tribal people was with the elements, with the possibility that wind and weather might be controlled for the common good. In simple agricultural societies religion was the expression of a deep desire that the crops should grow. Hunting inspired the worship of an animal (totemism).

Ever-present warfare demanded purification rites to rid a person of the evil spirits infesting one who came in contact with death. As war disappeared or became less pervasive, there was a transition to the aim of casting out the equally malignant spirit which caused illness and death.

Navajo religion has centered in the belief that "every daily act is colored by . . . supernatural forces, ever present and ever threatening." There are small daily observances, such as greeting the morning sun with prayer; rites of passage, such as death and puberty, are performed. The Navajos have been greatly afraid of ghosts, whom they believe to be witches from the world of the dead and who may appear as coyotes, mice, or even humans. These witches will chase people, throw dirt on them, or otherwise cause them ill. Witches, evil men or women who sometimes wear the hide of a coyote or a wolf, may cause loss of property, or sickness or death.

Perhaps the Navajo's greatest concern has been with disease. The actions of ghosts and witches or the "holy people" may cause sickness, and this can be cured by contacting supernatural forces rather than by dealing with the ailment directly. The sick man goes to a "hand trembler," who is a diagnostician and tells him the proper chant or "sing" which will cure. Next he goes to the appropriate medicine man or *shaman,* who in turn administers the correct chant. Among these are the Beauty Way Chant for propitiating snakes, the Mountain Top Way for difficulties with bears, and the Shooting Way if thunder and lightning are involved. The curing rite is based on a myth, reflecting the Navajo's imagination, sense of beauty, and poetry of soul.

The Navajo believes in many powerful beings; among them are the Changing Woman, the essence of nature and the seasons; the Twin War gods who rid the earth of monsters; and the Sun god, perhaps the most powerful of all. Navajo rituals are colorful, involving rich paraphernalia such as prayer sticks, rattles and other musical instruments, beautiful and elaborate sand-paintings, and masked, costumed dancers.

The Hopis have worked out a complex system of reciprocity between human beings and the supernatural. Apparently they believe that unless they perform certain specific rituals, the sun will not shine, the rain will not fall. Order prevails; and along the four-fold path of life marked by childhood, youth, adulthood, and old age, the stages are defined by appropriate ceremonies.

A ritual calendar establishes the cycle of Hopi ceremonies, which are given by secret religious societies. The more important ceremonies fall between the winter and summer solstices, lesser rites being held in the remaining six months of the year. Some of these include the *Powamu* or Bean ceremony, held in February for the initiation of young boys and stressing germination; *Niman*, the time of crop maturation and also the occa-sion for the return of the kachinas to their mountain-top homes; and the Snake Dance in August, to bring the late rains.

Kachinas are as important to the Hopi as they are difficult to define for the white man. They are spirits of the Hopis' ancestors — intermediaries between man and the gods. For one half of the year they live on top of the San Francisco Mountains and other peaks; the other half they are in the Hopi villages and may appear on occasion as costumed masked dancers. Colorful kachina dolls are carved and painted in bright colors and given to Hopi children, so that they may better recognize the embodiment when it appears in the village.

The Hopis have many gods, too. There is Masau'u, the god of the underworld and fire. "Spider Woman" is at the center of the universe; she gives the Hopis their major properties and skills but also witchcraft and death.

The Apache Indians have no religious societies, no ceremonial calendar, and in modern times not many native ceremonies. The main surviving ritual is the girl's puberty ceremony. The girl, her godmother, a medicine man, chanters and drummers, and the Crown dancers are the chief performers. Throughout the ceremony the girl is associated with White Painted Woman, a myth-ical being who embodies the ideal of Apache woman-hood. The Crown dancers perform in the evening by the light of great campfires.

Like other American Indians, the Apaches per-sonify the elements of nature around them — the sun, moon, stars, mountains, lightning, and many others. These personifications appear in their sandpaintings which form a part of their healing rites.

The religion of the Pima and Papago Indians of southern Arizona has also centered around nature wor-ship. The Pimas, however, have all but abandoned their native faith, while the Papagos retain a few religious observances of their own, among them the following: shamans perform rites for curing the sick, for weather, war, and the growth of crops; power is received in songs and dreams; singing is especially important. They "sing up" the corn, sing over the newborn babe. A scalp dance used to be performed, with old women dancing around a pole to the top of which was affixed an enemy scalp; the successful warrior had to be purified after his contact with death. Other significant ceremonies have been the drinking of wine made from saguaro fruit to bring the rain, and the *wiikita* or harvest rite, a masked performance of thanksgiving.

An especially interesting feature of the Arizona Yuman tribes' religion is the mourning rite. The Mohave custom is representative of this rite, shared by all tribes speaking the Yuman language. Formerly the rite was held at the time of death, culminating in the cremation of the deceased. Later it became customary to have a single ritual once a year, with all families who had lost a loved one gathered for the occasion. Images of the deceased were made, and at specified times the families

Ray Manley

Fig. 33.2   The Kachinas — spirits of the Hopi's ancestors.

gathered about and mourned. At the end of four days the images were all burned on a funeral pyre.

All Southwest tribes have a rich mythology. Stories are told of their origins, of the creation of the world and life, and of mountains and rivers. Coyote is a favorite rascal in many of the tales. All tribes have a number of deities, some conceptually clear and concise, others rather hazy and dim. Among the latter is a "high god" or "sky god" — among the Navajos, for instance — who seems to be or to have been in some way superordinate to all the others. This vague memory or tradition of a high god has been seen by some anthropologists as evidence of a "primitive monotheism" calling in question certain more usual assumptions of the unilinear cultural evolution of religious ideas. Possibly there has been devolution as well as evolution, and insights have been lost as well as gained.

All tribes have or have had rituals of some sort, simple or complex. The Hopis have priests and priesthoods; other tribes have shamans or medicine men. Ritual paraphernalia is simpler in some Arizona tribes, more elaborate in others. Not only does a deep and abiding faith in nature mark the religion of all the tribes, but through the centuries their religion has guided them in what seemed the right way of doing things; it has been a balance wheel, giving strength and a sense of well-being in a not too kindly environment.

When Spaniards entered Arizona with great missionary fervor, many natives became Catholics, and their descendants have remained within this faith. Later Anglo-Americans brought Mormonism and several Protestant denominations to the Indians, and today some tribes have embraced Christianity completely, while others are but partially converted. As late as the 1970s, however, the Indian tribes of Arizona still preserved the greatest number of aboriginal religious rituals of any group in the United States.

Catholicism in the New World

The Catholic church in Arizona dates from 1539. In that year Fray Marcos de Niza, a Franciscan priest from Mexico, penetrated the region in his quest for the fabled cities of Cibola. Whether or not one accepts as accurate the account of his investigations, there is no doubt that he came as a priest and announced the Gospel at various Indian villages along the way. So far as is known he was the first to carry the cross into these lands.

For the next 300 years the activities of the Catholic church in the state were of a missionary nature. Arizona stood at the frontier of Spain's colonial expansion, and the church's work lay in the labors first of the Jesuits and later of the Franciscans, who sought to Christianize the Indians and to establish among them missions as centers of Christian culture. To this era belong the names of the Jesuit, Padre Francisco Kino, a truly remarkable man celebrated in Herbert Bolton's

Fig. 33.3 Apache Crown Dancers are a vital part of ritual.

prize-winning biography, *Rim of Christendom;* the Franciscan, Padre Francisco Garcès; and a great company of other devoted priests from both of these orders.

Three centuries of missionary activity thus formed the backdrop for the flourishing Catholic life which continues in the latter half of the twentieth century.

With the Gadsden Purchase in 1854, ecclesiastical jurisdiction of the land south of the Gila was transferred from the Bishop of Sonora to the Bishop of Santa Fe. At first this new territory was attended by priests from New Mexico who made occasional visits to Tucson and the surrounding area. In 1866 Bishop Lamy of Santa Fe sent Father Jean Baptiste Salpointe and two other priests in Arizona to establish permanent parishes in Tucson and Yuma. Two years later Rome established Arizona as a separate jurisdiction, appointing Father Salpointe as the first Vicar Apostolic.

Father Salpointe went to his native diocese of Clermont in France to receive his episcopal consecration on June 20, 1869. He returned with six French priests who had volunteered for work in Arizona, and priests were stationed in the various towns which were springing up like mushrooms throughout the vicarate.

Priests were badly needed even in the more developed parts of the country, and for many years the bishops of Tucson had to rely upon France and other European countries for recruits to meet the religious needs of the new communities. To the young French seminarians of that day Arizona presented a missionary opportunity no less challenging than China or Africa.

The life and culture of Arizona were as different from France as one could find. Each new missionary had to learn at least two foreign languages — Spanish and English — and he had to adapt himself to a quite new mode of existence. Thus the Catholic rectory in Tucson became a kind of training school for volunteers in the Arizona missionary effort. As soon as they gained sufficient knowledge of the languages and people, missionaries were sent out to the larger communities of the territory to establish parishes often comprising several hundred square miles. For instance, the first pastor

of Florence had within his parish such far-flung settlements as Globe and Solomonville on the east, and Tempe and Phoenix on the west. The pastor of Prescott had the whole northern part of Arizona! The priests of Tucson cared for the entire southeastern part of the state, with missions at Benson, Tombstone, and Bisbee.

As settlements developed, new parishes were set up and the territory was divided. As late as 1923, when Bishop Gercke took over the diocese, St. Mary's in Phoenix was the only parish in Maricopa County. Its Franciscan fathers cared not only for the people of Phoenix but also for those living in Glendale, Peoria, Wickenburg, Tempe, Mesa, and Chandler.

The work of the Jesuit missionaries in the seventeenth century and of the Franciscan priests in the eighteenth had been principally among the Indians. Accordingly the Catholic church has always numbered among her adherents a great many members from the various Indian tribes of the state. A network of missions extends throughout the Papago land on the south to the Gila Valley, and through the Apache reserva-

Ray Manley

Fig. 33.4   Catholic Church activity from 1539 until mid-nineteenth century revolved largely around the missions.

Helga Teiwes Photos, Arizona State Museum, University of Arizona

Fig. 33.5   Church decorations by the Indians on the Papago Reservation show an intermingling of cultures and art styles.

tions in the White Mountains up to the Navajos in the north.

One of the first concerns of Bishop Salpointe when he began his administration in 1868 was to provide schools and hospitals. He appealed to the Sisters of Carondelet, in St. Louis, Missouri, who in 1870 sent seven teaching sisters to Tucson to open a school. Ten years later the same order staffed and opened St. Mary's Hospital in Tucson, the first general hospital in the Territory.

The initial convent school became St. Joseph's Academy and was the beginning of the widespread Catholic school system in Arizona. The order also established and operated an orphanage, open to all faiths, in Tucson. It closed in the 1930s. St. Joseph's Academy continued to serve as a preparatory school for girls, until in 1969, because of economic difficulties, it was closed.

Following the opening of St. Mary's Hospital, the nursing sisters of the St. Joseph's order built St. Joseph's in Phoenix and St. Joseph's in Nogales. To meet growing population demands, they not only expanded St. Mary's in west Tucson, but in the latter 1950s built a completely new and modern St. Joseph's Hospital on the east side to supplement it. New additions for both Tucson Catholic hospitals were being planned by 1970.

The Catholic church also established the Convent of the Good Shepherd in Phoenix to provide facilities for delinquent girls. In the 1950s a home for the aged was built there and was operated by the Little Sisters of the Poor.

The history of the Catholic church in Arizona has been one of continuing expansion, keeping pace with the growth and development of the state. Four bishops had ruled the Diocese of Tucson by the late 1960s: Bishop Salpointe, Bishop Bourgade, Bishop Granjon, and Bishop Gercke, who was succeeded at his death in 1964 by his auxiliary bishop, the Most Reverend Francis J. Green. From 1939, and still in the late sixties, the northern counties of the state were under the jurisdiction of the Most Reverend Bernard T. Espelage, O.F.M., the bishop of Gallup. The number of priests in the state increased from three in 1866 to nearly 350 in 1969, with some 175 secular priests attached to the two dioceses of Tucson and Gallup. The others were representatives of eight different religious orders. The ranks of the Sisters of St. Joseph have been augmented by sisters from twenty-two other religious communities, serving Catholics of the state through schools, hospitals, and institutions of social service.

Of necessity the church in Arizona has continued to draw heavily from other areas for its personnel, in particular France, Ireland, and the eastern United States. In 1956, however, the Regina Cleri seminary near Tucson was opened to educate young men for the priesthood; and several religious communities of sisters have established novitiates in the diocese to train young women for the various orders.

The church's story in Arizona should perhaps include mention of a contemporary spirit, moved to criticize and eventually to break with the religious establishment. In the years following World War II there appeared the controversial figure of Emmett McLoughlin, former Franciscan priest, founder of community centers, clinics and Memorial Hospital (formerly St. Monica's Clinic) in slum-ridden South Phoenix, and author of *People's Padre,* a book read by millions. He shaped the lives of many who had been without hope and influenced the thinking of many others on religious matters of our time and country.

The Latter-Day Saints

Arizona was known to the Latter-Day Saints from 1846, when the famous Mormon Battalion passed through the Territory on its march from the Missouri River to the Pacific coast. As early as 1865 LDS settlers were making their homes in Arizona, and in 1873 missionaries were called by the church authorities to locate settlements in the Territory. A number of teams with settlers proceeded as far as the Little Colorado that year but returned discouraged. In 1876, however, another attempt was undertaken which led to the founding of four settlements on the Little Colorado. These were organized into a stake of Zion, called the Little Colorado Stake. As the population grew, the eastern part of this stake was re-organized in 1879 as the Eastern Arizona Stake. Meanwhile, settlers on the lower Little Colorado became discouraged because of the frequent washing away of their dams. The original settlements there, with the exception of St. Joseph, were dissolved. The Eastern Arizona Stake was absorbed by the St. John's Stake and the Snowflake Stake, both organized in 1887. These were still in existence in 1971.

On the Gila and Salt rivers other settlements grew up, leading to the organization of two stakes of Zion in 1883, the St. Joseph Stake and the Maricopa Stake. These, occupying land in a lower, semi-tropical country, have also had a continuous existence.

As the membership of the LDS church in Arizona increased and the settlements of the Saints in the state were so far removed from the headquarters of the church or from the temples in Utah, a decision was made to erect a temple for Arizona, New Mexico, and southern California. The site chosen was in Mesa, Maricopa County, Arizona.

The temple at Mesa was dedicated October 23, 1927. Of strictly fireproof construction, modern, rectangular, and somewhat neoclassical in style, the temple has an independent reinforced concrete frame of floor slabs, columns, beams, and roof. Exterior walls are brick with terra cotta facing. At the four corners, in the frieze portion of the cornice, are sculptured panels depicting the gathering of Israel from all nations in this dispensation. On the exterior walls are splendid mural paintings, and in the baptismal room, which is finished

Fig. 33.6   Mesa, Arizona, is the site of the Latter Day Saints Temple for Arizona, New Mexico, and Southern California.

in colored faience tiles, the font rests on the backs of twelve life-size sculptured oxen.

The exterior of the temple proper measures 81 by 105 feet and rises three stories; the entire building, including the annex, measures 128 by 184 feet. This was the ninth of fourteen temples built by the Latter-Day Saints and one of eleven in the United States in 1971.

Latter-Day Saints elders have given special attention to the Indians and Mexicans in Arizona. The Papago Ward in the Maricopa Stake consists almost entirely of Indians, with members principally from the Papago and Maricopa tribes.

The Jews in Arizona

The Jewish community of Arizona has never been a large segment of the total population, but its impact culturally and civically has always been considerable. The early Jewish settlers came from San Francisco or took the long transcontinental trek from crowded cities of the East. Many of them were immigrants or children of refugees who had fled Europe in the time of the 1848 revolutions. They came to the New World seeking religious liberty, freedom of political expression, and economic opportunity. On the western frontier they demonstrated both initiative and a democratic spirit.

Herman Ehrenberg is a case in point. A mining engineer and former fighter for Texas independence, he came to the Territory immediately after the Gadsden Purchase and was closely associated with Charles D. Poston, "the father of Arizona." The town of Ehrenberg, named after him, was in its day the most important community in the Territory, a key shipping point via the Colorado River and a terminus of the Wickenburg-Ehrenberg stagecoach route. Ehrenberg was a member of the 1856 convention urging separation of Arizona from New Mexico. He was also a delegate in the first territorial convention of 1863. He served with Kit Carson and General Frémont, but his promising career ended when he was killed by Indians in 1866.

Other Jewish pioneers who gave their names to Arizona communities include Joe Mayer, Jacob Isaacson, and Isador Elkan Solomon. An especially colorful personality was David Abraham, one of the first discoverers of copper in Arizona, who insisted on carrying a complete set of Shakespeare at all times, even while building the first wagon roads, and was considered a literary authority in his day. Dr. Herman Bendell served under President Grant as superintendent of Indian affairs for Arizona. Selim Franklin, assistant United States attorney general, initiated the bill creating the University of Arizona.

Although there were probably less than fifty Jews in Arizona during the 1870s, by the turn of the century this number had increased to around 2,000. At that time the principal Jewish settlements were in Tucson, Phoenix, Prescott, Douglas, and Bisbee. Informal services were held on Sabbaths and festivals whenever a quorum of ten worshippers could be gathered together, usually in a private home or in rented quarters.

The first Jewish congregation organized in the Territory of Arizona was Temple Emanu-El, at 560 South Stone Avenue in Tucson. In 1949 the congregation moved to its new quarters at 225 North Country Club Road, which it was still occupying in 1969. A decade following Temple Emanu-El came Temple Beth Israel in Phoenix, located in 1969 at Tenth Street and Flower, and within another decade, Congregation Anshei Israel in Tucson. Other synagogues include Beth El Congregation and Beth Israel Congregation in Phoenix, and Young Israel Synagogue in Tucson.

Until 1940 Jews throughout the state did not exceed one-half of 1 percent of the total population, but increasingly in the last three decades they have joined their fellow Americans in finding the way to Arizona. Now numbering over twenty thousand, they still make up only a little more than 1 percent of the state's population. They continue, however, to play a highly significant role in civic and cultural life. Striking illustrations of this are the Jewish Community Centers in Phoenix and Tucson, where concerts, plays, dance recitals, arts and crafts workshops, community forums, and other worthwhile cultural and leisure-time activities take place. The various synagogues have cooperated in the building and maintenance of these centers, although use of their facilities is offered to the community at large.

Arizona's Protestant Sects

Protestantism in Arizona is little more than a hundred years old. Whereas Catholic missionaries had been active for centuries in the southern part of the state, and Mormons for decades in the north, Protestant ministers did not arrive until after the Civil War. In early 1868 the Reverend J. L. Dyer, a Methodist, is said to have conducted the first Protestant service in Arizona. In subsequent months James Skinner, sent as a nondenominational missionary by the American Bible Society, arrived in Tucson; and at about the same time a Presbyterian minister, the Reverend William Reid, who had accompanied the governor's party across the plains, also started services in Prescott. During the following year, in 1869, the Presbyterian missionary J. M. Roberts started a mission among the Navajos.

In 1870 the Methodist Episcopal Church South sent two ministers to Arizona — the Reverend Franklin McKean, who began work in Phoenix, and a Reverend Mr. Groves, who after establishing a congregation in Prescott, went to Phoenix where he alternately preached and farmed. Although living by his own toils, he managed to reach many communities in the area, especially the mining camps. During the same year the Reverend Charles Cook, of the Presbyterian church, started the Sacaton Agency and there established an early Indian school in Arizona, among the Pimas. This same clergy-man-missionary founded the Tucson Indian Training School which operated for seventy-five years until its closing in 1960. In 1873 a Presbyterian church was formed in Phoenix and was given free land. Until 1878, however, services were conducted out-of-doors, in the so-called "brush chapel."

By 1875 the Baptists had J. C. Bristow, an unlicensed but very effective preacher, at work near Prescott. His first sermon, preached under an old cottonwood tree, is still commemorated by Camp Verde residents. The first Protestant church building in Arizona was erected by Presbyterians in Phoenix in 1878 — an adobe structure; the first Methodist church, also in Phoenix, followed the next year. The founders of these two churches — the Reverend William Meyer and the Reverend George Adams, respectively — together with the Reverend J. E. Anderson, who went to Tucson in 1877, seem to have been the first regular and permanent Protestant pastors in the state.

The 1880s saw the coming of new denominations. The First Congregational Church of Tempe was established in 1880; Baptist churches in Prescott and Tucson were founded in 1881, along with St. Paul's Episcopal Church in Tombstone, Grace Episcopal in Tucson, and Trinity Presbyterian and First Congregational in the same city. By 1882 no less than twenty-five Protestant congregations were active in the Arizona Territory.

The record does not say much about the frontier people who made up the constituency of these churches. The clergy and missionaries would also have been nameless were it not for the response and support accorded them by the laity. The Reverend Uriah Gregory, founder of the First Baptist Church of Tucson, typified the frontier clergyman of that day at his best. Bearded and patrician of countenance and distinguished in bearing, he was tactfulness itself in winning over such recalcitrants as the lawyer from the South who "had always said that he would never hear a Northern man preach." The Reverend Mr. Gregory's coming to town was not going to alter that opinion, but it did. It was not beneath the Reverend Gregory's dignity to take part in the actual building of the church edifice, laying brick side by side with the Mexican laborers.

Fig. 33.7   Inspiration, for many moderns, resides in clarity and clean lines.

T. S. Montgomery

Fig. 33.8 Serving foothills residents west of Tucson is the Lutheran "Dove of Peace."

Bob Osbahr

Another colorful and effective clergyman who worked on the frontier was the Reverend Endicott Peabody. A young Episcopalian missionary-priest, he came from "the sheltered precincts of Cheltenham and Cambridge" to the rip-roaring boomtown of Tombstone in the 1880s. His Harvard education did not leave him unprepared for dealing with what he found there, adequately if not conventionally. He felt that St. Paul's Church should be enclosed by a neat, iron picket fence, and to this end he appealed for funds at Sunday morning service. Moneys collected, however, fell far short of the needed amount.

> Somehow or other . . . the gamblers at the Crystal Palace heard of the Rev. Peabody's disappointment. Being men of action they set up a kitty, and for the next fifty hours or so of their perpetual poker game every pot won with a hand above two pairs was assessed with a contribution toward the building of Endicott Peabody's picket fence. When a sum more than sufficient had been collected, a messenger delivered the proceeds to the parish house. A stodgier parson might have peered askance at the source of this manna, but the Rev. Peabody thanked the gentlemen for their generosity and built his fence.*

The Protestantism of the frontier was mostly a biblical literalism stressing the individual's personal experience of God. Because of the isolation and the leadership (few of the early ministers or preachers had been graduated from theological seminary or an illustrious eastern university), the Protestant who may have

---

*"Cards, Gentlemen?" by Stephen Shadegg; *Arizona Highways*, February, 1944, Vol. 20, No. 2, pp. 30-33.

Neil Koppes

Fig. 33.9 The Arizona Jewish community has several synagogues, including Phoenix Beth El Congregation.

been reared in Europe had to adjust to a less churchly type of Christian expression than prevailed in the Old Country. When a group of people, often primarily women, were able to find a clergyman who would consent to stay and nurture a flock of children and adults, a Protestant community would take shape. The children were educated in the faith, and adults were converted. Ties with the rest of the Protestant world were tenuous because they had to be maintained over long distances.

The circuit rider type of preaching was concerned with individual salvation, blended with a stern moralism. The frontiersman lived in a black and white world. Even in the first two or three decades of the twentieth century, the growth and development of Protestantism tended to follow this same pattern, to some extent reflecting the piety of the country as a whole during this period, but strongly predominating in the Territory because of the exigencies of frontier life.

Liberalizing of the Protestant message to include social concerns and to encourage a greater solidarity of the Christian family thus developed more slowly in Arizona than it did "back East." With numerical growth, indeed, came a strengthening of the separate denominations, through which the churches still function today.

The Arizona Council of Churches

The Arizona Council of Churches, represented in Phoenix and Tucson by city councils, for years was interested in the task of ministering to the migrants within the state, checking social legislation, and organizing councils in the smaller cities. The councils in Phoenix and Tucson worked with various minority groups, notably the NAACP. State · institutions were served through joint action in children's homes, hospitals, and jails. Cook Indian School in Phoenix has been represented on its board by major denominations of the National Council of Churches' Home Mission division.

It served in this manner in Tucson for twenty years prior to September 18, 1968, at which time its leaders joined with the leaders of the Roman Catholic church to form the Tucson Ecumenical Council and to hold its first delegate assembly on that date.

Membership in the Tucson Ecumenical Council was open to any Christian church in accord with its purposes. Its Assembly, which meets quarterly, is composed of two lay people and one cleric of each member local church. An executive board, which meets monthly or on call, is composed of a president, vice-president, secretary, treasurer, and a chairman and co-chairman of worship, education, and social outreach, each elected annually by the Assembly. The organization is supported by fees and pledges from the congregations making up its membership and by donations from individuals and businesses.

Its task forces extend into the fields of recreation, public welfare, problems of aging, housing needs for

older citizens, teaching, study groups, an audio-visual library, youth leader training and adult schools of religion, and other fields.

While opposition to legalized gambling was widespread in the state, the Council of Churches had a major part in the campaign against it, resulting in its defeat.

The council, in association with other groups, was involved in changes in the state's marriage laws, by supporting the successful initiative measure calling for a blood test prior to marriage (1956) and for the repeal, as unconstitutional, of the law which had held marriage between Caucasians and individuals of another race illegal. The test case, which involved an American-born Japanese and his white schoolteacher fiancée, originated in Tucson in 1962.

Work with students in the universities at Tucson and Tempe and Flagstaff has been done partly through denominational but increasingly through interdenominational sponsorship. A striking example of the latter is the United Christian Student Center, across Park Avenue from the University of Arizona campus. This well-planned building contains a chapel, a spacious library with books of Christian and non-Christian writers, and meeting rooms for religious as well as nonreligious groups.

There are nineteen religious groups serving the campus community at the University of Arizona, for example, ranging through the Christian, Hebrew, Mormon, and other faiths.

While these retain their sectarian nature, their services to the campus community have taken on more and more of an ecumenical pattern. This is true in varying degrees, depending on the extent of facilities available.

An instance of this is the Newman Catholic Student Center, which first appeared at the University of Arizona before 1930 as the Newman Club. Now, as the Newman Center, the Apostolate has, since 1966, dropped the "club" designation throughout the United States, to eliminate the exclusivist implication. While still Roman Catholic, the doors of the Newman Center, its chapel, general purpose hall, recreation rooms and lounges are open to all faiths of the campus community, and its four chaplains extend its worship services, spiritual, intellectual, and moral training to followers of all faiths.

The pattern is similar on the campus of the Arizona State University at Tempe and at Northern Arizona University at Flagstaff.

Parochial schools in Arizona have been maintained chiefly by Catholics, Lutherans, and Episcopalians. Mission schools for the Indians have also been fostered by the Presbyterians, the Baptists (Southern and Conservative), and in Mexico by the Mormons. Prescott College, a small liberal arts school noteworthy for its educational experimentation, was started by Congregationalists, although it is nonsectarian.

Rollie, Sedona

Fig. 33.10   The Chapel of the Holy Cross near Sedona invites everyone to "... rest, reflect."

The Baptists in Arizona have a story of their own. Since 1921 the Southern Baptists have built well over two hundred churches and more than eighty missions. Among the Indians, Mexicans, and Chinese they have almost fifty stations. Grand Canyon College in the northwestern area of Phoenix is a private, Southern Baptist liberal arts institution.

The Conservative Baptists had their beginnings in Arizona. The veteran pastor of the First Baptist Church in Tucson, Dr. R. S. Beal, led thirty churches out of the Northern Baptist Convention (in 1969 the American Baptist Convention) during the modernist-funda-

mentalist controversy besetting American Protestantism in the late 1920s and early 1930s. The Conservative Baptists have spread far beyond the borders of the state, and in 1969 they numbered more than 500,000.

A few groups, not numerically strong but recognizably Protestant although not associated with the foregoing churches, should be mentioned. Among these are the Seventh Day Adventists, known in Arizona as elsewhere for their schools, hospitals, and welfare work as well as for their more conventionally religious activities. Other fellowships include the Unitarians, the Christian Scientists, the Friends (both conservative and pacifistically "radical"), and syncretistic groups such as the Bahais, the Humanists, Unity, Ethical Culture, Transcendental Meditation, and others.

Spiritual Recovery

The ecumenical movement has found expression within Arizona in a variety of ways, but perhaps in none so distinctively as the Spiritual Life Institute of America, with its highly unusual and striking Chapel of the Holy Cross planted deep in the Red Rocks near Sedona. Here are "A Sign, a School, a Solitude," inviting people of all creeds "to come apart for a little, to celebrate, to rest, and reflect." The sign is the chapel itself, which literally hangs upon a gigantic concrete cross springing from the rocks enclosing it. The school is an "academy of theological humanism," a research center with a revolving staff of ecumenical scholars. Retreats, seminars, and summer sessions are held, in which "the central questions of our times . . . are discussed in a contemplative atmosphere." The school is thus inseparable from the solitude, a retreat center "where men and women can withdraw from turmoil and distraction to pursue that noblest of occupations: contemplation."

The Spiritual Life Institute was founded by Father William McNamara, O.C.D., a Carmelite friar, at the invitation of Pope John XXIII. Like the Chapel of the Holy Cross, it was Catholic in concept, but from the beginning it was open to all faiths.

In addition to the headquarters at Sedona, the Institute has a city center in New York, at Sunnyside Gardens, Long Island.

A visit to the Chapel of the Holy Cross is an unforgettable experience, and a longer stay at the Institute must have meant newness of life to many. This unique place and this unique fellowship are pointing men to a re-discovery of themselves — which may be what religion in Arizona, as anywhere else, is really all about.

34

COMMUNICATIONS: SIGHT AND SOUND

The Peripatetic Press

THE RECORDING OF ARIZONA'S DAILY LIFE by the printed word began long before statehood, even before Arizona was a territory.

In 1858, William Wrightson, superintendent of the Santa Rita mines, wanted a voice to impress Congress with the need for protection against the Apache Indians in southern Arizona.

He sent to his native Ohio for a press, had it shipped from Cincinnati around Cape Horn to the port of Guaymas and thence by ox cart to Tubac — headquarters and supply point for his company. It reached Tubac in January of 1859.

Wrightson imported Edward C. Cross, an eastern newspaperman, to publish the first paper in Arizona, the *Weekly Arizonian.* Its major mission was to obtain government military action against the Apaches for the protection of mining interests in the area.

With Cross as editor and Charles D. Poston, "The Father of Arizona," as a contributor, the *Arizonian* displayed amazing vigor in its campaign for more troops to protect the pioneer development of the area, and, for a time, to defeat territorial status for Arizona. It first appeared on March 3, 1859.

The paper, like others that followed it, featured news stories and bitter comment on every Apache atrocity, large or small, and saw to it that these reports received circulation in the East.

Cross's opposition to territorial status resulted in one of the most colorful incidents of early newspapering in the area — a duel, fought with rifles, which turned out to be bloodless. Cross came into direct conflict with Lieutenant Sylvester Mowry, a former West Pointer and owner of the Mowry Mine, who was energetically campaigning for the territorial designation. The dispute began even before the *Arizonian* was established. In articles written for eastern newspapers Cross accused Mowry of using false population figures to bolster his cause.

Mowry challenged Cross to a duel. Cross accepted and chose to duel with Burnside rifles at forty paces. Each man was to be allowed five shots.

Eight shots were exchanged without effect. Cross fired and missed again. Mowry's rifle failed to fire on his fifth shot, and the seconds agreed that he was entitled to fire again. But as Cross awaited the result, Mowry declared he could not shoot an unarmed man, fired his rifle into the air, and declared himself satisfied.

A formal account of the duel carried in the next issue of the *Arizonian,* explained the poor marksmanship of the participants. It said:

"It is proper to state at the time of the duel between Mr. Mowry and the editor of this paper, a high wind, amounting to almost a gale, was blowing across the line of fire, thereby preventing accurate aim.

"In this case the proverb 'It's an ill wind that blows no good' is aptly illustrated."

A short time after the duel Mowry purchased the paper and moved it to Tucson where it appeared as a Democratic organ and an all-out out proponent of territorial status, in August, 1859. At least five editors attempted to make a go of the paper before the beginning of the Civil War put an end to its journalistic troubles.

GHOST TOWN NEWSPAPERS. The late Estelle Lutrell, one-time librarian of the University of Arizona, in her bulletin *Newspapers and Periodicals of Arizona, 1859-1911,* recorded that before Arizona became a state 200 newspapers had been established in sixty towns. Dozens of these papers failed and in many instances the towns died with them, as the mine or mines which brought about their birth were bottomed and abandoned.

Communities such as Mesilla, Harshaw, Dos Cabezas, Salome, Mineral Park, Quijotoa, Arizona, and Pima are but a portion of such settlements where both press and community were short-lived.

After the Civil War halted the publication of the *Arizonian* in Tucson, there was no printed news or editorial comment in all of Arizona until 1864 when Richard C. McCormick, secretary of state in the new territorial government, established the *Arizona Miner* at Ft. Whipple and later moved it to Prescott.

The press used by McCormick was one he had brought out in one of the government wagons which transported Gov. John N. Goodwin and his official party to their frontier assignment.

It took only a small investment to start a weekly newspaper in the seventies and eighties, and they bloomed and faded in Arizona with great frequency. If a politician was at outs with the current editor of an existing publication, and could get no help from him, the candidate would set up his own paper and furnish his own editorial support.

One such newspaper was the *Arizona Citizen,* founded in 1870. As the *Tucson Daily Citizen* it is the oldest newspaper in the state. This paper was established by McCormick who, after serving a term as territorial governor, had been elected territorial delegate to Congress and was seeking a second term. By this time Pierson W. Dooner had re-established the old *Arizonian* in Tucson, changing its name to the *Arizonan.* Dooner and McCormick had a falling out and Dooner launched an anti-McCormick campaign in the *Arizonan.* McCormick established the *Citizen* to support his cause and hired as editor John Wasson. McCormick, after a campaign marked by vitriolic editorial exchanges between Dooner and Wasson, won re-election and soon after Dooner was forced to fold the *Arizonan.*

The *Citizen* flourished and eventually came under the direction of John P. Clum, an Indian agent who had resigned his post after differing with his Washington superiors over what he claimed was their inadequate care of Arizona Apaches. Clum moved the *Citizen* to Florence, then back to Tucson, and finally gave it up altogether to move to Tombstone where he founded the *Epitaph* in 1880. This was the same year Phoenix welcomed the founding of the *Arizona Gazette,* which became the *Phoenix Gazette* in 1929.

Most of the other daily newspapers among the 14 being published in Arizona in 1970 could trace their origins to territorial days.

The *Yuma Daily Sun and Arizona Sentinel* went back to the establishment in 1872 of the weekly *Arizona Sentinel,* which was merged in 1935 with the 30-year-old *Sun.*

The *Arizona Daily Star* emerged from C. H. Tully's *Daily Bulletin,* published for 28 days in March of 1877. L. C. Hughes, who later was territorial governor and University of Arizona chancellor, joined Tully in the publishing business in 1877, changed the name of the

paper to the *Arizona Star,* and brought it out three times a week, then weekly, and, in 1879, daily.

The *Coconino Sun* in Flagstaff is the descendent of the *Arizona Champion,* founded as a weekly in 1882. It first became the *Coconino Sun* in 1891, went through several more name changes through mergers, and permanently adopted its present name in 1898.

Another 1882 paper was the *Prescott Morning Courier* (now the *Evening Courier*), founded by John H. Marion who already had made a name for himself as the courageous, determined, plain-spoken editor of the weekly *Arizona Miner.*

The *Tempe Daily News* grew out of the weekly *Salt River Valley News,* established in 1886. One year later it became the *Tempe News* and began publishing daily in 1893.

The *Arizona Republic* was established in 1890 as the *Arizona Republican,* and assumed its present name in 1930.

The *Mesa Tribune* had its origins in the *Mesa Free Press,* an 1892 weekly that changed its name to the *Tribune* in 1921 and became the *Daily Tribune* in 1949.

The *Bisbee Daily Review* was founded as the weekly *Arizona Orb* in 1896 and took its present name in 1901. The *Douglas Dispatch* was established in 1902 as a weekly and the next year became the *Daily Dispatch.*

The state's three post-territorial dailies still publishing in 1970 were the *Nogales Herald,* founded in 1914; the *Scottsdale Progress,* established as a weekly in 1937 and as a daily in 1961, and the *Daily Reporter,* founded in Tucson in 1920 as a specialized newspaper devoted mostly to legal news.

In addition to the 14 daily newspapers being published in 1970, the Arizona Newspapers Association 1970 directory listed fifty-four weekly newspapers, published in Ajo, Apache Junction, Ash Fork, Bagdad, Benson, Bisbee, Buckeye, Bullhead City, Casa Grande, Chandler, Clifton, Coolidge, Cottonwood, Eloy, Flagstaff, Florence, Gilbert, Glendale, Globe, Green Valley, Hayden, Holbrook, Kingman, Lake Havasu City, Litchfield Park, Miami, Nogales, Parker, Payson, Phoenix, Peoria, Safford, San Manuel, Sedona, Show Low, Sierra Vista, St. Johns, Springerville, Sun City, Superior, Tombstone, Tucson, Wickenburg, Willcox, Williams, Window Rock, Winslow, Youngtown, and Yuma.

HALL OF FAME. Year by year the work of Arizona editors has been commemorated in the Arizona Newspaper Hall of Fame, originated at the University of Arizona in the 1950s by the late Douglas D. Martin, professor of journalism, with the cooperation of the Arizona Newspapers Association.

A lengthening row of copper plates in the University's Department of Journalism recalls the names of some of the men whose pens helped build the state, and points briefly to their services.

Members of the Hall of Fame in 1970 were William Wrightson and Edward C. Cross of the *Weekly Ari-*

zonian; John P. Clum of the *Tombstone Epitaph* and the *Citizen;* J. W. (Uncle Billy) Spear of the *Arizona Republic;* Anson H. Smith of the *Mohave County Miner;* John Wasson, Allan B. Jaynes and George H. Smalley of the *Tucson Daily Citizen;* Fred S. Breen of the *Coconino Sun;* Carmel Giragi of the *Winslow Mail;* Alfred Franklin Banta of the *St. Johns Observer* and the *Douglas Dispatch;* Aaron H. (Judge) Hackney of the *Arizona Silver Belt;* Thomas F. Weedin of the *Florence Blade-Tribune;* John W. Dorrington of the *Arizona Sentinel;* Robert C. Smith of the *Snowflake Herald;* John Marion of the *Arizona Miner* and the *Prescott Courier;* William P. Stuart, also of the *Courier;* Stanley C. Bagg of the *Tombstone Prospector* and *Tombstone Epitaph;* Charles H. Akers of the *Arizona Gazette;* Angela Hutchinson Hammer of the *Wickenburg Miner;* and Curt W. Miller of the *Tempe Daily News.*

Another journalism honor presented jointly by the Arizona Newspapers Association and the University of Arizona is the John Peter Zenger Award, given annually since 1954 to a person who has rendered outstanding service to the cause of Freedom of the Press and the people's right to know. Among those receiving this award have been James Reston and Arthur Krock of the *New York Times;* Herbert Brucker of the *Hartford Courant;* Eugene C. Pulliam and J. Edward Murray of the *Arizona Republic;* J. R. Wiggins of the *Washington Post;* Clark R. Mollenhoff of the *Des Moines Register;* Palmer Hoyt of the *Denver Post;* John S. Knight of Knight Newspapers; and West Gallagher of the Associated Press.

Book Publishing

A half century after the publication of *The Arizonian,* Frank Holme brought with him from Illinois a remarkably informal book publishing operation. Actually, Bandar Log Press had been started in a Chicago attic. The idea started with Booth Tarkington and a group of literary and artistic people, including many of the day's more gilt-edged names. They took the title from Kipling. Visitors to the garret took turns setting type, while Holme himself laboriously and skillfully whittled out woodcuts as illustration.

When health led him to Arizona, Holme packed Bandar Log with him. He set up shop north of Phoenix in a chicken coop with a hand press bought from a defunct Spanish-language newspaper.

The result was a series of thin paperbacks which might be described today as adult comic books. Irreverently philosophical, they followed the wry, pie-in-the-eye humor of the period, appearing in limited editions under such titles as "The Poker Rubaiyat" and "Handsome Cyril or The Messenger Boy with the Warm Feet."

Bandar Books sold for roughly five cents and appeared in Arizona for only a few years. Copies of any of them had become rarities in the mid-twentieth century.

Subsequently there have been spasmodic printings within the state, but usually of volumes of local interest.

In a class by itself was Arizona Silhouettes, a project conceived by George Chambers, a Tucson newspaper executive. When he started Arizona Silhouettes in 1950, it was Chambers' idea to reproduce long out-of-print Arizoniana.

He began with J. Ross Browne's *A Tour Through Arizona, 1864,* of which the first edition, brought out by Harpers, was all but non-existent.

The new edition was seized upon by collectors and history fans with such avidity that Chambers printed it again. He then drafted his wife and one son into the part-time publishing business, added a wing to his house as a print shop, and the project was well on its way.

Although Chambers planned and did stick to the idea of reprinting "out of print" Arizoniana to a great extent, he also published some first edition and some reprint works of living authors, all of which were concerned with the Southwest.

NORTHLAND PRESS. Stressing design, typography, and fine reproduction, this Flagstaff printer-publisher has won significant design awards during the 1960s and 1970s for its regional books, many of them on art.

THE UNIVERSITY OF ARIZONA PRESS. The University of Arizona Press imprint as of 1972 was carrying the name of the state around the globe on the covers and title pages of significant books and other book-length publications. As the book-publishing arm of the University it was concentrating on books of merit in the subject-matter fields with which the educational institutions of the state were identified, and other significant works, often historical, of regional nature about Arizona and the Southwest.

At the beginning of the 1970s the press was annually issuing some thirty new titles per year, with more than 200 active titles in print.

In 1972 the Press was fulfilling the complete responsibilities of a competent publisher: manuscript appraisal and selection; comprehensive editing and organization; meaningful design, quality production, and effective marketing. All books appearing under the imprint must have been approved formally by the Press publications committee, named from the faculty to uphold the standards of the University. A professional staff was executing the transformation from manuscripts to books of high standards in the field of scholarly publishing.

Manuscripts were being considered by the press from any authoritative writers — regardless of geographical location — if the works were in the publishing field in which the Press operates to maintain the scholarly intentions and emphasis followed in Arizona.

The Press itself in 1972 was publishing only English-language editions, but endeavoring to acquire foreign translation proposals from native publishing houses in other countries. This was among the responsibilities the Press was executing in fulfilling its role of the sharing of knowledge, and in serving its authors and readers in the countries of the world in which the Press English language versions were being distributed.

Books under the University of Arizona Press imprint were accorded numerous awards during the sixties for scholarly excellence and outstanding quality of production.

The Press from 1962 on has been an active member of the Association of American University Presses.

In addition to its work in the book field the Press has been publisher of the University of Arizona catalog and a number of educational reports, booklets and bulletins.

Magazines

Arizona has a number of magazines, divided roughly into general interest, special interest and scholarly journal fields.

Unique among these has been the *Arizona Highways* Magazine, which started in 1925 as the voice of the Arizona Highway Department. It featured some travel and engineering stories, and carried advertising from the heavy construction and machinery industries.

In 1937 Ray Carlson became the editor of the magazine and hired George Avey as its art director. They changed the entire format of the magazine, turning it into a spectacularly colorful chronicle of the scenic wonders of the state, carrying factual articles about Arizona and its people, old and new, and no advertising.

The outstanding success of the change was evident in several ways. The foremost color photographers of the West, an unusual number of whom have been Arizonans, were glad to place their work in *Highways,* which became a show window with circulation in every state in the Union and in ninety-one other countries.

At the beginning of the seventies the annual circulation was more than five million, which, with the price of sixty cents per copy, made the magazine practically self supporting despite the high cost of materials and color reproduction which were used in its content.

The *Highways* has been so adroitly edited that while many of its readers think of it as almost completely color in concept, usually a full half of the pages have been devoted to black and white photography and stories.

At the beginning of the 1970s, the *Arizona Publisher,* itself a magazine circulated for and to the membership of the Arizona Newspapers Association, listed eleven magazines published in Arizona as commercial ventures.

Only three of these, the *Arizona Highways, Arizona,* the *Arizona Republic's* Sunday magazine, and the *Phoenix Magazine* were listed as of general circulation. All of the rest (and there were more than 100) were either industrially or vocationally oriented: for example, *Arizona Medicine, The Arizona Teacher, Arizona Architect, Mining Journal,* the *Arizona Cattlelog,* published by the Arizona Cattle Growers' Association, and the *Arizona Journalist,* published by the Arizona Journalism Institute at the University of Arizona.

Also included in this specialized field of publishing were publications of the Navajo Indians, the Apaches, the Hopis and the Papagos, and such diverse publications as the *Arizona Wildlife and Sportsman* and *The Arizona Humane Society Record.*

Another magazine in a specialized field but with more general circulation has been *Hoof and Horns,* published in Tucson. As of 1970 *Hoof and Horns* was the official organ of the Rodeo business, maintaining the annual contest records of all major rodeos in the country, and the standing of the contestants.

SCHOLARLY PERIODICALS. Among the more scholarly magazines at the beginning of the 1970s was the *Arizona Quarterly* of the University of Arizona, devoted to selected literary material, and accepting meritorious work in its field from authors anywhere.

Arizona and The West, a quarterly journal of history was striving to present in an attractive manner the most authoritative writing on the Trans-Mississippi West. It was staffed by the history department of the University of Arizona, with an advisory board and consultants from various areas throughout the West.

The *Journal of Arizona History* was published quarterly by the Arizona Historical Society and sent to all members of the Society, as well as being sold by subscription to non-members.

Radio and Television

Radio and television broadcasting is an extensive activity in Arizona. In the spring of 1970 there were twelve commercial and two non-commercial television stations operating in the state and four more commercial facilities under construction. At the same time there were seventy-seven radio stations in service, including sixty AM and seventeen FM facilities. Among these were three non-commercial units, one of which was KUAT AM University of Arizona in Tucson, the most powerful educational AM station in the United States.

Broadcasting activities in Arizona followed by only two years the first radio broadcasts to the American public. Senator Barry Goldwater was one of three operators involved in starting an experimental amateur station in Phoenix with the call letters 6BBH. This facility went on the air in 1921, two years after the Westinghouse Company started experimental operations. The early Phoenix station later became KDYW and subsequently KOY which was still on the air in 1970.

Arizona's first commercially licensed station went on the air in Phoenix on June 21, 1922. The call letters were eventually changed to KTAR.

Arizona's early stations were located in the two major population centers — KTAR and KOY in Phoenix, and KTUC and KVOA (later KCUB) in Tucson. KTUC was established in 1926 and KCUB in 1929.

As the state developed and expanded, broadcasting continued to grow. In the ten-year period from 1959 to 1969, thirty-one radio stations went on the air. Literally every section of the state had radio coverage by 1970. In many instances programming was especially keyed to Mexican-American and Indian audiences. In particular KEVT and KXEW in Tucson and KFIN and KCAC in Phoenix offered one hundred percent of their programming in Spanish. Both KCLS in Flagstaff and KHAC in Window Rock offered substantial weekly programming in Navajo.

GROWTH OF TELEVISION. Arizona's first television station went on the air in Phoenix in 1949. KPHO TV originally presented local as well as filmed programs and was affiliated with all four of the national networks — CBS, NBC, ABC and DuMont. The Federal Communications Commission's freeze on television-station construction delayed the development of the industry in Arizona until 1953. In that year, five new television stations went on the air including KOPO-TV (later KOLD-TV), KTYL-TV in Mesa (later KVAR Phoenix); KVOA-TV, Tucson; KOOL-TV Phoenix and KIVA-TV in Yuma.

The first educational television facility in the state, KUAT-TV, went on the air in 1959 at the University of Arizona in Tucson. KAET-TV, the state's second non-commercial facility, began broadcasting in 1961 from the campus of Arizona State University in Tempe.

In the sixteen years from 1953 to 1969, the number of commercial television stations in Arizona doubled to a total of twelve. In 1970 it was predicted that most of the state would soon be directly serviced with television programming from stations based in Phoenix, Tempe, Nogales, Tucson, Yuma and Flagstaff. As of January, 1968, there were thirty-eight licensed television transmitters scattered throughout the state and a number of community cable systems to distribute programming to Arizona citizens.

In January, 1968, there were 487,800 households in the state. According to industry research figures, 447,700 of those homes, or ninety-two percent were equipped with television sets.

More than half of the television stations in Arizona were equipped to originate color programming and almost all were capable of transmitting color network material at the beginning of the seventies.

Fig. 35.1   The Grand Canyon of the Colorado is part of Arizona's heritage.

Ray Manley

Robert K. Johnson
Library Science

35

PRESERVING A HERITAGE

TO PRESERVE THE RECORD of the past for present and future generations to enjoy, Arizona has gradually established important libraries, archives, and museums. Its wealth of natural beauty is being preserved through the establishment of parks, monuments, and memorials.

Libraries

Early in Arizona's history the demand for libraries and the need for the state to provide them was apparent. The Howell Code of 1864, the original set of laws for the Arizona territory, created what has become the Arizona Department of Library and Archives. This was the first legally established public library in Arizona. The department's original book collection was assembled from various sources, some of them having been brought to Arizona with the initial territorial government party. From the original list of volumes held in 1865, including titles of classics, popular, legal and governmental publications, many are still in the state library collection. Through the years the department has survived a variety of name changes and responsibilities, although as late as 1970 appropriations to match the responsibilities had not been provided.

The United States Congress appropriated no funds for the library until 1871. For several years it existed on fees, and although a library extension division was approved by the state legislature in 1949, no funds were appropriated for its implementation until 1957 after the passage of the Library Services Act in 1956. In early years the state library was shifted from city to city in the struggle over which city was to become the state capital, and it was housed in various quarters from time to time. When the new wing to the capital building was completed in 1939, the state library was finally placed in quarters of its own, but this space, like that for a number of other state agencies, became badly over-crowded after a few years. During early years, jurisdiction over the library was held by a succession of offices, but in 1893 a board of curators was created to operate it, and as of 1970 that body continued to exist legally, although its authority had changed considerably from time to time.

The collection of the Arizona Department of Library and Archives by the end of the sixties included a book collection numbering over 767,000 volumes; it also had over 800,000 cubic feet of archives and other records as well as audio-visual material, microfilm, and a large collection of pictures, maps, and manuscripts. The Library Extension Service holdings exceeded 246,000 volumes. The extension service had one branch on demonstration serving Cochise and Santa Cruz counties out of Tombstone, and through this service the state library directly served public libraries not in regional systems and provided service to regional systems directly through county libraries.

The Maricopa County Free Library, established in 1929, was the state's first regional system and remained as late as 1970 the only complete county system in Arizona. The chief impetus for establishment of county systems came in 1957 after the Library Services and Construction Act of 1956, and there evolved by 1970 eight established county systems which contracted with city libraries: Coconino with Flagstaff, Graham with Safford, Mohave with Kingman, Pima with Tucson, Yavapai with Prescott, and Yuma County with Yuma. In Pinal County, all incorporated cities but one elected to join the County Free Library District.

EARLY PUBLIC LIBRARIES. Public libraries in Arizona as in other states generally were slow in coming into existence, often developing through the efforts of private individuals. In 1872 J. S. Mansfeld first advertised in Tucson the opening of a circulating (rental) library.

Fig. 35.2 Old and new libraries in Arizona
come in all sizes, shapes, and forms.

Arizona State University

Ray Manley

Hinton's Hand Book to Arizona, 1878, mentions the Prescott Library Association, "composed of leading citizens, with a public reading room containing over 50 newspapers from all points . . . and a library of 263 volumes." At the same time, it refers also to a "public library in Phoenix of 250 volumes, owned by a literary association." The Copper Queen Library at Bisbee began with a gift of books from New York in 1882. It was an example of a number of libraries opened to the public and operated by the mining companies, a generous gesture in their time. Although the Tucson Public Library originated in 1879, city libraries were not legally established until 1901. The first Carnegie library buildings in Arizona were erected in Tucson in 1899, Phoenix in 1902, and Yuma in 1917. In Globe, the Old Dominion Mine operated a library for the public beginning in 1904 and it was later taken over by the local women's club. In many instances, official and public support in later years have taken over the management and services of these libraries though at the start of 1970 far too many of them were still dependent upon contributions and volunteer help.

When the Arizona State Library Association was formed in 1926 under the leadership of Miss Estelle Lutrell, then librarian of the University of Arizona, there began a thirty-year struggle on the part of librarians and citizens to provide equitable, tax-supported, statewide library service for Arizona. This was climaxed during the late forties and early fifties by vigorous campaigning throughout the state, as members of the association and interested laymen sought to show citizens how good library service could be, and to stimulate them to demand adequate support for more dynamic and useful public libraries throughout Arizona.

Nevertheless, because of lack of official standing and tax support over the decades, many of Arizona's city libraries as of 1970 still did not have the resources, facilities, or personnel to offer good public library service.

In 1970 there were only twenty legally established city libraries in Arizona, twelve not legally established, four incorporated community libraries, twenty-nine unincorporated community libraries, and fourteen small deposit stations. A few of these libraries, such as the one at Nogales, serving a population of over 10,000, and Mesa serving fifty-five thousand, were in attractive buildings which were relatively new. Scottsdale's sixty thousand citizens had a new building dedicated in 1969; and the Yuma City-County Library erected a new and efficient building, serving a city-county population of over fifty-five thousand. But other communities such as Douglas with approximately thirteen thousand people, Chandler with over thirteen thousand, Tempe with over fifty thousand and Flagstaff with twenty-eight thousand had not been so fortunate in the matter of quarters, by the close of the sixties. The Phoenix Public Library, while serving a metropolitan area of more than five hundred thousand, had several branches, some of them new, but was badly in need of space for its patrons,

staff, and resources in its central building which was only sixteen years old; and the Tucson Public Library, with a service population nearing three hundred fifty thousand, while undergoing rejuvenation with a reorganization and expansion program begun in 1964, had three new branches, but struggled to give service out of an overcrowded central library building nearly seventy years old, as did Prescott for its nearly twenty thousand citizens. However, legislation in the sixties provided relief for the public in some areas: counties could cooperate with each other in joint support of library service, and the town of Sedona, lying astride the boundaries of Coconino and Yavapai counties, could now receive support from both whereas before it could be aided by neither.

Federal funds made available through the Library Services and Construction Act of 1956 made a marked improvement in some public library services throughout the state and have been responsible for aiding in the construction of several new library buildings. Such funds also enabled the state Library Extension Service to strengthen somewhat its bid to libraries on a statewide basis and to establish bookmobile service to isolated areas. Nevertheless, Arizona public libraries as of 1970 remained among the least adequately supported libraries in the nation.

GROWTH OF SCHOOL LIBRARIES. School libraries, like public libraries, were slow in developing but grew at a fast rate in the sixties because of several factors, including growth in numbers of students and changes in methods of teaching. Here again, federal funds available through the Elementary and Secondary Education Act of 1965, and the National Defense Education Act of 1958, assisted in improving elementary and secondary school libraries throughout the state by providing library materials to schools which did not have them before. Non-book materials also were usually included in these libraries. A school library consultant was placed in the State Department of Public Instruction as were library consultants, or coordinators, in twelve of the larger school districts. A number of the new school buildings provided handsome library rooms. Studies greatly instrumental in aiding school library development in the state were those which came from the office of the State Department of Public Instruction as well as from the *Arizona Library Survey.*

Other developments which have aided in the development of Arizona school libraries have included the increasing awareness and pride of the public in libraries and resource centers in new schools, upgrading of school library personnel together with pre-professional and professional training within the state, the demand in many areas for greater utilization of school libraries including extension of service beyond school hours and regular school terms, and increased activity to implement recommendations of professional and accrediting bodies.

Arizona's eleven institutions of higher learning — the three universities, two four-year colleges, and six junior colleges have established libraries of varying sizes, and federal funds, available through the Higher Education Act of 1963, have been used to help strengthen them and to help provide new buildings.

The libraries of the University of Arizona at Tucson and Arizona State University at Tempe ranked in 1970 as the oldest and strongest. The University of Arizona library, established in 1892, had a collection numbering 1,500,000 items, and was the largest library in the state. The library at Arizona State University which was founded in 1885 as the Arizona Territorial Normal School, making remarkable advances in the sixties, was the state's second largest collection with holdings nearing the one million mark. Both institutions had acquired well-rounded basic holdings and growing research collections supporting developing university programs. Their libraries were designated as official depositories for U. S. government documents. The science and technology collections at the University of Arizona in the sixties were moved to a separate science division library building completed in 1963 with a capacity of 180,000 volumes, and undergoing expansion in 1970. The Arizona State University Library moved into a new and excellently planned $4,000,000 building — the Charles Trumbull Hayden Library — in the summer of 1966. At Flagstaff, the Northern Arizona University Library

moved into a new building on its expanding campus in 1966 and its holdings in three years had increased to nearly 250,000. Of the state's three university libraries in 1970, only the one at the University of Arizona occupied quarters inadequate for its patrons and holdings in a building constructed in 1924, expanded in 1962-63, and by 1969, permanently outgrown.

SPECIAL LIBRARY FACILITIES. Among the oldest libraries in the state, besides that of the State Department of Library and Archives, were some of the special facilities such as the Pinal County Law Library established in 1880, and in Tucson the library of the Arizona Historical Society established in 1884. In Glendale, the long established Thunderbird Graduate School of International Management, formerly the American Institute of Foreign Trade, had a sizeable library. Libraries of this type have increased in number and have grown significantly since World War II, prior to that time largely being confined to the collection at the Department of Library and Archives in the state capitol, and a few working collections in such fields as law and medicine. There were in 1970 some one hundred special libraries throughout the state, two-thirds of them being located in the two main metropolitan centers and falling into three major groups.

The first of these were business and industrial

East High School, Phoenix

Fig. 35.3 Modern school libraries offer well-organized space, good lighting, and plenty of books close at hand.

Amerind Foundation Library, Dragoon

Fig. 35.4   Valuable research materials
are available in special libraries.

The library of the recently established College of Law at Arizona State University was quartered in the College's new building erected in the sixties, while the library of the University of Arizona College of Law was still in quarters badly outgrown in the College of Law building completed in 1960.

In 1970 the new College of Medicine at the University of Arizona had a rapidly growing library which occupied quarters in the College's basic science building and was planning to double its space with a building addition in 1971. Recent statewide and regional additions to its responsibilities resulted in a new name, The Arizona Medical Center Library.

Special libraries in Arizona have grown rapidly in size and number since 1954 as a result of increasing industrialization. It has been estimated that their combined holdings exceed 500,000 volumes, probably including considerable duplication but much unique material also. These libraries have cooperated in making their specialized holdings as readily available as possible and, like other types of libraries in Arizona, have worked through the Arizona State Library Association for improvement of services. Examples of such cooperation are the Union List of Medical Serials and the Arizona Medical Library Network, funded through the Arizona Regional Medical Program, whereby medical library resources throughout the state are to be available to any health sciences personnel needing them.

The state's larger academic, public, and special libraries engage in various types of interlibrary cooperation, and by means of an interlibrary loan network lend assistance to patrons of smaller collections. In 1970 the libraries were continuing to produce a union list of serials for Arizona in a cooperative project sponsored by the state library association. The first part of this list had been published and distributed by the end of the sixties.

libraries including those developed by such operations as manufacturing firms, banks, and newspapers. The special collections at Motorola in Scottsdale, AiResearch in Phoenix, Hughes Aircraft in Tucson, E.M.P. Electronics, Inc., in Tempe, and the Dickson Electronics Corp. in Scottsdale were representative of industrial concern library facilities. A second category was the society or foundation special library, established by historical, medical, legal, or religious organizations. The libraries of the Amerind Foundation in Dragoon, the Prescott Historical Society, the Maricopa County Law Library and the Cox Library of biography and genealogy in Tucson exemplify such special collections. The third category was institutional and governmental, and included special libraries in hospitals, special university collections and branches, various governmental and military installations in the state, including the technical library at the U.S. Army Electronic Proving Ground at Ft. Huachuca and the Veterans Administration centers, etc.

ARIZONA COLLECTIONS. Although the greatest collections of books about Arizona formerly existed in other states — the Ayer Collection in Chicago's Newberry Library, the Munk Collection in the Southwestern Museum in Los Angeles, and the Bancroft Library at the University of California—by 1970 noteworthy and expanding collections were in use at the libraries of the University of Arizona, Arizona State University, the Arizona Historical Society in Tucson, Northern Arizona University, and also at the State Department of Library and Archives. Publication of the quarterly journal, *Arizona and the West,* at the University of Arizona, *The Journal of Arizona History* (formerly known as *Arizoniana*) at the Arizona Historical Society, and the establishment of special collections departments at the libraries of the University of Arizona, Arizona State University, and Northern Arizona University are evidence of the state's awareness of its riches in books, historical manuscripts and other documents and of their importance to historical research.

Archives and Museums

Arizona has been referred to as a "natural anthropological laboratory." Much anthropological and natural history material is displayed in a number of museums, both large and small, some of which are found in the units of the national park system. What may have been Arizona's first museum was established in conjunction with a library when the Society of Arizona Pioneers was organized in Tucson in 1884. The Society's purpose was to collect "all the information calculated to exhibit faithfully the antiquities and the past and present condition . . . of the territory." The museum, located in the society's original library situated in the county courthouse, consisted of a glass-enclosed cabinet in which was displayed a large piece of petrified wood. Thirteen years after its founding, the society, by legislative action in 1897, officially became the Arizona Pioneers' Historical Society. Its growth was typical of most early museums and libraries; its historical collections being shunted about from one place to another, for many years being housed in a sort of "Old Curiosity Shop" beneath the stands of the west stadium at the University of Arizona. The Society's present territorial style building was completed at Tucson in 1955 near the university campus. The museum contained colorful displays, and as of 1970, the largest collection of Arizona historical antiquities in the state.

The first clearly defined museum in the state was established in 1893 by the Seventeenth Territorial Legislative Assembly as an integral part of the territorial university, which was to become the University of Arizona. Its purpose was defined as being "for the collection and preservation of the archaeological resources, specimens of the mineral wealth and the flora and fauna of the state." Today the Arizona State Museum houses, among numerous other items, the most complete collection in the world of the prehistoric Hohokam desert dweller culture of southern Arizona.

The first full-time director of the state museum was

Helga Teiwes Photo, Arizona State Museum, University of Arizona

Fig. 35.5   The Arizona State Museum at Tucson is widely known for its anthropological collections.

the late Byron Cummings who served from 1915 to 1938. Under his direction, pioneer archaeological explorations were conducted in various parts of the state. These resulted in greatly expanded collections and in 1930 special quarters were established for these materials in rooms under the west stadium of the University. Six years later the Arizona State Museum building was constructed at the main entrance to the University of Arizona campus.

In 1938 Emil W. Haury assumed the directorship of the state museum. Under his guidance the research and exhibition programs were greatly expanded, and an annual summer archaeological field school was inaugurated under the joint management of the museum and the Department of Anthropology. In 1961 a physical merging of the Department of Anthropology and the State Museum was accomplished when a four-story anthropology building was constructed immediately south of the museum and connected to it by two hallways. Haury relinquished the post of director in 1964 for the position of Museum Advisor, and was succeeded by Raymond H. Thompson.

The artistically designed exhibitions and rotating shows reflect the increasing research activity of the state museum in the varied fields of anthropology. The organization of the state museum and Department of Anthropology of the University under a single administrator was accomplished in recent years and has resulted in great benefits to both. In 1970, at Tucson, the state museum, with the Arizona Historical Society, was engaging in a cooperative statewide program of historic building preservation.

ART AND ANTHROPOLOGY. One of Arizona's outstanding museums, the Museum of Northern Arizona, is set in a pine grove near Flagstaff at the foot of the San Francisco mountains. These majestic peaks, legendary home of the Hopi gods, are framed in a huge picture window as the visitor steps inside the door. The museum appropriately is devoted largely to the ethnology and archaeology of the region with strong emphasis on the Hopi. A privately endowed institution founded in 1929 by Dr. Harold S. Colton, it has become one of the outstanding research institutions in the west with a staff to carry on significant ethnological and archaeological work. The museum also has acquired an excellent library.

In Phoenix in 1970 there were five museums. The Heard Museum of Anthropology and Primitive Arts was established by Mr. and Mrs. Dwight B. Heard; it also dates from 1929. Its collections are relatively small, but the high standards set by the late Mrs. Heard are reflected in the superb examples of aboriginal artifacts collected from many parts of the world. The 1960s have seen steady growth and expansion of the museum. In 1958 a junior museum and adult arts and crafts classes were inaugurated; one wing of the museum housed a colorful display of the daily life of the Navajo; and

research programs have been developing in several directions. In the year 1968-1969, the museum was doubled in size with a $650,000 addition. It held the Goldwater collection of approximately four hundred kachina dolls (other major significant kachina collections exist at the Museum of Northern Arizona and the Smithsonian Institution). The Heard Museum had a new gallery devoted to Indian artists, and featured its own collections as well as loan collections and special collections by contemporary Indian artists.

The newest and largest museum in Phoenix as of 1970 was the $500,000 Phoenix Art Museum, opened in 1959. It was expanded in 1964 and united with the Phoenix Public Library and the Phoenix Little Theatre into an integrated, block-size civic center. The two-story, windowless building housed two main galleries on the lower floor.

At Tempe near Phoenix are the university art collections of Arizona State University. They are housed in the Matthews Center which at the end of the sixties was being renovated. Its chief collection — the Oliver B. James Collection of American Art — is a composite historical collection of American painting from the eighteenth century to the present. Another outstanding group of art work is the Lenore and Lewis Ruskin collection of renaissance and baroque paintings. The university art collections also contain extensive holdings of original prints including the Read Mullan and Orme Lewis collections. At the start of the seventies contemporary ceramics were a chief field of emphasis in the art collections.

On the eastern edge of the city of Phoenix was established the unique, open-air museum of Pueblo Grande. A partially excavated archaeological site, it was a prehistoric Indian community but has been weatherproofed and opened to visitors via guided tours and recorded lectures. A small museum building houses Hohokam material culture items and helps illustrate the story of prehistoric irrigation on the very spot where modern irrigation has once more brought the valley back to fertility. The project was operating in 1970 as the Division of Archaeology within the Phoenix Parks and Recreation Department.

Also in Phoenix is the Arizona Museum devoted to Arizona pioneer history. Little Emma, the diminutive locomotive which hauled ore cars between Morenci and Clifton almost seventy-five years before rested outside the building as of 1970.

A major art collection of the state was housed from the late 1950s on in the new two-story gallery of the Fine Arts Center on the University of Arizona campus which was expanded late in the sixties by a large addition. The Tucson Fine Arts Association maintained another museum in a remodeled mansion in a once-fashionable west-side residential area dubbed "Snob Hollow." In 1970 plans were underway to construct a new building for this small but rapidly growing permanent collection. During the winter season the Association was presenting

Fig. 35.6   A research center for the ethnology and archaeology of the Flagstaff region.

Museum of Northern Arizona

a well-rounded series of traveling exhibits and exihibits of work by local artists.

A small but excellent archaeological museum is located at Dragoon, east of Tucson. It has been supported by the Amerind Foundation which was established by William Shirley Fulton for the promotion of archaeological research in the Southwest. The foundation has carried out important excavations in the San Pedro and Santa Cruz valleys, revealing much of the ancient life of the southwestern section of the state. Under the direction of archaeologist Charles Di Peso, the museum staff has conducted large-scale excavations at Casas Grandes in Chihuahua, Mexico, in collaboration with the Mexican government.

ECOLOGICAL MUSEUM. On the west slope of the Tucson Mountains overlooking the Avra Valley is the fascinating Arizona-Sonora Desert Museum. Its unique combination of indoor and outdoor exhibits tells the story of the plant and animal ecology of the desert life zones and the geology of the region. The visitor is offered living exhibits of cacti, desert animals, desert fish, and birds. A wonderful underground museum exhibits life

beneath the desert floor, a selected display of the rocks and minerals, and the extensive and absorbing Water Street, U.S.A., explores the story of water and its relation to the southwest. As of 1969, an otter pond with underground viewing windows was added and a similar beaver pond was being constructed. The Museum also includes a selected display of indigenous rocks and minerals.

In several of the counties rapidly growing historical museums placing emphasis on collecting, preserving, and displaying cultural artifacts of the local areas were established through the fifties and sixties and have been growing rapidly. Particularly outstanding have been those of the Sharlot Hall Museum at Prescott, the Pioneers' Museum at Flagstaff, and the Yuma, Mohave, Pinal, and Graham County historical societies. Most of these have been affiliated with the Arizona Historical Society.

Under the direction of the State Parks Board, historic parks and museums have been operating at Tombstone, Tubac, Yuma, Jerome, and at Buckskin Park on the Colorado River. As of the seventies, new parks and museum facilities were being added each year.

Fig. 35.7 At the Arizona-Sonora Desert Museum west of Tucson, center of ecological displays and research, a mother peccary, or javelina, guards her young.

Parks, Monuments, and Memorials

By the turn of the century, Arizona — only thirty-five years away from the Civil War which had seen her population almost vanish — was again growing and developing its cultural resources in natural historical and recreational sites as well as other areas.

One year before the Territorial Legislature had acted to establish (on paper at least) an archaeological museum, the Congress of the United States, acting on permissive legislation passed in 1889, authorized reservation of lands surrounding the four-story, six hundred-year-old combination Indian watchtower and community dwelling known as Casa Grande. This created Arizona's first national monument — though it was not officially so designated until 1918. The Casa Grande, built of packed earth by prehistoric Indian farmers, was the only surviving example of such structures which once dotted the Salt River Valley. It often surprises Arizonans accustomed to superlatives about their state, to discover it possesses yet another: more national monuments than any other state. Besides Grand Canyon and Petrified Forest national parks, there are two national recreation areas, one national memorial, sixteen national monuments, and two national historical sites. These areas as of 1970 comprised about two percent of the state's 72,688,000 acres.

EARLY PRESERVATION. Long before Congress established the National Park Service in 1916, a number of Arizona's natural and historic wonders had been set aside under the care of other agencies. Grand Canyon was created as a national monument by President Theodore Roosevelt in 1908, under the administration of the Forest Service, but it was not made a national park until 1919. One of the wonders of the world, Grand Canyon possesses so many scientific and scenic superlatives that it almost defies description. Whole books have been devoted to the canyon and the river which created it, and more are sure to be written. Most visitors get only the brief, two-dimensional view which is easily available at the rim. Really to see the park requires several days following trails, seeing museum exhibits, listening to talks by rangers, and especially going down into the vitals of the chasm where the muddy, turbulent river writhes, roars, and scours its way deeper into the earth.

To the west of the park is the Grand Canyon National Monument, somewhat inaccessible and infrequently visited but almost equally awesome. At one spot, Toroweap Point, there is a three thousand-foot view straight into the Colorado, a view not possible in the park. Lake Mead National Recreation Area, partly in Arizona, partly in Nevada, lies directly to the west. It includes Lake Mead and Lake Mohave, formed by the river and restrained by Hoover and Davis dams. Here, in the searing desert, fishermen catch fabulously big trout in the cold waters of the Colorado released from the bottom of the lake behind Hoover Dam.

Linking Grand Canyon National Park with the Glen Canyon Recreational Area, Marble Canyon National Monument was created early in 1969 to protect the entire course of the Colorado from below Hoover Dam to Moab, Utah.

Only a small portion of the Glen Canyon National Recreation Area is in Arizona (the much larger portion is in Utah). Here, the waters of Lake Powell, backed up by Glen Canyon Dam, provide easy access by boat to a region of fantastic rock formations, including the famous Rainbow Bridge, as well as to many recreational facilities.

Fig. 35.8   Casa Grande national monument is over 600 years old.

Ray Manley

Fig. 35.9   Towns were built on hilltops in Arizona at least 1,000 years ago — one of them was Tuzigoot, now a monument.

ARCHAEOLOGICAL MONUMENTS. One group of monuments is primarily of archaeological interest. Besides Casa Grande, these include Montezuma Castle, Tonto National Monument, Tuzigoot, Walnut Canyon, Wupatki, and Navajo National Monument. Tonto, overlooking the present Roosevelt Lake, contains a group of cliff dwellings which were occupied during the fourteenth century by the Salado Indians, possibly as a defensive site. Life must have been rugged for the Salado farmers. The nearest dependable spring was half a mile from the dwellings, while their fields were two to four miles away on the Salt River flood plain.

Northwest of Tonto is the lush Verde River Valley which was the home of agricultural Indians from at least one thousand years ago to as recently as the early fifteenth century. Toward the end of the period there seems to have been much competition for irrigable land, and defensive structures were essential. Towns or pueblos were built on hilltops, as at Tuzigoot, or where suitable in cliffs, as at Montezuma Castle.

Tuzigoot was strategically located at the end of a limestone ridge near the river and adjacent to farming land. Montezuma was high in a limestone cliff on Beaver Creek and close to rich farm land. It is a five-story, twenty-room structure, about ninety percent intact and original. However it rests so precariously on soft, friable, much-eroded stone that it was necessary some years ago to discontinue taking visitors through the building.

Farther north near Flagstaff is Walnut Canyon, known for the beauty of its heavily vegetated canyon slopes and hundreds of small cliff dwellings built in its natural caves and occupied by the Sinagua Indians, mainly during the eleventh to thirteenth centuries. Farming was made possible in this area by the eruption in about 1068 of the volcanic field in the San Francisco Peak area which created Sunset Crater, a one thousand-foot volcanic cinder cone which blew its top and blanketed the land with volcanic ash for many miles around. Indians, frightened away by the eruption, came back later to find the cinders and ash had made a fine moisture-retaining mulch. Word spread rapidly, and by A.D. 1100 an estimated four thousand Indians had come to the area.

At Wupatki National Monument, a few miles north of Sunset Crater, are hundreds of homesites which were built late in the twelfth and early in the thirteenth centuries. The excavated ruin of Wupatki shows the visitor that a highly developed agricultural community existed here. Drought conditions and probable drifting of moisture-conserving cinder into dunes caused general depopulation in the thirteenth century. The entire Wupatki Basin was abandoned by A.D. 1300.

Nearly one hundred miles northeast, near the Utah border, lies Navajo National Monument including the spectacular Keet Seel, the largest cliff ruin in Arizona, and two other large and well-preserved cliff dwellings, Betatakin and Inscription House. These were also deserted about the time the Wupatki area was abandoned.

In the heart of the Navajo Reservation is Canyon de Chelly National Monument, two deep canyons with towering, strangely wind-eroded, brilliant red rock walls — de Chelly and del Muerto. These canyons also sheltered Basketmaker and Pueblo Indians until about the year 1300, just as they later sheltered the Navajo. However, the monument is probably chiefly interesting to modern visitors for its rare and imposing natural beauty. It can be viewed from points on the rim, and arrangements may be made for trips along the canyon floor in a specially equipped car.

Fig. 35.10   Wupatki National Monument represents a thriving agricultural community, abandoned by A.D. 1300.

NATURAL WONDERS. Also in northern Arizona is the most spectacular display of petrified wood in the world, including a colorful portion of the Painted Desert. In Petrified Forest National Park there are six "forests," formed by silica which was picked up by ground water and carried into cell tissues of the wood to form the present petrified logs from trees which grew millions of years ago. Iron and manganese oxides were chiefly responsible for the varied coloring, both in the trees and the surrounding desert.

In the volcanic field northeast of Flagstaff, Sunset Crater has been set aside as a national monument. Its black, red-tipped cone is best seen in the afternoon as the sun begins to descend behind the San Francisco Peaks.

In the southern deserts, two national monuments have been established to protect and preserve the characteristic desert life for which this region is known over the world. Saguaro, near Tucson, includes what are probably the biggest specimens of the giant cactus in the United States. While the saguaro is the most spectacular feature, the entire plant community at lower elevations is picturesque. An astonishing variety of wild animals and birds also frequents the area.

Farther west, adjoining a lengthy strip of Sonora's

Fig. 35.11   Sunset Crater has been set aside as a national monument in the volcanic field north of Flagstaff.

Fig. 35.12   Saguaro National Monument has been created to preserve a cactus almost unique to Southern Arizona.

Fig. 35.13   A wonderland of rocks in the Chiricahua National Monument.

Fig. 35.14   Organ pipe cactus.

Ray Manley

Fig. 35.15   The Hubbell Trading Post at Ganado —
a national historic site.

northern boundary, Organ Pipe Cactus National Monument contains more than five hundred square miles of Sonoran desert. Here — in the wild beauty of desert mountains, vast stretches of surrounding *bajadas* (outwash plains) and a variety of grotesque vegetation — is the only large group of organ pipe cactus in the United States. Loop roads and trails offer good opportunities to see the desert as a place populated with living plants and animals.

East and south across the state is Chiracahua National Monument, something of a miniature opposite of the Grand Canyon. Instead of dramatizing what erosive forces have gouged out, nature has accumulated here innumerable bizarre-looking rock forms that erosion has left standing up, pointing away from the earth instead of into it. This wonderland of rocks is located high in a forested range, a mountain island in a desert sea.

The mountain range was the part-time home of the Chiricahua Apaches who, under the brilliant leadership of Cochise, for twelve years matched the strategy of the U.S. Army, forcing the establishment of Fort Bowie, one of the state's two national historic sites (on the northern flank of the mountains), to protect the overland stage route.

HISTORICAL MONUMENTS. The two historical monuments, Tumacacori and Pipe Spring, are almost a state's width apart. Tumacacori, some twenty miles north of Nogales, is the ruin of a typical Franciscan mission church of 150 years ago. It was built at the peak point of missionary achievement on the northern frontier of what was then New Spain. The shell of the building is well preserved and the fine museum explains vividly the missionary movement in the Arizona-Sonora region and the daily life of the padres. Its charming patio where gnarled olive trees surround a terraced fountain is one of the most delightful oases in southern Arizona.

Pipe Spring National Monument in the isolated Arizona Strip north of the Colorado River is named for a shooting exploit of Jacob Hamblin who led the first group of white men to visit the spring. The Mormon fort, built there for protection against Navajos and Paiutes in the 1860s, is an expression of the courage, foresight, and faith of the pioneers in general and the Mormons in particular.

Also in the north on the Navajo Reservation, the Hubbell Trading Post at Ganado has been designated a national historic site. The trading post and its warehouse and the adjacent Lorenzo Hubbell home, containing a treasure of paintings, rugs, baskets and furnishings, preserves a living feature of reservation life that is fast vanishing.

Coronado National Memorial, astride the southern tip of the Huachucas on the Mexican border, is also part of the historical picture. After a short climb from the parking area at Montezuma Pass the visitor reaches the top of Coronado Peak, 6,880 feet above sea level. To the south and the west stretches the majestic panorama of blue mountain and grassed valley through which the expedition of Coronado is believed to have passed leading the first white man into the southwest.

Fig. 35.16   Monument Valley, the Navajo Reservation in northern Arizona, has been named a tribal park.

PROBLEMS OF PRESERVATION. Arizona at the beginning of the seventies was in grave danger of losing its archaeological heritage. In the Tucson Basin alone, with its known three hundred village sites of prehistory as inventoried in the archaeological survey file of the Arizona State Museum, there was a strong likelihood that only one would have been preserved a few decades hence. This was the University Indian Ruin at the junction of the Pantano and Rillito drainages. As of 1970 this ruin was being "banked" for future development by the University of Arizona. Similar efforts to record information on other sites in the northern half of Arizona were being made by the staff of the Museum of Northern Arizona at Flagstaff.

The construction of superhighways, reservoirs, the reclamation of the desert for agriculture, and metropolitan and industrial expansion has already obliterated many ruins. It seemed likely at the start of the seventies that many more would suffer the same fate. A fact not readily appreciated is that man's archaeological resources are exhaustible. The day will likely come when the collections in the museums and the national monuments, preserved by the forward-looking planners of municipal, state, and federal agencies, will be the only remaining evidence of the prehistory of the state. The tragedy is that the loss is national in scope.

To cope with this problem, an independent committee was formed in 1945, known as the Committee for the Recovery of Archaeological Remains, with membership made up of representatives of the Society for American Archaeology, the American Anthropological Association, and the American Council of Learned Societies. The archaeological salvage program stimulated by this committee affects archaeological institutions

Fig. 35.17   Ventana Cave — a repository of ancient man.

Fig. 35.18 Tombstone Courthouse is part of a system of state parks and monuments.

within the state which have been active in studying resources before they are destroyed by the march of progress. Arizona has worked out effective arrangements with state and federal highway agencies to salvage the data and material from ruins doomed to destruction by highway building. Private industry (notably gas distributing companies) has cooperated most commendably in employing archaeologists, where necessary, to survey and dig, in pipeline rights-of-way.

Throughout the sixties the University of Arizona, through the Arizona State Museum, and the Museum of Northern Arizona at Flagstaff was engaging in cooperative salvage programs. Arrangements with the National Park Service and the Arizona State Highway Commission also were in effect, and other steps were planned.

But it is not just prehistoric sites that have suffered from neglect and willful destruction. Many of Arizona's most historic sites have also disappeared. To aid in preserving Arizona's heritage, historic as well as natural, the state legislature in 1957 created the Arizona State Parks Board. Under its direction is a growing system of state parks and monuments which as of 1970 included the Tubac presidio, the Tombstone courthouse, the Douglas mansion at Jerome, the old Territorial Prison at Yuma, the Civil War battleground at Picacho Peak, and parks at Buckskin Mountain, Lake Havasu, Lyman Lake, and Painted Rocks.

Acutely aware of the beauty of their own area which yearly attracts increasing numbers of visitors, the Navajo tribe in the sixties began establishment of a series of tribal parks. Best known has been Monument Valley, a region of towering, weirdly eroded red-rock formations through which the visitor moves, as the late

Joseph Wood Krutch has written, in perpetual astonishment. Private individuals also have involved themselves. Under the auspices of the Arizona Historical Society, the Committee for the Preservation and Restoration of Historical Sites in Arizona was formed in the 1960s. This committee, with statewide representation, has stated as its goal the surveying and marking of historic sites including the restoration of Fort Lowell and the Old Adobe Patio, both in Tucson.

Other groups have been working to preserve some of the state's natural attractions. Nature Conservancy has established the Patagonia-Sonoita Creek Sanctuary — more than a mile of tall cottonwoods and native ash bordering a perennial stream sixty miles south of Tucson. It is located on the flyway to Mexico, and over 2,000 species of birds have been recorded in the area.

In addition to the parks and monuments, a number of significant historical sites, both state and national — San Bernardino Ranch, San Xavier del Bac, Ventana Cave, for example — have been recognized in the National Register of Historic Places.

A THREATENED HERITAGE. All such efforts can be expected to aid in preserving Arizona's past. But by 1970 no effective way had yet been found to forestall the losses due to urban and agricultural expansion, nor the destruction wrought unwittingly by the private citizen, or wittingly by those who, in the face of federal and state antiquities laws, continued to vandalize ruins and historic sites for personal satisfaction and gain. An enlightened public, recognizing the value in understanding and preserving the relics, records, and reminders of America's and, locally, Arizona's past, is needed most desperately.

Fig. 36.1   Among the world's largest telescopes are those
operating from Kitt Peak National Observatory, south of Tucson.

Kitt Peak

Thomas C. Cooper
Communications

36

RESEARCH AND THE FUTURE

THE FUTURE OF ARIZONA, like that of the rest of the world, lies in research, which, in its broadest aspect, is the basis for progress everywhere. Man must continue to investigate, to observe, and to interpret his findings, for the resulting knowledge can enable him to minimize illness and pain, to augment the production and distribution of food, to increase his control over himself, his society, and his environment, and to improve international understanding.

One of the most important advantages afforded by Arizona's environment is the opportunity to study problems related to living in an arid region. Such problems and their solutions have significance far beyond the borders of the state and nation and give Arizonans an opportunity to contribute valuable knowledge to the other arid regions of the world.

Many of the difficulties of living in an arid region concern the health and welfare of the native and immigrant populations, the development of agriculture and industry, and of urban areas, through controlled use of water, the utilization of mineral resources, and the focus on special features of the area for scientific study.

Even before World War II, with the development of agricultural and mineral resources well under way, and with the continuing growth of the population and educational and research institutions, Arizonans were making great advances. Since the war, with increasing awareness of the problems of the native Indian peoples, with large growth in population, and with expanding industrialization and general diversification of the economy, Arizona has marked a path of progress unequaled in any other arid region.

Predictions in 1970 indicated that the population of Arizona would continue to grow, and it was estimated that by 1975 the population would be approximately 2,750,000. The primary cause of this growth has been the desire of many people to live under the conditions of dryness, sunshine, and warmth which are characteristic of Arizona. Through research new means of earning a livelihood are being sought for Arizona's expanding population.

Problems and Possibilities

Arizona needs research to increase the availability of water and to bring about more efficient utilization of already existent water; to make possible more efficient use of its limited arable lands; to devise better means of capitalizing upon its known mineral resources and of finding additional reserves; to discover and develop manufacturing processes and industries suited to the location and environment; and to make living in the state even more advantageous and enjoyable.

Research moves swiftly in these times. Complex mathematical computations that once required months or years of patient individual effort are the work of seconds for electronic computing equipment. In 1970 large computers were housed at the General Electric Computer Center at Arizona State University, at Fort Huachuca, at the Computer Center at the University of Arizona, and at the Kitt Peak National Observatory. The availability of these computers has contributed much to the development of research. The TRIGA Nuclear Reactor at the University of Arizona is capable of continuous operation at 100 kilowatts.

The study of rainfall, upper atmospheric changes, and cloud modification is the special province of atmospheric research, particularly at the Institute of Atmospheric Physics at the University of Arizona. The Institute was established in April of 1954 and later that year received a National Science Foundation grant for a study entitled *Natural Resources Survey of the Clouds*. Support for the Institute was continued by the National Science Foundation and the Office of Naval Research in succeeding years with a major grant providing a modern radar installation to study cloud physics, cloud seeding, and pulse-doppler radar.

Economic Demineralization of Saline Water was another major contract from the Office of Saline Water of the Department of the Interior in the amount of $76,000 in 1962. This initial research was followed in 1963 by a study that led to the amount of $98,165 for construction and operation of a multiple-effect solar-powered desalination pilot plant at Puerto Penasco, Sonora, Mexico. The success of this research attracted private foundation support in the development of a Unified Community Concept which is a plan to provide electricity, drinking water, and vegetables to an arid seacoast community for little more than the cost of the fuel for the diesel engines used to generate the electricity. The waste heat from the diesel engines is used to desalinate the seawater by an evaporation process, with some of the product water being used in a closed environment greenhouse system to produce amazing agricultural yields due to an increased carbon dioxide concentration obtained from a portion of the diesel engine exhaust.

More recently, the Shaikh of Abu Dhabi has contracted with the Environmental Research Laboratory of the Institute of Atmospheric Physics to perform the research necessary to design and construct a $3.2 million power, water, and food facility on an island in the Persian Gulf.

A large commercial greenhouse has been initiated in the Tucson area to produce tonnage quantities of exceptionally high-grade tomatoes by the application of research results from the Environmental Research Laboratory. Thus both local and international benefits have been derived from research in the Institute of Atmospheric Physics.

Study Centers

As man probes farther into the interstellar dark of outer space, the Lowell and the U.S. Naval observatories at Flagstaff, the Steward Observatory and the Lunar and Planetary Laboratory at the University of Arizona, and the Kitt Peak National Observatory forty miles southwest of Tucson are important centers of research. Some of the largest telescopes in the world are in Arizona. Kitt Peak National Observatory operates an 86-inch reflector and was finishing in 1970 a 150-inch reflector. Steward Observatory has its 90-inch reflector on

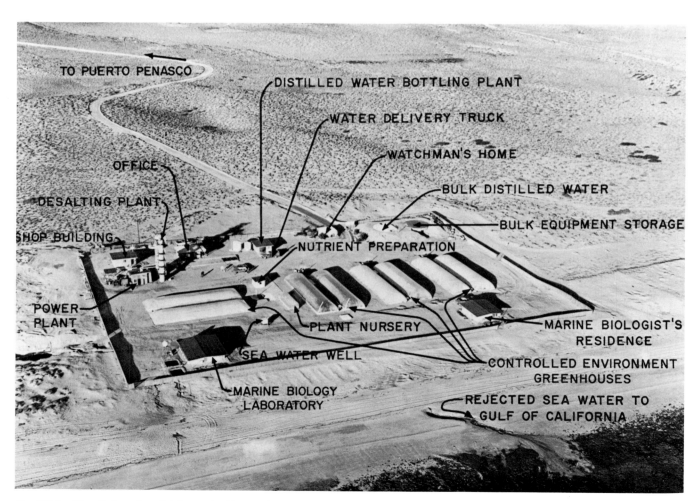

Fig. 36.2   The University of Arizona Institute of Atmospheric Physics is desalinating water for raising vegetables.

Fig. 36.3 Human beings and plants thrive in controlled atmospheric conditions at the Environmental Research lab.

Kitt Peak, and the Lunar and Planetary Laboratory has three 60-61-inch telescopes at its Catalina Station; Lowell Observatory has a 69-inch reflector.

Closely related to this activity is the analysis of lunar rock, dust, and core samples conducted by researchers in the University of Arizona Organic Geochemistry Laboratory on material returned from Apollo lunar missions. The work points to the confidence placed in UA researchers by the National Aeronautics and Space Administration.

In addition, Lunar and Planetary Laboratory scientists were entrusted to help select landing sites for early Apollo missions because of the University's extensive work in lunar mapping.

At Portal, Arizona, continuing the work of a long and distinguished line of private research foundations in Arizona, the Southwestern Research Station of the American Museum of Natural History offers biologists and other scientists a unique geographical situation which affords opportunity for study in five of the life zones.

Arizona has developed its own Academy of Science. Under the spread of this intellectual tent, many men and women of Arizona have joined in the search for solutions to problems of survival and better living. In addition, Arizona has twelve scientists honored by the prestigious National Academy of Science. Nine of the members are UA faculty members, two from Kitt Peak, and one from Lowell Observatory.

Military Research

The U.S. Army Electronic Proving Ground at Fort Huachuca is a major installation for military communications research. The Association for Applied Solar Energy, the University of Arizona, and Arizona State University work to harness the power of the sun for man's use. Cotton undergoes scientific testing continually by the University of Arizona's scientists and by cooperating scientists of the United States Department of Agriculture at the Cotton Research Center near Phoenix, as well as in the laboratory of the Agricultural Experiment Station in Tucson, where research has produced the leading varieties of high-quality fibers grown in the world today. Throughout Arizona many other state and federal agencies continue long records of important research activity.

Extensive research programs are also carried on by private industries throughout the state, including the mining companies. Work is done in the Phoenix area in solid state circuits by Motorola, in computer technology by General Electric, and in the field of components for electronics equipment by Sperry-Rand and AiResearch; in the Tucson area, work in missile research and production is carried on by Hughes Aircraft, in the water and waste-water treatment problems of nations by electronic instrumentation by Infilco, and in military communication by Burr-Brown. This industrial research is enhanced by research at the University of Arizona in many areas, including integrated circuits, all digital simulation, engineering reliability, and computer-aided design.

Throughout a thousand years of history, the main functions of the universities of Europe and the Americas have been to impart to each rising generation the accumulated knowledge and wisdom of the past and to seek continually through research new knowledge for the benefit of mankind. This tradition has been and continues to be a guiding principle in the development of higher education in Arizona.

Founded in 1885, the University of Arizona throughout the intervening years has served as the center of research for the state. The need for new knowledge for the development of the agricultural resources of the Territory was so great that the Agricultural Experiment Station was organized even before the university opened its doors to students. The subsequent addition of fifteen research divisions at the University of Arizona has been in response to the developing needs and the special opportunities afforded by the state. Nine of these divisions have been established since World War II. Over and above regularly budgeted research funds, the research grants and contracts from federal agencies, private foundations, corporations, and individuals amounted to $1.9 million in 1957-58 and ten years later reached in excess of $21 million.

Thus, Arizona is once again a frontier — this time a frontier where new knowledge gained through research points to a new day of technological progress in many fields, not only for Arizona but also for other arid regions of the nation and the world.

Fig. 36.4   Research for industry is carried on in plants such as this Integrated Circuits Center near Mesa, Arizona.

SUPPLEMENTARY
INFORMATION

TABLES

ARIZONA POPULATION STATISTICS — BY COUNTY

	1910	1920	1930	1940	1950	1960	1970
State Totals:	204,354	334,162	435,523	499,261	749,587	1,302,161	1,770,900
The Counties:							
Apache	9,196	13,196	17,765	24,095	27,767	30,438	32,298
Cochise	34,591	46,465	40,998	34,627	31,488	55,039	61,910
Coconino	8,130	9,982	14,064	18,770	23,910	41,857	48,326
Gila	16,348	25,678	31,016	23,867	24,158	25,745	29,255
Graham	23,999	10,148	10,373	12,113	12,985	14,045	16,578
Greenlee	—	15,362	9,886	8,698	12,805	11,509	10,330
Maricopa	34,488	89,576	150,970	186,193	331,770	663,510	967,522
Mohave	3,773	5,259	5,572	8,591	8,510	7,736	25,857
Navajo	11,471	16,077	21,202	25,309	29,446	37,994	47,715
Pima	22,818	34,680	55,676	72,838	141,216	265,660	351,667
Pinal	9,045	16,130	22,031	28,841	43,191	62,673	67,916
Santa Cruz	6,766	12,689	9,684	9,482	9,344	10,808	13,966
Yavapai	15,996	24,016	28,470	26,511	24,991	28,912	36,733
Yuma	7,733	14,904	17,816	19,326	28,006	46,235	60,827
Leading Cities:							
Phoenix	11,134	29,053	48,118	65,414	106,818	439,170	581,562
Tucson	13,193	20,292	32,506	35,752	45,454	212,892	262,933

Source: U.S. Department of Commerce, Bureau of the Census.

GROWTH IN PERSONAL INCOME
(in millions)

Rank	State	1960	1970	Percent Increase
1.	Nevada	$ 831	$ 2,267	173%
2.	Florida	9,746	24,938	156
3.	ARIZONA	2,684	6,418	139
4.	Georgia	6,489	15,345	136
5.	Hawaii	1,478	3,445	133

GROWTH OF BANK DEPOSITS
(in millions)

Rank	State	1960	1970	Percent Increase
1.	Alaska	$ 209.9	$ 688.5	228%
2.	Florida	4,887.4	14,091.3	188
3.	ARIZONA	1,285.1	3,550.8	176
4.	Georgia	2,942.5	7,779.6	164
5.	Nevada	441.9	1,152.7	161

Source: U. S. Department of Commerce, *Survey of Current Business.*

GROWTH IN NON-AGRICULTURAL EMPLOYMENT
(in thousands)

Rank	State	1960	1970	Percent Increase
1	Nevada	103.4	201.1	94.5
2	ARIZONA	333.8	544.8	63.2
3	Florida	1,323.7	2,155.7	62.8
4	Alaska	56.6	92.1	62.7
5	Hawaii	188.1	292.0	55.2
6	Georgia	1,051.1	1,545.7	47.0
7	North Carolina	1,195.5	1,745.9	46.0
8	Arkansas	367.3	532.0	44.8
9	South Carolina	582.5	839.4	44.1
10	Colorado	515.4	741.0	43.8
11	California	4,895.0	7,002.3	43.0
12	Mississippi	403.4	576.4	42.9

Source: U.S. Department of Labor, Bureau of Labor Statistics, *Employment and Earnings* Annual Supplement, Vol. 8, Number 12, June 1962 Vol. 17, Number 11, May 1971.

GROWTH IN MANUFACTURING EMPLOYMENT
(in thousands)

Rank	State	1960	1970	Percent Increase
1	ARIZONA	49.3	90.3	83.2
2	Arkansas	102.3	166.3	62.6
3	Florida	206.7	324.2	56.8
4	Mississippi	119.9	181.5	51.4
5	Tennessee	315.1	466.5	48.0
6	Kentucky	171.6	251.0	46.3
7	Alaska	5.8	8.1	39.6
8	South Carolina	244.8	340.0	38.9
9	North Carolina	509.3	698.9	37.2
10	Colorado	87.7	117.6	34.1
11	Idaho	30.1	40.1	33.2

Source: U.S. Department of Labor, Bureau of Labor Statistics, *Employment and Earnings* Annual Supplement, Vol. 8, Number 12, June 1962 and Vol. 17, Number 11, May 1971.

SUMMARY OF MAJOR CROPS IN ARIZONA
(in thousands of dollars)

CROP	1969	1970
All Cotton	70,886	58,375
Cottonseed	10,069	12,000
Barley	12,576	12,874
All Wheat	6,698	14,594
Sorghum for Grain	20,489	17,991
Corn for Grain	635	564
Safflower	2,145	1,311
Sugar Beets	5,570	3,515
Potatoes	8,538	8,489
Alfalfa Seed	380	289
All Hay	30,688	41,517
Broccoli, Winter	546	827
Cabbage, Winter	678	1,178
Cantaloups, Spring	10,417	11,624
Cantaloups, Early Summer	1,340	634
Cantaloups, Early Fall	360	794
Carrots, Spring	2,369	1,905
Cauliflower, Winter	705	936
Honeydews, Early Summer	924	1,503
Lettuce, Winter	20,924	14,672
Lettuce, Early Spring	24,408	13,735
Lettuce, Late Fall	22,774	10,234
Dry Onions, Late Spring	2,372	3,712
Watermelons, Early Summer	1,392	2,236
Grapes	3,800	3,706

Source: U. S. Department of Agriculture, Statistical Reporting Service, *Arizona Agricultural Statistics, 1972,* Bulletin S-7.

ALTITUDE, TEMPERATURE AND RAINFALL FOR ARIZONA CITIES

City	Elevation in Feet	Average Temperature	Normal Precipitation (Inches per year)
Ajo	1,763	71.5	9.06
Alpine	8,000	43.7	19.21
Benson	3,585	63.0	11.75
Bisbee	5,350	61.8	17.34
Casa Grande	1,390	69.9	8.02
Clifton	3,465	67.3	11.87
Douglas	4,098	63.1	11.72
Flagstaff	6,993	45.6	18.31
Florence	1,500	70.0	9.59
Gila Bend	737	72.2	5.62
Globe	3,510	62.0	15.37
Grand Canyon	6,927	49.7	14.34
Holbrook	5,069	55.2	7.74
Kingman	3,333	61.9	9.68
Litchfield Park	1,030	70.1	7.77
McNary	7,320	46.7	25.09
Mesa	1,225	68.5	7.53
Miami	3,603	63.7	18.47
Nogales	3,800	60.3	15.48
Oracle	4,450	61.7	18.78
Parker	405	71.8	4.53
Payson	4,902	53.2	20.57
Phoenix	1,083	69.0	7.20
Prescott	5,354	55.7	12.23
Safford	2,900	64.1	8.66
Springerville	6,964	48.6	12.10
Tempe	1,180	68.5	7.58
Tombstone	4,540	63.9	13.70
Tucson	2,423	68.1	10.47
Whiteriver	5,280	55.5	17.09
Wickenburg	2,070	66.1	10.85
Willcox	4,200	59.8	10.54
Williams	6,750	49.2	21.25
Winslow	4,880	55.7	7.23
Yuma	138	71.9	3.02

Source: U.S. Weather Bureau; Latest *Decennial Census of the U.S. Climate.*

Average Relative Humidity for Representative Cities
(11:00 AM Recordings)

	Jan.	Feb.	Mar.	Apr.	May	June	July	Aug.	Sept.	Oct.	Nov.	Dec.	Avg.
Phoenix, Arizona	45	39	34	24	18	18	29	37	37	28	40	48	33
Tucson, Arizona	40	34	28	21	16	16	32	39	31	29	31	38	30
Albuquerque, New Mexico	49	46	32	26	23	24	36	39	44	36	45	52	38
Billings, Montana	61	60	51	52	50	48	39	40	51	45	58	61	51
Boston, Massachusetts	61	59	57	58	54	55	50	58	61	52	62	59	57
Chicago, Illinois	63	61	61	59	51	50	54	57	55	47	61	72	58
Cleveland, Ohio	71	73	68	60	56	57	55	61	59	56	66	73	63
Denver, Colorado	42	47	42	35	36	40	33	37	41	30	43	44	39
Detroit, Michigan	68	66	63	57	54	52	51	58	57	54	65	70	60
El Paso, Texas	42	35	30	22	22	26	40	41	50	33	40	46	35
Houston, Texas	65	62	59	63	61	61	58	59	60	53	61	65	61
Los Angeles, Calif.	51	54	52	53	56	59	54	56	52	55	45	45	53
Miami, Florida	58	62	57	54	60	70	68	67	71	67	60	56	62
Minneapolis, Minnesota	67	66	67	57	56	55	56	58	64	56	66	70	61
New Orleans, Louisiana	67	65	59	60	60	63	66	66	65	58	59	67	63
New York, New York	60	59	55	52	53	55	55	58	58	55	59	60	57
Pittsburgh, Pennsylvania	67	67	61	55	52	52	51	55	56	48	59	68	57
Portland, Oregon	82	80	71	68	66	65	63	66	67	80	82	84	73
Reno, Nevada	69	51	41	36	33	34	29	35	38	40	63	70	45
St. Louis, Missouri	60	57	55	52	53	55	57	54	56	48	58	63	56
Salt Lake City, Utah	71	65	51	44	37	32	25	28	36	39	57	73	47
San Francisco, Calif.	68	66	62	64	66	68	75	74	67	62	62	70	67
Seattle, Washington	80	77	74	73	71	67	67	72	76	82	82	84	75
Spokane, Washington	82	78	67	56	51	47	38	45	48	67	83	86	62
Washington, D.C.	54	56	48	49	49	51	50	52	56	48	51	57	52

Source: U.S. Weather Bureau, Climatological Standard Normals (1931–1960).

CLIMATE COMPARISON
Average Percentage of Possible Sunshine for Representative Cities

	Jan.	Feb.	Mar.	Apr.	May	June	July	Aug.	Sept.	Oct.	Nov.	Dec.	Avg.
Phoenix, Arizona	77	79	83	88	93	94	84	85	89	88	84	77	86
Tucson, Arizona	81	84	86	91	93	93	76	80	87	90	86	81	86
Albuquerque, New Mexico	72	73	74	76	80	84	76	76	81	80	78	72	77
Billings, Montana	52	54	60	58	61	65	79	77	67	64	49	50	63
Boston, Massachusetts	52	57	58	55	59	64	66	66	64	61	53	54	60
Chicago, Illinois	44	47	51	53	62	68	70	68	64	63	43	42	58
Cleveland, Ohio	30	35	44	51	60	67	68	65	61	56	33	28	52
Denver, Colorado	73	70	70	65	64	71	72	73	75	76	66	69	70
Detroit, Michigan	44	34	50	45	65	81	66	67	61	67	22	24	52
El Paso, Texas	77	81	83	86	89	89	79	80	82	84	83	77	83
Houston, Texas	50	57	59	56	62	74	78	73	68	75	63	52	64
Los Angeles, Calif.	72	72	73	67	66	67	81	82	79	74	76	71	73
Miami, Florida	66	72	73	73	68	61	65	67	62	62	64	65	67
Minneapolis, Minnesota	51	57	53	55	58	62	69	66	60	59	41	42	58
New Orleans, Louisiana	49	50	57	63	68	65	58	59	64	69	60	46	59
New York, New York	50	55	57	59	62	65	66	64	63	61	53	50	60
Pittsburgh, Pennsylvania	40	39	48	49	57	64	67	64	66	61	47	37	54
Portland, Oregon	24	32	37	47	51	47	67	61	58	38	29	21	45
Reno, Nevada	66	70	74	79	78	84	92	93	91	82	72	63	80
St. Louis, Missouri	51	48	52	52	63	69	71	69	63	65	53	47	58
Salt Lake City, Utah	47	54	63	67	72	78	83	83	83	74	55	44	69
San Francisco, Calif.	56	62	68	71	71	73	65	65	71	70	63	53	66
Seattle, Washington	28	34	42	47	52	49	63	56	53	37	28	23	45
Spokane, Washington	26	39	54	62	63	66	81	76	71	52	29	20	57
Washington, D.C.	46	51	56	54	58	66	64	62	62	62	53	49	58

Source: U.S. Weather Bureau, Climatological Standard Normals (1931–1960).

Compiled by Donald M. Powell
Librarian

SELECTED ARIZONA READING MATERIALS

There are hundreds, nay, thousands of works on the many facets of Arizona. Some of them are technical, some are old, rare and hard to find, some are poorly written, and many — far too many to include in this list — are very fine.

The following is a highly selective list for the general reader who wishes to explore further the various topics covered in this volume. With few exceptions the books are currently available in bookstores, frequently in inexpensive editions, or, if out of print, can be found in most libraries.

General Histories

The March of Arizona History. Anne Merriman Peck. Arizona Silhouettes, Tucson, 1962. Written as general reading and as a text. A good book to begin with, but unfortunately out of print.

History of Arizona and New Mexico. Herbert H. Bancroft. Horn and Wallace, Albuquerque, 1962. Originally issued in 1888, so covers the story only until then, but still valuable.

Pioneer Days in Arizona. Frank C. Lockwood. Macmillan, N.Y., 1932. From the coming of the Spanish to statehood.

Arizona, the History of a Frontier State. Rufus K. Wyllys. Hobson and Herr, Phoenix, 1950. The careful, useful, but not very sprightly results of thorough research.

Land of Many Frontiers: A History of the American Southwest. Odie B. Faulk. Oxford University Press, N.Y., 1968. Arizona history woven into that of New Mexico, western Texas and southern California. Eminently readable.

Arizona Pageant: A Short History of the 48th State. Madeline F. Paré with the collaboration of Bert M. Fireman. Arizona Historical Foundation, Phoenix, 1965. Though written as a secondary school text, this will be useful for the general reader.

Indians Before the Conquest

Southwestern Archaeology. John C. McGregor. University of Illinois Press, Urbana, 1965. Largely deals with Arizona. A textbook but not unreadable. Second edition.

A History of the Ancient Southwest. Harold S. Gladwin. Bond Wheelright, Portland, Me., 1965. A longtime student of the region tells how man may have come into and developed in the Southwest.

Black Sand: Prehistory in Northern Arizona. Harold S. Colton. University of New Mexico Press, Albuquerque, 1960.

Prehistoric Indians of the Southwest. Hannah M. Wormington. Denver Museum of Natural History, 1951. Survey of prehistoric cultures briefly and ably done.

"First Masters of the American Desert: The Hohokam." Emil Haury. *National Geographic Magazine.* May 1967, pp. 670-695. A most readable thing on this desert culture, and, of course, profusely illustrated.

Indians After the Conquest

Southwestern Indian Tribes. Tom Bahti. KC Publications, Flagstaff, Arizona, 1968. Brief popular descriptions of the Arizona and New Mexico tribes, splendidly illustrated, partly in color.

Cycles of Conquest. Edward H. Spicer. University of Arizona Press, Tucson, 1962. Subtitle: "The impact of Spain, Mexico, and the United States on the Indians of the Southwest, 1533–1960." A monumental work of scholarship that no student of the subject can afford to ignore. Available in paperback.

Life Among the Apaches. John C. Cremony. Rio Grande Press, Glorieta, New Mexico, 1969. Classic, contemporary (1868) entertaining account, just back in print.

On the Border with Crook. John Gregory Bourke. Rio Grand Press, Chicago, 1962. Reprint of a classic concerned with the Apache wars — and the Apache. It is also army life in the 1870s.

The Warrior Apaches. Gordon Baldwin. D. S. King Publisher, Tucson, 1965. Good popular account of the culture of the Chiricahua and Western Apaches.

An Apache Life-Way. Morris Opler. Cooper Square Publishers, N.Y., 1965. Originally issued in 1941, this is more detailed and more scholarly than the title above. Considered by many the classic account of Apache life.

The Navajo. Ruth M. Underhill. Revised edition. University of Oklahoma Press, Norman, 1967. Excellent, sympathetic, well-written account by a trained anthropologist who also wrote *Here Come the Navaho!* (Haskell Institute, Lawrence, Kansas, 1953) with a somewhat different approach and profuse illustration.

The Enduring Navaho. Laura Gilpin. University of Texas Press, Austin, 1968. Probably the most beautiful book on the Navajo. The text is good, but the pictures — dozens of them — speak louder than words.

Traders to the Navajos. Frances Gillmor and Louisa Wade Wetherill. University of New Mexico Press, Albuquerque, 1967. Paperback reprint of the most beautifully written of a number of books on traders and their relations with The People. But look also at the splendid pictures in *Navaho Trading Days* by Elizabeth Hegemann (University of New Mexico Press, 1963).

Mission of Sorrows: Jesuit Guevavi and the Pimas, 1691–1767. John L. Kessell. University of Arizona Press, Tucson, 1970. An in-depth, vividly written study of a single missionary center that brings to life the forgotten men who struggled for three-quarters of a century to transform a native ranchería into an ordered mission community.

The Navaho. Clyde Kluckhohn and Dorothea Leighton. Revised edition. Natural History Library, Garden City, N.Y., 1962.

Me and Mine: The Life Story of Helen Sekaquaptewa. As told to Louise Udall. University of Arizona Press, Tucson, 1969. Story of quiet, successful adaptation to the best in two cultures. Recounts the story of the split between Hostiles and Friendlies in 1906.

The Hopis: Portrait of a Desert People. Walter O'Kane. University of Oklahoma Press, Norman, 1953. A sympathetic account and an enjoyable one.

The Hopi Indians. Ruth D. Simpson. Southwest Museum, Los Angeles, 1953. Thorough but rather prosaic survey of Hopi life and belief. Southwest Museum Leaflet 25.

The Snake Dance of the Hopi Indians. Earl Forrest. Westernlore Press, Los Angeles, 1961.

A Pima Remembers. George Webb. University of Arizona Press, Tucson, 1959. Charming reminiscences of the old ways some sixty and more years ago.

Pima Indian Legends. Anna Moore Shaw. University of Arizona Press, Tucson, 1968. Old and young can enjoy these tales retold by a Pima woman.

Angel to the Papagos. Charlsie Poe. Naylor Co., San Antonio, 1964. Popular, readable.

The Desert People: A Study of the Papago Indians. Alice Joseph, Rosamund Spicer and Jane Chesky. University of Chicago Press, 1949. A fine first section on the Papago way of life. The rest is written in a style so technical even an educated layman may find the going too rough.

Yuman Tribes of the Gila River. Leslie Spier. University of Chicago Press, 1933. Out of print, hard to find, but there is nothing else so good.

Yuman Indian Agriculture. Edward F. Castetter and Willis H. Bell. University of New Mexico Press, Albuquerque, 1951.

An Introduction to Southwestern Indian Arts and Crafts. Tom Bahti. KC Publications, Flagstaff, Arizona, 1962. Simple text and plentiful and pleasing illustrations, many in color.

Southwest Indian Craft Arts. Clara Lee Tanner. University of Arizona Press, Tucson, 1968.

American Indian Painting of the Southwest and Plains Areas. Dorothy Dunn. University of New Mexico Press, Albuquerque, 1968.

Southwest Indian Painting. Clara Lee Tanner. University of Arizona Press, Tucson, 1972. All three of these volumes are well worth your attention.

Spaniards and Missionaries

The Power Within Us. Haniel Long. Duell, Sloan and Pearce, N.Y., 1946. A beautifully written retelling of the odyssey of Cabeza de Vaca, the first Spaniard to set foot in our Southwest.

Coronado, Knight of Pueblo and Plains. Herbert E. Bolton. University of New Mexico Press, Albuquerque, 1964. The ill-fated search for phantom gold which brought the Spanish to Arizona and New Mexico superbly told in great detail. First published in 1949. See also *Coronado's Quest* by A. Grove Day, now in paperback, University of California Press.

The Rim of Christendom. Herbert E. Bolton. Russell and Russell, N.Y., 1960. Reprint of a masterful biography of the great missionary Francisco Eusebio Kino, written with deep understanding and love.

A Kino Guide. Charles Polzer, S. J. Southwest Mission Research Center, Tucson, Arizona, 1968. Subtitle: "A life of Eusebio Francisco Kino, Arizona's first pioneer, and a guide to his missions and monuments." An attractive and readable pamphlet.

A Record of Travels in Arizona and California, 1775–1776. Fr. Francisco Garcés. Translated and edited by John Galvin. John Howell Books, San Francisco, 1965. A handsome book in a small edition. There is nothing else so easily available on this famous Franciscan.

Biography of a Desert Church: The Story of Mission San Xavier. Bernard L. Fontana. The Westerners, Tucson, Arizona, 1961. This story of the famous mission embodies the results of research and is succinctly told.

Territorial Days and After

Arizona Place Names. Will C. Barnes. Revised and enlarged by Byrd H. Granger. University of Arizona Press, Tucson, 1960. Deserves a place on any list of important Arizona books in spite of its arrangement, an irritating pronunciation scheme and totally useless maps.

The Gila, River of the Southwest. Edwin Corle, Bisonbooks, University of Nebraska Press, Lincoln, 1964. A good deal of Arizona history strung on the thread of the river. A paper-bound reprint.

River of the Sun: Stories of the Storied Gila. Ross Calvin. University of New Mexico Press, Albuquerque, 1946. Eloquently, sometimes poetically written account of the river and adjacent territory. Unfortunately out of print.

Bartlett's West: Drawing the Mexican Boundary. Robert V. Hine. Yale University Press, New Haven, 1968. The story of the goings-on of the first commission to establish the boundary after the war with Mexico, illustrated with the commissioner's own drawings.

Camels to California: A Chapter in Western Transportation. Harlan D. Fowler. Stanford University Press, Stanford, California, 1950. The camels were not confined to Arizona but they were surely a part of its history.

Founding a Wilderness Capital: Prescott, A. T., 1864. Pauline Henson. Northland Press, Flagstaff, Arizona, 1965. The beginnings of Arizona Territory well told. For a more detailed treatment including background on territorial organization see *Be it Enacted: The Creation of the Territory of Arizona*. B. Sacks. Arizona Historical Foundation, Phoenix, 1964.

Pumpelly's Arizona: An Excerpt from "Across America and Asia." Raphael Pumpelly. Edited by Andrew Wallace. Palo Verde Press, Tucson, 1965. A lively account of mining and battling Apaches before the Civil War.

Vanished Arizona. Martha Summerhayes. Lippincott, Philadelphia, 1963. Life at several army posts in the 1870s seen by an army wife. It was rough. There have been several editions and even this, in paper, is now out of print.

Frontier Military Posts of Arizona. Ray Brandes. Dale Stuart Publisher, Globe, Arizona, 1960. Brief histories.

The Conquest of Apachería. Dan Thrapp. University of Oklahoma Press, Norman, 1967. The Apache wars of the 1870s and 1880s.

On the Bloody Trail of Geronimo. John Bigelow Jr. Westernlore Press, Los Angeles, 1968. A good picture of routine army life in the 1880s.

The Geronimo Campaign. Odie B. Faulk. Oxford University Press, New York, 1969. Historically accurate, well-paced narrative of the last army campaign against the Apache renegades, and its aftermath.

Vast Domain of Blood: The Story of the Camp Grant Massacre. Don Schellie. Westernlore Press, Los Angeles, 1968. Well researched and well written. The fictional devices in no way detract from its excellence.

Joseph Reddeford Walker and the Arizona Adventure. Daniel Ellis Conner. University of Oklahoma Press, Norman, 1956. The Apaches and mining in central Arizona in the early 1860s.

Apache Vengeance: True Story of Apache Kid. Jess G. Hayes. University of New Mexico Press, Albuquerque, 1954.

Pioneer Portraits. Frank C. Lockwood. University of Arizona Press, Tucson, 1968. A selection of the best character sketches by a devoted early Arizona historian.

Yuma Crossing. Douglas D. Martin. University of New Mexico Press, Albuquerque, 1954. Events at the crossing of the Colorado up to the time the railroad bridged the river. Breezy and readable.

Yuma Footprints. William H. Westover. Arizona Pioneers' Historical Society, Tucson, 1966. The best of this picks up where *Yuma Crossing* leaves off.

Tombstone's Epitaph. Douglas D. Martin. University of New Mexico Press, Albuquerque, 1951. Selections from the famous paper with Martin providing connecting links. Covers the Earps and the battle at the OK Corral.

Tombstone's Yesterday: Bad Men of Arizona. Rio Grande Press, Glorieta, New Mexico, 1968. Reprint edition.

The Last Chance: Tombstone's Early Years. John Myers Myers. Dutton, N.Y., 1950. Readable and good synthesis of the story of the feverish years. But for what is probably closest to the truth on the Earps read Frank Waters' *The Earp Brothers of Tombstone*. Clarkson N. Potter, N.Y., 1960.

The Peralta Grant: James Addison Reavis and the Barony of Arizona. Donald M. Powell, University of Oklahoma Press, Norman, 1960. Story of what was, perhaps, the greatest fraud ever perpetrated against a government by one of its citizens.

Arizona's Dark and Bloody Ground. Earle R. Forrest. Caxton Printers, Caldwell, Idaho, 1950. The definitive work on the Graham Tewksbury feud when the cattlemen and sheepmen fought it out.

Memories of an Arizona Judge. Richard E. Sloan. Stanford University Press, Stanford, California, 1932. Sloan was

the last territorial governor and his memories cover his life up to the time of statehood.

Brewery Gulch. Joe Chisholm. Naylor Company, San Antonio, 1949. Times past, times wild and times not so wild in the recent past of southern Arizona. Some of the material is firsthand and all of it is very good indeed.

Sheriff Thompson's Day. Jess G. Hayes. University of Arizona Press, Tucson, 1968. The career of a Gila County sheriff, probably typical for law enforcement officers.

The Killer Mountains: A Search for the Legendary Lost Dutchman Mine. Curt Gentry. New American Library, N.Y., 1968. There had to be one on this subject; here it is. There is also Sims Ely's *The Lost Dutchman Mine.* Morrow, N.Y., 1953, now out of print.

Horse and Buggy West: A Boyhood on the Last Frontier. Jack O'Connor. Alfred A. Knopf, New York, 1969. Delightful reminiscences of boyhood in Tempe at the beginning of the century.

A Cowman's Wife. Mary Kidder Rak. Houghton Mifflin, Boston, 1934. Splendid story of the vicissitudes and rewards of cattle ranching in the Chiricahua Mountains in the 1920's. Mrs. Rak also wrote *Mountain Cattle.* Houghton Mifflin, Boston, 1936.

Nine Months Is a Year at Baboquívari School. Eulalia Bourne. University of Arizona Press, Tucson, 1968. Not really the past but teaching young Mexican-Americans in the Altar Valley not so long ago. All remembered with good humor and affection.

Interpretations, Natural History

The Desert Year. Joseph Wood Krutch. William Sloane, N.Y., 1952. The reaction of a keen and inquiring mind to the life of the Sonoran desert has produced an enduring work that is as much philosophy as natural history. A paperback reprint is available. There is also the same author's *Voice of the Desert.* Sloane, N.Y., 1955.

The Sonoran Desert, Its Geography, Economy and People. Roger Dunbier. University of Arizona Press, Tucson, 1968. Scholarly, sometimes slightly technical, thorough. Covers the desert of Sonora, Mexico, as well as Arizona. Excellently illustrated.

Sky Island. Weldon Heald. Van Nostrand, N.Y., 1967. A love song to the Chiricahua Mountains where, for many years, the author made his home.

Gold on the Desert. Olga Wright Smith. University of New Mexico Press, Albuquerque, 1956. The formidable Lecheguilla Desert near the Colorado described with clarity and affection for its stark beauty.

Time and the River Flowing: Grand Canyon. François Leydet. Sierra Club, San Francisco, 1964.

Navajo Wildlands. Philip Hyde and Stephen C. Jett. Sierra Club, San Francisco, 1967. Two big, beautiful, and expensive books distinguished by outstanding color photography.

Grand Canyon: The Story Behind the Scenery. Merrill D. Beal. KC Publications, Flagstaff, Arizona, 1967. Succinct text, handsome color illustrations and diagrams and suggestions for further reading. For greater detail see *Grand Canyon, Today and All Its Yesterdays.* Joseph Wood Krutch, Sloane, N.Y., 1958.

The Romance of the Colorado River. Frederick Dellenbaugh. Rio Grande Press, Chicago, 1962. Reprint of a history of events along the river with an account of the first Powell expedition and of the second which included the author.

The Grand Colorado: The Story of a River and Its Canyons. T. H. Watkins and Contributors. American West Publishing Co., Palo Alto, California, 1969. All about the river, and very good it is.

The Changing Mile. James R. Hastings and Raymond M. Turner. University of Arizona Press, Tucson, 1965. Subtitle: "An ecological study of vegetation change with time in the lower mile of an arid and semiarid region." Dramatic then and now photographs of the hills and valleys of the oak woodlands and desert grasslands of the arboreal desert.

Flowers of the Southwest Deserts. Natt N. Dodge.

Flowers of the Southwest Mesas. Pauline Patraw.

Flowers of the Southwest Mountains. Leslie Arnberger.

Mammals of the Southwest Deserts. George Olin. Four excellent popular pamphlets published by the Southwest Parks and Monuments Association at Globe, Arizona.

100 Desert Wildflowers in Natural Color. Natt N. Dodge. Southwestern Monuments Association, Globe, Arizona, 1963. Another pamphlet for the amateur botanist illustrated with small but good color photographs.

Poisonous Dwellers of the Desert. Natt N. Dodge. Southwestern Monuments Association, Globe, Arizona, 1961. There have been a number of editions of this useful pamphlet.

The Birds of Arizona. Allan Phillips, Joe Marshall and Gale Monson. University of Arizona Press, Tucson, 1964. Technical ornithology, limited illustrations. The best book for popular identification is still Roger Tory Peterson's *A Field Guide to Western Birds.* Houghton Mifflin, Boston, 1941.

Southwestern Trees. Elbert Little Jr. U.S. Department of Agriculture, Washington, 1950. A guide to the native species of Arizona and New Mexico.

The Cacti of Arizona. Lyman Benson. 3rd edition, University of Arizona Press, Tucson, 1969. Technical, but not too difficult to use. *The Flowering Cactus,* edited by Raymond Carlson, McGraw-Hill, N.Y., 1954, has useful text and brilliant color photographs and is out of print.

Politics, Economics, and Other Matters

Arizona Territory, 1863–1912: A Political History. Jay Wagoner. University of Arizona Press, Tucson, 1969. The only political history of sixteen territorial administrations, both scholarly and readable; liberally illustrated.

Arizona Civilization. John S. Goff. Hooper Publishing Corp., Phoenix, 1968. History and present condition of state government with a glance at the civilization of the state. Designed as a text.

Constitution and Government of Arizona. Donald R. Van Petten. 3rd edition, Tyler Printing Co., Phoenix, 1960. Written as a text for a course in government, but useful.

Politics and Legislation: The Office of Governor in Arizona. Ray D. Morey. University of Arizona Press, Tucson, 1965. Background and the governor as legislative leader.

The Movement for Administrative Reorganization in Arizona. Robert E. Riggs, University of Arizona Press, Tucson, 1964.

Government Project. Edward Banfield. Free Press, Glencoe, Illinois, 1951. Story of the development and ultimate failure of the cooperative Casa Grande Farms in the 1930s.

The Politics of Water in Arizona. Dean E. Mann. University of Arizona Press, Tucson, 1963. A thorough study of all aspects of water management and research.

Arizona, an Adventure in Irrigation. Stephen C. Shadegg. Phoenix, 1949.

The Phoenix Story, an Adventure in Reclamation. Stephen C. Shadegg. Phoenix, 1958. Popular and well illustrated accounts of the development of the reclamation and irrigation systems of Arizona.

Tenth Arizona Town Hall: Do Agricultural Problems Threaten Arizona's Total Economy? Arizona Academy, Phoenix, 1967. Consideration of some recent questions about the agriculture of the state.

History of the Cattle Industry in Southern Arizona, 1540–1940. Jay Wagoner. University of Arizona Press, Tucson, 1952. A good study based on a thesis. It was a University of Arizona Bulletin, vol. 23, no. 2, and is out of print.

History of Extra-Long-Staple Cottons. Joseph C. McGowan. SuPima Association and Arizona Cotton Growers' Association, 1961.

Financing the Frontier: A Fifty-Year History of the Valley National Bank. Ernest J. Hopkins. Arizona Printers, Phoenix, 1950. Well-written account of the most influential bank in the state and a good deal of history.

A History of Phelps Dodge. Robert G. Cleland. A. A. Knopf, N. Y., 1952. A noted historian's account of the activities of one of the ruling copper corporations.

Pioneer Arizona Railroads. David F. Myrick. Colorado Railroad Museum, Golden, Colorado, 1968. Railroads existing and defunct, and a selection of fine railroad photographs.

The Economy of Arizona. Employment Security Commission of Arizona, Phoenix, 1964. A review of population, labor force, industry, and economic outlook, not yet wholly out of date.

Arizona Statistical Review. Valley National Bank, Phoenix. Annual, free.

Rock to Riches. Charles H. Dunning and Edward H. Peplow Jr. Southwest Publishing Co., Phoenix, 1959. Subtitle: The story of American mining, past, present and future as reflected in the colorful history of mining in Arizona, the nation's greatest bonanza.

A Layman's Guide to Arizona Public Schools. Dave Campbell, Phoenix, 1965. Helpful pamphlet.

Lamp in the Desert. Douglas D. Martin. University of Arizona Press, Tucson, 1960. Seventy-fifth anniversary history of the University of Arizona.

The Arizona State University Story. Ernest J. Hopkins and Alfred Thomas Jr. Southwest Publishing Co., Phoenix, 1960.

The Climate of Arizona. Howard V. Smith. University of Arizona Agricultural Experiment Station, Tucson, 1956. Can be understood by the layman. Experiment Station Bulletin 279.

INDEX

The state flag represents the copper star of Arizona rising from a blue field in the face of a setting sun. Blue and old gold are the colors of the state. The blue is of the same shade as that of the flag of the United States. The lower half of the flag is a blue field, the upper half divided into thirteen equal segments of rays which start at the center and continue to the edges of the flag, consisting of six yellow and seven red rays. A five-pointed copper star, symbolic of the state's enormous copper industry, is superimposed on the center of the flag.

STATE FLAG

SYMBOLS

STATE SEAL

In the background of the seal is a range of mountains with the sun rising behind the peaks. At the right side of the mountains there is a storage reservoir and dam, below which in the middle distance are irrigated farmlands and orchards. At the right, cattle are grazing. To the left, in the middle distance, is a quartz mill on a mountainside in front of which is a miner with pick and shovel. The year 1912 is the date of Arizona's admission to the Union as a state. The motto, "Ditat Deus," means "God Enriches."

Arizona's state bird, the cactus wren (*Heleodytes brunneicapillus couesi*) is a true lover of the desert country. The wren's nests in cactus plants are common. The more thornier plants serve as protection. A woody-brown bird, with a speckled breast, he will build not one, but several nests, using one as a home and the others as decoys from his enemies. Nesting time for the cactus wren begins as early as March and extends into June.

STATE BIRD